Woodwind
Solo and Study Material
Music Guide

compiled by
Himie Voxman & Lyle Merriman

The Instrumentalist Co.
1418 Lake St., Evanston, Illinois 60204

184240

Copyright 1975 by
The Instrumentalist Co.

Printed in the United States of America.

Library of Congress Catalog Card Number: 75-22523

PREFACE

The *Woodwind Solo and Study Material Guide* is the second in a series of bibliographies of the literature in print for wind and percussion instruments. Like its predecessor, the *Woodwind Ensemble Music Guide*, it is based on catalogs furnished by 319 publishers and foreign music information centers. The continuing changes in ownership of publishing firms and in agents add to the difficulty of listing actual publishers and sources for obtaining the compositions. As noted in our earlier volume, transfers of ownership are frequently accompanied by substantial deletions of material. These are usually not evident until much later when new catalogs become available.

Despite inaccuracies so created and our own errors we believe that the *Guide* represents the most complete listing of materials in print and should be useful to students, teachers, and publishers.

Lyle Merriman
Himie Voxman
Iowa City, Iowa USA
August 1975

ABBREVIATIONS

a	alto	nar	narrator
A	Alto voice	no(s)	number(s)
arr	arranger	ob	oboe
b	bass	opt	optional
B	Bass voice	org	organ
bar	baritone	perc	percussion
Bar	Baritone voice	pf	pianoforte
bc	*basso continuo	pic	piccolo
bk	book	rec	recorder
br	brass	rev	revised
bsn	bassoon	S	Soprano voice
c	contra	sax	saxophone
cel	celeste	sdr	snare drum
cemb	cembalo	str	string(s)
cl	clarinet	T	Tenor voice
comp	compiler	tamb	tambourine
ct	cornet	ten	tenor
db	double bass	timp	timpani
dr	drum	tpt	trumpet
ed	editor	tr	transcriber
ehn	English horn	trb	trombone
eu	euphonium	tri	triangle
fl	flute	tu	tuba
go	gong	V	Voice
guit	guitar	va	viola
hn	French horn	vc	violoncello
hp	harp	vib	vibraphone
hpcd	harpsichord	vn	violin
instr	instrument(s)	vol	volume
mar	marimba	ww	woodwind
MS	Mezzo Soprano voice	xyl	xylophone

see General Information

SYMBOLS

Instrumentation inside parentheses indicates alternate part:
  fl(ob) — flute or oboe

Slash between two instruments indicates doubling by one player:
  ob/ehn — oboe and English horn

Key signatures: (1) Upper case letter(s) indicate major key(s);
  (2) Lower case letter(s) indicate minor key(s).

v

GENERAL INFORMATION

Basso continuo. Since catalogs do not usually indicate whether or not a basso continuo part includes separate bass and keyboard parts, we have arbitrarily considered it to be a single keyboard part.

Unaccompanied solos; etudes. From the titles alone it is not possible to be sure that some items listed as unaccompanied solos do not more properly belong in the category of etude material. Conversely, some material listed as etudes may have been composed with public performance in mind.

Compositions with band or orchestral accompaniment. Without actual examination of the music, in a listing such as *Concerto for flute, strings, and piano,* one cannot be certain if the piano plays a solo or accompaniment role. We have arbitrarily placed such items in the category of two solo instruments and orchestra (strings). In some instances, then, a work listed under two (or more) instruments and orchestra, e.g., may actually be a solo work in which one of the listed instruments may be accompanimental.

BIBLIOGRAPHIC INFORMATION

Composer-Arranger, (Editor)   Publisher
    Title, Opus no., date of composition when given, key, no. of volumes
    Instrumentation

Titles are abbreviated as follows:

a. Catalog: Concerto in D Major, Opus 14, No. 3
    Bibliography: Concerto, D, op. 14/3

b. Catalog: Largo from Symphony No. 4
    Bibliography: Largo (Symphony No. 4)

CONTENTS

PREFACE. iii
ABBREVIATIONS AND SYMBOLS. v
GENERAL INFORMATION. vii

PICCOLO. 1

Unaccompanied Solos, 1; C Piccolo and Piano, 1; D♭ Piccolo and Piano, 2; Piccolo and Orchestra, 2; Piccolo and Band, 3; Methods and Studies, 3.

FLUTE. 3

Unaccompanied Solos (including alto and bass flutes), 3; Flute and Piano or Harpsichord, 13; Flute and Organ, 89; Alto Flute and Keyboard, 89; Flute and Orchestra, 90; Flute and Band, 100; Methods and Studies, 101.

OBOE. 111

Unaccompanied Solos, 111; Oboe and Piano or Harpsichord, 113; Oboe and Organ, 147; Oboe and Orchestra, 148; Oboe and Band, 155; Methods and Studies, 155.

ENGLISH HORN. 161

Unaccompanied Solos, 161; English Horn and Piano, 161; English Horn and Organ, 164; English Horn and Orchestra, 164; Methods and Studies, 164.

OBOE D'AMORE. 165

Oboe d'amore and Piano, 165; Oboe d'amore and Orchestra, 165.

E♭ CLARINET. 166

E♭ Clarinet and Piano, 166; E♭ Clarinet and Band, 166.

B♭ AND A SOPRANO CLARINET. 166

Unaccompanied Solos, 166; Clarinet and Piano, 171; Clarinet and Organ, 240; Clarinet and Orchestra, 240; Clarinet and Band, 246; Methods and Studies, 248.

ALTO CLARINET. 262

Alto Clarinet and Piano, 262; Methods and Studies, 265.

BASSET HORN 266

Basset Horn and Orchestra, 266.

BASS CLARINET 266

Unaccompanied Solos, 266; Bass Clarinet and Piano, 266; Bass Clarinet and Orchestra, 270; Bass Clarinet and Band, 270; Methods and Studies, 271.

CONTRABASS CLARINET 272

Contrabass Clarinet and Piano, 272; Contrabass Clarinet and Orchestra, 272.

BASSOON 272

Unaccompanied Solos, 272; Bassoon and Piano, 274; Bassoon and Organ, 293; Bassoon and Orchestra, 293; Bassoon and Band, 296; Contrabassoon and Piano, 296; Methods and Studies, 296.

SAXOPHONE 301

Unaccompanied Solos, 301; Soprano Saxophone and Piano, 302; Soprano Saxophone and Orchestra, 302; Soprano Saxophone and Band, 303; Alto Saxophone and Piano, 303; Alto Saxophone and Organ, 342; Alto Saxophone and Orchestra, 342; Alto Saxophone and Band, 344; C Melody Saxophone and Piano, 346; Tenor Saxophone and Piano, 347; Tenor Saxophone and Orchestra, 364; Tenor Saxophone and Band, 364; Baritone Saxophone and Piano, 365; Baritone Saxophone and Band, 367; Bass Saxophone and Piano, 367; Methods and Studies, 367.

MISCELLANEOUS 374

Treble Instrument, 374; Treble Instrument and Piano, 375; B♭ Instrument and Piano, 375; E♭ Instrument and Piano, 376; Miscellaneous Instrument, 376; Miscellaneous Instrument and Orchestra, 376.

MULTIPLE INSTRUMENTS WITH ORCHESTRA OR BAND . . . 376

2 Instruments with Orchestra, 376; 2 Instruments with Band, 383; 3 Instruments with Orchestra, 384; 3 Instruments with Band, 386; 4 Instruments with Orchestra, 387; 4 Instruments with Band, 388; 5 Instruments with Orchestra, 388; 5 Instruments with Band, 389.

Piccolo

Unaccompanied Solos

Persichetti, V.	Parable XII, op. 125	TP

C Piccolo and Piano

	Jewel Collection	CF
Avon, E.	Danse Joyeuse	CF
Balleron, L.	Le Moineau de Luxembourg	EdS
Balleron, L.	L'Oiseau tapageur	EdS
Barnard, G.	Gloriana	CF
Bent, R.	Swiss Boy	CF
Bois, R. du	Bewegingen. 1961	SD
Bullard, R.	Laura	Ken
Christensen, J.	Piccolo Espagnol	Ken
Clement, F.	Marching through Georgia	CF
Coppola, C.	The Piccolo Polka	BVC
Damare, E.	Cleopatra	CF
Damare, E.-Ryder	The Lark	CF
Damare, E.	Tourterelle	CF
Damare, E.-Lewis	La Tourterelle	CF
Damare, E.	Wren Polka	CF
Damm, A.	Through the Air	CF
Dubois, P.	La Piccolette	ERR
Dvořak, A.-Johnson	Air Gracile, op. 54/1	Rub
Fisher, C.	My Old Kentucky Home	CF
Fisher, C.	Nellie Gray	CF
Griffith, S.	Nesting Time	CF
Hartmann, J.-Prendiville	Auld Lang Syne	CF
Hartmann, J.-Rollinson	Whistle Polka	CF
Haydn, F.-Barnes	Gypsy Rondo	Lud
Hurrell, C.	The Dance of Elizabeth	Rub
Johnson, C.	Wind in the Pines	Rub
Koehler, E.-Dole	Nightingale Polka	CF
Koepke, P.	Meadowlark	Rub
Koepke, P.	Popinjay	Rub
Lake, M.	Moonlight	CF
Lake, M.	Squads Right	CF
Lax, F.	Bonnie Scotland, op. 101	CF
Morrissey, J.	Hoopla!	EBM
Occa, J.-Laurendeau	Kinloch of Kinloch	CF
Ostransky, L.	Pifferari No. 1	Rub
Ostransky, L.	Pifferari No. 2	Rub

C Piccolo and Piano

Presser, W.	Rondo. 1966	TP
Pryor, A.	The Whistler and His Dog	CF
Read, L.	Canary Polka	CF
Restorff, H.	The Bluebird's Call	CF
Telemann, G.-Voxman	Sonata, F (Der Getreue Musikmeister)	Rub
Thiere, C.	L'Oiseau du Bois	CF
Thiere, C.	Sylvia Scherzo	CF
Vivaldi, A.-Lesko	Concerto, a, F. VI No. 9	Ric
Vivaldi, A.	Concerto No. 13, C	EMT
Waddington, A.	Bob White	Wat
Waddington, A.	Piccolominnio	Wat
Waddington, A.	Pick-A-Piccolo	Wat
Walters, H.	Tarantella Festivo	Rub
Widdifield, T.	Oriole Polka	CF
Williams, E.	Sequoia Polka	CF

Db Piccolo and Piano

De Ville, P.-Goldman	Blue Bells of Scotland	CF
Dvořak, A.-Johnson	Air Gracile, op. 54/1	Rub
Fisher, C.	My Old Kentucky Home	CF
Griffith, S.	Nesting Time	CF
Hurrell, C.	Dance of Elizabeth	Rub
Johnson, C.	Wind in the Pines	Rub
Koepke, P.	Meadowlark	Rub
Koepke, P.	Popinjay	Rub
Lax, F.	Bonnie Scotland, op. 101	CF
Mendelssohn, F.-Weber	On Wings of Song	B-M
Ostransky, L.	Pifferari No. 1	Rub
Ostransky, L.	Pifferari No. 2	Rub
Telemann, G.-Voxman	Sonata, F	Rub
Thiere, C.	L'Oiseau du Bois	CF
Vivaldi, A.	Concerto, C	B-M
Walters, H.	Tarantella Festivo	Rub
Weber, F.	Autumn Leaves	B-M
Weber, F.	Peasant Dance	B-M

Piccolo and Orchestra

Benker, H.	Concertino. 1958	BrH
Bottje, W.	Concertino	ACA
Butt, J.	Concertino	Pet
Krek, U.	Concertino. 1967	HG

Piccolo and Orchestra

Vivaldi, A.-Smith & Baron	Concerto, C, F. VI, No. 4	B-M
Vivaldi, A.	Concerto, C, F. V, No. 5	Ric
Vivaldi, A.	Concerto, a, F. VI, No. 9	Ric
Vivaldi, A.-Oubradous	Concerto No. 13, C	EMT
Vivaldi, A.	Concerto, C	M&M
Vivaldi, A.-Lasocki	Concerto, C, P. 78	MR
Vivaldi, A.-Linde	Concerto, C (pic, str)	SS

Piccolo and Band

Boisson	Le Canari	EdR
Bouchel	Les deux cousins	EdR
Bridger	Shanghai Sailor	B&H
Chavatte	Follette	EdR
Damare, E.	L'Oiseau du paradis	EdR
Damare, E.	Le Rossignol de l'Opéra	EdR
Vivaldi, A.-Smith	Concerto, C, F. VI, No. 4	Ric
Vivaldi, A.-Reed	Concerto, C	Vol

Methods and Studies

Bettoney, H.	Chart of the Regular Fingering for the Bettoney Boehm Piccolo	CF
Koehler, E.	Method	WZ
Rusch, H. & A. Barto	Breath Control and Tuning and Intonation Studies	CF
Tulou, J.-Andreoni	Popular Method	Ric

Flute

Unaccompanied Solos

Classical Tunes for the Flute	Han

Acker, D.	Fioretten. 1972	B&B
Adler, S.	Flaunting	TP
Adler, S.	Harobed	SM
Alexander, J.	Monody	Gen
Alis, R.	Preludio y Cante, op. 34	EdA
Ameller, A.	Val-d'or	ALe
Ammann, B.	Successions	WZ
Amram, D.	Overture and Allegro	Pet
Amram, D.	Zohar	Pet
Amzalag, A.	Taksim. 1968	Isr
Andriessen, J.	Pastorale d'été. 1958	B&V
Apostel, H.	Sonatine	UE
Applebaum, L.	Essay	MCA
Arma, P.	Divertimento No. 3	Bil
Arma, P.	Sonatine	ESZ
Arnold, M.	Fantasy, op. 89. 1966	Fab
Baaren, K. van	Musica	SD
Bach, C.P.E.	Sonata, a	AlL
Bach, C.P.E.-Wittgenstein	Sonata, a	CF
Bach, C.P.E.-Niggemann	Sonata, a	FrH
Bach, C.P.E.-Siber	Sonata, a	FrH
Bach, C.P.E.-Wummer	Sonata, a	Int
Bach, C.P.E.-Moyse	Sonata, a	Sch
Bach, C.P.E.-Kurth	Sonata, a	Sim
Bach, C.P.E.-Leeuwen	Sonata, a	WZ
Bach, J.S.-Schmitz	Partita, a, BWV 1013	B&N
Bach, J.S.-Moyse	Sonata, a	ALe
Bach, J.S.-Le Roy	Sonata, a	Dur
Bach, J.S.	Sonata, a (Urtext)	GaM
Bach, J.S.-Rampal	Sonata, a	Int
Bach, J.S.-List	Sonata, a (Urtext)	Pet
Bach, J.S.-Schwedler	Sonata, a	Pet
Bach, J.S.-Moyse	Sonata, a	Sch
Bach, J.S.-Graf	3 Sonaten (Violin Sonatas and Partitas)	BrH
Bäck, S.	Sonata	Nor
Barati, G.	Searching	CoF
Bartolozzi, B.	The Hollow Man. 1968	ESZ
Baur, J.	Mutazioni. 1962	BrH
Bayr, G.	2 Caprices, op. 8	EdM
Becker, G.	3 Inventionen. 1957	WZ
Beckerath, A. von	Sonatine	MV
Becucci, E.	Tin-Tin	Dur
Bellenghi, G.	Voix de la briso	Dur
Benguerel, X.	Estructura II. 1959	See
Ben-Haim, P.	3 Songs Without Words	AlB
Benker, H.	Bavardage. 1957	BrH
Bennett, R.R.	Sonata	UE
Bennett, R.R.	A Flute At Dusk	Cha
Bentzon, N.	Variations, op. 93	WH

Berio, L.	Sequenza	ESZ
Bernier, R.	Monodie	ECM
Bhatia, V.	Flute Music	OxU
Binet, F.	La Chanson de Louisette	Dur
Blavet, M.-Vester	Gigue et Rondeau	B&V
Bois, R. du	Muziek. 1961	SD
Boismortier, J.-Ruf	6 Suiten	SS
Bon, M.	Caprichoso y Obstinada	GaM
Bonsel, A.	8 Concert-études. 1963	SD
Bonsel, A.	Elégie. 1961	SD
Bonsel, A.	Souvenir. 1959	SD
Booren, J. van den	Equilibrio (fl/fl in G/pic)	SD
Bornyi, L.	My Fish	Wat
Borris, S.	Partita, op. 27/1	Mit
Bossler, K.	Suite	HG
Bozza, E.	Image, op. 38	ALe
Bracquemond, M.	Sonatine	ALe
Brant, H.	Mobiles	MCA
Brant, H.	Temperamental Mobiles	Spr
Braun, G.	Aphorismen	HMo
Braun, Y.	3 Satze	ImV
Breuskine, G.	Hymenée	Dur
Brons, C.	Serenata. 1963	SD
Brown, R.	Sonatina	Wes
Brun, H.	Sonatina	ImV
Bucalossi	Gitana	Dur
Burghauser, J.	Deset skic	Art
Burkhard, W.	Suite, op. 98. 1955	B&N
Carles, M.	Anaphores (fl/pic/afl)	ALe
Chaminade, C.	Pièce romantique	Dur
Chaynes, C.	Prélude pour la flûte de jade	ALe
Childs, B.	Stances	See
Christoff, V.	Suite	Mau
Cohn, J.	Baroque Suite	EdM
Colaço Osorio-Swaab, R.	5 Pastoralen. 1959	SD
Colwell	Preludes and Voluntaries	S&C
Constant, M.	9 Mars. 1971	EdS
Cory, E.	Epithalamium	ACA
Couroupos, G.	Mutations	ERR
Crawford-Seeger, R.	Diaphonic Suite No. 1	AlB
Czibulka, A.	Gavotte de la Princesse, op. 334	ScF
Dahl, I.	Variations on a Swedish Folk Tune	TP
David, J.	Sonate, op. 31/1	BrH
David, T.	Sonate. 1951	BrH
Debras, L.	Sequenza I. 1968	See
Debussy, C.	Syrinx	B&V
Debussy, C.	Syrinx. 1912	Job
Dedieu-Peters	Sérénade	Dur
Demuth, N.	3 Pastorales d'après Ronsard	ALe

Dieny, A.	3 Improvisations	ALe
Dijk, J. van	Sonata. 1961	SD
Dijk, J. van	Sonatine. 1952	SD
Dobbelaere, R.	Bundel van drie stukken	Mau
Doflein, E. (ed)	16 Pieces	SS
Dohl, F.	Textur I. 1971	HG
Dohnanyi, E.	Passacaglia, op. 48/2	BB
Domenica, R. di	Variations on a Tonal Theme	EdM
Doran, M.	4 Short Pieces	Wes
Druckenmiller, W.	Theme and Variations	SM
Dubois, P.	Incantation et Danse	ALe
Durand, A.	Annette et Lubin	Dur
Durand, A.	Pomponnette	Dur
Efrein, L.	Attraction. 1964	AlB
Eisma, W.	Sonatine. 1959	SD
Eitler, E.	Piece	TP
Eitler, E.	Sentimiento Indefinido	TP
Eklund, H.	4 Sommarstycken. 1967	STI
Engelmann, H.	Variante, op. 20b. 1959	A&S
Erdmann, D.	Monodie. 1971	HG
Escher, R.	Air pour charmer un lézard. 1953	Als
Escher, R.	Monologue	SD
Escher, R.	Sonata. 1949	B&V
Evangelisti, F.	Proporzioni. 1958	AlB
Feld, J.	4 Pièces	ALe
Ferroud, P.	3 Pièces	EdS
Fink, R.	Sonata da Camera	Wes
Fink, S.	Improvisation und Umkehrung	OJ
Flothuis, M.	Aubade, op. 19a. 1944	B&V
Forsberg, R.	5 Interludier. 1969	STI
Fox, F.	Variables 2	See
Françaix, J.	Suite	SS
Franco, J.	Elegy	CoF
Franco, J.	4 Miniatures and an Encore	CoF
Franco, J.	Reflections	CoF
Franco, J.	3 Fluteries	CoF
Freundlich, R.	Theme and 8 Variations	B-M
Fühler, M.	Capricen	WMS
Fühler, M.	Suite	WZ
Fühler, M.	20 Impressionen	WZ
Fukushima, K.	Mei	ESZ
Fukushima, K.	Requiem	ESZ
Fumet, R.	Interpolaire	Bil
Funk, H.	6 Impressionen	Pet
Gaber, H.	Chimyaku (afl)	ACA
Gaslini, G.	Chorus	UE
Geiser, W.	Sonatine, op. 33b	B&N
Gelli, E.	Farfalla	Dur
Gennaro, M.	Sonate	Heu

6

Genzmer, H.	Sonata	SS
Gerber, S.	Epithalamion	ACA
Ghedini, G.	3 Pezzi. 1962	Edi
Glaser, W.	Sonat. 1966	STI
Glass, P.	Serenade	E-V
Godard, B.	Première gavotte	Dur
Goldberg, L.	Galante conversation	Dur
Goldman, R.	2 Monochromes	Sha
Gorecki, H.	3 Diagrams, op. 15. 1959	AP
Gornston, D. & B. Paisner	Beethoven Sonatas	SF
Grahn, U.	Canzona. 1968	STI
Grandis, R. de	3 Intermezzi	EdT
Green, R.	Dance Energies	AME
Guarnieri, M.	3 Improvisations	Ron
Gumbel, M.	Neue Spieltechniken	B&N
Guide, R. de	3 Nomes	EMe
Halffter, C.-Fibonaciana	Studie II. 1969	UE
Hamm, J.	3 Songs without Words	CF
Hartig, H.	Flötensolo. 1954	B&N
Hartley, W.	Sonatina. 1959	Cre
Hartzell, E.	Capriccio: Monolog IV. 1965	LDo
Haubenstock-Ramati, R.	Interpolation	UE
Hedwall, L.	Sonat. 1954, rev. 1957	STI
Hedwall, L.	Sonatin (afl)	STI
Hedwall, L.	2 Intermezzi. 1954	STI
Heininen, P.	Discantus I. 1956	EdF
Heiss	4 Lyric Pieces	SM
Heiss, H.	Modi. 1948	BrH
Hekster, W.	Fluxus. 1968	SD
Herman, V.	Melopée	EMU
Herman, V.	Singsong	EMU
Hermansson, A.	Suoni d'un flauto (afl)	EMf
Heussenstamm, G.	Windgate, op. 14/1	See
Hindemith, P.	8 Stücke. 1927	SS
Hitz, F.	Bonjour	Dur
Holliger, H.	Lied	HG
Holstein, J.	Quena	Bil
Honegger, A.	Danse de la Chèvre	EdS
Horn, P.	Inside	EBM
Hotteterre, J.-Bergmann	Echos	S&C
Hovhaness, A.	Sonata	Pet
Hsueh-Yung Shen	Adagio	NK
Huber, K.	Ein Hauch von Unzeit I. 1972	HG
Huber, K.	To ask the flutist. 1966	B&N
Hudadoff-arr	50 Standard Solo Series	PrA
Hufschmidt, W.	O Heiland, reiss die Himmel auf: Partita	B&N
Hultberg, S.	Cadenze. 1970	STI
Humble, K.	Arcade III. 1969	UE
Humel, G.	Praeludium und Scherzo.	

7

	1960	B&B
Ibert, J.	Pièce	ALe
Incerti, B.	Grenouilles et moustiques	Eul
Jacob, G.	The Pied Piper	OxU
Jemnitz, A.	Sonata, op. 43	M&M
Jeney, Z.	Soliloquium No. 1. 1967	EMB
Johanson, S.	Sonat. 1955	STI
Jolas, B.	Fusain	Heu
Jolivet, A.	Ascèses	Bil
Jolivet, A.	5 Incantations	B&H
Jolivet, A.	Incantation	Bil
Jones, K.	Rondo. 1963	Can
Jungk, K.	Appunti, op. 55	Pet
Kahowez, G.	Flachengitter	EMo
Kaiser, H.	Sonate	EMo
Kallstenius, E.	Sonat, op. 57, "Sonata biforme". 1962	STI
Kam, D.	5 Phases	MeP
Karg-Elert, S.	Appassionata Sonata, op. 140	SM
Karg-Elert, S.	Sonata (Appassionata), op. 140	WZ
Karkoff, M.	Liten svit, op. 42. 1959	STI
Karlins, W.	Fantasia on my Mother's Name	ACA
Keetbaas, D.	3 Miniatures. 1963	OxU
Keuning, H.	Op eigen benen	HU
Klerk, J. de	Impromptu No. 1	MM
Klusak, J.	1-4-3-2-5-6-7-10-9-8-11	HG
Koechlin, C.	Stèle Funéraire. 1950 (pic/ afl/bfl)	EME
Koechlin, C.	3 Sonatinas	EdS
Kolz, E.	6 Flötenweisen	LDo
Kolz, E.	2 Sonaten im alten Stil	LDo
Kondorossy, L.	Solos for Flute	AMC
Konietzny, H.	Marsyas	OJ
Koppel, H.	Little Suite from "Paw"	WH
Korevaar, A.	2 Impressions	B&V
Kotschoubey	Oh! dites-lui	Dur
Kounadis, A.	5 Sketches. 1958	EMo
Krebs, S.	Siva	See
Krenek, E.	Flötenstuck neunphasig. 1959	B&N
Krol, B.	Pastorella supra "Puer natus est," op. 24	B&B
Kroll, G.	Sonata (afl)	EMo
Kuhlau, F. -Gümbel	Fantasie, D	B&N
Kuhlau, F.	6 Divertissements, op. 68	CF
Kunc, B.	Soliloquy, op. 61	Ron
Lack, T.	Idilio	Dur
Lajtha, L.	2 Pièces. 1958	ALe
La Montaine, J.	Sonata, op. 24	BB
Lancen, S.	Monologues (3 Pieces)	HE

Lang, I.	Dramma breve	EMB
Lantier, P.	3 Pièces	Bil
Laporte, A.	Inclinations. 1967	EdT
Lateef, Y.	Tunis	FaM
Laudenslager, H.	Evocation	Cor
La Violette, W.	Suite	Wes
Lees, B.	Evocation	CCo
Leeuw, T. de	Night Music	SD
Leeuw, T. de	Reversed Night	SD
Leeuwen, A. van	Pan's Lament	SM
Lefort, A.	Chanson villageoise	Dur
Lefort, A.	Prière	Dur
Lehmann, H.	Regions. 1963	HG
Leister, F.	Fantaisie, op. 7	EdH
Leister, F.	9 Variations sur l'Air des Tyroliens	EdH
Lemmone, J.-Laube	Distant Voices	CF
Levi, M.	3 Pieces	Ken
Levy, B.	Orbs	WLP
Lewis, R.	Monophony I	LDo
Lidholm, I.	Sonat. 1946	EMf
Linthicum, D.	Pour la Flûte seule	CoA
Lorenzo, L. de	Suite mythologique, op. 38	WZ
Lourie, A.	The Flute of Pan	Ron
Lourie, A.	Sunrise	Ron
Louvier, A.	Promenade	ALe
Luening, O.	Suite No. 1	GaM
Lupi, R.	Nonephon. 1966	Car
Lutyens, E.	Variations	B-M
Maganini, Q.	Caprice Terpsichore, op. 12/2	CF
Maler, W.	Kleine Elegie. 1952	B&N
Malmlof-Forssling, K.	Sonata svickel	STI
Mamlok, U.	Variations. 1961	CoF
Mann, L.	Suite, op. 20B. 1963	Can
Manneke, D.	Jeux	SD
Mannino, F.	Melodie e contrappunti	Edi
Marais, M.-Schmitz	Les Folies d'Espagne	B&N
Marckhl, E.	Sonata. 1967	LDo
Martin, R.	En fanant	Dur
Martin, V.	2 Incantations	Com
Martino, D.	Quodlibets	M&M
Massenet, J.	Andante	Dur
Matsudaira, Y.	Rhymes for Gazzelloni. 1966	ESZ
Matsudaira, Y.	Somaksah	ESZ
Maury, L.	Lament	Wes
Maxwell	Voice in the Wilderness	Wes
McIntyre, P.	Abstract. 1963	Can
Mengelberg, K.	Soliloquio. 1952	SD
Michael, F.	Amun-Ra (Erotogramm II). 1970	WZ

Migot, G.	Le Mariage des Oiseaux	EMT
Migot, G.	Suite de 3 Pièces	ALe
Miller, E.	Song	M&M
Mills, C.	Larghetto and Allegro	CoF
Mills, C.	Variations on "Ite Missa Est"	CoF
Mimaroglu, I.	Capriccio. 1950	See
Moevs, R.	Pan	M&M
Moortel, A. van de	Sonata	Mau
Morel, F.	Nuvattuq. 1967 (afl)	Can
Morhange, E.	Marquis et Marquisette	Dur
Morhange, E.	Petite march militaire	Dur
Morley, C.	Les Bluets	Dur
Moroi, M.	Partita	ImV
Mortensen, F.	Sonata, op. 6	Nor
Morthenson, J.	Wechselspiel II	EMf
Moryl, R.	Particles	ACA
Moyse, L.	Pastorale (No. 3 of 7 ca-prices-études)	Bil
Mozart, W.	Don Juan	Dur
Mozart, W.	Tanzweisen (L. Mozart Notebook for Wolfgang)	NV
Muczynski, R.	3 Preludes	Sch
Müller, T.-Medek	Terzinen	Deu
Naumann, S.	Risposte I & II, op. 6	ESu
Naumann, S.	Sonat. 1949	EMf
Nielsen, C.	The Children Are Playing	WH
Nikiprowetzsky, T.	Sonatine	Bil
Nuten, P.	Improvisation	EMe
Ohana, M.	4 Improvisations	Bil
Osborne, W.	Fantasy	CoA
Pablo, L. de	Condicionado. 1962 (afl in G)	EdT
Paganini, N.-Pellerite	Caprice No. 23	TP
Paganini, N.-Pellerite	Caprice No. 24, a	Za
Paporisz, Y.	Miniaturen I-VI	HG
Parik, I.	Sonata	SHF
Paubon, P.	6 Pièces	EMT
Pentland, B.	Sonatina. 1954	Can
Pepin, C.	4 Monodies. 1955	MCA
Perle, G.	Monody I	TP
Persichetti, V.	Parable XII, op. 125	E-V
Peruzzi, A.	Tessiture. 1966	ESZ
Petrassi, G.	Souffle. 1969	ESZ
Petyrek, F.	3 Dances	UE
Pfister, H.	4 Esquisses	Hei
Pisk, P.	2nd Suite	ACA
Pisk, P.	Suite, op. 68	CoF
Polin, C.	Margoa	See
Polin, C.	o, Aderyn Pur	See
Polin, C.	Structures	E-V
Porcelijn, D.	Communications	Alb

Porcelijn, D.	Zen	SD
Porena, B.	D'Après. 1968	ESZ
Porret, J.	Les Succès francais, 26 morceaux célébres	EdR
Porret, J.	Le Tour du monde, 44 morceaux de tous les pays	EdR
Prosperi, C.	Filigrane	ESZ
Ramovs, P.	Expansion	EdD
Raphael, G.	Sonatas, op. 46/7, 8	WMS
Raphling, S.	Playthings of the Wind (Prelude)	EdM
Reinhardt, B.	12 mal 12. Spielstücke	ImV
Renosto, P.	Dinamica I	Ric
Reynolds, R.	Ambages	Pet
Riegger, W.	Suite, op. 8	TP
Rivier, J.	Oiseaux tendres	EdS
Rivier, J.	Virevoltes	Bil
Rivier, J.	Voltige	EdS
Rogers, B.	Study	Roc
Rollin, R.	2 Pieces	GaM
Rosenberg, H.	Sonat. 1959	ESu
Rothschild	Si vous n'avez rien a me dire	Dur
Ruiter, W. de	Solo	SD
Rychlík, J.	4 Partiten	Art
Rychlík, J.	4 Studi	Art
Sacco, P.	Moon Is Rising	Wes
Saint-Saens, C.	Mon Coeur s'ouvre a ta voix (Samson et Dalila)	Dur
Saint-Saens, C.	Printemps qui commence	Dur
Salmenhaara, E.	Prelude, Pop Tune and Fugue	EdF
Salzedo, C.	Volute and Rondel	SM
Saperstein, D.	Music	CoF
Saucier, G.	Expansion 9	Ken
Saucier, G.	Image	Ken
Schaeffer, B.	Cadenzas for Flute Concerti of the 18th Century	HSM
Schaffer, B.	2 Pieces	HMo
Schibler, A.	Solosonate, op. 9b	A&S
Schinstine, W.	Solitary Sequence	SM
Schmutz, A.	Nocturne	AlB
Schneider, G.-Marx	Variations, op. 44	M&M
Schneider, W.	Pan, drei Skizzen	SS
Schneider, W.	Sonata, op. 53	Hei
Schroeder	Sonata	MRL
Schroeder, H.	Sonata. 1971	HG
Schroeder, H.	Sonata No. 2	Pet
Schubert, M.	Sonata. 1966	Deu
Schumann, R.	Chant du soir	Dur
Scott, C.	Ecstatic Shepherd	SM
Scott, C.	The Ecstatic Shepherd	SS

Scott, S.	Egyptian Suite	SM
Sehlbach, E.	Musik, op. 53/1	MV
Shaughnessy, R.	Paradigm	See
Sheriff, N.	Arabesque. 1966	Isr
Sheriff, N.	Invention. 1967	Isr
Shevitz, A.	Improvisations	B-M
Sigtenhorst Meyer, B.	Sonatine. 1930, op. 34	Als
Sigtenhorst Meyer, B.	3 Rustical Miniatures, op. 24	Als
Sigtenhorst Meyer, B.	3 Rustical Miniatures, op. 40	Als
Sigtenhorst Meyer, B.	3 Rustical Miniatures, op. 45	Als
Siohan, R.	3 Pièces	EdS
Smith, B.	Andromeda M31	HE
Smith, H.	3 Brevities	CoF
Smolanoff, M.	Set of Three	See
Soderholm, V.	Vocaliser No. 1-3. 1966	STI
Soderholm, V.	Vocalis No. 4. 1968	STI
Soderholm, V.	Vocalis No. 5. 1970	STI
Soegijo, P.	Saih 1. 1971 (bfl)	B&B
Sorenson, T.	Sonat, "Fyra gravyrer"	EMf
Somers, H.	Etching--The Vollard Suite. 1964	Can
Sommerfeldt, O.	Divertimento, op. 9	Nor
Souffriau, A.	Sonate	Mau
Staeps, H.	Virtuose Suite	SS
Stamitz, J.-Gradenwitz	Capriccio-Sonata	BrH
Stamitz, J.-Gradenwitz	Rondo capriccioso	BrH
Steffens, W.	Structure de la Rose. 1970, op. 20	B&B
Steiger, C.	Gavotte	Dur
Steiger, C.	Menuet de Grand'Mère	Dur
Steiger, C.	Romance	Dur
Steiger, C.	Valse	Dur
Stein, L.	Sonata	CoF
Stern, M.	2 Pièces	Dur
Stockhausen, K.	Spiral	UE
Strang, G.	Sonata	B-M
Strange, A.	The Doug Meyers(') Playing Flute	MeP
Stringfield, L.	Pastoral Scene	MCA
Stutschewsky, J.	5 Pieces. 1956	Isr
Swack, I.	Invocation	CoF
Swisher, G.	Theme and Variations	Roc
Taira, Y.	Hierophonie IV	ERR
Takemitsu, T.	Voice	EdS
Tautenhahn, G.	Sonatina	See
Telemann, G.-Bopp	3 Suites	B&N
Telemann, G.-Larrieu	12 Fantaisies	Bil
Telemann, G.-Hauswald	12 Fantasien	B&N
Telemann, G.-Rampal	12 Fantasias	Int
Telemann, G.-Moyse	12 Fantasies	Sch

Thomson, V.	Sonata	E-V
Thorne, F.	Sonatina	Gen
Tomasi, H.	Les Cyclades	ALe
Tomasi, H.	Sonatina	ALe
Touma, H.	Studie Nr. 1	ImV
Touma, H.	Studie Nr. 2 "Combinations"	ImV
Tuthill, B.	3 Moods	SM
Ulrich, E.	Sonatina	TP
Varèse, E.	Density 21.5	B-M
Vivaldi, A.-Rousseau, Marx	Le Printemps	M&M
Voiculescu, D.	Piccola Sonata	EdR
Voss, F.	Musik. 1952	BrH
Voss, F.	Variationen. 1967	BrH
Wachs, P.	Pendant la cueillette	Dur
Wachs, P.	Le Petite Laitière	Dur
Wagner, R.	Choeur des fileuses (Le Vaisseau Fantome)	Dur
Wagner, R.	Lohengrin, Grand Duo	Dur
Wagner, R.	Romance de l'Etoile (Tannhauser)	Dur
Weiner, S.	Sonate, op. 30	Bil
Weisling, R.	This (afl)	MeP
Wellesz, E.	Suite, op. 57	Ron
Whittenberg, C.	Monade, op. 51	CoF
Widdoes, L.	Sonatina	TP
Wigglesworth, F.	Lake Music	TP
Wildberger, J.	Retrospective 1	HG
Wildberger, J.	Retrospective II. 1971	HG
Witkin, B.	Interludes	AMC
Wittinger, R.	Strutture simmetriche, op. 17. 1969	BrH
Wuorinen, C.	Flute Variations	M&M
Yannay, Y.	Statement in memoriam A. U. Boskovich. 1964	Isr
Zbinden, J.	4 Miniatures, op. 14	HG
Ziino, O.	Melos per Faja	Edi
Zimmermann, B.	Tempus loquendi. 1963	SS
Zindars, E.	Transposed Light	AMC
Zonn, P.	Grunge	CoF

Flute and Piano or Harpsichord

	Morceaux de Concours et pièces d'audition	ALe
	Easy to Play Pieces	Ash
	Intermediate Pieces	Ash

	51 Masterpieces	B-M
	Anthology--10 Pieces	BrH
	Celebrated Compositions (16 Classical and Romantic Pieces)	BrH
	Everyday Favorites	CF
	Flutist's Delight, 2 vols.	CF
	Pleasures of Pan, 6 vols.	CF
	Contemporary French Recital Pieces, 2 vols.	Int
	Easy Flute Solos	MS
	Flute Solos	MS
	More Easy Flute Solos	MS
	Selected Flute Solos	MS
	Modern Flute Music, 2 vols.	OxU
	Classic Pieces	Pet
	Indispensable Folio	Rub
	Radio Collection of National Songs & Hymns	Rub
	Sacred Solos	Rub
	Soloist Folio	Rub
	Broadway Showcase	War
	Devotional Solos	War
-Briccialdi, Wilkins	Carnival of Venice	Lud
-Martinotti	Concerto di Traverso	ESZ
-Bettoney	Dark Eyes	CF
-Harris	Deep River	CF
	Sonata, d	LDo
	Meditation (Sonatina in F)	NK
-Bettoney	Song of the Volga Boatmen	CF
Abel, C.	Concerto, C	B&N
Abel, C.-Peters	Concerto, C	Hei
Abel, C.	6 Sonates, op. 5, 2 vols. (fl, bc)	EdH
Abel, C.-Beechey	Sonata, op. 6/3, e (fl, bc)	OxU
Abel, C.-Beechey	Sonata, G, op. 6/6 (fl, bc)	B&N
Abel, C.-Sonntag	Sonata, C	Hei
Abel, C.-Sonntag	Sonata, D	Hei
Abel, C.-Sonntag	Sonata, F	Hei
Abel, C.-Bruggen	Sonate, G	B&V
Abel, C.-Riley	Sonata No. 3	SM
Abramson, R.	Evening Song	AMC
Abt, F.	O Ye Tears	CF
Adam, A.	O Holy Night	Rub
Adams, S.-DeLamater	The Holy City	Rub
Adolphus, M.	Opus 99	CoF
Ahnell, E.	Toccata, Adagio, Allegro	CoA
Akimenko, T.-Voxman	Idyll	Rub
Alain, J.	3 Mouvements	ALe
Albéniz, I.-Fleury	Berceuse	ALe
Albéniz, I.-Amaz	Mallorca. Barcarola	UME

14

Flute and Piano or Harpsichord

Albéniz, I.-Fleury	Le Printemps	ALe
Albéniz, I.-Amaz	Puerta de tierra	UME
Albinoni, T.	Adagio, g	GD
Albinoni, T.-Brinckmann, Ponten	Concerto, G	HSM
Albinoni, T.-Ruf	Concerto, G	B-M
Albinoni, T.-Schaffler	Sonata, a (fl, bc)	NV
Albrecht, G. von	Preludio e Fuga, op. 59	Be
Alderighi, D.	Divertimento	ESZ
Alessandro, R. d'	Serenade	EMP
Alessandro, R. d'	Sonate	EMP
Aletter, W.	Rendezvous	NK
Alexander, J.	Sonata	Gen
Alexeyev, M.	Sonata from the Cycle "Chuvash Melodies"	
Alpaerts, F.	Concertstuk	EMe
Alt, H.	Red Clouds	OxU
Altés, H.	La Vénitienne, op. 4	Bil
Altés, H.	L'Helvétienne, op. 5	Bil
Altés, H.	5th Solo de concours, g, op. 24	Bil
Altés, H.	6th Solo de concours, Bb, op. 25	Bil
Altmann, H.	Sonata, op. 37	HSM
Alwyn, W.	3 Easy Pieces	GaM
Amalie von Preussen, P. -Lenzewski	Sonata (fl, hpcd)	CFV
Ambrosius, H.	Concerto	RuE
Ameller, A.	Chicoutimi	ALe
Ameller, A.	Le Lys martagon	HLe
Ames, W.	Sonata	ACA
Ames, W.	Sonata	ACA
Amirov, F.	Piece on an Azerbaijan Folk Theme	MKE
Ancelin, P.-Rampal	Concerto Giocoso, op. 33	Bil
Anderberg, C.	Duo. 1957	STI
Andersen, J.-Rampal	Moto Perpetuo, op. 8	Bil
Andersen, J.-Heriche	Moto Perpetuo, op. 8	Bil
Andersen, J.	Variations Drolatiques, op. 26	CF
Andersen, J.	Variations Elégiaques, op. 27	CF
Andersen, J.	Opera Fantasy, op. 45/2 (Norma)	WH
Andersen, J.	Opera Fantasy, op. 45/4 (Merry Wives of Windsor)	WH
Andersen, J.	Intermezzo, op. 51/2	CF
Andersen, J.	Canzone, op. 53/1	CF
Andersen, J.-Voxman	Elegie, op. 55/1	Rub
Andersen, J.	Scherzino, op. 55/6	B-M
Andersen, J.	Scherzino, op. 55/6	CF
Andersen, J.-Voxman	Scherzino, op. 55/6	Rub
Andersen, J.-Cavally	Scherzino, op. 55/6	SM
Andersen, J.	Scherzino, op. 55/6	WZ
Andersen, J.-Cavally	Die Blumen, op. 56/2	SM

Flute and Piano or Harpsichord

Andersen, J.-Cavally	Im Herbst, op. 56/1	SM
Andersen, J.-Cavally	Tourbillon, op. 57/3	SM
Andersen, J.	Le Tourbillon, op. 57/3	WH
Andersen, J.	Introduction and Caprice, op. 58	WH
Andersen, J.	Ecossais, op. 59/2	WH
Andersen, J.	Russe, op. 59/3	WH
Andersen, J.	Suédois, op. 59/4	WH
Andersen, J.	Italien, op. 59/5	WH
Andersen, J.	Intermezzo, op. 62/2	WH
Andersen, J.	Dans la Gondole, op. 62/3	WH
Andersen, J.	Sérénade d'Amour, op. 62/4	WH
Andersen, J.	Ballad and Danse des Sylphes	SM
Andersen, J.	De lystige knoer, opera-fantasi	WH
Andersen, J.	Den hvide dame, opera-fantasi	WH
Andersen, J.	Der Freischutz, opera-fantasi	WH
Andersen, J.	Don Juan, opera-fantasi	WH
Andersen, J.-Cavally	The Mill	SM
Anderson, R.	Prelude & Rondo	AMC
Andriessen, H.	Kleine Suite	HU
Andriessen, H.	Variations on a Theme by Couperin	SD
Andriessen, L.	Paintings	HMo
Andriessen, L.	Sonata. 1956	SD
Andrieu, F.	Rossignol d'amour	Bil
-Dolmetsch	Greensleeves	S&C
-Kolz	3 Sinfonias (fl, bc)	LDo
-Staeps, Kolz	Sonata, d	LDo
-Rodemann	3 Sonatas (fl, bc)	NV
-Bouvet	Suite, F (fl, bc)	EME
Antheil, G.	Sonata	MS
Arambarri, J.	Ofrenda a Falla	UME
Arban, J.-Vanasek	Perpetual Motion	MCA
Arditi, L.	Il Bacio	Dur
Arma, P.	Divertimento No. 1	EMT
Arma, P.	12 Danses Roumaines de Transylvanie	HLe
Arnell, R.	Andante and Allegro, op. 58	S&C
Arnold, M.	Concerto	Pat
Arnold, M.	Sonatina	AlL
Arrieu, C.	Concerto, G. 1946	Amp
Arrieu, C.	Scherzo	E&C
Arrieu, C.	Sonatine	Amp
Atkinson, C.	Moods for Flute	PrA
Aubain, J.	Air Baroque	ALe
Aubert, J.-Barrère	Air	Sch
Aubert, J.	Gigue	EdM

Flute and Piano or Harpsichord

Aubert, L.	Introduction et Allegro	Dur
Aubert, L.	Madrigal, op. 9/1	Dur
Aubert, L.-Garban	Nocturne (3 Esquisses)	Dur
Aubert, L.-Garban	Romance	Dur
Aubin, T.	Air Baroque	ALe
Aubin, T.	The Calm of the Sea (Eolian Suite)	ALe
Aubin, T.	Concerto dell'Amicizia	ALe
Audran, E.-Genin	Gillette de Narbonne fantaisie	ECh
Audran, E.-Herman, Bull	La Mascotte (2 fantaisies)	ECh
Auric, G.	Imaginées	EdS
Avidom, M.	Concerto	ImV
Avon, E.-Klump	Danse Joyeuse	CF
Aydlette -Organn	Janina	Reb
Babell, W.-Tilmouth	Sonata, g	OxU
Bach, C.-Fischer	Spring's Awakening	CF
Bach, C.-Gallo	Spring's Awakening	CF
Bach, C.P.E.-Walther	12 Kleine Stücke	WZ
Bach, C.P.E.	Concerto, A	Eul
Bach, C.P.E.-Rampal	Concerto, A, Wq. 168	Int
Bach, C.P.E.-Rampal	Concerto, Bb, Wq. 167	Int
Bach, C.P.E.-Rampal	Concerto, C	Int
Bach, C.P.E.-Rampal	Concerto, d, Wq. 22	Int
Bach, C.P.E.-Redel	Concerto, d, Wq. 22	Leu
Bach, C.P.E.-Rampal	Concerto, G, Wq. 169	Int
Bach, C.P.E.-Lasocki	Concerto, G, Wq. 169	MR
Bach, C.P.E.-Laubenstein	Rondo Espressivo	CF
Bach, C.P.E.	2 Sonatas, a, D	EdK
Bach, C.P.E.	2 Sonatas, G, e	EdK
Bach, C.P.E.-Walther	Sonatas, G, e, Wq. 123, 124 (fl, bc)	B&N
Bach, C.P.E.-Walther	Sonatas, a, D, Wq. 128, 131 (fl, bc)	B&N
Bach, C.P.E.-Walther	4 Sonaten, WV 83-36, 2 vols.	BrH
Bach, C.P.E.-Walther	6 Sonatas (Wotq. 125-127, 129, 130, 134)	WZ
Bach, C.P.E.-Walther	Sonata No. 1, Bb	WZ
Bach, C.P.E.-Walther	Sonata No. 2, D	WZ
Bach, C.P.E.-Walther	Sonata No. 3, G	WZ
Bach, C.P.E.-Walther	Sonata No. 4, D	WZ
Bach, C.P.E.-Walther	Sonata No. 5, Bb	WZ
Bach, C.P.E.-Walther	Sonata No. 6, G	WZ
Bach, C.P.E.	Sonata, Bb, W. 161/2 (fl, hpcd)	MR
Bach, C.P.E.-Scheck, Ruf	Sonata, Bb (fl, bc)	Ric
Bach, C.P.E.	Sonata, C	CF
Bach, C.P.E.-Rampal	Sonata, C	Int
Bach, C.P.E.-Scheck, Ruf	Sonata, C, Wq. 87	Ric
Bach, C.P.E.-Leeuwen	Sonata, C	WZ
Bach, C.P.E.	Sonata, D	Ric

17

Flute and Piano or Harpsichord

Bach, C.P.E.-Schmitz	Sonata, G, Wq. 133 (fl,bc)	B&N
Bach, C.P.E.-Ruf	Sonata, G (fl,bc)	Ric
Bach, C.P.E.-Scheck, Ruf	Sonata, G	Ric
Bach, C.P.E.-Walther	Hamburger Sonate (fl,bc)	SS
Bach, J.C.-Marteau	Andante Cantabile	Lud
Bach, J.C.-Ruyssen	Concerto, 1st Movement	GD
Bach, J.C.	6 Sonatas, op. 16	Hei
Bach, J.C.-Küster	2 Sonatas, D. G. op. 16/1, 2	NV
Bach, J.C.-Küster	Sonata, A, op. 16/4	NV
Bach, J.C.	Sonata, op. 18/1	WH
Bach, J.C.-Hinnenthal	Sonate, F	BrH
Bach, J.C.-Marguerre	Sonata, F	HMo
Bach, J.C.-Ruf	Sonata No. 1, d (6 Sonatas)	SS
Bach, J.C.-Ruf	Sonata No. 2, D (6 Sonatas)	SS
Bach, J.C.F.-Meylan	Concerto, D	UE
Bach, J.C.F.-Schwedler	6 Sonatas	WZ
Bach, J.C.F.-Wittenbecher	Sonata No. 1, D	WZ
Bach, J.C.F.-Wittenbecher	Sonata No. 2, G	WZ
Bach, J.C.F.-Wittenbecher	Sonata No. 3, C	WZ
Bach, J.C.F.-Wittenbecher	Sonata No. 4, A	WZ
Bach, J.C.F.-Wittenbecher	Sonata No. 5, F	WZ
Bach, J.C.F.-Wittenbecher	Sonata No. 6, Bb	WZ
Bach, J.C.F.-Ruf	Sonata, D (fl, hpcd)	NV
Bach, J.C.F.-Hinnenthal	Sonata, F	BrH
Bach, J.S.-Brochlin	Adagio (Toccata & Fugue, C)	BrH
Bach, J.S.	Andante (Sinfonia)	MM
Bach, J.S.-Zverov	Andante (Sonata, a, violin)	SM
Bach, J.S.	4 Arias from Cantatas	Mit
Bach, J.S.-Taffanel	Aria, D	Dur
Bach, J.S.	Aria (Christmas Oratorio)	Pet
Bach, J.S.-Gaylord	Arioso (Cantata No. 156)	CF
Bach, J.S.-Barrère	Arioso	Sch
Bach, J.S.-Crossman	Art of the Fugue I	PMP
Bach, J.S.-Barrère	Badinerie	GaM
Bach, J.S.	Badinerie	Ham
Bach, J.S.-Barrère	Bourree (Suite, b)	Sch
Bach J.S.-Radeke, Haverkampf	Concerto, e (after BWV 1059 and 35)	BrH
Bach, J.S.-Lenzewski	Fuga canonica (Musical Offering)	CFV
Bach, J.S.	Italian Concerto	CF
Bach, J.S.-Schwedler	Italian Concerto	WZ
Bach, J.S.-Guenther	Minuet	B-M
Bach, J.S.-Voxman	2 Menuettos (Flute Sonata, C)	Rub
Bach, J.S.-Stouffer	Musette	Ken
Bach, J.S.-Marion	Partita	Bil
Bach, J.S.-Mueller, Berndsen	Partita, c	HSM
Bach, J.S.-Barrère	Polonaise	GaM

Bach, J.S.-Caratgé	Polonaise and Badinerie (Suite, b)	ALe
Bach, J.S.-Maganini	Polonaise and Badinage	CF
Bach, J.S.-Gaubert	Saraband (Suite in G)	ALe
Bach, J.S.-Fischer	Schlafe, mein Liebster	For
Bach, J.S.	Siciliano	EdM
Bach, J.S.-Buchtel	Siciliano	NK
Bach, J.S.-Barrère	Siciliano (Sonata, Eb)	Sch
Bach, J.S.-Frotscher	Sinfonia, b	B&N
Bach, J.S.-Moyse	Sonata No. 1, b	ALe
Bach, J.S.-Moyse	Sonata No. 2, Eb	ALe
Bach, J.S.-Moyse	Sonata No. 3, A	ALe
Bach, J.S.-Moyse	Sonata No. 4, a	ALe
Bach, J.S.-Moyse	Sonata No. 5, e	ALe
Bach, J.S.-Moyse	Sonata No. 6, E	ALe
Bach, J.S.-Moyse	Sonata No. 7, g	ALe
Bach, J.S.-Roth	Sonata No. 1, b	B&H
Bach, J.S.-Roth	Sonata No. 2, Eb	B&H
Bach, J.S.-Roth	Sonata No. 3, A	B&H
Bach, J.S.-Le Roy	Sonate No. 1, b	Bil
Bach, J.S.-Le Roy	Sonate No. 2, Eb	Bil
Bach, J.S.-Le Roy	Sonate No. 3, A	Bil
Bach, J.S.-Barrère	Bach Sonatas, 2 vols.	BM
Bach, J.S.-Silver, Francis	3 Sonatas	B&H
Bach, J.S.-Schmitz, Schneider	Sonatas, e, BWV 1034; E, BWV 1035; b, BWV 1030; A, BWV 1032	B&N
Bach, J.S.-Barge, Spiro, Todt	6 Sonatas, S. 1030-1035, 2 vols.	BrH
Bach, J.S.	Sonata No. 1	CF
Bach, J.S.	Sonata No. 2	CF
Bach, J.S.	Sonata No. 3	CF
Bach, J.S.	Sonata No. 4	CF
Bach, J.S.	Sonata No. 5	CF
Bach, J.S.	Sonata No. 6	CF
Bach, J.S.-Fleury	6 Sonatas, 2 vols.	Dur
Bach, J.S.-Kincaid, Polin	Sonatas	E-V
Bach, J.S.-Rampal	6 Sonatas, 2 vols.	Int
Bach, J.S.	Sonatas, 2 vols. (Urtext)	Pet
Bach, J.S.-Moyse	7 Sonatas, 2 vols.	Sch
Bach, J.S.-Wummer, Tournerie	6 Sonatas	SM
Bach, J.S.	Sonata, a	MKE
Bach, J.S.-Balet	Sonata, g, BWV 1020 (fl, hpcd)	B&N
Bach, J.S.-Rampal	Sonata, g	Int
Bach, J.S.	Sonata, BWV 1030	S&C
Bach, J.S.-Alkan	Sonata (fl, hpcd)	Bil
Bach, J.S.-Cavally	Sonata for Flute Alone	SM
Bach, J.S.-Sieber	Suite, b	B&H

Bach, J.S.-Eck	Suite, b	CF
Bach, J.S.-Johnson	Suite (Overture) No. 2, b	HE
Bach, J.S.-Wummer	Suite No. 2, b	Int
Bach, J.S.-List, Weyrauch	Suite, b (Overture No. 2)	Pet
Bach, J.S.-Moyse	Suite, b	Sch
Bach, J.S.-Callimahos	Suite, b, BWV 1067	SS
Bach, J.S.-Bopp	Suite, c	B&N
Bach, J.S.-Rampal	Suite, c	Int
Bach-Gounod	Ave Maria	CF
Bacon, E.	Burnt Cabin Branch	Ron
Badings, H.	Capriccio. 1936	SD
Badings, H.	Cavatina. 1952	SD
Bailey, P.	Sonata	TP
Baily, J.	Capriccio	ScF
Bak, M.	3 Pieces	MKE
Baker, M.	Sonata	SM
Baksa, R.	Aria da Capo	Sha
Balan, J.	2 Capriccios, op. 99	B&B
Balazs, F.	2 Dances	CoF
Balicourt, S.-Petit	Sonata No. 2 (fl, bc)	GD
Balleron, L.	Le Moineau du Luxembourg	EdS
Balleron, L.	Ode a Sainte-Cecile	EdS
Balleron, L.	L'Oiseau tapageur	EdS
Ballif, C.	Mouvements pour deux, op. 27	B&B
Ballif, C.	Sonate, op. 23	B&B
Banks, D.	3 Episodes. 1964	S&C
Bantai, V., Kovats, I	Small Performance Pieces	EMB
Bantock, G.	Pagan Poem	GaM
Barab, S.	Pastorals	GaM
Barati, G.	Hawaiian Bird-Catching Song	ACA
Barber, S.	Canzone (Piano Concerto, op. 38)	Sch
Bardwell, W.	Sarabande	S&C
Bariller, R.	Le Martyre de Marsyas	ALe
Bariller, R.	Pluies d'Avril	ALe
Barlow, F.	Pavane	HLe
Barnard, G.	Gloriana	CF
Barnard, G.	Moana Waltz	Bar
Barnes, M.	Sonata. 1965	Can
Barraine, E.	Elégie et Ronde	GrF
Barraud, H.	Concerto	B&H
Barre, M. de la -Viollier	Sonata, G	ERS
Barre, M. de la -Nagel, Radeke	Suite, F (fl, bc)	HSM
Barre, M. de la -Ruf	Suite, G (fl, bc)	Ric
Barrère, G.	Nocturne	Sch
Barsanti, F.-Ruf	Sonata, Bb (fl, bc)	B&N
Barsanti, F.-Ruf	Sonata, C (fl, bc)	B&N
Barsanti, F.-Ruf	Sonata, c (fl, bc)	B&N
Barsanti, F.-Bergmann	Sonata No. 1, d (fl, bc)	S&C

Barsanti, F.-Bergmann	Sonata, F (fl,bc)	S&C
Barsanti, F. -Bergmann	Sonata, g (fl,bc)	S&C
Barta, L.	Sonata	Art
Barthe, A.	Petite Suite Pittoresque	SM
Bartók, B.-Harris	Evening in the Country	Lud
Bartók, B.-Arma	Suite Paysanne Hongroise	EMB
Bartók, B.-Szebenyi	3 Chansons Populaires Hongroises	EMB
Bartók, B. -Arma	3 Popular Hungarian Songs	EMB
Bartos, J.	6 Praeludien. 1963	Art
Bartow, N.	Sonata	Sha
Bartsch, C.	Improvisation et Scherzo	Mau
Basart, R.	Fantasy. 1963	EdS
Basart, R.	Sonate	EdS
Bate, S.	Sonate	EdL
Bate, S.	Sonatina	S&C
Batiste -Taylor	Lament of Pan	B-M
Baton, C.-Neate	Premiere Suite	S&C
Baur, J.	Incontri. 1960	BrH
Bazlik, I.	5 Compositions	SHF
Beaucamp, A.	Fantaisie	ALe
Beaumont, P.	Con Amore	Cen
Beck, C.	Sonatine	SS
Beck, J.	Sonata	Uni
Beckerath, A. von	Sonate	MV
Beecroft, N.	3 Pezzi Brevi. 1962	UE
Beekhuis, H.	Rondo capriccioso. 1947	SD
Beers, J.	Sonata	EME
Beers, J.	Suite	SD
Beeson, J.	Song	Sha
Beethoven, L. van	Adagio (Sonata Pathetique)	CF
Beethoven, L. van -Buchtel	Adagio (Sonata Pathetique)	NK
Beethoven, L. van	Allegro (Sonata Pathetique)	CF
Beethoven, L. van -Gariboldi	Andante Cantabile, op. 97	GaM
Beethoven, L. van -Leeuwen	Largo	WZ
Beethoven, L. van -Gaubert	Melody	ALe
Beethoven, L. van -Trinkaus	Minuet	CF
Beethoven, L. van	Moonlight Sonata (Adagio)	Cen
Beethoven, L. van	Polonaise, op. 8	Ham
Beethoven, L. van -Roth	Serenade, op. 25	B&H
Beethoven, L. van	Serenade, op. 41, D	Pet
Beethoven, L. van -Katz	6 Allemandes	SF
Beethoven, L. van	6 Variierte Themen, op. 105 2 vols.	BrH
Beethoven, L. van -Jeney	6 Variierte Themen, op. 105	EMB
Beethoven, L. van -Hess	Sonata, Bb	BrH
Beethoven, L. van -Laube	Sonata	CF
Beethoven, L. van	Sonata	EdK
Beethoven, L. van -Leeuwen	Sonata	WZ
Beethoven, L. van	10 Variierte Themen, op. 107	

	5 vols.	BrH
Beethoven, L. van –Jeney	10 Variierte Themen, op. 107,	
	Vol. I, Nos. 1-5	EMB
Beethoven, L. van	Theme varié, op. 8	Ham
Beethoven, L. van –Guenther	Two Dances	B-M
Beethoven, L. van –Jarecki	Variationen über Volkweisen,	
	op. 105, 107	UE
Belaubre, L.-A. Marion	Concerto	Bil
Belval, E.	Coquerico	EdS
Benda, F.-Lebermann	Concerto, e	SS
Benda, F.-Ruetz	Sonata, G, op. 3/1 (fl, hpcd)	NV
Benda, F.-Ruf	Sonata, G, op. 3/1	SS
Benda, F.-Schoenbaum	Sonate, e (fl, bc)	B&N
Benda, F.	Sonata, F	EdM
Benda, G.-Janetzky	Sonata, C (fl, bc)	FrH
Benda, G.-Janetzky	Sonata, e	FrH
Bendik, M.-arr.	Leichte Original-Musik des	
	17. und 18. Jahrhunderts	SS
Ben-Haim, P.	3 Lieder ohne Worte	ImV
Benker, H.	Der Abreiss-Kalender,	
	Miniature Suite. 1955	BrH
Bennett, D.	Flute Royale	Bar
Bennett, R.	Flute Fresco	SM
Bennett, R.R.	Winter Music	B-M
Benoit, P.-Vieuxtemps	Poème Symphonique	ScF
Benoit, P.-Cavally	Symphonic Poem	SM
Bent, R.	Swiss Boy	CF
Bentzon, N.	Variations on an Original	
	Theme, op. 17	WH
Berbiguier, T.	Souvenir du Tyrol, op. 103	EdH
Berbiguier, T.	Les Regrets, op. 104	EdH
Berdiev, N.	Impromptu and Scherzo	MKE
Bereau, J.	Noir asile	ECh
Berger, J.	Suite	BB
Bergh, H.	Caprice No. 4	Wes
Berghmans, J.	The Sultan's Favorites (Scenes	
	from a Traveling Circus)	ALe
Bergmann, W.	Prelude	S&E
Beriot, C.	Adagio de la sonate	Ham
Berkeley, L.	Concerto	Che
Berkeley, L.	Sonatina	S&C
Berlioz, H.	3 Songs (Damnation of Faust)	EdM
Bermeiser, V.	Kleine Suite	LDo
Bernaud, A.	Incantation et Danse	ERR
Berry, W.	Duo	SM
Berthomieu, M.	Suite romantique	Com
Bertoni, F.-Haas	Canzona	Rub
Bertouille, G.	Aria et divertimento. 1956	CBD
Bettoney-Findlay -arr.	Pearls of the Old Masters,	
	2 vols.	CF

Beversdorf, T.	Sonata	SM
Bialas, G.	Concerto	WMS
Bialas, G.	Sonate. 1946	WMS
Binet, J.	Sonatine	EMP
Binkerd, G.	Sonatine	B&H
Bistritzky, Z	Sicilienne	SF
Bitsch, M.	3 Sonatines	ALe
Bitti, M.-Ruf	Sonatas, c, a (fl, bc)	B&N
Bitti, M.-Ruf	Sonatas, g, G (fl, bc)	B&N
Bizet, G.	Adagietto (L'Arlésienne)	EdM
Bizet, G.	Adagio (Symphony in C)	EdM
Bizet, G.	Aragonaise (Carmen)	EdM
Bizet, G.-Genin	L'Arlésienne fantaisie	ECh
Bizet, G.-Borne	Carmen fantaisie	ECh
Bizet, G.-Gariboldi	Carmen	ECh
Bizet, G.-Genin	Carmen (2 fantaisies)	ECh
Bizet, G.-Herman, Bull	Carmen fantaisie	ECh
Bizet, G.-Herman, Weber	Carmen fantaisie	ECh
Bizet, G.	Carmen	ES
Bizet, G.	Entr'acte (Carmen)	EdM
Bizet, G.-Spiegl	Intermezzo	OxU
Bizet, G.-Brooke	Minuet de l'Arlésienne	CF
Bizet, G.-Caso	Menuet (L'Arlésienne Suite No. 2)	CF
Bizet, G.-Delsaux	2e Menuet de l'Arlésienne	ECh
Bizet, G.	Minuet (L'Arlésienne)	EdM
Bizet, G.	Second Minuet (L'Arlésienne)	EdM
Bizet, G.	Menuet (L'Arlésienne)	MM
Bizet, G.	Minuet (L'Arlésienne)	NK
Bizet, G.-Voxman	Menuet (L'Arlésienne Suite No. 2)	Rub
Bizet, G.	Menuet (L'Arlésienne Suite No. 2)	Wat
Bizet, G.-Gariboldi	Les Pecheurs de perles	ECh
Bizet, G.	Petit mari, petite femme	Dur
Bizet, G.	Serenade Espagnole	EdM
Bizet, G.-Andraud	3 Pieces	SM
Bizet, G.-Roberts	Toreador Song	CF
Bjelik, M.	Dialog	LDo
Bjelinski, B.	Concerto	UE
Bjorkander, N.	Duo, op. 7	STI
Blacher, B.	Duo. 1972	B&B
Blavet, M.-Vester	Concerto, a	B&V
Blavet, M.-Ruf	Concerto, a	Ric
Blavet, M.-Kolneder	6 Sonatas, op. 2, 2 vols.	B&N
Blavet, M.-Ruf	Sonata, d, op. 2/2 (fl, bc)	SS
Blavet, M.-Ruf	Sonata, e, op. 2/3 (fl, bc)	SS
Blavet, M.-Fleury	Sonata No. 1, G, "L'Henriette"	B&H
Blavet, M.-Fleury	Sonata No. 2, d, "La Vibray"	B&H

Blavet, M.-Fleury	Sonata No. 3, e, "La Dhérou-	
	ville"	B&H
Blavet, M.-Fleury	Sonata No. 4, g, "La Lumagne"	B&H
Blavet, M.-Fleury	Sonata No. 5, D, "La Chaurel"	B&H
Blavet, M.-Fleury	Sonata No. 6, a, "La Bouget"	B&H
Blavet, M.	Sonata No. 3	CF
Blavet, M.	Sonata No. 4	CF
Blavet, M.-Ruf	Sonata, b (fl,bc)	B&N
Blezard, W.	Suite	Nov
Bloch, E.	Suite Modale	BB
Bloch, E.	2 Last Poems	BB
Blodek, V.	Concerto	ES
Blodek, V.-Cavally	Concerto	SM
Blumer, T.	Aus dem Pflanzenreich, op.57b	WZ
Blumer, T.	Aus der Tierwelt, op. 57a	WZ
Blumer, T.	Sonata, op. 61	WZ
Boccherini, L.	Celebrated Minuet	NK
Boccherini, L.-Upmeyer	Concerto, D, op. 27	B&N
Boccherini, L.-Vené	Concerto, D, op. 27	B-M
Boccherini, L.-Rampal	Concerto, D, op. 27	Int
Boccherini, L.-Redel	Concerto, D, op. 27	Leu
Boccherini, L.-Leeuwen	Concerto, D, op. 27	SM
Boccherini, L.-Gaubert	Minuet (Quintet, E)	ALe
Boccherini, L.	Menuet	CF
Boccherini, L.	Menuet	MM
Boccherini, L.	Sicilienne	Ham
Boehm, T.-Heriche	Nel cor piu, op. 4	Bil
Boehm, T.	Air suisse, op. 20	Bil
Boehm, T.	Le Desir, op. 21	Bil
Boehm, T.	Air allemand, op. 22	Bil
Boehm, T.-Bettoney	Souvenir des Alpes, op. 27/1	CF
Boehm, T.	Andante Pastorale, op. 31/5	CF
Boehm, T.-Haas	Andante (First Concerto)	Rub
Bohm, C.-Gilbert	The Bee	CF
Bohm, C.-Isaac	Perpetual Motion (Suite 3,	
	No. 6)	CF
Bois, R. du	7 Bagatelles. 1964	SD
Boisdeffre, R.	Au bord d'un ruisseau	Ham
Boisdeffre, R.-de Vroye	Mélodie, op. 20/1	E&C
Boisdeffre, R.-Cavally	Orientale, op. 21	SM
Boisdeffre, R.	Pastorale	Ham
Boisdeffre, R.	Sérénade	Ham
Boisdeffre, R.	Sonate No. 2	Ham
Boisdeffre, R.	3 Pièces	Ham
Boismortier, J.-Pincherle	Sonates, op. 91 (fl,hpcd)	Heu
Boismortier, J.		
-Parkinson	Sonata, e	OxU
Boismortier, J.-Ruf	Suite, b	SS
Boismortier, J.-Ruf	Suite, G, op. 35/2	SS
Bon, W.	5 Tours de Passe-passe,	

	op. 18	B&V
Bondon, J.	Mouvement Chorégraphique	ECh
Bonis, M.	Sonata	EME
Bonner	Over the Hills	EdM
Bononcini, G. -Richardson	6 Pieces from a Divertimento	B&H
Boone, C.	Oblique Formation	EdS
Bordier, J.	Berceuse	Dur
Borne, F. Le -Ephross	Carmen Fantaisie	SM
Borne, F. Le	Danse de la bayadere	ScF
Bornyi, L.	My Fish	Wat
Borodin, A. -Buchtel	Polovtsian Dance (Prince Igor)	NK
Borodin, A. -Walters	Polovtsian Dance((Prince Igor)	Rub
Borowski, F. -Buchtel	Adoration	NK
Borowski, F.	The Piping Faun	B-M
Borris, S.	Partita, op. 27/1	Mit
Borris, S.	Sonata, op. 22	Hei
Bortolotti	Simmetrie, G (fl/pic/afl, pf)	B-M
Bossi, M.	Improvviso	Bon
Bossler, K.	Kapriziose Musik	B&N
Bossler, K.	Sonatina, op. 33	MRL
Bossler, K.	Sonatine, op. 111	B&N
Bottje, W.	Episodes (fl, hpcd)	Col
Boucard	Petite pièce	EdR
Boughton, R.	Concerto	B&H
Bouillard, H.	En Benodet	GrF
Bouillard, H.	Fantaisie	GrF
Bouillard, H.	Tristesse	GrF
Boulanger, L.	Cortège	B-M
Boulanger, L.	D'un Matin de Printemps	Dur
Boulanger, L.	Nocturne	B-M
Boulanger, L.	2 Pieces, No. 2	Dur
Boulez, P.	Sonatine. 1946	Amp
Bourguignon, F. de	Sicilienne et scherzo, op. 60.	
	1939	CBD
Bournonville, A.	Danse pour Katia	Bil
Bournonville, A. -Cavally	Danse pour Katia	SM
Bousquet, N.	Gaule et France	EdS
Bousquet, N.	Golden Robin Polka	CF
Bousquet, N.	Malborough	EdS
Boutry, R.	Concertino	ALe
Bove, J.	Impromptu-Caprice	CF
Bove, J.	Melodie (Impressions of	
	Negro Life)	TP
Bove, J.	Praeludium	CF
Božič, D.	Sonata in cool, No. 1	EdD
Bozza, E.	Agrestide, op. 44	ALe
Bozza, E.	Aria	ALe
Bozza, E.	Concertino da Camera	ALe
Bozza, E.	Dialogue	Bil
Bozza, E.	Fantaisie Italienne	ALe

25

Bozza, E.	Soir dans les Montagnes	ALe
Bozza, E.	3 Impressions	ALe
Braga, G.	Angel's Serenade	CF
Braga, G.	Serenata	Dur
Brahms, J.	Berceuse	Ham
Brahms, J.	Danses hongroises, No. 1-8	Ham
Brahms, J.	Hungarian Dances	Pet
Brahms, J.	Hungarian Dance No. 5	CF
Brahms, J.-Steensland	Hungarian Dance No. 6	B-M
Brahms, J.	Hungarian Dance No. 6	CF
Brahms, J.	Intermezzo	Cor
Brahms, J.	Lullaby	CF
Brahms, J.-Tel-Oren	2 Clarinet Sonatas	M&M
Brant, H.	Colloquy	Spr
Braun, G.	Nocturnes	HMo
Braun, R.	Spirituals	YM
Braun, Y.	Concerto	ImV
Brehme, H.	Sonata piccola, op. 40	H-V
Brenet, T.	Le Faune	Com
Brepsant, E.	Swiss Air Varie	CF
Bresgen, C.	Sonate	SS
Bresgen, C.	Studies IV	LDo
Breval, J.-Ruyssen	Sonata	GD
Bréville, P. de	Une Flûte dans les bergers	EdS
Bréville, P. de	Sonatina	EdS
Briccetti, T.	Sonata, op. 14	M&M
Briccialdi, G.	Il Carnevale di Venezia, op. 77	CF
Briccialdi, G.-De Lorenzo	Il Carnevale di Venezia op. 78	CF
Briccialdi, G.	Il Vento, op. 112	CF
Briegel, G.	Little Shepherd	GFB
Briegel, G.	Mulberry Street Tarantella	GFB
Brogue, R.	Allegretto	AMC
Bronnemuller, E.	Sonata	HU
Broustet, E.	Badinerie	Dur
Brown, S.	Sister Sonji	PrA
Brun, F.	Un Andante et un scherzo	Bil
Brun, F.	Pastoral d'Arcadie	ALe
Brun, G.-Voxman	Romance, op. 41	Rub
Bruneau, A.	Romance	Ham
Brunner, A.	Sonate. 1936	B&N
Bryon, A.	2 Pieces	AMC
Buchtel, F.	At the Ball	NK
Buchtel, F.	Attila	NK
Buchtel, F.	Beau Brummel	NK
Buchtel, F.	Chant d'amour	Vol
Buchtel, F.	Chromatica Waltz	NK
Buchtel, F.-arr.	Cielito Lindo	NK
Buchtel, F.	Crescent March	B-M

Buchtel, F.	Drum Major March	NK
Buchtel, F.	Fandango	NK
Buchtel, F.	First Book of Solos for Flute	Col
Buchtel, F.	The Flatterer	B-M
Buchtel, F.	Fun and Frolic	NK
Buchtel, F.	Golden Dreams	NK
Buchtel, F.	Golden Glow Waltz	B-M
Buchtel, F.	Happy Prince	NK
Buchtel, F.	Harlequin	NK
Buchtel, F.	Hercules	NK
Buchtel, F.	Jean Waltz	B-M
Buchtel, F.	Jovial Mood	NK
Buchtel, F.	Princess Helene	NK
Buchtel, F.	Saucy Sally	NK
Buchtel, F.	Serenade	NK
Buchtel, F.	Silver Sails	NK
Buchtel, F.	Tango	NK
Buchtel, F.	Tarantelle	NK
Buchtel, F.	Twilight Shadows	NK
Buchtel, F.	Valse Romantique	Vol
Buchtel, F.	Waltz Medley	NK
Buck, L.	Enchantment	NK
Bullard, R.	Eunice	Ken
Bullard, R.	Laurel	Ken
Bullard, R.	Marlis	Ken
Burghauser, J.	Sonatina	Art
Burgstahler, E.	Amoroso	PrA
Burgstahler, E.	Flutella	PrA
Burgstahler, E.	The Piper	PrA
Burgstahler, E.	The Spinning Wheel	PrA
Burian, E.	Verlorene Serenaden	ES
Burkhard, W.	Suite en miniature, op. 71/2. 1944	B&N
Burton, E.	Sonatina	CF
Busch, C.	4 Miniatures	CF
Busoni, F.	Albumblatt. 1916	BrH
Busoni, F.-Weill	Divertimento, Bb, op. 52	BrH
Busser, H.	Andalucia	ALe
Busser, H.	Danse de Mirrhina (Les Noces Corinthiènnes)	ECh
Busser, H.	Petite Suite, op. 12	Dur
Busser, H.	Prelude and Scherzo, op. 35	ALe
Busser, H.	Sicilienne, op. 60	ALe
Busser, H.	The Squirrels	ALe
Busser, H.	The Swans	ALe
Busser, H.	Theme Varié, op. 68	ALe
Busser, H.-Ephross	Theme Varié	SM
Bussotti, S.	Sette Fogli: Couple	UE
Butting, M.	Concerto, op. 72	Pet
Byrne, A.	3 Bagatelles	HE

Flute and Piano or Harpsichord

Cabus, P.	Sonate	Mau
Callaerts -Taylor	Dance of the Pixies	B-M
Camilleri, C.	Danse Lente	Wat
Camilleri, C.	Meditation	Wat
Camilleri, C.	Sonata Antica	Nov
Campagnoli, B.	Concerto, D, op. 3/2	B&N
Campagnoli, B.-Sonntag	Concerto, D, op. 3/2	Hei
Campra, A.-Boulay	Carnival of Venice	GD
Campra, A.-Gaubert	Minuet and Jig (L'Europe galante)	ALe
Camus, P.	Chanson et Badinerie	ALe
Cannabich, C.-Peters	Concerto, D	Leu
Caplet, A.	Improvisations (d'après Le Pain Quotidien)	Dur
Caplet, A.-Wummer	Reverie & Petite Valse	Int
Caplet, A.	Reverie and Petite Valse	SM
Carazo, C.	Spanish Moment	E-V
Carles, M.	Vieille Chanson	ALe
Carman -Dorson	Conte de Noël	EdS
Carol, H.	Melodie	GaM
Carse, A.	Pipe Tune	GaM
Carse, A.	Romance	GaM
Carter, T.-Bettoney	Boston Commandery March (Onward, Christian Soldiers)	CF
Casadesus, R.	Fantaisie, op. 59	Dur
Casadesus, R.	Sonate, op. 18. 1934	Dur
Casella, A.	Barcarola & Scherzo	EdS
Casella, A.	Sicilienne et Burlesque	ALe
Casterede, J.	Sonate en forme de Suite	ALe
Castiglioni, N.	Gymel	ESZ
Castro, R. de	Anoranza	SM
Catherine, A.-Medicus	Arabesque	CF
Catherine, A.	Nocturne	CF
Catherine, A.	Nocturne	Dur
Catherine, A.	Tarantelle	E-V
Cavally, R.-arr.	15 Concert Pieces	SM
Cavally, R.	7 Original Etudes	SM
Cavally, R.-arr.	6 Brilliant Pieces	SM
Cavally, R.-arr.	Solos for the Debutante Flutist	SM
Cavally, R.-arr.	24 Short Concert Pieces	SM
Cazden, N.	Sonata	AMC
Cecconi, M.	Bucolique	Com
Cechvala, A.	3 Short Pieces	PrA
Cere, R.	Bolero (Souvenirs de San Sebastian)	EME
Chagrin, F.	4 Lyric Interludes	Nov
Chailley, J.	3 Pièces en Courte-pointe	ALe
Chaminade, C.	Air de ballet, op. 30	E&C
Chaminade, C.	Concertino, op. 107	B&H
Chaminade, C.	Concertino, op. 107	CF

Flute and Piano or Harpsichord

Chaminade, C.	Concertino, op. 107	E&C
Chaminade, C.-Moyse	Concertino, op. 107	Int
Chaminade, C.-Moyse	Concertino, op. 107	Sch
Chaminade, C.	Concertino, op. 107	SM
Chaminade, C.	Pastorale Enfantine	CF
Chaminade, C.	Pastorale Enfantine	E&C
Chaminade, C.	Serenade to the Stars, op. 142	B-M
Chaminade, C.	Sérénade aux étoiles, op. 142	E&C
Chandler, M.	Holiday Tunes	Nov
Chapelle -Catlin	Une Serenade	CF
Chapiro, F.	Sonatine. 1962	SD
Chapuis, A.	3 Pièces	Dur
Charpentier, J.	Esquisse	ALe
Charpentier, J.	Pour Syrinx	ALe
Chaynes, C.	Sonatina	ALe
Chaynes, C.	Variations on a Tanka	ALe
Chédeville, N.	Scherzo	EdM
Chédeville, N.-Ruf	Sonata, e	SS
Childs, B.	Sonata	CoF
Chopin, F.	Nocturne, op. 9/2	CF
Chopin, F.-Taffanel	Nocturne, op. 15/1	ALe
Chopin-Taffanel -Medicus	Nocturne, op. 15/1	CF
Chopin-Taffanel -Medicus	Nocturne, op. 15/2	CF
Chopin, F.-Taffanel	Nocturne, op. 15/2	Int
Chopin, F.-Taffanel	Valse, op. 64/1	ALe
Chopin, F.-Taffanel	Valse, op. 64/1	CF
Chopin, F.-Taffanel, Medicus	Valse, op. 64/1	CF
Chopin, F.-Cavally	Etude, f	SM
Chopin, F.-LaFleurance	6 Etudes, 2 vols.	Dur
Chopin, F.	Minute Waltz, op. 64/1	GFB
Chopin, F.-Steensland	Nocturne, Eb	B-M
Chopin, F.-Gaubert	Prelude No. 15	ALe
Chopin, F.	Variations for Flute	AP
Chopin, F.	Variations for Flute	EBM
Chopin, F.-Rampal	Variations on a theme by Rossini	Int
Chou, Wen-Chung	Cursive	Pet
Christensen, J.	Flute Portrait	Ken
Christensen, J.	Holiday on Ice	Ken
Ciardi, C.	Nocturne, op. 133, No. 1	CF
Ciardi, C.	Nocturne, op. 135, No. 3	CF
Cinna, O. de la	Malaguena, op. 369	E&C
Ciortea, T.	Sonata. 1962	EdR
Cirri, G.	Arioso	EdM
Clarke, I.-arr.	25 Christmas Carols	BM
Clarke, I.-arr.	25 Hymns	BM
Classens, H.	Canzonne	Com
Classens, H.	Fantaisie	Com
Classens & Leroy-arr.	La Flute Classique, 4 vols.	Com

Flute and Piano or Harpsichord

Clement, F.	Marching Thro' Georgia	CF
Clement, F.	Silvertone Polka	Vol
Clementi, M.	3 Sonates, op. 2	EdH
Clementi, M. -Rampal	Sonata, op. 2/3	Int
Clérisse, R.	Au fil de L'eau	ALe
Clérisse, R.	Ballade	Bil
Clérisse, R.	D'un manoir	Com
Clérisse, R.	Eglogue	Bil
Clérisse, R.	Fantaisie	ALe
Closson, E.	Nocturne	ScF
Cockshott, G.	Serenade	Ron
Coedes-Mongin, A. -Cochrane	Tarentelle (Suite)	CF
Cohen, S.	Spring Morning	B-M
Cohn, J.	Baroque Suite	EdM
Colaço Osorio-Swaab, R.	4 korte stukken. 1958	SD
Cole, H.	Capriccio	Nov
Colin	Sonata, op. 33	ScF
Collier	Waterfront, Night Thoughts	Ken
Conley, L.	Leprechaun Tune	Ken
Conley, L.	Pastorale	Ken
Constant, F.	Evocation	ALe
Constantinescu, D.	Sonata. 1967	EdR
Cooke, A.	Sonatina	OxU
.Coolidge, R.	Music for a Rhapsody by Shelley	Ken
Coolidge, R.	Weeping Dancer	Ken
Cooper, P.	Sonata	Che
Cope, David	Triplum	CoA
Copland, A.	Duo	B&H
Coppola, C.	Flute Flight	BVC
Coppola, C.	The Piccolo Polka	BVC
Corbeel, R.	Allegretto	Mau
Corbeel, R.	Comédia	Mau
Corbeel, R.	Moderato	Mau
Corbeel, R.	Nocturno	Mau
Corelli, A.	Air and Dance	EdM
Corelli, A. -Krainis	La Follia, op. 5/12	M&M
Corelli, A.	Gavotte and Gigue	EdM
Corelli, A.	Gigue	EdM
Corelli, A.	Sonata, F	EdM
Corelli, A.	Suite, Bb	EdM
Coriolis, E. de	Humoresque	ALe
Corrette, M. -Guy-Lambert	Airs	ERS
Corrette, M. -Döflein	Sonatilles, op. 19/5, 6 (fl, bc)	SS
Corrette, M. -Ruf	Sonata, e, op. 20/4 (fl, hpcd)	SS
Corrette, M. -Ruf	Sonata, e, op. 25/4	SS
Corrette, M. -Petit	Sonata No. 2	GD
Corrette, M. -Boulay	Sonatille (fl, bc)	EMT
Corrette, M. -Ruf	Suite, C (fl, bc)	Ric
Cortés, R.	Elegy	SMP
Cortese, L.	Introduction and Allegro, op. 40	B-M

Flute and Piano or Harpsichord

Cortese, L.	Melodia, op. 41	Edi
Cosacchi, S.	Berceuse, op. 5	HG
Couperin, F.-Boulay	4e Concert Royal (fl, bc)	EMT
Couperin, F.-Rampal	Concert Royal No. 4	Int
Couperin, F.	Concerto No. 6	GD
Couperin, F.-Fleury	Le Rossignol en Amour	S&C
Couperin, F.-Fleury	12 Transcriptions	Dur
Course, W.	Happy-Go-Lucky	Rub
Coursey, R. de	10 Sketches	B-M
Cowell, H.	Two-Bits	CF
Cox, H.	Sonate	Bil
Cramer-Francis, Silver	Etude	AlL
Cras, J.	Suite en Duo	EdS
Crawford, R.-Kent	The Army Air Corps	CF
Croebelis, D. Del	The New Dutch Playhouse	HeE
Crooke, S.	Novelette	Sim
Crosse, G.	Carol, op. 7	OxU
Cui, C.-Taylor	Bagatelle	B-M
Cui, C.	Cantabile, op. 36	CF
Cui, C.	Orientale, op. 50/9	CF
Cui, C.	Orientale	NK
Cui, C.	Scherzetto	Heu
Cumberworth, S.	6 Sketches	AMC
Curtis, N.	Sonata	AMC
Czernik, W.	Concertino	WZ
Czibulka, A.	Gavotte Stephanie	ScF
Czibulka, A.	Pavane Rodolphe	ScF
Dahl, I.	Variations on an Air by Couperin	JB
Dahl, I.	Variations on a French Folktune	JB
Damare, E.	Bolero	EdS
Damare, E.	Cleopatra	CF
Damare, E.-Ryder	The Lark	CF
Damare, E.	Turtle Dove	CF
Damare, E.	The Wren	CF
Damm, S.	Lyrisk svit No. 1	EMf
Danican-Philidor-Ruf	Sonata, d (fl, bc)	B&N
Danks, H.	Silver Threads among the Gold	CF
Dannatt, R.	Sonata	SM
Danzi, F.-Anspacher	Concerto No. 1, G, op. 30	Hei
Danzi, F.-Anspacher	Concerto No. 2, d, op. 31	Hei
Danzi, F.	Concerto No. 3, op. 42	WMS
Danzi, F.-Niggemann	Sonatina, D	FrH
Danzi, F.-Lebermann	Sonatine, D	SS
Dao, N.	Tay Nguyen	EdS
Darke, H.	Meditation on 'Brother James's Air'	OxU
Dautremer, M.	A petits pas	ALe
Dautremer, M.	Traversiana	ECh

Dávid, G.	Preludio. 1964	EMB
Dávid, G.	Sonata. 1955	EMB
Davidson, J.	More Or Less	PMP
Dearnley, C.-arr.	8 Easy Pieces by Classical Composers	Che
Dearnley, C.-arr.	More Easy Pieces by Classical Composers	Che
De Bueris, J.	Musette	CF
Debussy, C.-Platonov	Afternoon of a Faun	Int
Debussy, C.	Prélude a L'Après Midi d'un Faune	Job
Debussy, C.	Air de Lia (L'Enfant Prodigue)	EdM
Debussy, C.	1st Arabesque	Dur
Debussy, C.-Laube	Second Arabesque	CF
Debussy, C.	2nd Arabesque	Dur
Debussy, C.	Ballade	Job
Debussy, C.	Clair de Lune	Job
Debussy, C.	En bateau (Petite Suite)	Dur
Debussy, C.-Roques	La Boite a joujoux: Danse de la poupée	Dur
Debussy, C.	The Little Negro	ALe
Debussy, C.	Mandoline	EdM
Debussy, C.	Menuet	Dur
Debussy, C.-Davidson	Page d'Album	PMP
Debussy, C.-Hennebains	Le Petit berger (Children's Corner)	Dur
Debussy, C.	Il Pleure dans mon Coeur	EdM
Debussy, C.-Roques	Printemps	Dur
Debussy, C.	Valse Romantique	Job
Decsényi, J.	Sonatina Pastorale. 1956	EMB
Dedrick, C.	Twilight	Ken
Defossez, R.	Les Arpèges en congé	ALe
Delalande, M.-Boulay	Air, Musette et Passepied (fl, bc)	GD
Delano, J.	Sonatina	SMP
Delaunay, R.	Au fil de l'eau	Bil
Delaunay, R.	Sérénade matutinale	Bil
Delibes, L.-Brooke	Pas des Fleurs (Naila)	CF
Delibes, L.-Cavally	Waltz of the Flowers	SM
Dello Joio, N.	The Developing Flutist	EBM
Delmas, M.	Complainte et air de ballet	Bil
Delmas, M.	Conte rose	Bil
Delmas, M.	Faunesse	Bil
Delmas, M.	Incantation et danse	Bil
Delmas, M.	Soir d'été	Bil
Delmas, M.	Variation tendre	Bil
DeLone, R.	Recitative and Arioso (fl, hpcd)	Za
Delrez, J.	Ballade	EMb
Delvaux, A.	Prélude. 1948	CBD
Delvincourt, C.	Contemplation	ALe
Demarquez, S.	Sonatine	EMT

Demersseman, J.	Fantaisie, op. 2/1	Bil
Demersseman, J.	Bolero, op. 2/2	Bil
Demersseman, J.	Ballade, op. 2/6	Bil
Demersseman, J.-Moyse	The Tremolo (Grand Air, op. 3)	ALe
Demersseman, J.	Souvenirs de Bayonne, op. 5	Bil
Demersseman, J.	Introduction et variations sur le carnival de Venise, op. 7	Bil
Demersseman, J.	Petite fantaisie sur le carnival de Venise, op. 7 bis	Bil
Demersseman, J.-Moyse	Air with Variations and Polonaise, op. 8	ALe
Demersseman, J.	Air varié et polonaise, op. 8	Bil
Demersseman, J.	Polonaise, op. 9/1	Bil
Demersseman, J.	Sérénade espagnol, op. 9/3	Bil
Demersseman, J.	2nd Solo de concert, Eb, op. 20	Bil
Demersseman, J.	1st Duo, Ab, op. 25	Bil
Demersseman, J.	6 Fantaisies faciles, op. 28, No. 1 Balladine, Simplicité	Bil
Demersseman, J.-Moyse	Homage to Tulou, op. 43	ALe
Demersseman, J.-Moyse	Brillant Fantasy on Duprato's "The Goddess and the Shepherd"	ALe
Demersseman, J.-Moyse	Concert Solo No. 6, F	ALe
Demersseman, J.-Ephross	Evening Echoes	SM
Demersseman, J.-Moyse	Grand Concert Fantasia on Weber's "Oberon"	ALe
Denisov, E.	Sonata	MKE
Denissoff	Sonata	Pet
Dentato, J.	Jazz Flute	Big
De Roxlo, G.	Bajo la reja (Spanish Suite)	CF
De Roxlo, G.	Jota (Spanish Suite)	CF
De Roxlo, G.	Playera (Spanish Suite)	CF
Desenclos, A.	Bucoliques	ALe
Desportes, Y.	Pastorale Joyeuse	EdS
Desportes, Y.	Pastourelle	EdS
Desprez, F.	Apaisement	Mau
Desprez, F.	Exaltation	Mau
Devienne, F.-Szebenyi, Nagy	Concerto No. 1, D	EMB
Devienne, F.-Rampal	Concerto No. 2, D	Int
Devienne, F.-Szebenyi	Concerto No. 4, G	SS
Devienne, F.-Szebenyi	Concerto No. 8, G	SS
Devienne, F.-Rampal	Sonata No. 1, e	Int
Diabelli, A.-Bergmann	Sonatina, C	S&C
Diemer, E.	Sonata	SM
Diethelm, C.	Sonata, op. 108	S-V
Diethelm, C.	Sonatine, op. 109	S-V
Dietrich, O.	Suite, g	LDo
Dieupart, C.	Suite VI, f (fl, bc)	Pel
Dillon, R.	Petite Etude	B&H
Dilsner, L.	Tumbleweed	PrA

Dindale, E.	Bucolique	EMb
Dindale, E.	Canzonetta	EMb
Dindale, E.	Danse Paysanne	EMb
Dodge, C.	Duo	CoF
Dohl, F.	Julianische Minuten	GBV
Döhl, F.	Oculapis	GBV
Dohnányi, E. von	Aria, op. 48/1	AMP
Domenica, R. di	Sonata	EdM
Donahue, R.	Sonatine No. 2	Bar
Donizetti, G.-Wienandt	Cavatina	SM
Donizetti, G.-Meylan	Sonata, C	Pet
Donjon, J.-Medicus	Adagio Nobile	CF
Donjon, J.-Medicus	Invocation	CF
Donjon, J.-Maganini	Offertoire, op. 12	CF
Donjon, J.-Medicus	Offertoire, op. 12	CF
Donjon, J.	Offertory	GD
Donjon, J.-Medicus	Pan!	CF
Donjon, J.-Cavally	Pan, Pastorale	SM
Donjon, J.-Medicus	Pipeaux	CF
Donjon, J.	Rossignolet	CF
Donjon, J.-Medicus	Spirale	CF
Doppler, F.-Cavally	Berceuse, op. 15	SM
Doppler, F.	Nocturne, op. 17	ECM
Doppler, F.	Fantaisie Pastorale Hongroise, op. 26	CF
Doppler, F.	Fantaisie Pastorale Hongroise, op. 26	SS
Doppler, F.	Wallachian Fantasy	MKE
Doran, M.	Poem	Wes
Dorlay, G.	Scherzo Brillante	GaM
Dornel, A.-Aubert	Première Suite	ERS
Dorsselaer, W. van	Au petit Trianon	Bil
Dorsselaer, W. van	Le Chant du gaulois	Bil
Dorsselaer, W. van	Feux Follets	MM
Dorsselaer, W. van	Will O' the Wisp	HeE
Douliez, V.	Feuille d'album	Mau
Drake, R.-arr.	Let Us Have Music	CF
Drdla, F.-Damm	Souvenir	CF
Driessler, J.	4 Kleine Stücke, op. 8/2	B&N
Drigo, R.-Damm	Serenade	CF
Drigo, R.-Safronow	Serenade	CF
Dubois, P.	A tempo classico	ERR
Dubois, P.	Concerto	ALe
Dubois, P.	9 Préludes faciles	ECh
Dubois, P.	Novelette	ALe
Dubois, P.	Pop-Variations	ALe
Dubois, P.	Sonata	ALe
Duckworth, A.	En Passant and Thistledown	HE
Duckworth, A.	Frolic for Flute	HE
Dukas, P.-Fleury	Alla Gitana	ALe

Dukas, P.-Samazeuilh	La Plainte, au loin, du Faune	Dur
Duport, F.	Romance	Spr
Durand, A.-Medicus	First Valse, op. 82	CF
Durand, A.-Taffanel	1st Valse, op. 83	Dur
Durand, E.	Le Biniou	EdS
Durand, J.	Romance	Dur
Durey, L.	Sonatine, op. 25	JB
Dutilleux, H.	Sonatina	ALe
Duvernoy, A.	Concertino, op. 45	BM
Duvernoy, A.-Cavally	Concertino, op. 45	SM
Duvernoy, A.-Medicus	Intermezzo, op. 41/2	CF
Duvernoy, A.	Intermezzo	Ham
Duvernoy, A.	Lamento	Ham
Duysburgh, F.	Andantino Cantabile	Mau
Dvoracer, J.	Dialogy	CHF
Dvořak, A.-Sargent	Humoreske	CF
Dvořak, A.	Humoreske	NK
Dvořak, A.	Larghetto	NK
Dvořak, A.	Largo (New World Symphony)	CF
Dyck, V.	Invocation à Euterpe	EdS
Dyson, G.	In Pixieland	GaM
Dzherbashian, S.	2 Pieces	MKE
Echevarria, V.	Divertimento	UME
Eckard, W.-arr.	Highlights of Familiar Music	TP
Edelson, E.	Autumn Sunset	PrA
Edelson, E.	Chant	CF
Edelson, E.	The Gay Gendarme	PrA
Edelson, E.	Mirage	PrA
Edelson, E.	Night Song	EdM
Edelson, E.	Shadows	PrA
Edelson, E.	Soliloquy	PrA
Eder, H.	Sonatine, op. 34/4	LDo
Eisenhardt, G.	From the life of a red Indian	Deu
Elgar, E.-Bettoney	Love's Greeting	CF
Elgar, E.-Trinkaus	Love's Greeting	CF
Elgar, E.-Akers	Pomp and Circumstance	CF
Elgar, E.	Salut d'amour, op. 12	SS
Eller, H.	3 Pieces	MKE
Emch, W.	Rondino	CF
Enesco, G.	Cantabile and Presto	B&H
Enesco, G.	Cantabile et Presto	E&C
Enesco, G.	Cantabile and Presto	EdK
Enesco, G.	Cantabile and Presto	Int
Enesco, G.	Cantabile et Presto	SM
Ensor, C.-arr.	20 Baroque Pieces	Spr
Ephross, A. (ed)	Program Solos, 2 vols.	TP
Erbse, H.	Sonate, op. 25 (fl/afl, pf)	B&B
Erdmann, D.	Aphorismen	Hei
Ernst, H.	Elegie	CF
Etgen, M.	Andante cantabile	Com

35

Evans, B.	Caprice	Sha
Evans, E.	Sweet and Dainty	CF
Exaudet, A.	La Cour de la Marquise	EdM
Fabribeckers, E. de	Foret	ScF
Färber, O.	Sonata, op. 72	LDo
Fair, R.	Bouree Solo	Col
Fair, R.	Ghosts of the Pecatonia	Col
Fair, R.	Minuet No. 2	Col
Fair, R.	The Tarantella	Col
Fair, R.	Via Crucis	Col
Fair, R.	The Wood Serenade	Col
Farkas, F.	Rumanian Folk Dances. 1950	EMB
Farkas, F.	Third Sonatina. 1959	EMB
Faulx, J.	Polonaise de Concert	EMb
Fauré, G.-Barrère	Andantino	Sch
Fauré, G.	Berceuse de Dolly	Ham
Fauré, G.	En Prière	EdM
Fauré, G.	Fantaisie, op. 79	B-M
Fauré, G.	Fantasy, op. 79	EdK
Fauré, G.	Fantaisie, op. 79	Ham
Fauré, G.	Fantasy, op. 79	Int
Fauré, G.	Fantaisie, op. 79	SM
Fauré, G.	Pavane	Ham
Fauré, G.	Pénélope--Les Joueuses de flûte	Heu
Fauré, G.-Doney	Pièce	ALe
Fauré, G.	Sicilienne, op. 78	Ham
Fauré, G.	Sicilienne, op. 78	Int
Fauré, G.-Cavally	Sicilienne (Pelléas et Mélisande), op. 78	SM
Fauré, G.	Soir	Ham
Fauré, J.	The Palms	CF
Fekete G.	3 Duos	B&H
Feld, J.	Concerto	Art
Feld, J.	Sonata	ALe
Feld, J.	3 Kompositionen	ES
Felderhof, J.	Suite. 1933	SD
Feldman, L.	Burlesca. 1959	EdR
Feline, J.	Serenade	EME
Fenigstein, V.	4 Rufspiele	Eul
Fenigstein, V.	Vortragsstuck	Eul
Ferguson, H.	3 Sketches	B&H
Fernström, J.	Concertino, op. 52	EMf
Ferrari, G.	Sonata. 1957	Edi
Ferrari-Trecate, L.	Ariette	ALe
Ferritto, J.	Affigliazione	CoF
Fesch, W. de-Kaplan	Canzonetta	Spr
Fievet, C.	Canzonetta	Com
Filas, T.	Chanson	Big
Fils, A.	Concerto, D	ES
Finch, R.	Sonata	S&C

Fine, A.	Sonatina	AMC
Finger, G.-Hunt	Sonata, G	B&H
Finger, G.-Hunt	Sonata, d	B&H
Finger, G.-Dinn	Tempo di Minuetto	S&C
Finke, F.	Sonata	BrH
Finney, R.	Pastorale	AMC
Fiocco, J.-Balbo	Allegro (Première Suite)	SF
Fisher, C.	Nellie Gray	CF
Fisher, T.	Sonatina	CoA
Fitzgerald, B.	4 Gaelic Miniatures	TP
Flagello, N.	Concerto Antoniano	BM
Flegier, A.	Villanelle du Midi	EdM
Fleming, R.	Almost Waltz	OxU
Fleury, L.-arr.	Klassische Stücke aus dem 18 Jh.	SS
Fleury, L. (ed)	Oeuvres originales des XVII et XVIII Siècles	ALe
Flothuis, M.	Ronde champêtre, op. 19b. 1945 (fl, hpcd)	SD
Flothuis, M.	Sonata da camera, op. 17. 1943	SD
Flowers, G.	A Plaintive Air	Nov
Focking, H.	Sonate, op. 1	B&V
Focking, H.-Schouwman	Sonata, G, op. 1/2 (fl, bc)	EdH
Focking, H.	Sonata, G, op. 1/6	B&V
Fontaine	7 Pieces brèves	GrF
Fontaine, C.	Fleur Printaniere	ScF
Fontaine, C.	3 Morceaux--Andante; Valse de concert; Tarentelle	ScF
Fontyn, J.	Sonate. 1952	CBD
Foote, A.-Zverov	Night Piece	SM
Forsman, J.	Sonatina divertante, op. 16a	B&N
Fortner, J.	Cantilenae	E-V
Fortner, W.	Sonata. 1947	SS
Foster, I.	2 Pieces	OxU
Foster, S.-Fisher	My Old Kentucky Home	CF
Frackenpohl, A.	Ballad and Tango	SM
Frackenpohl, A.	Introduction and Romp	Sch
Françaix, J.	Concerto	SS
Françaix, J.	Divertimento	SS
Franck, C.	Sonate, A	Ham
Franck, C.-Rampal	Sonata, A	Int
Francl, J.	Pastoral Suite	ES
Franco, J.	Ballade	ACA
Franco, J.	Night Fable	CoF
Franco, J.	Ode of Praise	CoF
Franco, J.	Ode of Supplication	CoF
Franco, J.	Theme and Variations	ALe
Frank, M.	Concerto, C	Bou
Frank, M.	Evening Reverie	Ken
Frank, M.	Holiday for Pipers	Bou

Frank, M.	Impromptu	SF
Fransella, A.	Concert Etude, F	GaM
Fraser, S.	Prelude and Scherzino	B&H
Frederick the Great	Solo per il Flauto Traverso, b, No. 122	For
Frederick the Great	Ausgewählte Sonaten, 2 vols.	BrH
Frederick the Great -Lenzewski	3rd Concerto, C	CFV
Frederick the Great -Lenzewski	4th Concerto, D	CFV
Frederick the Great	Rondo	EdM
Frederick the Great -Pillney	3 Flötenstücke	B&N
Frederick the Great -Sonntag	Sonata, A, No. 117 (fl, bc)	HSM
Frederick the Great -Müller, Rodemann	4 Stücke	NV
Frederick the Great -Mueller	3 Movements (Flute Sonatas 182, 189, 217)	WZ
Freed, I. -Kincaid	Scherzino	CF
Freedman, H.	Soliloquy. 1970	MCA
Frešo, T.	Composition	SHF
Fried, G. -Stepanian	2 Pieces	MKE
Friedel, K.	Sonata	MV
Friedel, K.	Suite	MV
Friess, H.	Sonate. 1950	MV
Friml, R. -Simon	The Donkey Serenade	Sch
Fritsch, J.	Oktober 70	B&N
Frohne, V.	Pendulum, op. 29	B&B
Frotscher (ed)	Noels, 2 vols.	Hei
Frumerie, G. de	Pastoral-Suite	Nor
Frumerie, G. de	Svit	EMf
Fuerst, P.	Concerto, op. 50	LDo
Fürstenau, A. -Eck	Concertino	B-M
Fürstenau, A. -Richter	Concerto, D, op. 84	WZ
Fürstenau, A. -Rampal	Introduction et Variations, op. 72	Bil
Fuerstner, C.	Nocturne and Dance	Za
Fukushima, K.	Kadha Karuna	ESZ
Fukushima, K.	3 Pieces from "Chu-u"	Pet
Fuleihan, A.	Pastoral Sonata	SMP
Fuleihan, A.	Suite Concertante	B&H
Fulton, N.	Scottish Suite	S&C
Funk, H.	Sonatine, op. 116	FrH
Fussan, W.	Musik, op. 13	B&B
Fuste-Lambezat, M.	Sicilienne	Com
Gabaye, P.	Etude pour Rire	ALe
Gaber, H.	Scambio	ACA
Gagnebin, H.	Hiver et Printemps	ALe
Gagnebin, H.	23 Pièces récréatives et progressives	ALe
Gal, H.	Concertino, op. 82	UE

Flute and Piano or Harpsichord

Gallet, J.	Berceuse Modale et Scherzetto	Bil
Gallois-Montbrun, R.	Divertissement	ALe
Gallois-Montbrun, R.	6 Pièces musicales d'étude	ALe
Gallois-Montbrun, R.	Valse-Caprice	ALe
Gallon, N.	Improvisation & Rondo	EME
Gallon, N.	Recueillement	ALe
Gallon, N.	Suite	ALe
Galuppi, B.-Brinckmann	Concerto, G	B&N
Ganne, L.	Andante et scherzo	Bil
Ganne, L.	Andante et Scherzo	B-M
Ganne, L.	Andante et Scherzo	CF
Ganne, L.	Andante et Scherzo	SM
Ganne, L.	La Czarine	E&C
Ganne, L.	Marche Lorraine	E&C
Ganne, L.	Villanelle	E&C
Gardner, J.	Little Suite, C	OxU
Garsnek, M.	2 Pieces (Sonatina, Concert Piece)	MKE
Gatti, G. (ed)	Antologia di Pezzi Scelti da Autori Classici	EBe
Gaubert, P.	Ballade	Heu
Gaubert, P.	Berceuse	E&C
Gaubert, P.	Divertissement Grec	ALe
Gaubert, P.	Fantaisie	EdS
Gaubert, P.-Ephross	Fantasy	SM
Gaubert, P.	Madrigal	B-M
Gaubert, P.	Madrigal	E&C
Gaubert, P.	Nocturne et Allegro scherzando	E&C
Gaubert, P.	Nocturne and Allegro Scherzando	Int
Gaubert, P.	Nocturne and Allegro Scherzando	SM
Gaubert, P.	Orientale	Heu
Gaubert, P.	Romance	ALe
Gaubert, P.	Romance	E&C
Gaubert, P.	Sicilienne	Heu
Gaubert, P.	Soir sur la Plaine	Heu
Gaubert, P.	Sonate	Dur
Gaubert, P.	2nd Sonata	Heu
Gaubert, P.	3rd Sonata	Heu
Gaubert, P.	Sonatine	Heu
Gaubert, P.	Suite	Heu
Gaubert, P.	2 Esquisses	Heu
Gaultier, P.-Favre	Suite, G	ERS
Gee, H.	Ballade	PrA
Geehl, H.	Serenade	GaM
Geist, C.	Andante Pastorale, op. 13	CF
Geminiani, F.	Sonata, e	B&N
Genin, P.	Air napolitan, op. 8	Bil

Genin, P.	Carnival de Vénise, op. 14	Bil
Genin, P.	Mélodie, op. 7	Bil
Genin, P.	Méditation, op. 49	Bil
Genin, P.	Petite fantaisie concertante	Bil
Gentilucci, A.	Figurazioni. 1966	B-M
Genzmer, H.	Sonata No. 1	R&E
Genzmer, H.	Sonata No. 2	SS
George, T.	Concerto	Roc
Geraedts, J.	Canzonetta. 1944	SD
Geraedts, J.	Sarabande. 1948	SD
Geraedts, J.	Sonatine. 1949	SD
Gerhard, R.	Capriccio	B-M
German, E.	Pastorale Dance	CF
German, E.	Valse Graceuse	CF
Gerschefski, E.	"America" Variations for Winds, op. 44/2	CoF
Gerschefski, E.	"America" Variations for Winds, op. 44/3	CoF
Gerschefski, E.	"America" Variations for Winds, op. 45/3	CoF
Gerschefski, E.	"America" Variations for Winds, op. 45/4	CoF
Giannini, V.	Sonata	B-M
Gibbs, C.	Suite, A	OxU
Gilbert	Miniatures	ScF
Gilbert, A.	The Incredible Flute Music	SS
Gillet, E.	La Lettre de Manon	E&C
Gillis, D.	North Harris	B&H
Gillis, D.	Three Short Pieces	B-M
Giordani, G.	An 18th Century Air (Caro Mio Ben)	EdM
Girnatis, W.	Concerto	B&N
Glanville-Hicks, P.	Sonatina	S&C
Glière, R.	Mélodie, op. 35/1	HSM
Glière, R.	Melody, op. 35/1	MCA
Glière, R.	Valse Triste, op. 35/1	CF
Glière, R.	Walzer, op. 35/1	HSM
Glière, R.	Waltz, op. 35/2	MCA
Gluck, C.-O'Neill	Andante and Maestoso (Orpheus)	Wat
Gluck, C.-Steensland	Ballet of the Shepherds	B-M
Gluck, C.-Gaubert	Burial Scene (Iphigenia in Tauris)	ALe
Gluck, C.	Concerto, G	EdK
Gluck, C.-Scherchen	Concerto, G	Hug
Gluck, C.-Francis, Silver	Dance of the Blessed Spirits	AlL
Gluck, C.-Klengel	Dance of the Blessed Spirits	BrH
Gluck, C.-Hunt	The Dance of the Blessed Spirits (Orpheo)	S&C
Gluck, C.-Gaubert	Echoes of the Naiad (Armide)	ALe
Gluck, C.-Taffanel, Gaubert	Elysian Fields (Orpheus)	ALe

Gluck, C.-Voxman	Gavotte (Don Juan)	Rub
Gluck, C.-Barrère	Gavotte	Sch
Gluck, C.-Gaubert	Hymn (Iphigenia in Tauris)	ALe
Gluck, C.	Largo	Pet
Gluck, C.-Barge	Melodie (Orpheus)	CF
Gluck, C.-Brooke	Minuet and Dance of the Blessed Spirits	CF
Gluck, C.-Cavally	Minuet and Dance of the Blessed Spirits	SM
Gluck, C.	Minuet and Dance (Orpheus)	TP
Gluck, C.	Orpheus	MM
Gluck, C.-Leeuwen	Reigen seliger Geister	WZ
Gluck, C.	Scène de Champs-Elysées	Ham
Gluck, C.-Barrère	Scenes from "Orpheus"	Sch
Gluck, C.-Voxman	Spirit Dance (Orpheus)	Rub
Gluck, C.-Barrère	Tambourin	Sch
Gobbaerts, L.	Le Concert dans le feuillage, op. 33	ScF
Godard, B.	Allegretto, op. 116/1	CF
Godard, B.-Cavally	Allegretto, op. 116	SM
Godard, B.-Bettoney	Berceuse (Jocelyn)	CF
Godard, B.-Trinkaus	Berceuse (Jocelyn)	CF
Godard, B.-Wagner	Berceuse (Jocelyn)	CF
Godard, B.-Hahn	Canzonette (Concerto Romantique)	CF
Godard, B.	Idyll, op. 116/2	CF
Godard, B.-Cavally	Idylle, op. 116	SM
Godard, B.	Légende Pastorale	SM
Godard, B.	Suite de 3 morceaux, op. 116	Dur
Godard, B.	Valse, op. 116/3	CF
Godfrey, K.	Dolente	PrA
Godfrey, K.	Melodie for Flute	PrA
Godfrey, K.	Petite Serenade	PrA
Godfrey, K.	Scherzo	PrA
Godron, H.	Suite Bucolique. 1939	SD
Goedicke, A.	12 Transcriptions, 2 vols.	MKE
Goehl, H.	Serenade	GaM
Goehr, A.	Variations, op. 8	S&C
Gold, E.	Sonatina	Sim
Goldman, R.	Divertimento	Sha
Golestan, S.	Sonatina	EdS
Golterman, C.	Tarantelle	NK
Goodenough, F.	Lament	CoF
Goossens, E.	Scherzo fantasque	ALe
Goossens, E.	Three Pictures	Che
Gossec, F.-Andreoni	Gavotte	Ric
Gossec, F.-Bettoney	Gavotte	CF
Gossec, F.-Leeuwen, Maganini	Gavotte	CF
Gossec, F.	Gavotte	MM

Flute and Piano or Harpsichord

Gossec, F.	Gavotte	NK
Gossec, F.-Voxman	Gavotte	Rub
Gossec, F.-Leeuwen	Gavotte	WZ
Gossec, F.-Leeuwen	Tambourin	WZ
Gounod, C.	Adagio and Valse Lento (Faust)	CF
Gounod, C.-Alard, Herman	Fantaisie de concert (Faust)	ECh
Gounod, C.-Alard, Carles	Fantaisie de concert (Romeo et Juliette)	ECh
Gounod, C.-Gariboldi	Faust	ECh
Gounod, C.-Génin	2 Fantaisies (Faust)	ECh
Gounod, C.-Herman, Bull	2 Fantaisies (Faust)	ECh
Gounod, C.-Brooke	Helen's Dance and Maiden's Entry (Faust)	CF
Gounod, C.-Génin	2 Fantaisies (Mireille)	ECh
Gounod, C.-Génin	2 Fantaisies (Romeo et Juliette)	ECh
Gounod, C.	Souvenir d'un bal, Air de ballet	ECh
Gounod, C.-Daubel Bretonnière	Valse de Faust	ECh
Graener, P.	Suite, op. 63	WZ
Gramatges, H.	Duo	PIC
Granados, E.-Amaz	Spanish Dance No. 2, Oriental	UME
Granados, E.-Amaz	Spanish Dance No. 5, Andaluza	UME
Granados, E.-Amaz	Spanish Dance No. 6, Rondalla Aragonesa	UME
Grandis, R. de	Studi. 1960	EdT
Granom, L.-Fleury	Sonata, G	Ric
Grassi, E.	Complainte Laotiènne	EdS
Grassi, E.	Sukhanimitra	EdS
Graun, C.	Concerto, e	WMS
Graun, C.-Ruf	Sonata, D	Hei
Graupner, C.-Hoffmann	2 Sonatas, g	B&N
Green, H.	Sky Castles	PMP
Gregoir, E.	Dernière pensée, de Nicolo Paganini	ScF
Gretchaninoff, A	Brimborions, op. 138	GaM
Gretchaninoff, A.	En Avant; Mazurka	GaM
Gretchaninoff, A.	En Route!; Pastorale	GaM
Gretchaninov, A.-Voxman	First Waltz	Rub
Gretchaninoff, A.	La Demande; Le Soir	GaM
Gretchaninoff, A.	La Fête; Plainte	GaM
Gretchaninoff, A.	2 Miniatures, op. 145	ALe
Gretchaninoff, A.	Sévère Réprimande; L'Adieu	GaM
Gretchaninoff, A.	Travail du Matin; Une Journée Grise	GaM
Grétry, A.	Concerto, C	B&N
Grétry, A.-Sonntag	Concerto, C	Hei
Grétry, A.-Rampal	Concerto, C	Int
Grétry, A.-Leeuwen	Concerto, C	SM
Grétry, A.	Gigue Gracieuse (Céphale et Procis	CF

Grétry, A.-Gaubert	Musette (La Fausse Magie)	ALe
Grétry, A.-Barrère	Passepied	GaM
Grétry, A.-Gaubert	Sérénade (L'amant jaloux)	ALe
Grieg, E.	Berceuse	CF
Grieg, E.-Steensland	Elf Dance	B-M
Grieg, E.-Hahn	Puck (Lyric Pieces)	CF
Grieg, E.	To Spring	Cen
Griffes, C.-Barrère	Poem	Sch
Griffith, S.	Nesting Time	CF
Grimm, C.	A Dorian Suite	SM
Grimm, C.-Cavally	Concerto Miniature	SM
Grooms, C.-arr.	Dark Eyes (Russian Song)	Cen
Groven, E.	Sun Mood	HL
Grovlez, G.	Concertino	Com
Grovlez, G.	Divertissement (Coeur de Rubis)	EME
Grovlez, G.	Romance et scherzo	Bil
Grovlez, G.	Romance and Scherzo	SM
Gruber-Kent	The Caissons Go Rolling Along	CF
Guarnieri, A.	Diaphonia (fl, hpcd/pf)	ESZ
Guarnieri, C.	Sonatina	TP
Gubaidulina, M.	Allegro	ChM
Gubaidulina, M.	Allegro	MKE
Gümbel, M.	Lern und Spielbuch, 2 vols.	B&N
Gümbel, M.	3 Chansons (fl, hpcd)	Pet
Guenther, R.	Canzona	B-M
Guenther, R.	Echo Song	B-M
Guenther, R.	Improvisation	SM
Guenther, R.	Little Waltz	B-M
Guenther, R.	March for Flutists	B-M
Guenther, R.	La Petite Danse	B-M
Guenther, R.	Reflections	B-M
Guenther, R.	Reverie	B-M
Guenther, R.	Shepherd's Song	B-M
Guignon, J.-Ruf	Sonata, A, op. 1/8 (fl, bc)	SS
Guillemain, L.-Ruf	Sonata, G (fl, bc)	SS
Guiraud, E.-LaFleurance	Piccolino	Dur
Guiraud, G.	Legende & Danse Slaves	EME
Guiraud, G.	Rêverie Tendre	EME
Guiraud, G.	Scherzetto-Valse	EME
Guridi	Tirana, Homenaje a Sarasate	UME
Gutierrez Heras, J.	Sonata Simple	SMP
Guy, B.	4 Miniatures	Nov
Guyonnet, J.	Polyphonie I	UE
Gyulai, E.	Sonatina	EMB
Haass, H.	Kleine Suite	HG
Hába, A.	Fantasie	CHF
Hässler, J.	Short Sonatas, D, G	Mit
Hässler, J.	2 Sonatas	EdK
Hässler, J.-Gloder	Sonatas, G, D (6 Easy Sonatas)	NV
Hahn, L.	Hahn's Transcriptions of	

	Familiar Melodies	CF
Hahn, R.	L'Enchanteuse	Heu
Hahn, R.	Romanesque	Heu
Hahn, R.	2 Pièces	Heu
Hahn, R.	Variations on a Theme	Heu
Hahn, R.	Variations on a theme by Mozart	Int
Hahn, T.-Hahn	Valse Scherzo	CF
Haidmayer, K.	Flute Sonata. 1962	LDo
Haigh, M.	Serenade	TP
Hajdu, M.	Hungarian Shepherd's Song. 1953	EMB
Halevy, J.-Balogh	Valse de Concert	Lud
Haller, H.	6 Inventionen (fl, hpcd)	Hei
Hallnas, H.	Lyrisk svit. 1964	STI
Halphen, F.	Sicilienne	E&C
Halvorsen-Andersen	Bojarernes indtogsmarch	WH
Hamilton, I.	Sonata	TP
Hammer	Canzonetta	Ham
Hammer	Intermezzo "Clair de Lune"	CF
Hand, C.	Petite Suite Champêtre	B&H
Handel, G.-Voxman	Bourrée and Menuet (Flute Sonata No. III)	Rub
Handel, G.	Cantilena	NK
Handel, G.-Taffanel	Celebrated Largo	Dur
Handel, G.-Knepper	Concerto No. 13	SM
Handel, G.-Gaubert	Larghetto (2nd Organ Concerto)	ALe
Handel, G.	Largo	CF
Handel, G.-Gaubert	Little March	ALe
Handel, G.	Menuet	B&H
Handel, G.	Menuet	Dur
Handel, G.-Voxman	Petite Gavotte	Rub
Handel, G.-Leeuwen	Praeludium	WZ
Handel, G.	3 Dances and an Air	EdM
Handel, G.-Bopp	Sonatas, op. 1/1, 5, 9, Vol. 1 (fl, bc)	B&N
Handel, G.-Bopp	Sonatas, op. 1/2, 4, 7, 11, Vol. 2 (fl, bc)	B&N
Handel, G.-Seiffert	Chamber Sonata, e, op. 1/1a, No. 1 (fl, bc)	BrH
Handel, G.-Seiffert	Chamber Sonata, e, op. 1/1b, No. 2 (fl, bc)	BrH
Handel, G.-Seiffert	Chamber Sonata, g, op. 1/2, No. 3 (fl, bc)	BrH
Handel, G.	Chamber Sonata, a, op. 1/4 (fl, bc)	BrH
Handel, G.-Seiffert	Chamber Sonata, G, op. 1/5, No. 6 (fl, bc)	BrH
Handel, G.-Seiffert	Chamber Sonata, g, op. 1/10 (fl, bc)	BrH

Flute and Piano or Harpsichord

Handel, G.-Seiffert	Chamber Sonata, a,	
	op. 1/16, No. 17 (fl,bc)	BrH
Handel, G.-Hunt	4 Sonatas, op. 1/2, 4, 7, 11	S&C
Handel, G.-Fleury	Sonatas, 2 vols.	B&H
Handel, G.-Barrère	Handel Sonatas, 2 vols.	BM
Handel, G.-Schmitz	11 Sonatas, op. 1/1a, 1/1b, 5,	
	9, Hallenser Sonatas 1, 2, 3	
	(Includes 4 recorder sonatas)	B&N
Handel, G.	7 Sonatas and Prelude	CF
Handel, G.-Rampal	10 Sonatas, 2 vols.	Int
Handel, G.	Sonatas Nos. 1 & 7	MKE
Handel, G.-Shvedler	Sonatas 1-3	MKE
Handel, G.	Sonatas Nos. 4-7	MKE
Handel, G.-Dancker	3 Sonatas	NV
Handel, G.-Schwedler	7 Sonatas	Pet
Handel, G.	10 Sonatas (Urtext), 3 vols.	
	(fl,bc)	Pet
Handel, G.-Dart	3 Fitzwilliam Sonatas	S&C
Handel, G.	7 Sonatas and Largo, 2 vols.	EdK
Handel, G.-Moyse	7 Sonatas	Sch
Handel, G.-Cavally	7 Sonatas	SM
Handel, G.	Sonata No. 1	CF
Handel, G.	Sonata No. 2	CF
Handel, G.	Sonata No. 3	CF
Handel, G.	Sonata No. 4	CF
Handel, G.	Sonata No. 5	CF
Handel, G.	Sonata No. 6	CF
Handel, G.	Sonata No. 7	CF
Handel, G.-Cavally	Sonata No. 1	SM
Handel, G.-Cavally	Sonata No. 2	SM
Handel, G.-Cavally	Sonata No. 3	SM
Handel, G.-Cavally	Sonata No. 4	SM
Handel, G.-Cavally	Sonata No. 5	SM
Handel, G.-Cavally	Sonata No. 6	SM
Handel, G.-Cavally	Sonata No. 7	SM
Handel, G.-Fleury	Sonata, b	B&H
Handel, G.	Sonata, b	CF
Handel, G.-Mann	Sonata, Bb	B&H
Handel, G.-Scheck & Ruf	Sonata, c (fl,bc)	Ric
Handel, G.-Fleury	Sonata, e	B&H
Handel, G.	Sonata, F	EdM
Handel, G.	Sonata, G	ES
Hannisian, R.	Encounter & Diversion	Sha
Hanson, H.	Serenade, op. 35	CF
Hanus, J.	5 Impromptus, op. 45	Art
Hanus, J.	Short Stories No. 1	Gen
Harris, F.	Ballroom Echoes	Lud
Harris, F.	2 Larks	Lud
Harris, F.	2 Marionettes	Lud
Harrison, P.	Badinage	Cha

Harsanyi, T.	3 Pièces	EdS
Hartley, W.	Fantasia	Cre
Hartley, W.	4 Sketches	TP
Hartley, W.	Sonata. 1965 (fl, hpcd)	TP
Hartley, W.	Suite	Cre
Hartmann, J.	Weber's Last Waltz	CF
Hartmann, J.	Whistle Polka	CF
Hasbrouck, C.	El Romance Antiguo	BM
Hasbrouck, C.	Tuneful Twaddle	BM
Hasse, J.	Canzone	EdM
Hasse, J.-Walther	Konzert, b	BrH
Hasse, J.	12 Sonaten, op. 1/1, 2 (fl, bc)	RuE
Hasse, J.-Walther	Sonata No. 1, D (fl, bc)	NV
Hasse, J.	Sonate, d	B&V
Hasse, J.-Engländer	Sonata, G	FrH
Hasse, J.-Niggemann	Sonata, G	FrH
Hasse, J.-Ruf	Sonata, G (fl, bc)	SS
Hasse, J.-Niggemann	Sonatina, G	FrH
Haubiel, C.	Fear	See
Haubiel, C.	Gentle	See
Haubiel, C.	Jocose	See
Haubiel, C.	Plaintive	See
Haubiel, C.	Still	See
Hauck, F.	Concertino	HG
Haufrecht, H.	From Washington's Time (fl, hpcd/pf)	Bou
Haufrecht, H.	Minuet, Gavotte & Jig	CoF
Haug, H.	Prelude and Rondo	ALe
Hauser, M.-Haas	Song Without Words	Rub
Hayashi, H.	Sonata	TP
Haydn, F.-Moyse	Adagio and Presto	ALe
Haydn, F.	Capriccietto	Pet
Haydn, F.-Kaul-Zanke	Flute Concerto, D	AlL
Haydn, F.	Concerto, D	Int
Haydn, F.-Kowatscheff	Concerto, D	Leu
Haydn, F.-Moyse	Concerto, D	SM
Haydn, F.-Feltkamp	Cadenzas for the Haydn Concerto, D	B&V
Haydn, F.-Graf	Divertimento, D	Hug
Haydn, F.-Barnes	Gypsy Rondo	Lud
Haydn, F.-Brearley	Larghetto	Cur
Haydn, F.	Largo Cantabile	Ham
Haydn, F.-Guenther	Minuetto, C	B-M
Haydn, F.	Oxen Minuet	CF
Haydn, F.	Sérénade	CF
Haydn, F.	Serenade	Ham
Haydn, F.-Voxman	Serenade	Rub
Haydn, F.-Perry	Sonata, G	B&H
Haydn, F.	Sonata, G	Int
Haydn, F.	Sonata No. 8, G	Pet

46

Flute and Piano or Harpsichord

Haydn, F.-Muller	Sonatine I	Mau
Haydn, F.-Muller	Sonatine II	Mau
Haydn, F.-Tillmetz	6 Trios, 2 vols.	WZ
Haydn, F.	Valse Scherzo	CF
Haydn, M.-Vécsey	Concerto. 1776	EMB
Haydn, M.-Boehm	Concerto	Sch
Haydn, M.-Byrns	Concerto, D	TP
Haydn, M.-Beyer	Sonata (Divertimento), G	Pet
Head, M.	By the River in Spring	B&H
Hedges, A.	Count Down	BrH
Heiden, B.	5 Short Pieces	SM
Heiden, B.	Sonata. 1958	AMP
Heilman, H.	Sonata	Lud
Heimbern, L.	Fantaisie de concert	ScF
Heinichen, J.-Fischer	Concerto, G	CFV
Heiser, W.-Stern	Das Grab auf der Heide, op. 30	MRL
Helm, E.	Sonata	SS
Helm, E.	Sonata No. 2	AMC
Hemel, O. van	Pastorale suite. 1956	SD
Henkemans, H.	Epiloog (Hommage a Willem Pijper)	B&V
Hennebains, A.	Rêverie-Caprice	ALe
Henneberg, A.	Concertino, op. 39	CGM
Henze, H.	Sonatine	SS
Herbert, V.-Harris	Csardas "Fortune Teller"	Lud
Herbert, V.	Gypsy Love Song	NK
Herbert, V.-Voxman	Serenade	Rub
Herman, A.-arr.	Soirées du jeune flûtiste	Heu
Herman, J.	Fantaisie pastorale	ECh
Herman, J.	Grande fantaisie romantique	ECh
Herman, J.	Grande Valse	ECh
Herman, J.	Impromptu-valse	ECh
Herman, J.	Rondo turc	ECh
Herman, J.	Tarentelle	ECh
Hernried, R.	Dance Interlude	GFB
Herrera	Badinage, op. 11	EdS
Herrmann, T.	Air varie, op. 34	ScF
Herrmann, T.	Mignonne, op. 61	ScF
Hertel, J.	Partita No. 3, d (fl, hpcd/org)	Pet
Hervelois, C. d'	Suite	GD
Hess, W.	8 Recital Pieces, op. 70, 2 vols.	HE
Hess, W.	Thema mit Variationen, op. 27	Eul
Hess, W.	11 Tonstucke, op. 74	Eul
Hessenberg, K.	Elegy and Burlesque	ALe
Hessenberg, K.	Sonata, op. 38	SS
Hessenberg, K.	Suite, op. 77	SS
Hetu, J.	4 Pieces	Bil
Heyl, M.	Sonatine, op. 48	HMo
Hibbard, W.	Portraits	ECS
Hill	Dancing Fawn	B&H

Hindemith, P.	Echo. 1942	S&C
Hindemith, P.	Sonata. 1936	SS
Hinkson, A.	Valse Petite	Rub
Hirsch, H.	Sonata	Pet
Hlouschek, T.	Kleines Kaleidoskop	BrH
Hodgson -arr.	Flute Album, 2 vols.	Pet
Höller, K.	Sonate 1, op. 45. 1947	WMS
Höller, K.	Sonata No. 2, C, op. 53	SS
Hoff, G.	Scherzo	CF
Hoffmeister, F.	Concerto, D	EMB
Hoffmeister, F. -Sonntag	Concerto, D	HSM
Hoffmeister, F. -Szebenyi	Concerto, D	SS
Hoffmeister, F. -Rampal	Concerto, G	Int
Hoffmeister, F. -Schmitz	Sonata, C	B&N
Hofmann, H.	Concert Piece, op. 98	CF
Hofmann, H. -Cavally	Concertstuck, op. 98	SM
Hoiby, L.	Pastoral Dances	Sch
Holewa, H.	Sonatin. 1947	STI
Holzbauer, I.	Concerto, D	B&N
Holzbauer, I. -Gronefeld	Concerto, D	Leu
Honegger, A.	Romance	Int
Hook, J. -Salkeld	2 Sonatinas	S&C
Hopkins, A.	Flirtatious Fancy	S&C
Hopkins, A.	Sensuous Sarabande	S&C
Hopkins, A.	Wanton Waltz	S&C
Hosmer, J.	Rhapsody	M&M
Hotteterre, J. -Scheck, Ruf	Suite, D	Ric
Hotteterre, J. -Ruf	Suite, e (fl, bc)	B&N
Houdy, P.	Pastourelle	ALe
Houdy, P.	Sonate	ALe
Hovhaness, A.	The Garden of Adonis	OxU
Hovland, E.	Suite	Nor
Howard	Still Waters	EdM
Howe, C.	Valse Caprice	CF
Howe, C.	Valse Caprice	NK
Hrisanide, A.	Sonata	EMU
Hrisanide, A.	Sonata No. 2. 1969	EdR
Hubeau, J.	Idylle. 1967	Dur
Hudadoff, I. -arr.	15 Intermediate Solo Series	PrA
Hudadoff, I. -arr.	Marches	PrA
Hudadoff & Spire -arr.	11 Classic Solos	PrA
Hüe, G.	Fantaisie	Bil
Hüe, G.	Gigue	ALe
Hüe, G.	Gigue	CF
Hüe, G.	Nocturne	ALe
Hüe, G. -Doney	Petite Pièce, G	ALe
Hüe, G.	Serenade	CF
Hüe, G. -Cavally	Serenade	SM
Hughes -Pelz	Moods and Contrasts	SF
Hugon, G.	Sonata	EMT

48

Flute and Piano or Harpsichord

Humel, G.	Concerto. 1961	B&B
Hummel, H.	American Patrol	Rub
Hummel, J.-Riessberger	Sonata, G, op. 2/2	LDo
Hummel, J.-Sonntag	Sonata, D, op. 50	Hei
Hummel, J.-Riessberger	Sonata, D, op. 50	LDo
Hummel, J.-Riessberger	Sonate, A, op. 62	LDo
Hurd, M.	Sonatina	Nov
Hurník, I.	Partita, A	ES
Hurník, I.	Le Petit Faune	ALe
Hurrell, C.	Bingo	GFB
Hurrell, C.-arr.	The Lonely Birch Tree	Rub
Huzella, E.	Concertino lirico	EMB
Ibert, J.	Allegro scherzando (Concerto)	ALe
Ibert, J.	Aria	ALe
Ibert, J.-Moyse	La Cage de cristal (Histoires)	ALe
Ibert, J.	Concerto	ALe
Ibert, J.-Moyse	Le Cortège de Balkis (Histoires)	ALe
Ibert, J.-Moyse	Dans la Maison triste (Histoires)	ALe
Ibert, J.	Jeux	ALe
Ibert, J.-Moyse	La Marchande d'eau fraiche (Histoires)	ALe
Ibert, J.-Moyse	La Meneuse de tortues d'or (Histoires)	ALe
Ibert, J.-Moyse	Le Petit âne blanc (Histoires)	ALe
Iglo, M.	Miniature	ES
Ihlau, F.	Poème passionnel	Hei
Indy, V. d'-Samazeuilh	Chanson (Karade)	Heu
Infante, M.	Chanson gitane	EdS
Inghelbrecht, D.	Sonatina	ALe
Isaac, M.	Album of Favorite Flute Solos	Col
Isaac, M.	Midsummer Morning	CF
Isaac, M.	Music for the Flute	Col
Isaac, M.-arr.	Strolling	CF
Istrate, M.	Sonata. 1958	EdR
Ito, H.	Apocalypse. 1965	ESZ
Jacob, G.	Concerto	GaM
Jacobi, F.	Night Piece and Dance	B&H
Jacque-Dupont	Aulos	ALe
Jacquet-arr.	Album of 17 Popular Pieces	Sch
Jadassohn, S.-Cavally	Concert Piece	SM
Jaffe, G.	Lamentation and Dance	SM
Janácek, L.	Ballada	JB
Járdányi, P.	Sonata. 1952	EMB
Járdányi, P.	Sonatina. 1952	EMB
Jarnach, P.	Sonatine, op. 12	MRL
Jeanjean, P.	Heureux temps	Bil
Jeanjean, P.	Rêverie de printemps	Bil
Jenni, D.	Musica	PE
Jenni, D.	Musique Printanière	PE
Jensen, A.-Quensel	Murmuring Breezes	CF

Flute and Piano or Harpsichord

Jessel, L.-Schuman	Parade of the Wooden Soldiers	EBM
Jimenez M.	Cinco Piezas	PIC
Joachim, O.	Expansion. 1962	Can
Jolivet, A.	Capers	Int
Jolivet, A.	Chant de Linos	ALe
Jolivet, A.	Concerto	Heu
Jolivet, A.	Fantaisie-Caprice	ALe
Jolivet, A.	Sonata	Heu
Joly, D.	Eglogue	Bil
Jones	Rondo	Wat
Jones, W.	2 Pieces	AMC
Jongen, J.	Danse Lente	Che
Jongen, J.	Sonate, op. 77. 1924	CBD
Josephson, W.	Trilogy da Camera	SM
Kabalevsky, D.-Seay	Waltz (The Comedians)	Spr
Kadosa, P.	Sonatina, op. 56. 1961	EMB
Kai, N.	Andante	ALe
Kaláš, J.	Die Nachtigall und die Rose	Pan
Kalinnikov, V.	Chanson Triste	EdM
Kalmár, L.	Sonata	EMB
Kannon, V.	Ballade	EBM
Kantor	Dialogue	Wes
Kaplan, R.	Notturno, op. 35	Bra
Kapr, J.	Intermezzo	CHF
Kardos, I.	Scherzo Variato	Gen
Karg-Elert, S.	Suite pointillistique, op. 135	WZ
Karkoschka, E.	Variationen über das islandische Volkslied "Sumri hallar". 1952	GBV
Kauder, H.	Sonata	SM
Kaufmann	Sonate	Ham
Kaufmann, A.	Sonatine, op. 53/3	LDo
Kawaski	Essay On a Day	CF
Keiper, W.	Capriccietto	HG
Keldorfer, R.	Sonata ritmica	LDo
Kelkel, M.	Prière pour un vagabond	B-M
Keller, G.	Chant de Parthenope	EME
Keller, H.	Sonata	CoF
Kempe, H.	3 Danser	STI
Kempter, L.	Capriccio, op. 32	WZ
Kenins, T.	Concertante. 1966	B&H
Kennan, K.	Night Soliloquy	CF
Kennaway, L.	Interrupted Serenade	HE
Kepner, F.-McCathren	The Silver Thrush	CF
Kern, F.	Flötenserenade, op. 62	LDo
Kerr, H.	Suite	B&H
Kesnar, M.	Legend	CF
Ketelbey, A.	Italian Twilight	Bos
Ketelbey, A.	Scherzo de Concert	CF
Ketting, P.	Sonata. 1930	SD

Keuning, H.	De koning danst	HU
Keuning, H.	Van ver en dichtbij	HU
Keuning, H.	Wie het kan mag het spelen	HU
Khachaturian, A.-Rampal	Concerto (violin)	Int
Kilpatrick, J.	Suite Semplice	CoF
Kimmell, N.	Expression	TP
King-Garrison	Song of the Islands	EBM
King, K.	Night in June	Bar
Kinyon, J.	Program Pieces	War
Kinyon, J.	Recital Pieces	War
Kirnberger, J.-Weigart	Sonata, G (fl, bc)	SS
Kirnberger, J.-Sonntag	2 Sonatas, G, g (fl, bc)	WMS
Kittler, R.	Sonata. 1956	AMP
Klebe, G.	9 Duettini, op. 39	B&B
Klerk, J. de	De Rattenvonger van Hamelin	MM
Knight-Clement	Rocked in the Cradle of the Deep	Vol
Koch, E. van	Concertino Pastorale	BrH
Koch, P.	In Dulci Jubilo	Aug
Kochan, G.-Hauer	Concertino	Pet
Kochurov, Y.-Trizno	Romance (Alexander Popov)	MKE
Kocsár, M.	Repliche (fl, hpcd)	EMB
Kocsár, M.	Saltus Hungaricus	EMB
Koechlin, C.	14 Pièces	EdS
Koechlin, C.	Sonate	EdS
Köhler, E.	Berceuse, op. 30/2	CF
Köhler, E.	Butterfly, op. 30/4	CF
Köhler, E.-Cochrane	Concert Fantasie, op. 62 (Moskwa)	CF
Köhler, E.-Dole	Nightingale Polka	CF
Köhler, E.	Serenade, op. 59	WZ
Köhler, E.	25 Etudes Romantiques, op. 66	Bil
Koepke, P.	Andante con Moto (Sonata, Bb)	Rub
Koepke, P.-Voxman	Bergamask	Rub
Koepke, P.	Chanson Pastorale	Rub
Koepke, P.	Poplars in the Wind	Rub
Koepke, P.	Sonata, Bb	Rub
Koepke, P.	3 Aquarelles	Rub
Koepke, P.	Villanella	Rub
Koerppen, A.	Sonate, Bb. 1956	BrH
Kohn, K.	Encounters I	CF
Kohn, K.	3 Pieces	CF
Kolb, B.	Figments	CF
Kolz, E.	Petites Nocturnes. 1962	LDo
Kopelent, M.	Kleine Suite	Art
Kopp, F.	Portrait of a Woman	See
Koppel, H.	Capriccio	ALe
Kořínek, M.	Concerto	SHF
Kořínek, M.	Sonatina. 1960	SHF
Korn, P.	Aloysia Serenade, op. 19	B&H
Kornauth, E.	Sonatine, op. 46a	LDo

184240

Flute and Piano or Harpsichord

Kósa, G.	Notturno	EMB
Kosik, G.	Suite im alten Stil, op. 8	Art
Kosma, J.	3 Movements	EME
Kotlar, I.	Monte-Cristo	E&C
Kotonski, W.	Piece for Flute and Piano	AP
Kougel, A.	Scherzino	E-V
Kounadis, A.	Blues. 1970 (fl, hpcd/pf)	B&B
Kounadis, A.	Duo	EMo
Koutzen, B.	Nocturne	MCA
Kovalov, P.	Suite, op. 11	Be
Kox, H.	Studies in contrapunt. 1962 (fl, hpcd)	SD
Kraft, L.	Fantasy	JB
Krantz, A.-Brooke	Whirlwind	CF
Krebs, J.	6 Kammersonaten, 2 vols. (fl, hpcd)	B&N
Krebs, J.	Sonata, A	WH
Krebs, J.-Scheck, Ruf	Sonata, C	Ric
Krebs, J.-Ermeler	Sonata, D	Hei
Krebs, J.-Ermeler	Sonata No. 4, e	B&N
Krein, M.	Melody	MKE
Kreisler, F.-Van Leeuwen	Liebesfreud	CFo
Kreisler, F.-Van Leeuwen	Liebeslied	CFo
Kreisler, F.-Van Leeuwen	The Old Refrain	CFo
Kreisler, F.-Van Leeuwen	La Précieuse	CFo
Kreisler, F.-Van Leeuwen	Schön Rosmarin	CFo
Kreisler, F.-Van Leeuwen	Sicilienne and Rigaudon	CFo
Krenek, E.	Flute Piece in Nine Phases. 1959	B&N
Krenek, E.	Suite. 1954	B&N
Krenek, E.	Suite	Ron
Kreutzer-Ermeler	Sonata, D	Hei
Kreutzer	Sonata, op. 35, G	Pet
Křička, J.	Sonatine, e, op. 103	Art
Krieger, E.	Miniatures	PIC
Krieger, J.	Absence and Return	GD
Krol, B.	Reminiscenza, op. 47 (fl, hpcd)	Sim
Kronke, E.-Cavally	Caprice Impromptu	SM
Kronke, E.	Kolibris, Kleinste leichte Stücke, op. 210	WZ
Kronke, E.-Eck	Suite in Ancient Style	B-M
Kronke, E.	Suite im alten Stil, op. 81	WZ
Kronke, E.	2nd Suite im alten Stil, op. 160	WZ
Krumpholtz, J.-Zingel	Sonata, F	NV
Kruyf, T. de	Pas de deux, op. 22	B&B
Kruyf, T. de	Sonatina. 1960	SD
Kubik, G.	Nocturne	Sch
Kuhlau, F.	Menuett	CF
Kuhlau, F.	Menuett	NK
Kuhlau, F.-Voxman	Menuett	Rub

Flute and Piano or Harpsichord

Kuhlau, F.-Rampal	Grande Sonate Concertante, E, op. 51/2	Bil
Kuhlau, F.-Rampal	Grande Sonate Concertante, A, op. 51/3	Bil
Kuhlau, F.	3 Grand Solos, op. 57 (sold separately)	Bil
Kuhlau, F.	3 Grand Solos, op. 57/1	CF
Kuhlau, F.	3 Grand Solos, op. 57/2	CF
Kuhlau, F.	3 Grand Solos, op, 57/3	CF
Kuhlau, F.	Variations sur la romance d'Euryanthe, op. 63	Bil
Kuhlau, F.	Introduction and Variations, op. 63, on a Theme from C.M. von Weber's "Euryanthe"	B&N
Kuhlau, F.	Grande sonate, Eb, op. 64	Bil
Kuhlau, F.-Rampal	6 Divertissements, op. 68, 2 vols.	Bil
Kuhlau, F.	6 Divertissements, op. 68	EdK
Kuhlau, F.-Taffanel	6 Divertissements, op. 68	Int
Kuhlau, F.	Grand duo, e, op. 71	Bil
Kuhlau, F.	Sonate, F, op. 79/1	Bil
Kuhlau, F.-Sonntag	Sonata, G, op. 83/1	WMS
Kuhlau, F.-Sonntag	Sonata, C, op. 83/2	WMS
Kuhlau, F.-Rampal	Duo sonate, g, op. 83/3	Bil
Kuhlau, F.	Introduction et rondo, op. 98	Bil
Kuhlau, F.	Variations sur un thème écossais, op. 104	Bil
Kuhlau, F.	Variations sur un thème irlandais, op. 105	Bil
Kuhlau, F.	3 Duos brillants, op. 110 (sold separately)	Bil
Kukuck, F.	Sonata	MV
Kummer, G.	Carnival of Venice, op. 157	CF
Kummer, H.	Eine Handvoll Feldblumen, 7 Stücke, op. 33	WZ
Kunert, K.	Konzert, op. 21	BrH
Kupferman, M.	Hallelujah the Hills	BM
Kupferman, M.	Quiet Piece. 1971	Gen
Kurtz, S.	Notturno	SF
Kutsch, B.	Der junge Flötist	WZ
Labate, B.	Dancing Doll	Spr
Labate, B.	Pastorale	CF
Labate, B.	Rondino	CF
Labate, B.	Venetian Serenade (Barcarolle)	CF
Labitzky, A.-Ambrosio	Herd Girl's Dream	CF
Labitzky, A.-Bettoney	Herd Girl's Dream	CF
Lacombe, P.	Sérénade	Ham
Laderman, E.	Sonata	OxU
Lago, N.	Lullaby	GD

Lajtha, L.	Sonate en concert. 1958	ALe
Lakner, Y.	Sonata	ImV
Lalinov, M.	Armenian Dance	MKE
Lalo, E.	Chants russes	Ham
La Monica, J.	Primavera, op. 51	CF
La Monica, J.	Autumno, op. 57/3	CF
Lamote de Grignon, J.-Amaz	Canço de Maria	UME
Lamote de Grignon, J.-Amaz	Reverie (Schumanniana)	UME
Lancen, S.	Printanières. 5 Pieces	HE
Lancen, S.	Vahinee	MM
Lancen, S.	Week-end	Bil
Lane-Edwards	Penny Whistle Rock	B-M
Lane, R.	Sonata. 1967	CF
Lange, G.	Blumenlied	CF
Langer, F.	Concerto	MKE
Langer, F.-Cavally	Concerto	SM
Langer, G.	Gavotte	Ham
Langer, G.	Grand'maman	Ham
Langer, G.	Grand-Papa	Ham
Lannoy, J. de	Introduction et thème varié	ScF
Lannoy, R.	Pastourelle and Rigaudon	ÀLe
Lanshe, R.	Vignette	Roc
Lantier, P.	Danse sur un thème lydien	Bil
Laparra, R.	Suite	Heu
Làpis, S.-Ruf	3 Leichte Sonaten, op. 1/3, 4, 8 (fl, bc)	SS
Lara, A.	Granada	SMP
Larsson, L.	Concertino, op. 45/1	B&H
Lasala, A.	Poema del pastor coya	Ric
Lateef, Y.	Sonata	FaM
Latham, W.	Fantasy Concerto	Spr
Latham, W.	Sonata No. 2	Spr
Latham, W.	Suite in Baroque Style	S-B
Laube, P.	Alsatian Dance	CF
Lauber, J.	4 Danses mediévales, op. 45	WZ
Lauber, J.	Fantasie, op. 46	WZ
Lavigne, P. de-Hillemann	Sonata, C, No. 1 (La Barssan) (fl, bc)	Hei
Lavigne, P. de-Hillemann	Sonata, c, No. 2 (La d'Acut) (fl, bc)	Hei
Lavigne, P. de-Hillemann	Sonata, C, No. 3 (La Dubois) (fl, bc)	Hei
Lavigne, P. de-Hillemann	Sonata, C, No. 4 (La Beaumont) (fl, bc)	Hei
Lavigne, P. de-Hillemann	Sonata, G, No. 5 (La Persan) (fl, bc)	Hei
Lavigne, P. de-Hillemann	Sonata, G, No. 6 (La Simianne) (fl, bc)	Hei
La Violette, W.	Sonata	TP
Lavrans, E.	Suite	AMC

Flute and Piano or Harpsichord

Law, A.	Champagne	ATL
Lawrence, S.	Driftwood	PrA
Lawton, S. -arr.	The Young Flautist, 3 vols.	OxU
Lax, F.	Bonnie Scotland	CF
Lax, F. -Cavally	Tarantelle	SM
Lazare-Lévy	Sonatina, op. 32	ECh
Leclair, J. -Rampal	Concerto, op. 7/3	Int
Leclair, J. -Redel	Concerto, C, op. 7/3	Leu
Leclair, J. -Scheck, Ruf	Concerto, C, op. 7/3	Ric
Leclair, J. -Wummer	Concerto, C, op. 7/3	SM
Leclair, J.	Concerto, C	EMT
Leclair, J.	Dance Provençale	EdM
Leclair, J. -Barrère	Gigue	Sch
Leclair, J. -Barrère	Musette	Sch
Leclair, J.	Sarabande and Tambourin	Pet
Leclair, J. -Ruf	Sonata, C, op. 1/2 (fl, bc)	SS
Leclair, J. -Ruf	Sonata, G, op. 2/5 (fl, bc)	B&N
Leclair, J.	Sonata, C, op. 3/2	EME
Leclair, J. -Polnauer	Sonata, op. 9/2	Che
Leclair, J. -Ruf	Sonata, e, op. 9/2 (fl, bc)	SS
Leclair, J. -Ruf	Sonata, G, op. 9/7 (fl, bc)	SS
Leclair, J. -Bouillard	Sonata, e, No. 1	SS
Leclair, J. -Zanke	Sonata I, e	WZ
Lecuona, E. -Simon	Andalucia	EBM
Lecuona, E. -Simon	Malaguena	EBM
Leduc, J.	Divertissement, op. 12. 1962	CBD
Leduc, J.	Sonata, op. 21. 1966	CBD
Leeuw, T. de	Andante en Vivace. 1955	SD
Leeuw, T. de	Sonata. 1949	SD
Leeuwen, A. van	A Bird's Call	CF
Leeuwen, A. van -Cavally	Capricetta, op. 12/2	SM
Leeuwen, A. van	In a Great Hurry	SM
Leeuwen, A. van -Cavally	7 Artistic Solos	SM
Leeuwen, A. van	Soliloquy and Dance Sacral	Spr
Leeuwen, A. van -Cavally	Tarantella, op. 19/6	SM
Leeuwen, A. van	A Whimsical Thought	CF
Lefèbvre, C. -Waln	Piece Romantique	NK
Leffloth, J. -Ruf	Concerto, D	NV
Le Fleming, C.	Air and Dance	Che
Legendre	Air varié	EdS
Lehar, F. -Klickmann	Frasquita Serenade	EBM
Lehmann, T.	Elegie, op. 2/2	WH
Lehmann, T.	Idyll, op. 6/2	WH
Lehner, F.	Sonatine	GBV
Leigh, W.	Sonatina	S&C
Lemacher, H.	"Eia, Weihnacht"	HG
Lemare, E. -Maganini	Andantino	CF
Lemare, E. -Long	Andantino	Vol
Lendvay, K.	4 Duos. 1965	EMB
Lenom, C.	Lullaby	CF

Flute and Piano or Harpsichord

Lentz, D.	Sonance	CF
Leroux, F.	Une Soirée près du Lac	Heu
Leroux, X.	Romance, a	ALe
Lester, J.	Moment Orientale	Wes
Lester, L.	Crimson Blushes	Cen
Lewallen, J.	Andantino	B-M
Lewallen, J.	Aries	B-M
Lewallen, J.	Country Dance	B-M
Lewallen, J.	Fantasie	B-M
Lewallen, J.	Notturno	B-M
Lewallen, J.	Poeme Petite	B-M
Lewallen, J.	Taurus	B-M
Lewallen, J.	Valse Romantique	B-M
Liedbeck, S.	2 Stycken	EMf
Lieurance, T.	The Bridesmaid	CF
Lieurance, T.	Ranchita Twilight	CF
Lilien, I.	Divertimento. 1950	SD
Lincke, P.-Schuman	Glow-Worm	EBM
Lincke, P.	Glow-Worm	NK
Lincke, P.-Walters	The Glowworm	Rub
Linicke, J.-Schroeder	Concerto, G	Hei
Linicke, J.	Sonata, C	Mit
Lisenko, N.	Fantasy on Two Ukrainian Themes, op. 21	MKE
List, G.	Scherzino and Memoir	Spr
Liszt, F.-Hahn	Liebestraum	CF
Lluge, F.	Sonata	B&V
Locatelli, P.-Scheck	3 Sonatas (fl, bc)	B&N
Locatelli, P.	3 Sonatas	EdK
Locatelli, P.-Ruf	Sonata, Bb (fl, bc)	SS
Locatelli, P.-Rampal	Sonata, D	Int
Locatelli, P.-Kowatscheff	Sonata, F	Hug
Locatelli, P.-Rampal	Sonata, G	Int
Locatelli, P.	Sonate II	B&V
Locatelli, P.	Aria	EdM
Lockwood, N.	Sonata	ACA
Löhlein, G.-Sonntag	Sonata, G	Hei
Loeillet, J.	Courante	EdM
Loeillet, J.B.-Hinnenthal	Sonatas, op. 1/1-3 (fl, bc)	B&N
Loeillet, J.B.-Poulteau	Sonata, e, op. 3/7 (fl, bc)	ALe
Loeillet, J.B.-Ruf	Sonata, G, op. 3/8	SS
Loeillet, J.B.-Hinnenthal	Sonatas, op. 3/9, 4/9, 4/10 (fl, bc)	B&N
Loeillet, J.B.-Poulteau	Sonata, D, op. 3/11 (fl, bc)	ALe
Loeillet, J.B.-Hinnenthal	Sonatas, op. 3/12, 4/11, 4/12 (fl, bc)	B&N
Loeillet, J.B.	Sonata, e, op. 5/1	MR
Loeillet, J.B.	Sonate V	B&V
Loeillet, J.B.	Sonate X	B&V
Loeillet, J.B.-Fleury	Sonata, C	ALe

Flute and Piano or Harpsichord

Loeillet, J. B. -Lovering	Sonata, e	B&H
Loeillet, J. B. -Béon	Sonata, F	Int
Loeillet, J. B.	Sonata No. 14, g	CF
Loeillet, J. B. -Béon.	Sonata, g	Int
Lonque, A.	In verhaaltrant (Historiette)	Mau
Lonque, A.	Sonate, op. 21	EMb
Lora, A.	Improvisation and Burlesque	AMP
Lora, A.	Rhapsody	AMC
Lora, A.	3 Humorous Pieces	CF
Lora, A.	2 Sketches. 1960	AMP
Lorenzo, L. de	Scherzino, op. 18/1	CF
Lorenzo, L. de	Idillio, op. 67	Pet
Lorenzo, L. de	Il Pastorello Polacco, op. 68	Pet
Lorenzo, L. de	Improvviso, op. 72	Pet
Lorenzo, L. de	Allegro di Concerto, op. 74	Pet
Lothar, F.	Sonata, op. 72	B&N
Lotti, A.	Arietta	EdM
Lovec, V.	Sonata (fl, hpcd)	EdD
Lowthian, C.	Venetia	Dur
Lucke, G.	Studie. 1967	GBV
Lucky, S.	Sonata	CHF
Luening, O.	Fantasia brevis	GaM
Luening, O.	Second Suite	B-M
Luening, O.	Short Sonata	PE
Luening, O.	2 Pieces	CoF
Luigini, A.	Romance	GD
Lully, J. -Gaubert	Ariette en rondeau (Les Ballets du Roi)	ALe
Lully, J.	Dances for the King	EdM
Lully, J. -Leeuwen	Gavotte	WZ
Lully, J. -Gaubert	Gavotte en rondeau (Les Ballets du Roi)	ALe
Lully, J. -Gaubert	Minuet and Bourrée (Phaéton)	ALe
Lully, J. -Gaubert	Saraband and Gavotte (Les Ballets du Roi)	ALe
Lully, J.	20 Pieces	EdK
Lully, J. -Matthes	20 Pieces	Hug
Lyon, D.	3 Miniatures	InM
Maasz, G.	Flötenbuch für Gisela	WMS
Maasz, G.	6 Leichte Stücke	WZ
Macbeth, A.	Forget Me Not	CF
MacDowell, E. -Isaac	To a Wild Rose	CF
Macilwham, G.	Highland Suite	Cha
Macudzinski, R.	Fantasia. 1954	SHF
Madatov & Yagudin -arr.	5 Pieces by Russian Composers	MKE
Madatov & Yagudin -arr.	5 Pieces by Russian and Ukrainian Composers	MKE
Maderna, B.	Honeyreves	ESZ
Maertens, J.	Contrast	Mau
Maes, J.	Arabeske en Scherzo	EMe

Flute and Piano or Harpsichord

Maganini, Q.	Ancient Greek Melody	EdM
Maganini, Q.	Biskra (An Algerian Serenade)	CF
Maganini, Q.	Clouds and the Moon	CF
Maganini, Q. -arr.	Concert Album	EdM
Maganini, Q.	Evening Bells	CF
Maganini, Q.	Japanese Suite	EdM
Maganini, Q.	Lake at Sunset	EdM
Maganini, Q.	Moonlight on the Painted Desert	EdM
Maganini, Q.	Moto-Kago-Machi from Above	EdM
Maganini, Q.	Night Piece	EdM
Maganini, Q. -arr.	Paris Soir	EdM
Maganini, Q.	Peaceful Land	EdM
Maganini, Q.	La Romanesca	EdM
Maganini, Q.	Serenade	CF
Maganini, Q.	Song of a Chinese Fisherman	EdM
Maganini, Q.	Titania's Wedding March	CF
Mahaut, A.	6 Sonatas, op. 1 (fl, bc)	EdH
Mahault, A. -Schmitz	Sonata, G	B&N
Mai, P.	Concertino	FrH
Mai, P.	Sonatina	FrH
Maillot, J.	Ballade	Com
Maillot, J.	3 Danses	EMT
Mailly, A.	Sérénade française	ScF
Malipiero, G.	Concerto	Ric
Maltby, R.	The Slopes of Powderhorn	Ken
Manen, J.	Belvedere	B-M
Manicke, D.	Concerto	B&N
Manigold, J. -Cavally	Concerto	SM
Mann, H.	Jazz Flute Solos	War
Mann, L.	5 Improvisations, op. 10. 1954	Can
Marais, M. -Kestner	Menuette (Pièces de viole)	FrH
Marais, M. -Boulay	Suite (fl, bc)	EMT
Marcello, B.	Sonate, op. 1/4	B&V
Marcello, B. -Ermeler, Kluge	Sonata, Bb, op. 1/6	Hei
Marcello, B. -Ermeler, Kluge	Sonata, a, op. 1/11	Hei
Marcello, B. -Ermeler, Kluge	Sonata, G, op. 1/12	Hei
Marcello, B. -Tassinari, Toma	12 Sonatas, op. 2, 2 vols. (fl, bc)	EDS
Marcello, B. -Glode	2 Sonatas, C, Bb (fl, bc)	B&N
Marcello, B. -Glode	2 Sonatas, F, d (fl, bc)	B&N
Marcello, B. -Glode	2 Sonatas, g, e (fl, bc)	B&N
Marcello, B. -Martucci, Veggetti	4 Sonatas	EDS
Marcello, B.	Sonata, a	OHN
Marcello, B.	Sonata, Bb (fl, bc)	B&N
Marcello, B. -Pearson	Sonata, Bb	OxU
Marcello, B. -Whitney	Sonata, F	Hei
Marcello, B. -Slater	Sonata, F	OxU

Marcello, B.-Slater	Sonata, G, No. 12	OxU
Marcello, B.-Zanke	Sonata, G	WZ
Marchetti, F.-Hurrell	Fascination	Rub
Marcus	A Song for Flute	Tem
Margola, F.	Partita	GZ
Margola, F.	3 Pieces	Bon
Mari, P.	Divertissement	Bil
Marie, G.	La Cinquantaine	CF
Marie, G.	La Cinquantaine	Bil
Marie, G.	Danse de Jeunes Filles	EdS
Marie, G.	Serenade "Badine"	CF
Marie, G.	Slovakiana	ECh
Marpurg, F.-Scarmolin	Minuet	Lud
Marpurg, F.-Scarmolin	Rondo	Lud
Marsick, A.	Cadence et Danse Orientales	ALe
Marsick. A.	Tableaux Grecs	Heu
Martelli, H.	Fantaisiestuck, op. 67	Bil
Martelli, H.	5 Etudes Caprice	Amp
Martin, F.	Ballade	UE
Martin, V.	Barcarolle	Com
Martini, P.	Air with Variations	EdM
Martini, P.	Plaisir d'Amour	EdM
Martino, A. di	Allegro da concerto	Edi
Martinon, J.	Sonatine	Bil
Martinu, B.	Scherzo (Divertimento)	Art
Martinu, B.	Sonata No. 1	AMP
Marx, K.	Sonatine, C, op. 48/3	B&N
Mascagni, P.-Guenther	Intermezzo	B-M
Mascagni, P.	Intermezzo (Cavalleria Rusticana)	CF
Mascagni, P.	Intermezzo (Cavalleria Rusticana)	Heu
Maschat, M.	Sonatine	Hei
Mason, D.	Variations	SF
Massenet, J.	Andante	CF
Massenet & Saint Saens	Andante and Le Cygne	CF
Massenet, J.	Clair de Lune (Werther)	Heu
Massenet, J.-Trinkaus	Elegy	CF
Massenet, J.-Taffanel	Meditation (Thais)	CF
Massenet, J.	Méditation (Thais)	Heu
Massenet, J.	Mélodie-Elégie des Erinnyes	Job
Massenet, J.-Cavally	Mélodie-Elégie, op. 10	SM
Massenet, J.	Virgin's Last Slumber	CF
Masseus, J.	Introduzione en capriccio, op. 18. 1953 (fl/afl, pf)	SD
Masseus, J.	Sonata, op. 28. 1955	SD
Massias, G.	Concert 52	Bil
Masten, I.	Bonnie Eloise	Lud
Mateiciuc, P. (tr)	5 Piese	EdR
Matej, J.	Concertino	Art

Flute and Piano or Harpsichord

Matsudaira, Y.	Sonatine	Sha
Mattheson, J.	12 Sonatas, 2 vols.	EdK
Mattheson, J.-Leeuwen	12 Kammersonaten, 2 vols.	WZ
Mattheson, J.-Ruf	Sonata, A	SS
Maurat, E.	Petites Inventions, op. 39/1	EME
Maury, L.	Reflection	Wes
Maw, N.	Sonatina	Che
Mazellier, J.	Divertissement Pastoral	ALe
McBride, R.	In the groove	B-M
McCaughey, W.	Enchanted Isle	CF
McCaughey, W.	Mignonette	CF
McCauley, W.	5 Miniatures	MCA
McCoy, S.-Stuart	Trio (Lights Out)	CF
McKay, F.	Buckboard Blues	Bar
McKay, F.	Dream Waltz	Bar
McKay, F.	Hallowe'en Time	Bar
McKay, F.	Hernando's Holiday	Bar
McKay, F.	Jig for Jeanine	Bar
McKay, F.	The Powdered Wig	Bar
McKay, F.	Siciliano	Bar
McKay, F.	Ye Traveling Troubador	Bar
McKay, G.	Arietta and Capriccio	BM
McKay, G.	Concert Solo Sonatine	BM
Meacham, F.-Kent	American Patrol	CF
Medek, T.	Duo. 1966 (fl/pic/afl/pf)	JB
Medek, T.	Terzinen. 1966	Deu
Meier, D.	Cygne (fantaisie)	ECh
Melik-Muradian, G.	Lyric Piece	MKE
Melyan, T.	Soliloquy	Sha
Mendelssohn, F.	Mosquito Dance	NK
Mendelssohn, F.-Trinkaus	Nocturno	CF
Mendelssohn, F.-Weber	On Wings of Song	B-M
Mendelssohn, F.-Bettoney	On Wings of Song	CF
Mendelssohn, F.-Trinkaus	On Wings of Song	CF
Mendelssohn, F.	On Wings of Song	NK
Mendelssohn, F.-Hahn	Rondo Capriccioso	CF
Mendelssohn, F.-Altés	Scherzo (A Midsummer Night's Dream)	CF
Mendelssohn, F.	Scherzo (Midsummer Night's Dream)	M&M
Mendelssohn, F.-Francis, Silver	Song Without Words, op. 85/4	AlL
Mendelssohn, F.-Francis, Silver	Song Without Words, op. 102/3	AlL
Mendelssohn, F.-Francis, Silver	Song Without Words, op. 102/5	AlL
Mendelssohn, F.-Zverov	Song Without Words	SM
Mendelssohn, F.	Spring Song	CF
Mendelssohn, F.-Ward, Race	Venetian Boating Song, op. 19/6	Ken
Menéndez, J.	Nocturne	UME

Mercadante, S.-Girard	Concerto, e	ESZ
Merlet, M.	En tous sens	ALe
Merlet, M.	Sonatine en trois mouvements	ALe
Mersey, R.	Flutesville	SF
Messiaen, O.	Le Merle Noir	ALe
Metzler, F.	Konzert	R&E
Metzler, F.	Sonate	MRL
Meulemans, A.	Sonate No. 2. 1955	CBD
Meyer	Conte en gris	Com
Meyer, J.	Pastel	GD
Meyerbeer, G.-Trinkaus	Coronation March (The Prophet)	CF
Meylink, C.	Capriccioso	EdH
Mezö, I.	Suite. 1956	EMB
Miari, G.	Preludio e Divertimento	GZ
Miaskovsky & Goedicke		
-Voxman	2 Russian Songs	Rub
Michael, E.	Nocturne	EMT
Michaelis	Patrouille turque	Ham
Michalsky, D.	Partita Piccola	Wes
Micheelsen, H.	Suite	WMS
Micheelsen, H.	3 Stücke	B&N
Middeleer, J. de	Recitativo e allegro. 1970	CBD
Mieg, P.	Concerto. 1962	B&B
Migot, G.	Fantaisie No. 1	EdO
Migot, G.	Sonata in 5 parts	ALe
Mihalovici, M.	Melody	ALe
Mihalovici, M.	Pastourelle triste	ALe
Mihelic, P.	Sonatina	EdD
Milford, R.	Sonata, C	GaM
Milford, R.	Sonatina, F	OxU
Milford, R.	3 Airs	OxU
Milhaud, D.	Sonatine	Dur
Miller, M.	Sonata	AMC
Milsen	Memorandum, Eb, No. 2	EBM
Mimaroglu, I.	Antistrophes, 1967	See
Mimart, P.	Air varié	EdS
Miroglio, F.	Phases	UE
Missud, J.-Catlin	Magnolia Serenade	CF
Moeschinger, A.	Sonatine	Bil
Mohler, P.	Capriccio, op. 19	SS
Mohler, P.	Concertino, op. 28	WMS
Mohr, W. (ed)	Flauto domestico	WMS
Mole, C.	Danse Espagnole	CF
Molique, B.-Maganini	Andante (Concerto, d)	CF
Molique, B.-Medicus	Andante (Concerto No. 1)	CF
Molique, B.	Andante (Concerto, d)	SM
Molique, B.	Concerto, d	SM
Molnár, A.	Fantasy. 1910	EMB
Molter, J.	Flute Concerto	MR
Monath, N.	Parisienne Promenade	ShB

Flute and Piano or Harpsichord

Monti, V.-Roberts	Czardas	CF
Moortel, A. van de	Improvisation sur un thème de choral, op. 41	ScF
Moreau, L.	Dans la forêt enchantée	ALe
Moreno, T.	Dedicatoria	UME
Morlacchi, P.-Wilkins	Swiss Shepherd	CF
Morlacchi, P.	Il Pastore svizzero	Ric
Morra, G.	Nocturnal Serenade	CF
Morrissey, J.	Hoopla!	EBM
Moser, R.	Pezzo. 1967	SS
Moszkowski, M.	Serenata, op. 15/1	Bos
Moszkowski, M.	Serenade	CF
Moszkowski, M.-Hahn	Serenata, op. 15/1	CF
Moszkowski, M.	Serenade	NK
Moszkowski, M.	Spanish Dance, op. 12/1	Ric
Mouquet, J.-Wummer	Sonata "La Flûte de Pan"	Int
Mouquet, J.	Flûte de Pan	SM
Moyse, L.-arr.	Album of Sonatinas for Young Flutists	Sch
Moyse, L.	The Castle by Moonlight. Variations on a Japanese Song.	M&M
Moyse, L.	Fantaisie	ALe
Moyse, L. (ed)	Flute Music by French Composers	Sch
Moyse, L. (ed)	Flute Music from the Baroque	Sch
Moyse, L.-arr.	40 Little Pieces in Progressive Order	Sch
Moyse, L.	Pastorale	EdR
Moyse, L. (ed)	Solos for the Flute Player	Sch
Moyse, L.	3 Pièces faciles (Published separately.)	ALe
Moyse, L.	Variations	SM
Moyse, M.	The Golden Age of the Flutists, 2 vols.	Z-O
Moyse, M.	Tone Development through Interpretation	M&M
Mozart, F.-Ermeler	Rondo, e	Hei
Mozart, W.-Caratgé	Adagio (Flute Quartet)	ALe
Mozart, W.-Lentz	Adagio	B-M
Mozart, W.	Adagio (Clarinet Concerto)	CF
Mozart, W.-Buchtel	Adagio	NK
Mozart, W.-Scarmolin	Allegretto	Lud
Mozart, W.-Isaac	Allegro (Eine kleine Nachtmusik)	CF
Mozart, W.-Caratgé	Andante, C	ALe
Mozart, W.-Wolff	Andante, C, K. 315	B&H
Mozart, W.-Burchard	Andante, C, KV 315	BrH
Mozart, W.-Boehm, Medicus	Andante, op. 86	CF
Mozart, W.-Boehm, Voxman	Andante, C. KV 315	CF
Mozart, W.	Andante, C, K. 315	EdK

Flute and Piano or Harpsichord

Mozart, W.	Andante, C, K. 315	ES
Mozart, W.-Rampal	Andante, C, K. 315; Rondo, D, K. 184	Int
Mozart, W.-Voxman	Andante, C, K. 315	Rub
Mozart, W.-Lutz	Andante, KV 315	S&C
Mozart, W.-Walther	Andante, C, K. 315	WZ
Mozart, W.-Bettoney	Andante, F	CF
Mozart, W.-Isaac	Andante (Piano Sonata No. 1)	CF
Mozart, W.-Cole	Andantino	TP
Mozart, W.-Gaubert	Arietta (Cosi fan tutte)	ALe
Mozart, W.-Guenther	Cradle Song	B-M
Mozart, W.-Leeuwen	Deutscher Tanz	WZ
Mozart, W.-Moyse	Duport's Minuet	ALe
Mozart, W.-Gaubert	Figaro's Aria (Le Nozze di Figaro)	ALe
Mozart, W.-Leeuwen	Gavotte (Les petits riens)	WZ
Mozart, W.-Gaubert	Invocation (Die Zauberflöte)	ALe
Mozart, W.-Pellerite	Largo and Allegro (Sonata, Bb)	Za
Mozart, W.-Steensland	Magic Flute	B-M
Mozart, W.	Marche turque	Ham
Mozart, W.-Steensland	Melody (Don Giovanni)	B-M
Mozart, W.	Menuett, D	CF
Mozart, W.-Voxman	Menuett Paysanne	Rub
Mozart, W.-Leeuwen	Menuet, D	WZ
Mozart, W.-Vecchio	Menuetto	CF
Mozart, W.-Voxman	Menuetto (Eine Kleine Nacht- musik)	Rub
Mozart, W.-Barrère	Menuetto	Sch
Mozart, W.-Leeuwen	Menuetto, F	WZ
Mozart, W.-Gaubert	Minuet (Don Giovanni)	ALe
Mozart, W.	Minuetto	Ham
Mozart, W.-Moyse	Rondo, D	ALe
Mozart, W.-Sonntag	Rondo, D, KV 184	Hei
Mozart, W.-Boehm, Laube	Rondo-Andante	CF
Mozart, W.-Irmer, Marguerre	Serenade No. 1, KV 439b	B&N
Mozart, W.-Irmer, Marguerre	Serenade No. 2, KV 439b	B&N
Mozart, W.-Irmer, Marguerre	Serenade No. 3, KV 439b	B&N
Mozart, W.-Irmer, Marguerre	Serenade Nos. 4 & 5, KV 439b	B&N
Mozart, W.-Bopp	6 Sonatas, K. 10-15, 2 vols.	B&N
Mozart, W.	6 Sonatas, K. 10-15, 2 vols.	EdK
Mozart, W.-Moyse	3 Sonatas	Sch
Mozart, W.-Cavally	Sonata No. 1, K. 378	SM
Mozart, W.	2 Sonatinas after K. 439b	Pet
Mozart, W.	Concerto, G	ALe
Mozart, W.-Weissmann	Concerto No. 1, K. 313	B&H
Mozart, W.-LeRoy	Concerto, G, No. 1	Bil

Mozart, W.-Horn	Konzert, G, No. 1, K. 313	BrH
Mozart, W.	Concerto, G, No. 1, K. 313	CF
Mozart, W.	Concerto, G, K. 313	EdK
Mozart, W.-Rampal	Concerto, G, No. 1, 313	Int
Mozart, W.-List, Thiele	Concerto, G, K. 313	Pet
Mozart, W.	Flute Concertos 1, 2	Sch
Mozart, W.-Leeuwen	Concerto, G	SM
Mozart, W.	Concerto, D	ALe
Mozart, W.-Roth	Concerto No. 2, K. 314	B&H
Mozart, W.	Concerto, D, No. 2	Bil
Mozart, W.-Burchard	Konzert, D, No. 2, K. 314	BrH
Mozart, W.	Concerto No. 2, KV 314	CF
Mozart, W.	Concerto, D, No. 2, K. 314	EdK
Mozart, W.	Concerto, D, No. 2	EdR
Mozart, W.-Rampal	Concerto, D, No. 2, K. 314	Int
Mozart, W.-Burkhardt	Concerto, D, No. 2	MKE
Mozart, W.-List	Concerto, D, No. 2	Pet
Mozart, W.-Leeuwen	Concerto, D (Includes 6 Donjon, Andersen cadenzas)	SM
Mozart, W.	Concerto for Flute and Harp	CF
Mozart, W.-Andersen, Tillmetz	Cadenzas for K. 313, K. 314, K. 315	CF
Mozart, W.-Barrère	Cadenza for the Mozart Flute Concerto, G, K. 313	GaM
Mozart, W.-Barrère	Cadenza for the Mozart Flute Concerto, D, K. 314	GaM
Mozart, W.-Bartuzat	Cadenzas to Concertos, G, D	WZ
Mozart, W.-Belaubre, Marion	Cadenzas for Mozart Concertos	Bil
Mozart, W.-Blumenthal	Cadenzas to Concerto, KV 314	PrM
Mozart, W.-Bozza	3 Cadenzas for the Concerto, G	ALe
Mozart, W.-Donjon	3 Cadenzas for the Concerto, D	ALe
Mozart, W.-Donjon, Andersen	Cadenzas for Concerto, D	SM
Mozart, W.-Flothuis	Cadenzas to Mozart's Concertos, D, G, and Andante, C	B&V
Mozart, W.-Müller	3 Cadenzas to Mozart's Concerto	Mau
Mozart, W.-Solum	Cadenzas for Mozart's Works for Flute	M&M
Mozart, W.-Taffanel, Gaubert	3 Cadenzas for the Concerto, D	ALe
Mozart, W.-Taffanel, Gaubert	3 Cadenzas for the Concerto, G	ALe
Mozart, W.-Tillmetz	Cadenzas to Concertos, G, D, Andante, C	WZ
Mozart, W.-Müller	Sonatine	Mau
Muczynski, R.	Sonata, op. 14	Sch

Flute and Piano or Harpsichord

Müller -Medek	Kernberg-Suite	PG
Müller -Zuric, P.	Capriccio	Eul
Müthel, J.-Hinnenthal	Sonata, D	B&N
Mulder, H.	Sonata No. 2, op. 40. 1943	SD
Mulder, H.	Sonatine, op. 100. 1956	SD
Muldermans, J.	Fantasie Varié	Lud
Murgier, J.	3 Pièces	EdS
Murrill, H.	Sonata	OxU
Nabokov, N.	Concerto Chorale	Be
Nagovitzin, V.	Sonata	MKE
Nagy, F.	Zigany	Lud
Napoli, C.	Introduzione	Edi
Nardini, P.	Shepherd's Pipes	EdM
Naudot, J.-Gurgel	6 Sonatas, op. 1 (fl, bc)	B&N
Naudot, J.-Ruf	Sonata, G (fl, bc)	B&N
Nelhybel, V.	Suite	BM
Nerini, E.	Pages d'album	EdS
Nerini, E.	Sonata	EdS
Nessler, R.	Dialoge	EMo
Neugeboren, H.	Sonata	EMT
Neukomm, S.-Kaplan	Aria	Spr
Nevin, E.-Hummel	Narcissus	Rub
Nguyen-Thien-Dao	Tay Nguyen	EdS
Nicolai, O.-Perrin	Merry Wives of Windsor	B-M
Nielsen, C.	Concerto	SPD
Nielsen, C.	The Fog Is Lifting	WH
Niemann, W.	4 Stücke, op. 121a	WZ
Niemann, W.	Kleine Sonate, op. 181	WMS
Nigg, S.	Concerto	Job
Nikolayev, A.	2 Pieces	MKE
Niverd, L.	Elégie	Bil
Niverd, L.	Impromptu	Bil
Niverd, L.	Musette et tambourin	Bil
Niverd, L.	Pastourelle	GD
Niverd, L.	6 Bagatelles	GrF
Nixon, R.	Nocturne	TP
Noble, H.	Le Petit-Rouet	ALe
Noordt, S. van	Sonata	HU
Norden, H.	Capriccio	CF
Nordenstrom, G.	Rondo. 1948	B&N
Nowak, L.	Short Suite	CoF
Nussio, O.	Bagatellen	WZ
Nussio, O.	Concerto (violin)	Car
O'Bryan, C.	Maiden's Dance	CF
Occa, J.	Kinloch of Kinloch	CF
Očenáš, A.	Concertino, op. 27	SHF
Offenbach, J.	Barcarolle	CF
Offenbach, J.	La Musette	CF
Offenbach, J.-Steensland	Offenbach Ballet	B-M
Offenbach, J.	Waltz "La Perichole"	NK

Flute and Piano or Harpsichord

Oliver	Menuettons	Spr
Ollone, M. d'	Andante et allegro en style ancien	Heu
O'Preska, J.	Mist	CoA
Organn, R.	The Brook	Reb
Organn, R.	Even Song	Reb
Organn, R.	Sérénade et Danse	Reb
Ortolani, O.	More (Mondo Cane)	EBM
Osieck, H.	Ballade	SD
Ott, J.	Cihpronap	CBP
Paderewski, I.-Laube	Minuet, op. 14/1	CF
Paderewski, I.-Trinkaus	Minuet a l'Antique	CF
Paganini, N.	Rondo (de la danse des sorciers), Bk. 2	Bil
Paladilhe, E.	Mandolinata	Heu
Palau, M.	Dolcainers	UME
Palenıček, J.	Concerto. 1957	CHF
Pannain, G.	Sonatina	Edi
Papandopulo, B.	Zwiegesprach. 1968/69 (fl, hpcd)	HG
Papineau-Coutre, J.	Suite. 1944-45	Can
Paray, P.	Sérénade	Job
Parcham, A.-Dart	Solo	OxU
Parès, G.	Crépuscle	Bil
Parès, G.	Fantaisie-caprice	Bil
Parodi	Concerto	Ric
Parsadanian, B.	Concertino	MKE
Pascal, C.	6 Pièces variées	Dur
Pasfield, W.	Humoresque	GaM
Pasfield, W.	Skyscapes	Bos
Passani, E.	Concerto	Bil
Passani, E.	Serenite	Com
Paubon, P.	A un enfant	EPC
Pauer, J.	Capricci	Art
Paul, B.	Sonata	HSM
Paulson, J.	Concert Etude	PrA
Paulson, J.	Impromptu	GFB
Paulson, J.	2 Moods	PrA
Paulson, J.	Valse Chromatique	B-M
Pearson, W.	3 Flute Tunes	Cha
Peck, D. (ed)	Easy Original Flute Solos	MS
Pelemans, W.	Sonata (fl, hpcd)	Mau
Pendleton, E.	Concerto alpestre	EdS
Pepin, A.	Impromptu	ALe
Pepping, E.	Sonate. 1957	B&N
Pepusch, J.-Ruyssen	Sonata	GD
Pergament, M.	Elegi. 1966	STI
Pergament, M.	Sonat. 1968	STI
Pergolesi, G.-Rampal	Concerto, D	Int
Pergolesi, G.-Meylan	Concerto, G.	B&H
Pergolesi, G.-Brinckmann,		

Flute and Piano or Harpsichord

Mohr	Concerto, G	HSM
Pergolesi, G.	Concerto, G	Int
Pergolesi, G.-Barbirolli	Concerto	OxU
Pergolesi, G.-Elkan	Se Tu M'Ami	HeE
Pergolesi, G.	Sicilian Air	EdM
Pergolesi, G.	Sonata No. 12	EdM
Perilhou, A.	Ballade	Heu
Perilhou, A.-Cavally	Ballade	SM
Pernette, R.	Crépuscle	ECh
Perrin, M.	Frolic	B-M
Perrin, M.	Taurus	B-M
Perry, H.-arr.	Classical Album	B&H
Pessard, E.	Andalouse, op. 20	ALe
Pessard, E.	Andalouse, op. 20	CF
Pessard, E.-Brooke	Andalouse, op. 20	CF
Pessard, E.	Andalouse	NK
Pessard, E.-Voxman	Andalouse	Rub
Pessard, E.-Cavally	Andalouse	SM
Pessard, E.	Bolero, op. 28/2	CF
Pestalozza, A.	Ciribiribin	NK
Peter, H.	Bagatelle	AMP
Peter, H.	Pastorale	AMP
Petit, P.	Petite Suite	ALe
Petrassi, G.	Concerto	ESZ
Petrič, I.	Sonata	EdD
Petrovics, E.	Concerto. 1957	EMB
Pez, J.-Bergmann	Adagio & Presto	S&C
Pez, J.-Schroeder	Concerto, e	Pet
Phillips, B.	3 Nostalgic Songs	TP
Phillips, B.	4 Figures in Time	E-V
Phillips, I. (ed)	Beginner's Repertoire, 2 vols.	OxU
Pierné, G.-Petiot	Canzonetta	ALe
Pierné, G.-Bettoney	March of the Little Tin Soldiers	CF
Pierné, G.	March of the Soldiers	NK
Pierné, G.	Nocturne	Ham
Pierné, G.	Serenade, op. 7	ALe
Pierné, G.	Sonate, op. 36	Dur
Pietsch, E.	Woodland Fantasie	SM
Pijper, W.	Sonata. 1925	SD
Pillois, J.	Bucoliques	EdS
Pillois, J.	Chagrin d'amour	Dur
Pillois, J.	Jour de l'an japonais	Dur
Pillois, J.	Solitude	Dur
Pinchard, M.	Sonate concertante	Bil
Pisk, P.	Introduction and Rondo	SMP
Pisk, P.	Sonata, op. 82	CoF
Piston, W.	Sonata	AMP
Plain, G.	For Piano & Flute	AMC
Platamone, S.	Duet	EDS

Platt, R. (ed)	Music for Flute and Basso Continuo, 1700–1750 (fl, bc)	OxU
Platti, G. -Waln	Adagio and Allegro	NK
Platti, G. -Jarnach	Sonata, A	SS
Platti, G. -Scheck, Ruf	Sonata, D	Ric
Platti, G. -Ruf	Sonata, G, op. 3/6	SS
Platti, G. -Jarnach	Sonata, e	SS
Ple, S.	Conte	EdS
Pleskow, R.	2 Pieces. 1963	See
Pless, H.	Divertimento, op. 49	LDo
Pleyel, I. -Rampal	Concerto	Int
Pleyel, I. -Alberti	Sonata, Bb, No. 3	Eul
Pleyel, I. -Alberti	Sonata, A, No. 4	Eul
Pleyel, I.	Sonata No. 5	Pet
Pleyel, I. -Alberti	Sonata, D, No. 6	Eul
Poldini, E. -Guenther	Oiseaux de Passage	B-M
Poldini, E.	Waltzing Doll	NK
Poldini, E. -Andreoni	Poupée valsante	Ric
Polin, C.	Sonata No. 1	SM
Ponce, M. -Weber	Estrellita	B-M
Ponce, M.	Estrellita (My Little Star)	CF
Ponse, L.	2 Caprices, op. 20. 1956	SD
Ponse, L.	Variations, op. 31/2. 1962 (fl, hpcd)	SD
Poot, M.	Ballade	EME
Poot, M.	Légende	EME
Poot, M.	Sicilienne	ALe
Pope, P.	Sonatina	S&C
Popp, W. -Medicus	Birdsong	CF
Popp, W.	Concert-Fantasie, op. 382	ECM
Popp, W. -Pellerite	The Nightingale	TP
Popp, W.	Nightingale Serenade	CF
Popp, W.	Polka de bravoure, op. 201	ECM
Popp, W.	Schwedisches Konzert, op. 266	ECM
Porpora, N. -Maynard	Sinfonia, d	M&M
Porret, J.	Concertino No. 11	EdR
Porret, J.	Concertino No. 12	EdR
Porret, J.	le Solo de Concours	MM
Porret, J.	2e Solo de Concours	MM
Porter, Q.	Blues Lointains	CoF
Poser, H.	Miniaturen, op. 60	MV
Poulenc, F.	Sonata	Che
Pouwels, J.	Sonata. 1950	SD
Presle, J. de la	Orientale	ALe
Presser, W.	Prelude and Dance	TP
Prokofiev, S. -Voxman	Gavotta (Classical Symphony)	Rub
Prokofiev, S.	Kije's Wedding	EdM
Prokofiev, S.	Romance	EdM
Prokofiev, S.	Sonate No. 2, op. 94	ChM
Prokofiev, S.	Sonata No. 2, op. 94	HSM

Flute and Piano or Harpsichord

Prokofiev, S.-Rampal	Sonata, op. 94	Int
Prokofiev, S.	Sonata, op. 94	MCA
Pryor, A.-Roberts	Whistler and His Dog	CF
Pryor, A.-Stuart	Whistler and His Dog	CF
Ptaszynska, M.	Wariacje (Variations)	PWM
Puccini, G.-Isaac	Mimi and Musetta	CF
Pütz, E.	Improvisation Modale. 1966	EdT
Purcell, D.-Fleury	Sonata, F	Ric
Purcell, D.-Slater	Sonata	OxU
Purcell, D.-Jarnach	Sonata, F	SS
Purcell, D.-Hunt	Sonatina, d	S&C
Purcell, H.	Dance Suite	EdM
Purcell, H.	Nymphs and Shepherds	NK
Purcell, H.-Kaplan	Saraband	Spr
Purcell, H.	Sonata, g	EdM
Purcell, H.-Revell	2 Pieces	B&H
Pyle, F.	Sonata	SM
Quantz, J.-Taffanel	Adagio	Dur
Quantz, J.	Arioso and Presto	CF
Quantz, J.-Cavally	Arioso and Presto	SM
Quantz, J.	Concerto, A	Eul
Quantz, J.-Sonntag, Krainer	Concerto, c	Hei
Quantz, J.-Sonntag	Concerto, C	WMS
Quantz, J.	Concerto, d	MR
Quantz, J.-Walther	Concerto, D, "Pour Potsdam"	B&N
Quantz, J.-Nagy	Concerto, D	EMB
Quantz, J.	Concerto, D, No. 17	For
Quantz, J.-Sonntag	Concerto, e	HSM
Quantz, J.-Barge	Concerto, G	BrH
Quantz, J.	Concerto, G	CF
Quantz, J.	Concerto, G	EdK
Quantz, J.	Concerto, G	EMB
Quantz, J.-Rampal	Concerto, G	Int
Quantz, J.-Schroeder	Concerto, G	Pet
Quantz, J.-Wummer	Concerto, G	SM
Quantz, J.-Bresser	Cadenzas for the Concerto, G	B&V
Quantz, J.	3 Sonatas (fl, bc)	BrH
Quantz, J.-Sonntag	6 Sonatas, D, G, e, G, D, A (fl, bc)	WMS
Quantz, J.	Sonata, a	CF
Quantz, J.-Fischer	Sonata, a, No. 1	For
Quantz, J.-Fischer	Sonata, Bb, No. 2	For
Quantz, J.-Fischer	Sonata, c, No. 3	For
Quantz, J.-Fischer	Sonata, D, No. 4	For
Quantz, J.-Fischer	Sonata, e, No. 5	For
Quantz, J.-Fischer	Sonata, D, No. 6	For
Quantz, J.-Fischer	Sonata, D, No. 8	For
Quantz, J.-Ruf	Sonata, b (fl, bc)	SS
Quantz, J.-Nagel	Sonata, Bb, op. 1/2	Hei
Quantz, J.-Nagel	Sonata, c, op. 1/3	Hei

Flute and Piano or Harpsichord

Quantz, J.-Hinnenthal	Sonata, D (fl, bc)	B&N
Quantz, J.-Sonntag	Sonata, D	B&N
Quantz, J.-Schreiter	Sonata, e	BrH
Quantz, J.-Ruf	Sonata, e	SS
Quensel, A.	Andante, op. 7	CF
Quensel, A.-Cavally	Scherzo	SM
Quentin, B.-Ruf	Sonata, d (fl, bc)	B&N
Quinet, M.	Concertino. 1959	CBD
Quinet, M.	Sonate. 1968	CBD
Rachmaninoff, S.	Polka Italienne	EdM
Rachmaninoff, S.	Sérénade	Ham
Rachmaninoff, S.	Vocalise	EdM
Radauer, I.	Duo Concertante	Pet
Raff, J.	Cavatina, op. 85/3	CF
Raff, J.	Fileuse	Ham
Rafter, L.	5 Satires	Bos
Rakov, N.	3 Pieces	MKE
Ralston, A.	3 English Folk Tunes	B&H
Rameau, J.	Dardanus, Rigodon	Dur
Rameau, J.	Gavotte (Temple de la Gloire)	Pet
Rameau, J.-Voxman	Menuet (Platée)	Rub
Rameau, J.	Minuet and Passepied (Castor and Pollux)	Pet
Rameau, J.-Horusitzky	Pièces de Clavecin	EMB
Rameau, J.	Rigodon de Dardanus	EdM
Rameau, J.-Barrère	Sarabande	GaM
Rampal, J.-Yashiro	Jean-Pierre Rampal Flute Favorites	TP
Ranger, A.-arr.	The Old Refrain	CF
Ranish, J.-Platt	Sonata, op. 2/3 (fl, bc)	OxU
Raphael, G.	Concertino, op. 82. 1956	BrH
Raphael, G.	Sonate, e, op. 8. 1925	BrH
Raphling, S.	Square Dance	EdM
Raphling, S.	Warble for Lilac-Time	Gen
Rateau, J.	Matinale	ALe
Ravel, M.	Berceuse sur le nom de Fauré	Dur
Ravel, M.-Roques	Menuet (Sonatine)	Dur
Ravel, M.	Menuet antique	E&C
Ravel, M.	Pavane de la Belle au Bois dormant	Dur
Ravel, M.-Bettoney	Pavane	CF
Ravel, M.-Walters	Pavane	Rub
Ravel, M.	Pavane	SS
Ravel, M.	Pavane pour une Infante défunte	EdM
Ravel, M.-Fleury	Pavane pour une Infante défunte	EME
Ravel, M.-Kochanski	Pavane pour une Infante défunte	EME
Ravel, M.	Petit Poucet	Dur

Flute and Piano or Harpsichord

Ravel, M.	Pièce en forme de Habanera	ALe
Ravin, I.	Meditation	AMC
Read, G.	Threnody	See
Read, L.	Canary Polka	CF
Read, T.	Concatenation	CoA
Rebikov, V.	A Little Girl Rocking her Doll	EdM
Rebikov, V.-Guenther	On the Meadow	B-M
Rebikov, V.-Grunes	Valse (The Christmas Tree)	SF
Reck, D.	3 Short Constructions	SM
Reed, A.	Pastorale	BM
Reger, M.	Allegretto grazioso	OJ
Reger, M.-Schwedler	Romanze, G	BrH
Reicha, A.	Sonata, G, op. 54	Pet
Reicha, A.-Lebermann	Sonata, D, op. 103	SS
Reichardt, J.-Wiltberger	Sonata, C	BrH
Reif, P.	Banter. 1966	See
Reinecke, C.	Konzert, D, op. 283	BrH
Reinecke, C.	Sonata "Undine," op. 167	EdK
Reinecke, C.	Undine Sonata, op. 167	For
Reinecke, C.	Sonata "Undine," op. 167	Int
Reiner, K.	6 Studien	CHF
Reinl, F.	Minuet & Modern Dance	Sim
Reizenstein, F.	Partita	S&C
Relmes, L.	Intermezzo	Bil
Renosto	Mixage (fl/afl, pf)	Ric
Renzi, A.	Mnemosyne	GZ
Resch	Amour discret	Ham
Resch	Salut au printemps	Ham
Restorff, H.	The Bluebird's Call	CF
Reuter, H.	Barcarolle	ALe
Reutter, H.	Rondeau	ALe
Revel, P.	5 Pièces	Dur
Reynaud, J.	Adam et Eve	EdS
Reynaud, J.	Ah! Vous dirai-je Maman?	EdS
Reynaud, J.	L'Arabesque	EdS
Reynaud, J.	Chant d'alouette	EdS
Reynaud, J.	Hylda	EdS
Reynaud, J.	Merle et Pinson	EdS
Reynolds, R.	Mosaic	Pet
Reynolds, V.	Sonata	CF
Rhené-Baton	Bourrée, op. 42	Dur
Rhené-Baton	Passacaille, op. 35	Dur
Ribari, A.	Dialogues	Gen
Richter, F.	Concerto, D	WMS
Richter, F.-Gronefeld	Concerto, e	Leu
Richter, F.-Upmeyer	Sonatas, D, G, A (6 Sonatas, op. 2) (fl, bc)	B&N
Ries, F.	Introduction & Polonaise	MR
Ries, F.-Schmitz	Sonata, Eb, op. 169	B&N
Ries, F.	Sonate Sentimentale, op. 169	MR

Flute and Piano or Harpsichord

Rieti, V.	Sonatina	Bon
Rieunier, J.	Dialogue	ALe
Riker, H.	All on a Summer's Day, op. 4	CF
Riker, H.	3 Oriental Carpets	CF
Rimsky-Korsakov, N.	Chanson indoue	Com
Rimsky-Korsakov, N.-Cavally	Flight of the Bumble Bee	BM
Rimsky-Korsakov, N.	Hummelflug	BrH
Rimsky-Korsakov, N. -Bettoney	Flight of the Bumble Bee	CF
Rimsky-Korsakov, N. -Iasilli	Flight of the Bumble Bee	CF
Rimsky-Korsakov, N. -Wilkins	Flight of the Bumble Bee	Lud
Rimsky-Korsakov, N. -Glinsky-Safronov	Flight of the Bumble Bee	MKE
Rimsky-Korsakov, N. -Trizno	Flight of the Bumble Bee	MKE
Rimsky-Korsakov, N. -Voxman	Flight of the Bumble Bee	Rub
Rimsky-Korsakov, N.-Cavally	Flight of the Bumble Bee	SM
Rimsky-Korsakov, N. -Bettoney	Hymn to the Sun	CF
Rimsky-Korsakov, N.	Sonnenhymne (Der goldene Hahn)	For
Rimsky-Korsakov, N.-Isaac	Song of India	CF
Rimsky-Korsakov, N.-Laube	Song of India	CF
Rimsky-Korsakov, N.-Vachey	Song of India	GD
Rimsky-Korsakov, N.-Davis	Song of India	Rub
Rivier, J.	Ballade	EMT
Rivier, J.	Concerto	Bil
Rivier, J.	Sonatine	EMT
Rivier, J.	3 Silhouettes	JB
Rizzo, Blalock-Robinson	The Flea	SF
Robbins, G.	Danse	ALe
Robbins, G.	Sonatina	ALe
Robles, D.	El Condor Pasa	EBM
Rodrigo, J.	Aria antigua	UME
Roelens -Mule	Menuet vif	Job
Roesgen-Champion, M.	Sonata	ALe
Rössler-Rosetti, F.-Szebenyi	Concerto, D	SS
Rössler-Rosetti, F.-Szebenyi	Concerto, G	SS
Roger-Ducasse, J.	Berceuse (Petite suite)	Dur
Roger-Ducasse, J.	Souvenance (Petite Suite)	Dur
Rogers, B.	Soliloquy	CF
Rohwer, J.	Sonata	MV
Rollinson, T.	Columbia	NK
Roman, J.-Brinckmann, Mohr	Sonata, D, No. 12 (fl, bc)	HSM
Roman, J.-Senn	2 Sonatas, G, b (fl, bc)	B&N
Roman, J.	Sonatas 4, 7	EMf
Roman, J.	Sonatas 5, 8	EMf
Roman, J.	Sonata, b (fl, bc)	Mit

Rootham, **C.**	Suite in Three Movements	Che
Ropartz, J.	Sonatine	Dur
Rorem, N.	Mountain Song	PIC
Rosas, J.	Over the Waves	Cen
Rose, D.	Holiday for Flutes	BVC
Roseingrave, T.-Platt	Sonata, a, No. 1	Fab
Roussel, A.	Andante et Scherzo	Dur
Roussel, A.	Aria	ALe
Roussel, A.	Krishna	Dur
Roussel, A.	Monsieur de la Péjaudie	Dur
Roussel, A.	Pan	Dur
Roussel, A.	Tityre	Dur
Rovics, H.	Sonata	PE
Rowley, A.	Pastoral Elegie	Gam
Rowley, A.	Pavan and Dance	B&H
Roxlo, G.	Bajo la Reja	CF
Rozmann, A.	Improvisazione	EMB
Rubinstein, A.-Guenther	Melodie	B-M
Rubinstein, A.	Melodie in F	CF
Rubinstein, A.	Mélodie en fa	Ham
Rubinstein, A.	Melody in F	NK
Rubinstein, A.	Romance, op. 44	Ham
Rubinstein, A.	Romance	SF
Rubinstein, A.-Long	Romance	Vol
Rudolf, B.	Divertissement	LDo
Rueff, J.	Diptyque	ALe
Rumeau, G.	3 Pièces	EME
Russell, L.	Suite One	B&H
Russell, R.	Duo	Gen
Russell, R.	Pan	Gen
Ruyneman, D.	4 Chansons Bengalies. 1950	SD
Ruyneman, D.	Sonata da camera. 1942	SD
Ruyneman, D.	Sonatina. 1952 (fl, hpcd)	SD
Sacchini, A.	Andantino Grazioso (Renaud)	CF
Sacchini, A.	Andantino Grazioso	NK
Sacchini, A.	Gavotte (Renaud)	CF
Saint-Jacome	Le Roi Dagobert	EdS
Saint-Saens, C.-Barrère	Airs de Ballet	GaM
Saint-Saens, C.	Airs de Ballet (Ascanio)	SM
Saint-Saens, C.-Taffanel	Ascanio, Air de ballet	Dur
Saint-Saens, C.	Danse Macabre	CF
Saint-Saens, C.	Danse Macabre, op. 40	Dur
Saint-Saens, C.	Danse des Prêtresses de Dagon	Dur
Saint-Saens, C.-Taffanel	Déluge, op. 45	Dur
Saint-Saens, C.	Etienne Marcel, "O beaux rêves évanouis"	Dur
Saint-Saens, C.-LaFleurance	Fantaisie	Dur
Saint-Saens, C.	My Heart At Thy Sweet Voice	Cen
Saint-Saens, C.-Brooke	My Heart At Thy Sweet Voice	CF
Saint-Saens, C.	Odelette, op. 162	Dur

Saint-Saens, C.-Barrère	Pavane	BM
Saint-Saens, C.-Taffanel	Pavane	Dur
Saint-Saens, C.-Taffanel	Proserpine, Pavane	Dur
Saint-Saens, C.-Taffanel	Rêverie du Soir, op. 60	Dur
Saint-Saens, C.	Rêverie du Soir (Scènes Algériennes)	EdM
Saint-Saens, C.	Romance, op. 37	Dur
Saint-Saens, C.-Taffanel	Romance, op. 51	Dur
Saint-Saens, C.	Sérénade	ECh
Saint-Saens, C.-Voxman	Serenade	Rub
Saint-Saens, C.-Barrère	The Swan	BM
Saint-Saens, C.-Perrin	The Swan	B-M
Saint-Saens, C.-Langenus	The Swan	CF
Saint-Saens, C.-Trinkaus	The Swan	CF
Saint-Saens, C.-Taffanel	Le Cygne	Dur
Saint-Saens, C.-Mittell	The Swan	Sch
Saint-Saens, C.	2 Pavanes	EdM
Saint-Saens, C.	Volière (Carnival of the Animals)	Dur
Saint-Saens, C.-Pellerite	Volière	Za
Salieri, A.	Danse (Tarare)	EdM
Samazeuilh, G.	Esquisse d'Espagne	Dur
Samazeuilh, G.	Luciole	Dur
Sammartini, G.-Preisler	Allegro	HeE
Sammartini, G.	Concerto No. 1	Sch
Sammartini, G.	6 Sonaten, op. 3/1, 2 (fl, bc)	RuE
Sammartini, G.-Rampal	Sonata, D	Int
Sammartini, G.-Berger	Sonata, G	Hei
Sammartini, G.	Sonata, g	B&N
Sancan, P.	Sonatine	Dur
Sangiorgi	Little Sonata	Ric
Sangiorgi	Rondo	Ric
Sárai, T.	Studio. 1964	EMB
Sarasate, P. de-Rogers	Zigeunerweisen	CF
Sári, J.	Contemplazione	B&H
Sárközy, I.	Sonata da camera. 1965	EMB
Sáry, L.	Pezzo concertato	EMB
Sas, A.	Sonatina-Fantasia	SMP
Sauguet, H.	Sonatina	EdS
Saunders, R.	Round the Clock	GaM
Scarlatti, A.-Ewerhart	2 Sonatas, G, F (fl, bc)	WMS
Scarlatti, D.-Rofe	Sonata, d, op. 1/2	B&H
Scarlatti, D.-Leeuwen	Sonata, g	Sch
Scarlatti, D.-Leeuwen	Sonata, e	Sch
Scarlatti, D.-Benjamin	Suite	B&H
Scarmolin, L.	Busy Bee	PrA
Schafer, R.	Sonatina, 1958 (fl, hpcd or pf)	Can
Schaffrath, C.-Ruf	Duetto, Bb (fl, hpcd)	Hei
Schaffrath, C.-Ruf	Duetto, D, op. 1/2	Hei
Schampaert, J.	Notturno e danza	EMe

Flute and Piano or Harpsichord

Schelb, J.	Sonata	WMS
Schers, S.-Bopp	Sonata, e, No. 1	Hug
Schers, S.-Bopp	Sonata, D, No. 2	Hug
Schers, S.-Bopp	Sonatas, b, a, Nos. 3, 4	Pet
Schers, S.-Bopp	Sonatas, G, D, Nos. 5, 6	Pet
Schevenhals, F.	Berceuse Expressive	ScF
Schibler, A.	Lyrisches Konzert, op. 40	A&S
Schickhardt, J.	Concerto, g	WMS
Schindler, G.	Melusine	Bos
Schlemm, G.	Sonate. 1948	BrH
Schmidek, K.	Sonatine, op. 42	LDo
Schmidt, E.	Le Chevrier D'Erymanthe	ALe
Schmidt, O.	Suite	WH
Schmidt, W.	Sonatina	Wes
Schmidt, W.	Variations	Wes
Schmit, G.	1er Solo, op. 5	ScF
Schmitt, F.	Scherzo pastoral	Ham
Schmitt, F.	Scherzo-Pastorale, op. 17/2	Int
Schmitt, F.	Suite, op. 129	Dur
Schmutz, A.	Nocturne	AlB
Schneider, W.	Concertino	MV
Schneider, W.	Sonata serena	MV
Schoenberg, A.-Greissle	Sonata (Wind Quintet, op. 26)	UE
Schollum, R.	Sonatine, op. 55/5	LDo
Schouwman, H.	4 stukken, op. 39. 1944	SD
Schroeder, H.	Konzert, op. 37	HG
Schubert, F.	Ave Maria	CF
Schubert, F.	Entract II (Rosamunde)	NK
Schubert, F.-Gaubert	Impromptu, op. 90/3	ALe
Schubert, F.-Wirth	Variations on "Trockne Blumen"	B&N
Schubert, F.-Delius	Introduction and Variations on "Ihr Blümlein alle"	BrH
Schubert, F.-Rampal	Introduction and Variations, op. 160	Int
Schubert, F.-Richter	Introduction and Variations on "Trockne Blumen," op. 160	Pet
Schubert, F.	Moment Musical	CF
Schubert, F.	Rosamunde (Theme)	NK
Schubert, F.-Voxman	Round Dance	Rub
Schubert, F.	Serenade	Cen
Schubert, F.	Serenade	CF
Schubert, F.-Isaac	3 Themes	CF
Schubert, F.-Popp	Through the Leaves	CF
Schule, B.	Spiel mit musikalischen Formen, op. 83	GBV
Schulhoff, E.	Sonata	Che
Schumann, R.	Berceuse, op. 124	Dur
Schumann, R.-Gaubert	Chorale and Cantabile (Album für die Jugend)	ALe

Schumann, R.	Einsame Blumen	Spr
Schumann, R.-Gaubert	Lullaby (Albumblätter)	ALe
Schumann, R.	L'Oiseau prophete	Ham
Schumann, R.-Guenther	Melody	B-M
Schumann, R.-Gaubert	Rêverie (Träumerei from Kinderscenen)	ALe
Schumann, R.-Taffanel	Rêverie, op. 15	Dur
Schumann, R.	Rêverie	Ham
Schumann, R.	Romance	CF
Schumann, R.-Hervig	Slumber Song, op. 124/16	Rub
Schumann, R.	Träumerei	CF
Schumann, R.	Träumerei	Pet
Schurmann, G.	Sonatina	Nov
Schütz, A.	Suite	BrH
Schuyt, N.	5 Dramatische nocturnes. 1954	SD
Schwadron, A.	Sonatina	Ken
Schwarenka, X.	Polish Dance	CF
Schwartz, E.	Sonata	Gen
Schwindl, F.-Meylan	Flötenkonzert, D	BrH
Scott, C.	Aubade	S&C
Scott, C.-Wummer	Lotus Land	GaM
Scott, C.-Arnold	Lotus Land	SF
Scott, C.	Scotch Pastoral	WH
Scott, C.	Sonata	Elk
Search, S.	Allegro Giocoso	AMC
Searle, H.	Divertimento	S&C
Sebestyén, A.	Rondo Burlesco	EMB
Seeboth, M.	Sonatina	Hei
Segerhammar, R.	Lazy Waterfall	PrA
Segerhammar, R.	The Whistler	PrA
Seghers, F.-Moyse	Souvenir de Gand	ALe
Sehlbach, E.	Kleine Lyrik, op. 102/1	MV
Sehlbach, E.	Sonate, op. 53	MV
Seiber, M.	Pastorale und Burleske	S&C
Sellenick, A.-Gariboldi	Célèbre marche Indienne	ALe
Semegen, D.	Quattro	ACA
Semler-Collery, A.	Interlude	EPC
Semler-Collery, J.	Introduction et Saltarelle	EME
Semler-Collery, J.	Pastorale et Caprice	ALe
Senaille, J.	Entrée et Cotillon	MM
Senstius, K.	Concertino, op. 5. 1921	SPD
Serini, G.-Pilgrim	Sonata, D	OxU
Sermon, E.	Légende	EMb
Sermon, E.	Petite Pièce	EMb
Serradell	La Golondrina	Cen
Seter, M.	Partita. 1965	Isr
Sgrizzi, L.	Capriccio	ESZ
Shevchenko, S.	Etude, op. 2	MKE
Shevitz, A.	Sonata, A	B-M
Shinohara, M.	Kassouga	ALe

Shinohara, M.	Relations	HMo
Shostakovitch, D.	Danses Fantastiques	EdM
Shostakovitch, D.	4 Preludes	EdM
Shostakovitch, D.	Polka (The Age of Gold)	EdM
Shostakovitch, D.	Satirical Dance (The Bolt)	EdM
Sibelius, J.-Amans	Nocturne	CF
Sibelius, J.	Valse Triste (Kuolema)	CF
Siebert, F.	Concertino	Eul
Siefert, E.	Sonata	EdS
Siegl, O.	Sonata. 1968	LDo
Siegmeister, E.	Concerto	MCA
Siegmeister, E.	Nocturne	MCA
Siennicki, E.	Memphis Ridge	NK
Siennicki, E.	Valse Ballet	Bar
Sikorski, K.	Concerto. 1957	AP
Silcher, F.-Dahmen	Variations	NV
Šilva, P. de	Praeludium (fl, hpcd)	B&B
Simeonov, B.	4 Moments	Wat
Simon	Lullaby for Johnny	EdM
Simon, L.	Sonatina	Art
Sinopoli, G.	Numquid et Unum. 1970 (fl, hpcd)	ESZ
Siqueira, J.	3 Etüden	Deu
Sitt, H.	Barcarolle	CF
Šivic, P.	Sonata	EdD
Skilton, C.-Barrère	Sioux Flute Serenade	CF
Sköld, Y.	Liten svit. 1966	STI
Sköld, Y.	Sonatin, op. 57. 1956	ESu
Sköld, Y.	En Valsmelodi	EMf
Skolnik, W.	Sonatina. 1965	EdM
Slater, J.	Chanson Caprice	Che
Slater, J.	Rapsodie	Che
Slechta, T.	Father of Waters	CF
Smit, A.	Diptyque	Mau
Smit, L.	Sonata. 1943	SD
Smit Sibinga, T.	Suite. 1952	SD
Smith-arr.	Suite Classique	EdM
Smolsky, D.	Sonata	MKE
Socarras, A.	Meditation	Pod
Söderholm, V.	Partita	EMf
Solazzo, M.	Meditation and Dance	Ken
Solin, L.	Sonatina	MKE
Sollberger, H.	Music	M&M
Solo, C.	A Grand Sonata, op. 31	EdH
Sontag	An Evening Serenade	CF
Soproni, J.	Sonata	B&H
Sorge, E.	6 Variationen über ein englisches Volkslied	Hei
Souderes, V.	Minuet-Fantasy	AmP
Sousa, J.	Stars and Stripes Forever	NK

Sousa, J.-Walters	The Stars and Stripes Forever	Rub
Spadi, G.-Horsley, Davenport	Anchor Che Col Partire. Diminutions for a solo instrument on a Madrigal by de Rore	AMP
Spelman, T.	Rondo	Che
Spencer, W.	Silvatones	CF
Sporck, G.	Caprice	EdR
Sporck, G.	Chanson d'Antan	Bil
Sporck, G.	Méditation	Bil
Sporck, G.	Orientale	Bil
Sprongl, N.	Suite, op. 98	LDo
Squarzoni, F.	Canzone invernale	GZ
Squarzoni, F.	Sacada--Concerto	GZ
Šrámek, V.	Sonatine	ES
Šrámek, V.	Suite. 1955	Art
Ssinissalo, G.	3 Miniaturen	FrH
Staempfli, E.	Concerto. 1957	B&B
Staempfli, E.	Duo. 1965	B&B
Staempfli, E.	5 Stücke. 1954	B&B
Stamitz, A.	Concerto, D	BrH
Stamitz, J.-Kölbel	Concerto, C	B&N
Stamitz, J.	Concerto, C	Hug
Stamitz, K.	Andantino	EdM
Stamitz, K.-Lebermann, Haverkampf	Concerto No. 3, D	BrH
Stamitz, K.-Gradenwitz	Konzert, D	BrH
Stamitz, K.-Sonntag	Concerto, D	HSM
Stamitz, K.-Rampal	Concerto, G	Int
Stamitz, K.-Gronefeld	Concerto, G	Leu
Stamitz, K.-Lebermann	Concerto, G, op. 29	SS
Stamitz, K.-Bodart	Concerto, G	WZ
Stanley, J.-Caldwell	8 Solos, op. 1, 4 vols.	OxU
Stanley, J.-Weigart	Sonatas 1, 2 (6 Sonatas)	SS
Stanley, J.-Weigart	Sonatas 3, 4 (6 Sonatas)	SS
Stanley, J.-Fleury	Sonata, A	B-M
Stanley, J.-Kirby	Solo, g, op. 1/2	B&H
Stanley, J.-Kirby	Solo	OxU
Stanley, J.-Finzi	Solo, D, op. 4/5	B&H
Starer, R.	Recitation	SMP
St. Clair, F.	Admiration	Vol
St. Clair, F.	Dream Time	Vol
St. Clair, F.	Golden Days	Vol
Steckmest, W.	Amid the Roses	NK
Steensland, D., Weber, F.	Flute soloist (Level I)	B-M
Steffens, W.	La Femme Fleur, op. 11	BrH
Steffens, W.	Triade, op. 15. 1970	B&B
Steffes, G.	Desert Shadows	Hal
Stein, L.	Rhapsody	CoF
Steiner	Arabian love song	B-M
Steiner, G.	Jouissance. 1965	See

Flute and Piano or Harpsichord

Stevens, H.	Sonatina	BB
Stevens, H.	Sonatina Piacevole	CoF
Stewart, J.	Four Dimensions	Ken
Stewart, R.	Recitative	CoA
Stockhausen, K.	Aus den sieben Tagen	UE
Stoker, R.	Sonatine	HE
Stone	Caprice Tzigane	EBM
Stout, A.	Music	PE
Stoutamire, A.	Twilight Tune	PrA
Stratton, D.	Suite	Cor
Strauss, J.-Bettoney	Blue Danube	CF
Strauss, J.-Bettoney	Tales from the Vienna Woods	CF
Strauss, O.-Harris	A Waltz Dream	Lud
Strauss, R.-Buchtel	Andante (Violin Concerto)	NK
Strauss, R.-Heldburg	Rosenkavalier Album	B&H
Strauss, R.	Zueignung	EdM
Strauwen, J.	Elégie	EMb
Stravinsky, I.	Berceuse (Firebird)	EdM
Stravinsky, I.	Dance of the Princesses	EdM
Stravinsky, I.	Pastorale	EdM
Stravinsky, I.-Grunes	Supplications (The Firebird)	SF
Strens, J.	2 Impromptus, op. 33. 1941	CBD
Strimer, J.	Pastorale caucasienne	Dur
Stringfield, L.	Mountain Dawn	EdM
Stringfield, L.	Serenade (Indian Sketches)	CF
Stringfield, L.	To a Star	EdM
Strungk, N.	Suites and Airs (fl, bc)	Pet
Stuart, H.-arr.	BMCO Famous Flute Favorites	BM
Stuart, H.	Danzetta	CF
Stuart, H.	Essay	BM
Štuhec, I.	3 Bagatelles	EdD
Sugar, R.	Concertino	EMB
Sullivan, A.	The Lost Chord	CF
Sumerlin, M.	Adobe	B-M
Sumerlin, M.	Fiesta	B-M
Sumerlin, M.	Gaucho	B-M
Sumerlin, M.	Night Gypsy	B-M
Sumerlin, M.	Rustique	B-M
Sumerlin, M.	Serenade	B-M
Sumerlin, M.	3 Dances. 1946	Man
Suppé, F. von -Long	Andante Maestoso (Poet and Peasant)	Vol
Surdin, M.	Takeone. 1968	Can
Svendsen, J.-Hahn	Romance, op. 26	CF
Swain, F.	Paspy	Cha
Swinstead, F.	Pastorale	GaM
Sydeman, W.	Duo. 1960	See
Szalowski, A.	Concertino	Amp
Székely, E.	Capriccio. 1964	EMB
Szeligowski, A.	Miniatures	AP

Szervánszky, E.	Concerto. 1952	EMB
Szervánszky, E.	Sonatina. 1952	EMB
Szollosy, A.	3 Pezzi	JB
Taffanel, P.	**Andante Pastoral et** Scherzettino	E&C
Taffanel, P.	Andante Pastoral & Scherzettino	Int
Taffanel, P.-Cavally	Andante, Pastorale and Scherzettino	SM
Tailleferre, G.	Pastorale	E-V
Taktakishvili, O.	Sonata	MKE
Tamba, A.	Pièces a danser	ALe
Tamba, A.	Sonata	ERR
Tansman, A.	Concertino	EME
Tansman, A.	Sonatina	EdS
Taranu, C.	Sonata. 1963	EdR
Tardos, B.	Preludium and Rondo	EMB
Tarp, S.	Concertino, op. 30. 1938	SPD
Tartini, G.-Ticciati	Andante Cantabile	OxU
Tartini, G.-Rampal	Concerto, F	Int
Tartini, G.-Brinckmann, Mohr	Concerto a 5, G	HSM
Tartini, G.	Introduction and Allegro Assai	EdM
Taubert, K.	Variationen über ein Quarten-Motiv	R&E
Taubert, W.-Fahrbach	Wiegenlied, op. 46/4	MRL
Taylor, L.	Arabian Jugglers	Hal
Taylor, L.	Avignon	Hal
Taylor, L.	Moonlight Waltz	Hal
Tchaikovsky, P.	Adagio Lamentoso (Symphony No. 6)	CF
Tchaikovsky, P.-Bettoney	Allegro con Grazia (Symphony No. 6)	CF
Tchaikovsky, P.-Emch	Autumn Song (The Seasons)	CF
Tchaikovsky, P.	Barcarolle	Ham
Tchaikovsky, P.-Hanson	Canzonetta	Lud
Tchaikovsky, P.-Schinstine	Canzonetta (Violin Concerto)	SM
Tchaikovsky, P.	Chanson Triste	CF
Tchaikovsky, P.-Popp	Dance of the Reed Flutes	CF
Tchaikovsky, P.-Hummel	Danse des Mirlitons	Rub
Tchaikovsky, P.	Mignon's Lament, op. 6	CF
Tchaikovsky, P.	The Minstrel's Canzonet	EdM
Tchaikovsky, P.-Bettoney	Sleeping Beauty	CF
Tchaikovsky, P.-Bettoney	Song without Words	CF
Tchaikovsky, P.-Laube	Song without Words	CF
Tchaikovsky, P.	Suite (The Children's Album)	EdM
Tchaikovsky, P.-Hurrell	2 Dances (Nutcracker Suite)	Rub
Tchaikovsky, P.-Guenther	Waltz	B-M
Tchaikovsky, P.-Harris	Waltz	Lud
Tchaikovsky, P.-Laube	Waltz of the Flowers, op. 71/13	CF

Flute and Piano or Harpsichord

Telemann, G.-Barnes	Arie (Pimpinone)	Spr
Telemann, G.-Pätzold	15 Stücke (7 mal 7 und ein Menuett)	MRL
Telemann, G.-Pätzold	Ein fröhlicher Tugendspiegel in 12 Marschen	MRL
Telemann, G.-Pätzold	Heldenmusik in 12 Märschen	MRL
Telemann, G.	Little Pieces	EdK
Telemann, G.-Winschermann	Ouverture, e	HSM
Telemann, G.-Polnauer	6 Menuette	SS
Telemann, G.-Woehl	6 Partiten (fl, bc)	B&N
Telemann, G.-Hinnenthal	Solo, b (Tafelmusik) (fl, bc)	B&N
Telemann, G.-Degen	Spielstücke (Der getreue Musikmeister) (fl, bc)	B&N
Telemann, G.-Lauschmann	6 Suites, 2 vols. (fl, bc)	Pet
Telemann, G.	Suite, a	EMT
Telemann, G.-Salter	Suite, a	Eul
Telemann, G.-Rampal	Suite, a	Int
Telemann, G.-Moyse	Suite, a	Sch
Telemann, G.-Wummer	Suite, a	SM
Telemann, G.-Hinnenthal	6 Concertos (Published separately) (fl, bc)	B&N
Telemann, G.-Hinnenthal	Concerto, a	B&N
Telemann, G.-Hinnenthal	Concerto, b	B&N
Telemann, G.-Rampal	Concerto, D	Int
Telemann, G.-Hinnenthal	Concerto, D	Leu
Telemann, G.-Schroeder	Concerto, D	Leu
Telemann, G.	Concerto, D	Pet
Telemann, G.-Brinckmann, Mohr	Concerto a 5, D	HSM
Telemann, G.	Concerto, e	Eul
Telemann, G.-Rampal	Concerto, G	Int
Telemann, G.-Kölbel	12 Sonaten, 4 vols. (fl, bc)	Hei
Telemann, G.-Wittgenstein	4 Sonatas	Sch
Telemann, G.-Seiffert	Sonata, b (Tafelmusik) (fl, bc)	BrH
Telemann, G.-Silver	Sonata, b	Che
Telemann, G.-Bergmann	Sonata, C	S&C
Telemann, G.-Rampal	Sonata, C	Int
Telemann, G.	2 Sonatas, d, C (Essercizii Musici)	Pet
Telemann, G.-Ruf	Sonata, D (Essercizii Musici) (fl, bc)	SS
Telemann, G.-Ruf	Sonata, G (Essercizii Musici) (fl, bc)	SS
Telemann, G.-Seiffert	12 Methodische Sonaten, 6 vols. (fl, bc)	B&N
Telemann, G.-Seiffert	Sonaten, a, G (12 Methodische Sonaten) (fl, bc)	B&N
Telemann, G.-Seiffert	Sonaten, b, c (12 Methodische Sonaten) (fl, bc)	B&N
Telemann, G.-Seiffert	Sonaten, d, C (12 Methodische	

	Sonaten) (fl, bc)	B&N
Telemann, G.-Seiffert	Sonaten, E, B (12 Methodische Sonaten) (fl, bc)	B&N
Telemann, G.-Seiffert	Sonaten, e, D (12 Methodische Sonaten) (fl, bc)	B&N
Telemann, G.-Seiffert	Sonaten, g, A (12 Methodische Sonaten) (fl, bc)	B&N
Telemann, G.-Seiffert	Sonata, c (Methodischen Sonaten, No. 2) (fl, bc)	Kis
Telemann, G.-Seiffert	Sonata, Bb (Methodischen Sonaten, No. 4) (fl, bc)	Kis
Telemann, G.	Sonate, d	B&V
Telemann, G.-Upmeyer	Sonata, D (fl, bc)	NV
Telemann, G.	Sonata, C (Getreuer Musik-meister)	Pet
Telemann, G.-Rampal	Sonata, f	Int
Telemann, G.	Sonate, F	B&V
Telemann, G.	Sonata, F	ES
Telemann, G.	Sonata, F	HMP
Telemann, G.-Dohrn	Sonata, F (fl, bc)	Int
Telemann, G.-Bopp	Sonata, F	Pet
Telemann, G.-Bergmann	Sonata, F	S&C
Telemann, G.-Rampal	Sonata, G	Int
Telemann, G.-Feltkamp	Sonata, G	SS
Telemann, G.-Moyse	Suite, a	Sch
Templar, J.	Sonnet	Ken
Tenaglia, A.	Aria	Pet
Tenaglia, A.	Aria Antica	EdM
Terschak, A.-Brooke	Le Babillard, op. 23	CF
Terschak, A.-Haas	A Little Gem	Rub
Terschak, A.-Medicus	Melancolie Hongrois, op. 149	CF
Terschak, A.-Cavally	Reproche, op. 19/1	SM
Tessarini, C.-Schmitz	Sonata, F (fl, bc)	B&N
Testi, F.	Musica da concerto op. 12, No. 4	Ric
Thärichen, W.	Concerto, op. 29	B&B
Thiele, S.	Cantilena und Allegro	Deu
Thiele, S.	Concertino	Pet
Thiere, C.	L'Oiseau du Bois	CF
Thilman, J.	Sonatine, op. 31	WMS
Thiry	Dialogue	MM
Thiry	Pont du Gard	MM
Thomas, A.-Gatley	Mignon	CF
Thomason	Concerto	B-M
Thomé, F.	Andante	Ham
Thomé, F.	Simple Aveu	CF
Thomé, F.-Taffanel	Simple Aveu	Dur
Thomé, F.	Sous la feuilée	Dur
Thomson, V.	Concerto	B-M

Flute and Piano or Harpsichord

Thornowitz, H.-Dawes	Sonata da Camera, F	S&C
Thornowitz, H.-Dawes	Sonata da Camera No. 5	S&C
Tillmetz, R.-Cochrane	Roumanian Pastoral Fantasie, op. 34	CF
Tisné, A.	Concerto	Bil
Tisné, A.	Sonate	Bil
Titcomb, E.	Suite	CF
Titl, A.-Roberts	Serenade	CF
Titl, A.	Serenade	Com
Tittel	Sonatine	Pet
Toeschi, C.-Münster	Concerto, G	Leu
Togni, C.	Fantasia Concertante	ESZ
Togni, C.	Sonata, op, 35	UE
Toldra, E.-Amaz	Ave Maria	UME
Toldra, E.-Amaz	Dels Quatre Vents	UME
Toldra, E.-Amaz	La Font	UME
Toldra, E.-Amaz	Oracio al Maig	UME
Toldra, E.-Amaz	Soneti de la Rosada	UME
Tomasi, H.	Concertino, E.	ALe
Tomasi, H.	Concerto, F	ALe
Tomasi, H.	Concerto de Printemps	ALe
Tomasi, H.	Le Petit chevrier corse	ALe
Ton-That Tiet	Vision II	EMT
Torroba, F.	Dedicatoria	UME
Tosti, F.-Crosby	Good Bye	CF
Touchemoulin, J.	Concerto, A	Eul
Tower, J.	Movements	ACA
Townsend, D.	Dance Improvisation and Fugue, op. 3/2	Pet
Tremais	Sarabande and Minuet	Pet
Tremblot de la Croix, F.	Etoile Vesper	ALe
Trépart, E.	Evocations Sylvestres	EdS
Trinkaus, G.	Lament	CF
Trinkaus, G.	Pan's Serenade to Spring	CF
Trinkaus, G.-arr.	World's Best-Known Pieces	CF
Tromlitz, J.-Ruf	Sonata, G	Hei
Tull, F.	Erato	SM
Tulou, J.-Rampal	Concerto, D, No. 3	Int
Tulou, J.-Rampal	3rd Grand Solo, op. 74	Bil
Tulou, J.-Rampal	Grand Solo, op. 94/12	Bil
Tulou, J.-Rampal	5th Grande Solo, op. 79	Bil
Tzibin, V.	Andante	MKE
Tzibin, V.	Concert Etudes Nos. 1-10	MKE
Tzibin, V.	Concerto Allegro No. 1	MKE
Tzibin, V.	Concert Etudes Nos. 1-3	MKE
Tzibin, V.	Concert Etudes Nos. 4-6	MKE
Tzibin, V.	Concert Etudes Nos. 7-10	MKE
Tzibin, V.	Concert Allegro No. 3	MKE
Tzibin, V.	Tarantella	MKE
Ulrich, B.	8 Miniatures	EMT

Uray, E.	Minnelied	LDo
Uray, E.	Rondo, Eb	LDo
Urbanner, E.	8 Pieces	UE
Urbanner, E.	Flute Concertino. 1958	LDo
Uyttenhove, Y.	Sonate	Mau
Vaccai, N.-Wienandt	Arietta	SM
Vachey, H.	Aubade	ALe
Vachey, H.	Eolienne	ALe
Vachey, H.	Intermezzo	ALe
Vachey, H.	Sicilienne	ALe
Vackar, T.	Concerto recitativo	Art
Vainberg, M.	Concerto, op. 75	MKE
Valentine, R.-Rodemann	3 Sonatas, d, d, F (fl, bc)	NV
Valentine, R.-Rodemann	3 Sonatas, F, C, Bb (fl, bc)	NV
Valentine, R.-Peter	3 Sonaten	MRL
Valentine, R.-Peter	4 Sonaten	MRL
Vallee, G.	4 Short Pieces	GD
Vasilenko, S.-Brook	In Spring, op. 138	MCA
Vasilenko, S.	In Spring, op. 138	MKE
Vaughan Williams, R.-Douglas	Suite de Ballet	OxU
Veach, D.	Meadow Mist	PrA
Velden, R. van der	Concertino. 1965	CBD
Vellère, L.	Intermède	Mau
Veracini, F.	12 Sonatas, 4 vols. (fl, bc)	Pet
Veracini, F.-Paumgartner	Sonata Prima	B&H
Veracini, F.-Ricci	Sonata Prima (fl, bc)	GZ
Veracini, F.-Paumgartner	Sonata Seconda	B&H
Veracini, A.-Polnauer	Sonata da Camera	Che
Verbesselt, A.	Concerto	Bil
Verdi, G.-Steensland	Themes from La Traviata	B-M
Vereecken, B.	Bouquet des Fleurs Serenade	Bar
Veretti, A.	Concertino	ALe
Verhey, T.-Cavally	Concerto, d	SM
Verhey, T.	Concerto, a, op. 57, No. 2	WZ
Verrall, J.	Sonata	ACA
Vibert, P.	Libellule	ALe
Vibert, P.	L'Oasis	ALe
Vibert, P.	Scherzando	ALe
Vieru, A.	Concerto. 1965	EdR
Vilec, M.	Summer notes. 1959	SHF
Villetard, A.	Sous les ombrages	Bil
Villette, P.	Complainte	ALe
Vincent, T.-Dawes	Sonata, D	S&C
Vinci	Nenia	Bon
Vinci, L. da-Bopp	Sonatas, D, G (fl, bc)	B&N
Vinci, L. da	Sonata, G	EdK
Vinci, L. da	Sonata, D, No. 1	Pet
Vinci, L. da	Sonata, G, No. 2	Pet
Vittadini, F.	Elegy	ALe

Flute and Piano or Harpsichord

Vivaldi, A.	Giga	EdM
Vivaldi, A.	Rain ("Winter" from The Seasons)	EdM
Vivaldi, A.-Smith, Kardt	Concerto, F, F. VI, No. 1	Ric
Vivaldi, A.-Pigato	Concerto, G, F. VI, No. 6	Ric
Vivaldi -Ephrikian	Concerto, G, F. VI, No. 8	Ric
Vivaldi, A.-Smith	Concerto, D, F. VI, No. 10	Ric
Vivaldi, A.-Rampal	Concerto, F, op. 10/1 (La Tempesta di Mare)	Int
Vivaldi, A.-Kolneder	Concerto, op. 10/1 (La Tempesta di Mare)	SS
Vivaldi, A.-Rampal	Concerto, g, op. 10/2 (La Notte)	Int
Vivaldi, A.-Kolneder	Concerto, op. 10/2 (La Notte)	SS
Vivaldi, A.	Concerto, D, op. 10/3	Eul
Vivaldi, A.-Rampal	Concerto, D, op. 10/3 (The Bullfinch)	Int
Vivaldi, A.-Kolneder	Concerto, op. 10/3 (Il Cardellino)	SS
Vivaldi, A.-Rampal	Concerto, G, op. 10/4	Int
Vivaldi, A.-Kolneder	Concerto, op. 10/4	SS
Vivaldi, A.-Rampal	Concerto, F, op. 10/5	Int
Vivaldi, A.-Kolneder	Concerto op. 10/5	SS
Vivaldi, A.-Rampal	Concerto, G, op. 10/6	Int
Vivaldi, A.-Kolneder	Concerto, op. 10/6	SS
Vivaldi, A.	Concerto, C, op. 44/11	Eul
Vivaldi, A.	Concerto, C, op. 44/11	HE
Vivaldi, A.	Concerto, op. 44/19, P. 440	Pet
Vivaldi, A.-Rampal	Concerto, D, P. 205	Int
Vivaldi, A.-Rampal	Concerto, a	Int
Vivaldi, A.-Arbatsky	Concerto, C	M&M
Vivaldi, A.-Nagy, Hartlay	Concerto, c	EMB
Vivaldi, A.-Rampal	Concerto, c	Int
Vivaldi, A.	Concerto, c	MR
Vivaldi, A.	Concerto, G, No. 6	EMT
Vivaldi, A.-Barbe	Concerto, g (fl, bc)	Pet
Vivaldi -Upmeyer	Il Pastor fido (6 Sonatas) (fl, bc)	B&N
Vivaldi, A.-Rampal	6 Sonatas (Il Pastor Fido), 2 vols.	Int
Vivaldi, A.-Marx	Il Pastor Fido (Sonata, g, No. 6)	M&M
Vivaldi, A.-Silver	Sonata, C	Che
Vivaldi, A.	Sonata, C	EBe
Vivaldi, A.-Nagel	Sonata, C	Hei
Vivaldi, A.	Sonata, d (fl, bc)	B&N
Vivaldi, A.-Nagel	Sonata, d	Hei
Vivaldi, A.-Lasocki	Sonata, e (Stockholm) (fl, bc)	MR
Vivaldi, A.-Bruggen	Sonate, F	B&V
Vivaldi, A.	2 Sonatas, F, d (fl, bc)	Pet
Vivaldi, A.-Bodky	Sonata, g	M&M
Vivaldi, A.-Edmunds	Sonata	CF

Flute and Piano or Harpsichord

Vivaldi, A.	Suite, c	EdM
Vlad, R.	Il Magico Flauto di Severino	ESZ
Vlad, R.	Sonatina	ESZ
Von Kreisler, A.	3 Miniatures	SM
Voss, F.	Pan exzentrisch. 1962	BrH
Votquenne, V.	Fioriture	EMb
Voxman, H. (ed)	Concert and Contest Collection	Rub
Vredenburg, M.	Rondoletto. 1951 (fl, hpcd)	SD
Vredenburg, M.	3 Stukken. 1963	SD
Vreuls, V.	Elegie	Bos
Waddington	Bob White	Wat
Waddington	Impromptu	Wat
Waddington	Larry Grogan	Wat
Waddington	Piccolominnio	Wat
Waddington	Pretty Minka	Wat
Waddington	Tyrolienne	Wat
Wagenseil, G.	Concerto, G	Hug
Wagenseil, G.-Kölbel	Concerto	B&N
Wagenseil, G.-Scholz	Sonata, D	LDo
Wagner, H.-comp.	Flutist's Concert Album	CF
Wagner, R.	Albumleaf	CF
Wagner, R.-Hahn	Albumleaf	CF
Wagner, R.-Haas	Albumleaf	Rub
Wagner, R.	Dreams	CF
Wagner, R.-Roberts	Song to the Evening Star	CF
Wagner, R.	Song to the Evening Star	CF
Wagner, R.-Trinkaus	Walther's Prize Song (Meistersinger)	CF
Wahlberg, R.	Pan och nymfer. 1966	STI
Wahren, K.	Frétillement. 1965	B&B
Walacinski, A.	Dichromia	PWM
Waldteufel, E.	A toi	Dur
Waldteufel, E.	Bella bocca	Dur
Waldteufel, E.	Berceuse	Dur
Waldteufel, E.	Dolorès	Dur
Waldteufel, E.-Lacome	Estudiantina	E&C
Waldteufel, E.-Chabrier	Espana	E&C
Waldteufel, E.	Etincelles	Dur
Waldteufel, E.	Je t'aime	Dur
Waldteufel, E.	Les Patineurs	Dur
Waldteufel, E.	Pluie de diamants	Dur
Waldteufel, E.	Pomone	Dur
Waldteufel, E.	Mon rêve	Dur
Waldteufel, E.	Sirènes	Dur
Waldteufel, E.	Souviens-toi	Dur
Waldteufel, E.	Tendres baisers	Dur
Waldteufel, E.	Toujours ou jamais	Dur
Waldteufel, E.	Tout à vous	Dur
Waldteufel, E.	Très jolie	Dur
Waldteufel, E.	Vergissmeinnicht	Dur

Flute and Piano or Harpsichord

Walker, R.	Album Leaf	B-M
Walker, R.	Petit Rian	Hal
Walker, R.	Valse Casuel	BM
Wallbank, N.	Sonata, op. 31	AlL
Walter, F.	Der Paradiesvogel	WZ
Walter, H.	Partita impulsiva (fl, hpcd)	LDo
Walters, H.-arr.	Amazing Grace	Rub
Walters, H.	Sakura, Sakura (Cherry Blossoms)	Rub
Walters, H.	Shindig (Folksong Fantasy)	Rub
Walters, H.-arr.	When the Saints Go Marching In	Rub
Wanhal, J.-Tuthill	Sonata	M&M
Wanhal, J.-Klement	Sonata, G, No. 2	Art
Warren, D.	Sonatina	Lud
Waters, C.	Courante in Canon	B&H
Waters, C.	2 Flute Solos (Winter Tune, Summer Tune)	Bos
Watson, W.	Essay	Sha
Webber, C.-arr.	First Solo Album	TP
Webber, L.	Mulberry Cottage	AHC
Webber, R.	Romany Caprice	TP
Webber, W.	Sonatina, D	HE
Weber, A.	Scherzetto	ALe
Weber, C.M. von-Taffanel	Fantasy on Freischutz	ALe
Weber, C.M. von	Invitation to the Waltz	CF
Weber, C.M. von	Romanza Siciliana	MRL
Weber, F.	Autumn Leaves	B-M
Weber, F.	Peasant Dance	B-M
Weegenhuise, J.	Sonatina. 1957	SD
Weigl, K.	Pictures from Childhood	B&H
Weinberg, M.	Concerto	ChM
Weinberger, J.	Sonatine	CF
Weinzweig, J.-Perry	Divertimento I	B&H
Wendel, M.	Capriccio. 1969	BrH
Wendling, J.-Ade	Sonata, G	I-V
Werdin, E.	Greensleeves--Variations	LDo
Wesly, E.	Confidences	EdS
Wesly, E.	Fiançailles	EdS
Wesly, E.	Hyménée	EdS
Wesly, E.	Joyeux ébats	EdS
Wesly, E.	Rêverie d'automne	EdS
Westergaard, P.	Divertimento on Discobbolic Fragments	AlB
Wetzger, P.	Brook in the Wood, op. 33	CF
White, D.	Glimpses	SM
White, J.	Duettino	ALe
Widdifield, T.	Oriole Polka	CF
Widdoes, L.	Sonatina	TP
Widor, C.	Romance (Suite, op. 34)	Heu
Widor, C.-Wummer	Romance and Scherzo (Suite,	

	op. 34)	Int
Widor, C.-Maganini	Scherzo, op. 34/2	CF
Widor, C.	Sérénade	Ham
Widor, C.	Suite, op. 34	Heu
Wiefler, F.	Sonatine, op. 15/1	LDo
Wijdeveld, W.	Sonatine. 1948	SD
Wilder, A.	Sonata	SF
Wilder, A.	Sonata No. 2	SF
Wildgans, F.	Kleine Sonatine. 1935	LDo
Williams, E.	Sequoia Polka	CF
Willis, R.	Recitative & Dance	TP
Willson, M.	Suite	BM
Winkler, T.-Cavally	Romanze, op. 4	SM
Wisse, J.	Limitazione. 1961	SD
Wolff, A.	Concerto	ECh
Wolff, H.	Sonata, op. 38	MV
Wolfurt, K. von	Sonatine, op. 49	WMS
Wolpe, S.	Piece in Two Parts	M&M
Wood, W.	Let 'Er Go	Cen
Woodle, J.	Diversion	SM
Wouters, A.	Idylle, op. 70	ScF
Wuensch, G.	Cameos	MCA
Wuensch, G.	Divertimento, G, op. 5	Can
Wüsthoff, K.	3 Mobiles (fl/afl/pic, pf)	WZ
Wummer, J. (ed)	Album of 30 Classical Pieces, 2 vols.	Int
Wuorinen, C.	Sonata	CoF
Wurmser, L.	Barcarolle	Bil
Wurmser, L.	Fantasia	EMT
Wurmser, L.	Frivolle	Bil
Wurmser, L.	Lied	Com
Wurmser, L.	Piecettes	Bil
Wurmser, L.	Tristesse	Com
Wyttenbach, J.	Paraphrase	SS
Yagudin, J.	Easy Songs	MKE
Yun, I.	Garak. 1963	B&B
Zachert, W.-arr.	Classical Flute Album	SS
Zafred, M.	Concerto	Ric
Zagwijn, H.	Andante. 1908	Als
Zagwijn, H.	Canzone en Riddone. 1952 (fl/afl, pf)	SD
Zagwijn, H.	Capriccio. 1949	SD
Zagwijn, H.	Sonata. 1949 (fl, hpcd)	SD
Zamacois, J.-Amaz	Serenada d'Hivern	UME
Zamara, A.	Capriccietto	LDo
Zaninelli, L.	Canto	E-V
Zanke, H.	Sonata in Olden Style, op. 14	EdK
Zanke, H.	Sonate im alten Stil, op. 14	WZ
Zanke, H.	Idée musicale, op. 12	WZ
Zanke, H.	3 Humoresken, op. 8	WZ

Flute and Piano or Harpsichord

Zbinden, J.	Fantasie, op. 22	BrH
Zbinden, J.	4 Miniatures, op. 14	HG
Zbinden, J.	Sonatine, op. 5	SS
Zecchi, A.	Divertimento	Bon
Zechlin, R.	Sonatine	Pet
Železny, L.	Concerto. 1965	Art
Zender, H.	Musik. 1950	B&B
Zieritz, G. von	Bilder vom Jahrmarkt	R&E
Zieritz, G. von	Bokelberger Suite	R&E
Zilcher, H.	Konzertstuck, op. 81	BrH
Zimmerman -arr.	Play a Song of America	TP
Zimmerman -arr.	Play a Song of Christmas	TP
Zipoli, D.-Ralston	Gigue	B&H
Zipoli, D.-Setaccioli	Sarabande and Gigue	Ric
Zipp, F.	Au clair de la lune. 1963	WMS
Zipp, F.	Sonatine, op. 23a	SS
Zipp, F.	Suite, op. 35a	Pet
Zonn, P.	Well Pursed	ACA
Zuckert, L.	Little Spanish Dance. 1970	Can
Zverev, V.	Lyric Piece on a Russian Theme	MKE
Zverev, V.	Suite	MKE
Zykan, O.	O, Santa Caecilia und andere Pusztavögel	LDo

Flute and Organ

Badings, H.	Dialogues	SD
Beyer, F.	Tiento. 1965	B&N
Bornefeld, H.	Choralsonate I "Auf meinen lieben Gott"	B&N
Borris, S.	Lauda, op. 110/2	S-V
Bottje, W.	Little Sonata	ACA
Bremen, A. von	Musik	MV
Brown, R.	Sonata	Wes
Glaser, W.	Le Tombeau d'une dame. 1965-66	STI
Hovhaness, A.	Sonata, Ryuteki & Sho	Pet
Kropfreiter, A.	4 Pieces	LDo
Martin, F.-Desarzens	Sonata da Chiesa	UE
Rohlig, H.	A Little Shepherd Music	Con
Rohlig, H.	Variations on "Es kommt ein Schiff, geladen"	Con
Runback, A.	Andante religioso	EMf
Studer, H.	Petite fantaisie pastorale. 1952	B&N
Urbanner, E.	Burleske	LDo
Verrall, J.	Serenade and Pastorale	PE
Zagwijn, H.	Andante. 1946	SD

Alto Flute and Keyboard

Ahlgrimm, H.	Sonate	MRL
Bartolozzi, B.	Cantilena. 1970	ESZ
Budd, H.	The Edge of August	CPE

Fukushima, K.	Ekagra	ESZ
Guyonnet, J.	Polyphonie I	UE
LaMonaca, J.	Autumno	CF
LaMonaca, J.	Primavera	CF
Lentz	Kishore	Tem
Louvier, A.	Promenade	ALe
Masseus, J.	Fantasie, op. 12. 1952	SD
Mozart, W.-Pellerite	Larghetto	SM
Parfrey, R.	Lyric Moment	JE
Rovics, H.	Cybernetic Study No. 1	See
Thilman, J.	3 Essays	Pet
Von Kreisler, A.	Berceuse	SM
Von Kreisler, A.	Serenata	SM

Flute and Orchestra

-Martinotti	Concerto di Traverso	ESZ
Abel, C.-Peters	Concerto, C	Hei
Albinoni, T.-Brinckmann	Concerto, G	HSM
Ancelin, P.	Concerto gioioso, op. 33	Bil
Andersen, J.	2nd Morceau de Concert, op. 61	WH
Anderson, R.	Prelude & Rondo	AMC
Andriessen, H.	Variations on a Theme of Couperin. 1944	SD
Andriessen, J.	Concerto. 1951	SD
Arma, P.	Divertimento de Concert No. 1 (fl, str)	EMT
Armando, G.	Concerto	Schu
Arnold, M.	Concerto	Pat
Arnold, M.	Flute Concerto No. 2, op. 111. 1972	Fab
Arrieu, C.	Concerto, G	Amp
Atterberg, K.	Adagio amoroso. 1967 (fl, str)	STI
Aubin, T.	The Calm of the Sea (Eolian Suite)	ALe
Aubin, T.	Concerto dell' Amicizia	ALe
Avidom, M.	Concerto (fl, str)	AlB
Bach, C.P.E.-Kneiks	Concerto, A	Eul
Bach, C.P.E.-Altmann	Concerto, a	Eul
Bach, C.P.E.-Rampal	Concerto, A	Int
Bach, C.P.E.-Rampal	Concerto, Bb	Int
Bach, C.P.E.-Rampal	Concerto, d	Int
Bach, C.P.E.-Redel	Concerto, d	Leu
Bach, C.P.E.-Rampal	Concerto, G	Int
Bach, C.P.E.-Lasocki	Concerto, G, Wq. 169	MR
Bach, J.C.-Meylan	Concerto, D	UE
Bach, J.C.F.	Minuets from a serenata	MV
Bach, J.S.-Applebaum, Gordon	Concerto, a, No. 1	B-M
Bach, J.S.-Mohr	Concerto, C (Flute Sonata, A, BWV 1032)	Hug

90

Flute and Orchestra

Bach, J.S.-Radeke, Haverkampf	Concerto, e, BWV 35	BrH
Bach, J.S.	Sinfonia, b (fl, str)	MV
Bach, J.S.-Frotscher	Sinfonia, b (Cantata BWV 209)	WMS
Bach, J.S.	Suite, b, No. 2	BrH
Bach, J.S.	Overture (Suite), b, BWV 1067 (fl, str)	CF
Bach, J.S.-Soldan, Landshoff	Suite No. 2	Pet
Bach, J.S.-Von Bulow	Suite, b (fl, str)	UE
Badings, H.	Flute Concerto. 1956	SD
Barclay, A.	Elegie	Che
Barclay, A.	Idylle	Che
Bariller, R.	Le Martyre de Marsyas	ALe
Bartók, B.-Arma	Suite Paysanne hongroise (fl, str)	UE
Bauer, M.	Prelude and Fugue, op. 43 (fl, str)	ACA
Becerra, G.	Concerto	OxU
Beck, J.	Capriccio (fl, str)	MV
Beckhelm, P.	Cantilena	CF
Benda, F.-Lebermann	Concerto, e	SS
Benker, H.	Rondo scherzando. 1959	BrH
Benoit, P.	Poème symphonique	ScF
Bentzon, N.	Orchester-Sonate, op. 27	WH
Bentzon, N.	Concerto, op. 147	WH
Berghmans, J.	The Sultan's Favorites (Scenes from a Traveling Circus)	ALe
Berio, L.	Serenata	ESZ
Berio, L.	Tempi Concertati	UE
Berkeley, L.	Concerto	Che
Bertouille, G.	Aria et Divertimento. 1956	CBD
Beyer, F.	Concerto	B&N
Bjelinski, B.	Concerto (fl, str)	UE
Bloch, E.	Suite Modale (fl, str)	BB
Bloch, E.	2 Last Poems (Maybe...)	BB
Blodek, V.	Concerto	Art
Boccherini, L.-Upmeyer	Concerto, D, op. 27	B&N
Boccherini, L.	Concerto, op. 27 (fl, str)	CF
Boccherini, L.	Concerto, op. 27	SM
Bonsel, A.	Suite. 1929	SD
Bordier, J.	Berceuse	Dur
Borris, S.	Concertino, op. 71 (fl, str)	S-V
Boutry, R.	Concertino	ALe
Bozza, E.	Concertino da camera	ALe
Braal, A.	Concertino. 1950	SD
Bräutigam, H.	Musik, op. 55b. 1938	BrH
Brant, H.	Colloquy	Spr
Broustet, E.	Badinerie	Dur
Bughici, D.	Dramatic Dialogues	EMU
Busoni, F.-Nussio	Albumblatt	BrH
Busoni, F.	Divertimento, op. 52	BrH

91

Busser, H.	Andalucia	ALe
Camillo, A.	Elegy for Flute	Sha
Campagnoli, B.-Sonntag	Concerto, D, op. 3/2	Hei
Cannabich, C.-Peters	Concerto, D	Leu
Casella, A.	Sicilienne et Burlesque	ALe
Castiglioni, N.	Consonante	SS
Chaminade, C.	Concertino	E&C
Chaminade, C.	Concerto, op. 107	EdK
Chopin, F.-Cavally	Etude No. 14	SM
Clementi, A.	Ideogrammi No. 2	ESZ
Collum, H.	Konzert, d	BrH
Coriolis, E. de	Humoresque	ALe
Corrette, M.-Ruf	Concerto, e, op. 4/6	SS
Dalla Vecchia, W.	4 Momenti musicali (fl, str)	GZ
Danzi, F.-Foerster	Concerto, d, op. 31, No. 2	Eul
Danzi, F.-Anspacher	Concerto, d, op. 31, No. 2	Hei
Danzi, F.-Sonntag	Concerto, d, op. 42	WMS
Danzi, F.-Foerster	Concerto, D, op. 43, No. 4	Eul
Danzi, F.-Peters	Concerto	WH
Darke, H.	Meditation on Brother James's Air	OxU
David, J.	Konzert. 1934	BrH
Delden, L. van	Concerto, op. 85. 1965	SD
Devienne, F.-Dudley	Concertos Nos. 1, 5	Heu
Devienne, F.-Szebenyi	Concerto, G, No. 4	SS
Dijk, J. van	Ballade. 1970 (fl in G, O)	SD
Dijk, J. van	Jardin Public; Divertissement. 1967	SD
Dijk, J. van	Simple music. 1969 (fl, str)	SD
Dittersdorf, K. von	Concerto, e	MV
Dobrzynski, I.	Andante and Rondo alla polacca	AP
Donatoni, F.	Puppenspiel 2. 1966	ESZ
Donizetti, G.-Hofmann	Concertino	Pet
Dresden, S.	Concerto. 1949	SD
Dubois, P.	Concerto	ALe
Duvernoy, A.	Serenade	SM
Erdmann, D	Concertino	HG
Farina, E.	Fantasia	B-M
Farkas, F.	Sérénade concertante. 1967 (fl, str)	EMB
Fasch, J.-Winschermann	Concerto, D	HSM
Feld, J.	Concerto	Art
Feld, J.	Sonata	ALe
Felderhof, J.	Concerto. 1955	SD
Fesch, W. de -Ruf	Concerto, D, op. 10/7	B&N
Fils, A.	Concerto, D	Art
Fiocco, J.-Carroll	Suite No. 1 (fl, str)	Pet
Flagello, N.	Concerto Antoniano	Gen
Flothuis, M.	Concerto, op. 19. 1944	SD
Flothuis, M.	Per sonare ed ascoltare,	

	5 canzoni	SD
Foote, A.	A Night Piece	SM
Forsberg, R.	Concertino. 1960 (fl, str)	STI
Foster, S.	A Village Festival	EdM
Fraenkel, W.	Musik	UE
Franco, J.	Thème et variations	ALe
Frederick the Great	Concerto, C	CF
Frederick the Great		
-Lenzewski	3rd Concerto, C	CFV
Frederick the Great		
-Lenzewski	4th Concerto, D	CFV
Fridolfson, R.	Concerto	STI
Frumerie, G. de	Pastoral-Suite	Nor
Fürstenau, A.	Concerto op. 58, No. 6	EdH
Fürstenau, A.-Richter	Concerto, D, op. 84	WZ
Fürstenau, A.	L'Illusion (Norma), op. 133	BrH
Fukushima, K.	Hi-Kyo (fl in G, O)	ESZ
Furst, P.	Concerto, op. 50 (fl, str)	LDo
Fussan, W.	Concertino. 1957 (fl, str)	SS
Gabrielsky, W.	Grand Concerto op. 90, No. 4	EdH
Galuppi, B.-Schroeder	Konzert, D	BrH
Galuppi, B.	Concerto, G	B&N
Galuppi, B.-Brinckmann	Concerto, G	WMS
Gentilucci, A.	Fantasia No. 2. 1968	ESZ
Genzmer, H.	Concerto	SS
George, T.	Concerto	Roc
Gesensway, L.	Concerto	TP
Ghedini, G.	Sonata da Concerto	Ric
Gibbs, C.	Suite, A	OxU
Gillis, D.	North Harris	B&H
Gillis, D.	Three Short Pieces	B-M
Giuffre, G.	Lyrismes	B-M
Glaser, W.	Concerto. 1934 (fl, str)	STI
Glodeanu, L.	Concerto	EMU
Gluck, C.	Alceste, Marche religieuse	Dur
Gluck, C.-Scherchen	Concerto, G	Pet
Gluck, C.-Barge	Melodie, Dance of the Blessed	
	Spirits (Orpheus)	CF
Godard, B.-Cavally	Suite of 3 Pieces	SM
Goodman, J.	Concerto, G	TP
Goossens, E.	3 Pictures	Che
Grabner, H.	Gasteiner Serenade	Kis
Grant, W.	Scherzo, op. 33	ACA
Graun, C.-Brinckmann	Concerto, e	Pet
Graupner, C.	Concerto, D	MV
Grétry, A.-Sonntag	Concerto, C	Hei
Grétry, A.	Concerto	SM
Griffes, C.	Poem	Sch
Grimm, C.	A Dorian Suite	SM
Groot, C. de	Concerto. 1940	SD

93

Guerrini, G.	Egloga	Car
Haidmayer, K.	Concerto	LDo
Halffter, C.	Fibonaciana. 1969	UE
Hallnäs, H.	Concerto da camera. 1963	ESu
Hallnäs, H.	Concerto. 1958, rev, 1968	STI
Halphen, F.	Sicilienne	E&C
Handel, G.	Concerto, D	MV
Handel, G.-Hudson	Concerto III, G, op. 3	B&N
Hannikainen, V.	Variations pastorales. 1933	Fin
Hanson, H.	Serenade, op. 35	CF
Hasse, J.-Mohr	Concerto, A	Pet
Hasse, J.	Konzert, b	BrH
Hasse, J.-Engländer	Concerto, D	Pet
Hasse, J.-Jeney	Concerto, F	Eul
Hasse, J.-Engländer	Concerto, G	B&N
Hasse, J.	Concerto (fl, str)	Eul
Hayakawa, M.	Requiem santi (fl, str)	WZ
Haydn, F.-Kaul, Zanke	Concerto, D	AIL
Haydn, F.-Kowatscheff	Concerto, D (fl, str)	Leu
Haydn, F.	Concerto, D	RS
Haydn, F.-Moyse	Concerto, D	SM
Haydn, F.-Nagel	Divertimento, D (fl, str)	Pet
Haydn, F.-Scherchen	Divertimento, D (fl, str)	Pet
Haydn, M.-Landon	Concerto	UE
Heinichen, J.-Fischer	Concerto, G	CFV
Heiss, H.	Concerto	BrH
Hemel, O. van	Concerto. 1962	SD
Hemel, O. van	Suite. 1937	SD
Henkemans, H.	Concerto. 1945-46	SD
Henneberg, A.	Concertino, op. 39	CGM
Hindemith, P.	Plöner Musiktag: D-- Abendkonzert II	AMP
Hobson, M.	Concerto	Che
Hobson, M.	3 Tänze	Che
Hoeller, K.	Divertimento, op. 53a (fl, str)	Pet
Hoffmeister, F.-Sonntag	Concerto, D	HSM
Hoffmeister, F.-Szebenyi	Concerto, D	SS
Hofmann, W.	Divertimento (fl, str)	Pet
Hoiby, L.	Pastoral Dance, op. 4	Sch
Holzbauer, I.-Gronefeld	Concerto, D (fl, str)	Leu
Hosmer, J.	Rhapsody (fl, str)	M&M
Hovhaness, A.	Elibris (fl, str)	PIC
Huber, K.	Alveare Vernat (fl, str)	SS
Hüe, G.	Gigue	ALe
Hüe, G.	Nocturne	ALe
Humel, G.	Concerto. 1961	B&B
Hurník, I.	Concerto. 1955	CHF
Hurník, I.	Partita (fl, str)	ES
Ibert, J.	Allegro Scherzando (Concerto)	ALe
Ibert, J.	Concerto	ALe

Flute and Orchestra

Illin, E.	Rapsodie. 1958	CHF
Jablonski, H.	Concerto. 1962	AP
Jacob, G.	Concerto (fl, str)	GaM
Jacob, G.	Suite	OxU
Jirko, I.	Concerto	CHF
Johnson, H.	For an Unknown Soldier	NVM
Jolivet, A.	Concerto (fl, str)	Heu
Kalas, J.	The Nightingale and the Rose	Art
Kapr, J.	Variations (fl, str)	ES
Karaš, R.	Concerto, op. 11. 1961	CHF
Kelterborn, R.	Nuovi Canti. 1973	B&N
Kempter, L.	Capriccio, op. 32	Pet
Kennan, K.	Night Soliloquy	CF
King, H.	Concerto. 1962	SD
Koch, E. von	Concertino pastorale. 1963	BrH
Kořínek, M.	Concerto	SHF
Kox, H.	Concerto. 1957	SD
Krenek, E.	Suite	B&N
Krommer, F.	Konzert	Art
Kronke, E.-Cavally	Caprice Impromptu	SM
Kruyf, T. de	4 Pas de deux, op. 30. 1972	SD
Kučera, V.	Der Rattenfanger. Stereo-concertino	ES
Kummer, G.	Concertino, op. 42	EdH
Kunert, K.	Konzert, op. 21	BrH
Laderman, E.	Celestial Bodies (fl, str)	OxU
Landowski, M.	Concerto (fl, str)	ECh
Landré, G.	Symphonic Music. 1947–48	SD
Langer, F.-Cavally	Concerto	SM
Lanshe, R.	Vignette	Roc
Larsson, L.	Concertino, op. 45/1	CGM
Leclair, J.	Concerto, op. 7/3	SM
Leclair, J.-Oubradous	Concerto, C	EMT
Leduc, J.	Divertissement, op. 12. 1962	CBD
Leeuwen, A. van-Cavally	Tarantelle	SM
Lemacher, H.	Musica festiva (fl, str)	HG
Lerche, N.	Fairy Tale Suite. 1939–54	Fin
Lessel, F.-Perkowski	Variations	AP
Liedbeck, S.	Suite. 1964	STI
Linicke, J.-Schroeder	Concerto, G	Hei
Loeillet, J.-Ruf	Concerto, D	B&N
Luening, O.	Concertino	Pet
Luening, O.	Lyric Scene (fl, str)	Pet
Lundkvist, P.	Silverflöjten	STI
Maderna, B.	Dimensioni III	ESZ
Madey, B.	Concerto. 1960	AP
Maganini, Q.	La Romanesca	EdM
Mahaut, A.	Concerto	SD
Malipiero, G.	Concerto	Ric
Manicke, D.	Concerto	RS

Martin, F.	Ballade	UE
Martin, F.-Desarzens	Sonata da Chiesa (fl, str)	UE
Marx, K.	Konzert, Eb, op. 32 (fl, str)	B&N
Matěj, J.	Concerto. 1966 (fl, str)	Art
Mengelberg, R.	Concertino. 1943	SD
Metzler, F.	Konzert	R&E
Meyer, K.	Concerto da Camera	HMo
Meyerowitz, J.	Concerto	EBM
Micco, D. de -Boelger	Concerto, G	HSM
Michael, E.	Nocturne	EMT
Mieg, P.	Concerto. 1962	B&B
Milano, R.	Essay No. 4	AMC
Molter, J.	Flute Concerto	MR
Moreau, L.	Dans la forêt enchantée	ALe
Moszumanska-Nazar, K.	Variazioni concertanti. 1965-66	AP
Motte, D. de la	Konzert	B&N
Mouquet, J.	La Flûte de Pan	SM
Mourant, W.	Idyl (fl, str)	ACA
Moyzes, A.	Concerto, op. 61	SHF
Mozart, W.	Andante, C, K. 315	BrH
Mozart, W.	Andante, K. 315	CF
Mozart, W.	Andante, K. 315	EdK
Mozart, W.	Concerto, G, K. 313, No. 1	BrH
Mozart, W.	Concerto, G, K. 313, No. 1	CF
Mozart, W.	Flute Concerto K. 313, No. 1	EdK
Mozart, W.	Concerto, D, K. 314, No. 2	BrH
Mozart, W.	Concerto, D, K. 314, No. 2	CF
Mozart, W.	Flute Concerto K. 314, No. 2	EdK
Mozart, W.-Sonntag	Rondo, D, KV 184	Hei
Mueller-Zurich, P.	Sinfonia No. 2 (fl, str)	A&S
Myslivecek, J.-Munclinger	Concerto, D	B&N
Myslivecek, J.	Concerto	ES
Nabokov, N.	Concerto Corale	Be
Naudot, J.-Petit	Concerto, op. 11/4 (fl, str)	Bil
Naudot, J.-Thilde	Concerto, op. 11/4 (fl, str)	Bil
Nielsen, C.	Concerto for Flute. 1926	SPD
Nigg, S.	Concerto	Job
Nussio, O.	Bagatelles (fl, str)	Pet
Nussio, O.	Concerto (fl, str)	Car
Nystroem, G.	Partita. 1953	ESu
Očenáš, A.	Concertino, op. 27 (fl, str)	SHF
Olsen, S.	Serenade	WH
Paccagnini, A.	La Citta del Miracolo	
	(afl/bfl/pic,O)	UE
Páleníček, J.	Concerto. 1957	CHF
Palubicki, K.	Concerto. 1957	AP
Pehm, R.	Concertino im alten Stil, op. 57	LDo
Pendleton, E.	Concerto alpestre	EdS
Pepin, A.	Impromptu	ALe
Pergolesi, G.-Meylan	Concerto, G	B&H

Pergolesi, G.-Brinckmann, Mohr	Concerto, G	HSM
Pergolesi, G.-Barbirolli	Concerto	OxU
Perilhou, A.	Ballade	Heu
Petit, P.	Petite Suite	ALe
Petrovics, E.	Concerto. 1957	EMB
Pez, J.	Concerto, e	Eul
Podešva, J.	Concerto. 1965	Art
Poradowski, S.	Concerto, op. 59. 1954	AP
Pouwels, J.	Concerto. 1957	SD
Quantz, J.	Concerto, C	MV
Quantz, J.-Sonntag	Concerto, C	Pet
Quantz, J.-Sonntag	Concerto, c	Hei
Quantz, J.	Concerto, d (fl, str)	MR
Quantz, J.-Upmeyer	Concerto, D (Potsdam) (fl, str)	B&N
Quantz, J.	Flute Concerto, D	EdK
Quantz, J.	Concerto, D	MV
Quantz, J.-Sonntag	Concerto, e	HSM
Quantz, J.-Weissenborn	Concerto, G	BrH
Quantz, J.	Flute Concerto, G	EdK
Quantz, J.-Schroeder	Concerto, G	Eul
Quantz, J.-Weissenborn	Concerto, G	M&M
Quensel, A.-Cavally	Concert Etude	SM
Quinet, M.	Concertino. 1959	CBD
Ramovš, P.	Contrasts	EdD
Ramovš, P.	Odmevi (Echoes). 1965	HG
Ramovš, P.	Nasprotja	HG
Raphael, G.	Concertino, op. 82	BrH
Raphling, S.	Warble for Lilac Time	EdM
Ravel, M.	Pavane	EdM
Ravel, M.	Pièce en forme de Habanera	ALe
Read, G.	Threnody	See
Řehoř, B.	Chamber concerto. 1963	CHF
Reinecke, C.	Konzert, D, op. 283	BrH
Revel, P.	5 Pièces	Dur
Rhené-Baton	Passacaille, op. 35	Dur
Richter, F.-Gronefeld, Kraus	Concerto, e	AMP
Rimsky-Korsakov, N.-Cavally	Flight of the Bumblebee	SM
Rössler-Rosetti, F.-Szebenyi	Concerto, G	SS
Rössler-Rosetti, F.-Szebenyi	Concerto, D	SS
Rogers, B.	Soliloquy	CF
Rohwer, J.	Chamber Concerto, D, on a theme of Vivaldi	MV
Roos, R. de	Rapsodie e Danza. 1972-73	SD
Roos, R. de	Danses. 1940	SD
Roussel, A.	Aria	ALe
Rudolf, B.	Divertissement	LDo
Ryausov, S.	Concerto (fl, str)	MKE
Rybicki, F.	Concertino, op. 51. 1951	AP
Saeverud, H.	Divertimento op. 13, No. 1	WH

Saint-Saens, C.	Adagio et Variation (Ascanio)	Dur
Saint-Saens, C.	Odelette, op. 162	Dur
Saint-Saens, C.	Romance, op. 37	Dur
Saint-Saens, C.	Romance, op. 37	EdK
Samazeuilh, G.	Luciole	Dur
Sammartini, G. -Jenkins	Concerto No. 1	Sch
Santa Cruz, D.	Sinfonia Concertante, op. 21	PIC
Sarri, D. -Meylan	Sonata, a	AMP
Scarlatti, D. -Benjamin	Suite	B&H
Schibler, A.	Lyrisches Konzert, op. 40	A&S
Schickhardt, J. -Brinckmann, Mohr	Concerto, g	WMS
Schmidt, O.	Suite, op. 23	WH
Schmitt, F.	Suite, op. 129	Dur
Schneider, W.	Concertino	MV
Schroeder, H.	Concerto, op. 37	HG
Schwickert, G.	Concertino, op. 9	R&E
Schwindl, F. -Meylan	Flötenkonzert, D	BrH
Seiber, M.	Pastorale and Burlesque (fl, str)	S&C
Semler-Collery, J.	Pastorale et Caprice	ALe
Senstius, K.	Concertino, op. 5. 1921	SPD
Siegmeister, E.	Concerto	MCA
Siennicki, E.	Rondo (fl, str)	NK
Sikorski, K.	Concerto. 1957	AP
Simon, L.	Concertino. 1960	CHF
Sinigaglia, L.	Egloga d'autunno, op. 45/2	Car
Sinigaglia, L.	4 Piccoli pezzi	Car
Sinigaglia, L.	Suite, op. 45	Car
Škerjanc, L.	Concertino	EdD
Slowinski, W.	Concerto. 1957	AP
Spinks, C.	Suite (fl, str)	AlL
Spoljaric, V.	Concerto (fl, str)	DSS
Staempfli, E.	Concerto. 1957	B&B
Stamitz, A. -Lebermann	Concerto, D	BrH
Stamitz, J. -Koelbel	Concerto, C	Pet
Stamitz, J. -Gradenwitz	Konzert, D	BrH
Stamitz, J. -Lebermann	Concerto, D	Eul
Stamitz, K. -Lebermann	Flute Concerto, D, No. 3	BrH
Stamitz, K.	Flute Concerto, D	EdK
Stamitz, K.	Concerto, D	EdL
Stamitz, K. -Sonntag	Concerto, D	HSM
Stamitz, K.	Concerto, G	EdL
Stamitz, K. -Gronefeld	Concerto, G	Leu
Stamitz, K. -Lebermann	Concerto, G, op. 29	SS
Stölzel, G. -Tessmer	Concerto, e	HSM
Stringfield, L.	Mountain Dawn	EdM
Suchý, F.	Concerto. 1939	CHF
Suppé, F. von	Concertino (Dichter und Bauer)	B&B
Svatoš, V.	Concerto	CHF
Swierzynski, A.	Concerto. 1952	AP

Flute and Orchestra

Swisher, G.	Cancion	Roc
Szabelski, B.	Concerto. 1964	AP
Szalonek, W.	Concertino. 1960-62	AP
Szalowski, A.	Concertino	Amp
Tamas, J.	Kleine ungarische Suite	Eul
Tarp, S.	Concertino, op. 30. 1938	SPD
Tartini, G.	Andante Cantabile	OxU
Tartini, G.-Nagel	Concerto, G	HSM
Tartini, G.-Brinckmann, Mohr	Concerto a 5, G	HSM
Telemann, G.-Schlövogt	Concerto, c	AMP
Telemann, G.-Braun	Concerto, D	Eul
Telemann, G.-Rampal	Concerto, D	Int
Telemann, G.-Hinnenthal	Concerto, D	Leu
Telemann, G.-Schroeder	Concerto, D	Leu
Telemann, G.-Schroeder	Concerto, D	Pet
Telemann, G.-Brinckmann, Mohr	Concerto a 5, D	HSM
Telemann, G.	Flute Concerto, e	EdK
Telemann, G.-Schroeder	Concerto, e	Eul
Telemann, G.-Upmeyer	Concerto, G (fl, str)	B&N
Telemann, G.-Winschermann	Ouverture, e	HSM
Telemann, G.-Buettner	Suite, a	Pet
Telemann, G.-Wummer	Suite, a (fl, str)	SM
Thärichen, W.	Concerto, op. 29. 1953	B&B
Thomson, V.	Concerto	B-M
Thyrestam, G.	Sommarpastoral. 1969	STI
Tisné, A.	Concerto (fl, str)	Bil
Toeschi, C.-Münster	Concerto, G	Leu
Tomasi, H.	Concertino, E	ALe
Tomasi, H.	Concerto, F	ALe
Tomasi, H.	Concerto de Printemps	ALe
Touchemoulin, J.-Braun	Concerto, A	Pet
Urbanner, E.	Flötenconcertino	LDo
Vasilenko, S.	In Spring, Suite, op. 138	MKE
Verbesselt, A.-Rampal	Concerto	Bil
Veretti, A.	Concertino	ALe
Verhaar, A.	Concerto, op. 17. 1940	SD
Villette, P.	Complainte	ALe
Vinter, G.	Little Island Rhapsody	UE
Vivaldi, A.-Fortner	Concerto, F, op. 10/1 (La Tempesta)	AMP
Vivaldi, A.-Fortner	Concerto, g, op. 10/2 (La Notte)	AMP
Vivaldi, A.-Oubradous	Concerto, g, No. 6 (La Nuit)	EMT
Vivaldi, A.-Fortner	Concerto, D, op. 10/3 (Il Cardellino)	AMP
Vivaldi, A.-Lenzewski	Concerto, op. 10/3	CFV
Vivaldi, A.	Concerto, op. 10/3	EdK
Vivaldi, A.-Einstein	Concerto, D, op. 10/3	Eul

Vivaldi, A.-Fortner	Concerto, G, op. 10/4	AMP
Vivaldi, A.-Fortner	Concerto, F, op. 10/5	AMP
Vivaldi, A.-Fortner	Concerto, G, op. 10/6	AMP
Vivaldi, A.-Schroeder	Concerto, C, op. 44/11	Pet
Vivaldi, A.-Braun	Concerto, D, P. 205	Pet
Vivaldi, A.-Redel	Concerto, F	Pet
Vivaldi-Smith	Concerto, F, F. VI, No. 1	B-M
Vivaldi, A.-Ephrikian	Concerto, G, F. VI, No. 8	Ric
Vivaldi-Smith	Concerto, D, F. VI, No. 10	B-M
Vlijmen, J. van	Serenata II. 1964	SD
Voss, F.	Pan exzentrisch. 1962	BrH
Vries Robbé, W. de	Concertino (fl, str)	SD
Vries Robbé, W. de	Concerto Pastorale. 1962	SD
Wagenseil, G.-Koelbel	Concerto, G	Pet
Walacinski, A.	Sequenze. 1963	AP
Wildberger, J.	Contratempi	HG
Wilder, A.	Air	Bou
Wishart, P.	Aubade (fl, str)	Pet
Wolff, A.	Concerto	ECh
Wolpert, F.	Banchetto musicale op. 25, No. 1	BrH
Wouters, A.	Idylle, op. 70	ScF
Zafred, M.	Musica Notturna (fl, str)	Ric
Zagwijn, H.	Concertante. 1941	SD
Zbinden, J.	Fantasy, op. 22. 1954	BrH
Železny, L.	Konzert. 1965	Art
Zieritz, G. von	Bilder vom Jahrmarkt	R&E
Zilcher, H.	Konzertstuck, op. 81	BrH
Zipoli, D.-Selvaggi	12 a Canzone dall'organo (fl, str)	UE
Zipp, F.	Au clair de la Lune. 1963 (fl, str)	WMS
Zipp, F.	Suite, op. 35	Pet
Zöllner, H.	Serenade, op. 95	R&E

Flute and Band

-Briccialdi, Wilkins	Carnival of Venice	Lud
Barnes	Caprice for a flock of flutes	B-M
Beethoven, L. van -Colant	Romance, F	EdR
Bennett, D.	Flute Fresco	SM
Bennett, D.	Flute Royale	Bar
Chaminade, C.	Concertino	CF
Chaminade, C.-Wilson, Stickles	Concertino, op. 107	CFC
Chopin, F.-Cavally	Etude No. 14	SM
Conley, L.	Pastorale	Ken
Course, W.	Happy-Go-Lucky	Rub
Hanson, H.-Ebbs	Serenade	CF
Kennan, K.	Night Soliloquy	CF
Kinyon, J.	Petite Chanson	CFC
Kronke, E.-Cavally	Caprice Impromptu	SM

Flute and Band

Maltby, R.	The Slopes of Powderhorn	Ken
Masten, I.	Bonnie Eloise	Lud
Morrissey, J.	Hoopla!	EBM
Ostling, A.	Skip to my flute based on "Skip to my Lou"	B-M
Pyle, F.	The Edged Night	CF
Reynolds	Quick Silver	CFC
Rimsky-Korsakov, N.-Cavally	Flight of the Bumblebee	SM
Tchaikovsky, P.-Schinstine	Canzonetta (Violin Concerto)	SM
Telemann, G.-Reed	Suite, a, Part I	SM
Telemann, G.-Reed	Suite, a, Part II	SM
Telemann, G.-Reed	Suite, a, Part III	SM
Titl, A.	Serenade	CF

Methods and Studies

	Bandman's Flute Repertoire, 2 vols.	CF
	Military Band Studies for the Flute and Piccolo	CF
	Fun with Flute	War
	L'Idéal du flûtiste, 2 vols.	Dur
	Pro Art Flute Method, 2 vols.	PrA
	Rubank Instrumental Chart	Rub
Alassio	Short Method	B-M
Alassio	16 Short Progressive Exercises	B-M
Altés, H.-Caratgé	Method, 2 vols.	ALe
Altés, H.	Method for the Boehm Flute	CF
Altés, H.-Barrère	26 Studies	Sch
Andersen, J.	24 Etudes de virtuosité, op. 15, 2 vols.	Bil
Andersen, J.	24 Etudes, op. 15	CF
Andersen, J.-Wummer	24 Studies, op. 15	Int
Andersen, J.-Fenboque	24 Etudes Artistiques, op. 15	SM
Andersen, J.-Moyse	24 Etudes, op. 15	Sch
Andersen, J.	24 Etudes, op. 21	Bil
Andersen, J.	24 Studien, op. 21	ECM
Andersen, J.-Wummer	24 Studies, op. 21	Int
Andersen, J.-Barrère	24 Studies, op. 21	Sch
Andersen, J.	24 Etudes instructives, op. 30	Bil
Andersen, J.-Wummer	24 Studies, op. 30	Int
Andersen, J.-Cavally	24 Instructive Studies, op. 30	SM
Andersen, J.	24 Petites Etudes, op. 33	Bil
Andersen, J.	24 Exercises, op. 33	CF
Andersen, J.-Wummer	24 Studies, op. 33	Int
Andersen, J.	24 Progressive Studies, op. 33	SM
Andersen, J.	24 Petits Caprices, op. 37	Bil
Andersen, J.-Wummer	26 Little Caprices, op. 37	Int
Andersen, J.	26 Short Caprices, op. 37	Sch
Andersen, J.-Cavally	26 Small Caprices, op. 37	SM
Andersen, J.	26 Small Caprices, op. 37	WH

Flute — Methods and Studies

Andersen, J.-Heriche	18 Petites études, op. 41	Bil
Andersen, J.-Wummer	18 Studies, op. 41	Int
Andersen, J.-Barrère	18 Studies, op. 41	Sch
Andersen, J.-Cavally	18 Studies, op. 41	SM
Andersen, J.-Wummer	24 Grand Studies, op. 60, 2 vols.	Int
Andersen, J.	24 Virtuosity Studies, op. 60	SM
Andersen, J.	Schule der Virtuosität, 24 grosse Studien, op. 60, 3 vols.	WZ
Andersen, J.-Heriche	24 Etudes Techniques, op. 63, 2 vols.	Bil
Andersen, J.-Wummer	24 Technical Studies, op. 63, 2 vols.	Int
Andersen, J.	24 Etude Techniques, op. 63, 2 vols.	Sch
Andersen, J.-Cavally	24 Etudes Techniques, op. 63	SM
Andersen, J.	24 Technical Studies, op. 63, 2 vols.	WH
Andersen, J.	School of Virtuosity, 2 vols.	EdK
Andraud, A. (ed)	Modern Flutist	SM
Anzalone, V.	Breeze-Easy Method, 2 vols.	War
Arnold, J.	Modern Fingering System	ShB
Arnold, J.	The Very First Flute Method	Han
Arx, D. von	Schule	Hug
Bach, J.S.-Spiegl	Bach for Unaccompanied Flute	OxU
Bach, J.S.-Mols	20 Concert Studies	SM
Bach, J.S.-Schindler	24 Flute Extracts from the works of J.S. Bach, 2 vols.	BrH
Bach, J.S.-Schindler	24 Flute Concert Studies	SM
Bach, J.S.-Baker	The Flute Solos from the J.S. Bach Cantatas, Passions and Oratorios	Sch
Bach-Corroyez	22 Pièces de J.S. Bach	EdR
Bach, J.S.-Vester	Flute Obbligatos from the Cantatas	UE
Bach & Handel-Bartuzat	Orchestral Studies	FrH
Barrère, G.	The Flutist's Formulae	Sch
Bartuzat, C. (ed)	Orchestral Studies, 5 vols.	FrH
Beltran	Metodo completo	UME
Berbiguier, T.-Altés	18 Etudes (2nd fl ad lib)	Bil
Berbiguier, T.-Stringfield	18 Exercises or Etudes	CF
Berbiguier, T.	18 Exercises ou Etudes dans les tons	EdH
Berbiguier, B.	Method, 2 vols.	EdS
Berbiguier, B.-Wummer	18 Studies	Int
Berbiguier, T.-Barrère	18 Exercises	Sch
Bergman & Filas	Do's and Don'ts of Flute Playing	Col
Bitsch, M.-Rampal	12 Etudes	ALe
Boehm, T.	12 Etudes	Bil

Boehm -Wummer	12 Studies (Etudes), op. 15	CF
Boehm, T.	12 Studies, op. 15	EdK
Boehm, T.-Rampal	12 Studies, op. 15	Int
Boehm, T.-LeRoy	24 Caprices, op. 26	Bil
Boehm -Wummer	24 Caprices, op. 26	CF
Boehm, T.-Rampal	24 Etudes-Caprices, op. 26	Int
Boehm, T.-Caratgé	24 Studies, op. 37	ALe
Boehm -Wummer	24 Melodious Studies, op. 37	CF
Bouillard, H.	Méthode	EdS
Bousquet, N.	12 Grand Caprices, 2 vols.	EdS
Boustead, A. & Chambers, C.	Essential Repertoire for Flute	UE
Bozza, E.	10 Etudes sur des modes karnatiques	ALe
Bozza, E.	14 Etudes Arabesques	ALe
Bretonnière	18 Etudes brillantes	ECh
Briccialdi, G.	Exercice indispensable	Bil
Briccialdi, G.-Vinci	6 Grand Studies, op. 31	Bon
Briccialdi, G.	24 Studies, op. 31	Bon
Brooke, A.	Harmonic Fingerings	CF
Brooke, A.-Pappoutsakis	Method for the Flute, 2 vols.	CF
Bruckner & Tchaikovsky -Bartuzat	Orchestral Studies	FrH
Bruggen, F.	Studies for Fingercontrol	B&V
Brun, F.	Etudes de virtuosité	GrF
Buyssens, P.	25 Exercices journaliers, 2 vols.	ALe
Camus, P.	12 Studies	ALe
Caratgé, F.	12 Etudes faciles d'après Samie	ALe
Carbone, E.	Metodo teorico-pratico	Car
Carnaud	8 Exercises et 20 Etudes	EdR
Castérède, J.	12 Studies	ALe
Cavally, R. (ed)	Famous Flute Studies and Duets	SM
Cavally, R.	Flute Fingering and Trill Chart	SM
Cavally, R.	Melodious and Progressive Studies, 3 vols.	SM
Cavally, R.	Original Melodious and Progressive Studies for the Beginning Flutist	SM
Cerny & Bok	Schule für Flöte	ES
Crunelle, G. (ed)	Difficult Passages	ALe
Dalby	All Melody Method, 2 vols.	PrA
Damare, E.	Nouvelle Etudes, 2 vols.	EdS
Damare, E.	New Method, 3 vols.	EdS
Daneels	The Budding Flutist	ScF
Demersseman, J.	50 Etudes mélodiques, op. 4, 2 vols.	Bil
De Michelis, V.-Vinci	24 Exercises, op. 25	Ric
Dentato	How To Play Jazz Flute	Han
Devienne, F.-Gariboldi,		

Gaubert	Method, 2 vols.	ALe
Dobbelaere, R.	25 Etudes, 2 vols.	Mau
Dressler, R.	6 Caprices ou Etudes, op. 20	EdH
Drouet, L.	Etude modulée	EdH
Drouet, L.	18 Préludes et 6 Cadences	EdH
Drouet, L.-Fleury, Merry	25 Famous Studies	ALe
Drouet, L.	47 Etudes	B&V
Dubois, P.	13 Etudes de moyenne difficulté	ALe
Duschenes, M.	12 Studies	Ber
Duvergés, J.	Méthode de Flûte Boehm	Job
Eck, E.	Eck Method for Flute, 2 vols.	B-M
Eck, E.	Flute Trills	B-M
Eck, E.	Practical Flute Studies	B-M
Eck, E.	Tone Development for Flute	B-M
Edlen, H.	Grepptabell for the Boehm Flute	Nor
Edlen, H.	Studies	Nor
Eisenhauer, W.	Elementary Supplement Series	Alf
Eisenhauer & Gouse	Flute Method, Bk. 2	Alf
Endresen, R.	Supplementary Studies	Rub
Eördögh, J.	Medium-grade Technical and Reading Exercises, 2 vols.	EMB
Eriksson, G.	Flöjtspelets ABC	Nor
Fair, R.	Flute Method, 2 vols.	Col
Falk, J.	15 Etudes atonales	ALe
Filas, T.	Top Register Studies	CF
Fischer, O.	Scale and Chord Studies	Pet
Fischer, O.	Tonleiter- und Akkordübungen	For
Fontbonne, L.	Méthode complète	Bil
Freillon-Poncein, J.	La véritable manière d'apprendre a jouer en perfection du hautbois, de la flûte et du flageolet (reprint of 1700 edition)	MiR
Froseth, J.	The Individualized Instructor, 4 vols.	GIA
Fürstenau, A.	Exercices ou études, op. 15	Bil
Fürstenau, A.	12 Grand Studies	CF
Fürstenau, A.	26 Studies, op. 107, 2 vols.	CF
Fürstenau, A.-Eck	Fuerstenau Studies, op. 125	B-M
Fürstenau, A.-List	24 Etudes, op. 125	FrH
Fürstenau, A.-List	26 Studies, op. 107	FrH
Galli, R.	Indispensable Method	B-M
Galli, R.-Veggetti	30 Exercises, op. 100	B-M
Gariboldi, G.	30 Easy and Progressive Studies, 2 vols.	EdK
Gariboldi, G.	30 Easy and Progressive Studies, 2 vols.	GaM
Gariboldi, G.-Merry	Complete Method, op. 128, 2 vols.	ALe
Gariboldi, G.	L'Indispensable	EdM

Gariboldi, G.	15 Etudes Amateures	B&V
Gariboldi, G.-Merry	20 Etudes chantantes, op. 88	ALe
Gariboldi, G.-Merry	Daily Exercises, op. 89	ALe
Gariboldi, G.-Prill	First Exercises	Pet
Gariboldi, G.-Merry	Complete Study of the Scales, op. 127	ALe
Gariboldi, G.-Merry	Etudes mignonnes, op. 131	ALe
Gariboldi, G.-Merry	20 Little Studies, op. 132	ALe
Gariboldi, G.	20 Little Etudes, op. 132	Int
Gariboldi, G.-Merry	Grand Studies in Style, op. 134	ALe
Gariboldi, G.-Merry	Grands Exercises, op. 139	ALe
Gatti, G.	15 Studi	EBe
Gatti, G.	Invito al Flauto	EBe
Gavinies, P.-Herman	22 Exercices (24 matinées)	ECh
Gekeler, K.-Hovey	Belwin Flute Method, 3 vols.	B-M
Genzmer, H.	Neuzeitliche Etüden, 2 vols.	SS
Giampieri, A.	16 Daily Studies	Ric
Gibbons, A.	First Step Series--Flute	KPM
Gillet, F.	Exercices pour la technique superieure	ALe
Gillet, F.	Übungen für den fortgeschrittenen Unterricht der Flöte	B&N
González, F.	Metodo elemental	UME
González, F.	20 Exercises	UME
Gornston, D.	Advanced Method	Ash
Gornston, D.	Intermediate Method	Ash
Gornston, D.	Very First Flute Method	Ash
Gornston, D. & B. Paisner	Chopin Studies	SF
Gornston, D. & B. Paisner	Playing with Chords	SF
Gümbel, M.	Lern- und Spielbuch	B&N
Hart, A.	Introduction to the Flute	OxU
Hegvik, R.	Modern Course for the Flute, 5 vols.	HeE
Hendrickson	Handy Manual of Fingering Charts	CF
Herfurth, C. & H. Stuart	Sounds of the Winds, 2 vols.	CF
Herfurth, P.	A Tune A Day, 2 vols.	BM
Heriche, R.	Exercices Journaliers	E-V
Heriche, R.	24 Petites Etudes et 4 Recréations	Bil
Hetzel, J.	Photographic Fingering Chart	TP
Hofmann, R.	Melodic Studies, 2 vols.	FrH
Hugues, L.	30 Studies, op. 32	Ric
Hugues, L.	40 New Studies, op. 75	Ric
Hugues, L.-Veggetti	40 Exercises, op. 101	Ric
Hugues, L.-Moyse	40 Studies, op. 101	Int
Hugues, L.-Veggetti	24 Selected Studies	Ric
Jacobs	Flute Method	Alf
Jeanjean, P.	Modern Studies	ALe

Jeney, Z.	Flute Tutor, 3 vols.	EMB
Karg-Elert, S.	30 Capriccios, op. 107	CF
Karg-Elert, S.	30 Studies, op. 107	Int
Kelemen, M.	Study for Flute Alone	ImV
Keller, E.	12 Etudes, op. 33 (Bk. 2)	MKE
Keuning, H.	Van de bovenste plank; 8 etudes	HU
Kincaid, W.-Polin	The Art and Practice of Modern Flute Technique, 3 vols.	MCA
Kliment, J.	Anfängerschule für Flöte	JKM
Kliment, J.	Grifftabelle für Flöte	JKM
Knape, W.	2 Suites, op. 66	WMS
Koebner, R.-Skornicka	Master Method	B&H
Köhler, E.	35 Exercises, op. 33, 3 vols.	CF
Köhler, E.-Wummer	The Progress in Flute Playing, op. 33, 3 vols.	Int
Köhler, E.	Der Fortschritt im Flötenspiel, op. 33, 3 vols.	WZ
Köhler, E.-Cavally	15 Easy Melodic Etudes, op. 33/1	SM
Köhler, E.-Cavally	12 Moderately Difficult Studies, op. 33/2	SM
Köhler, E.-Cavally	8 Difficult Studies, op. 33/3	SM
Köhler, E.-Cavally	Romantic Etudes, op. 66	SM
Köhler, E.-Heriche	25 Etudes romantiques, op. 66	Bil
Köhler, E.	25 Romantische Etüden, op. 66	WZ
Köhler, E.	30 Virtuosen-Etüden, op. 75, 3 vols.	WZ
Köhler, E.	Schule der Geläufigkeit, op. 77	WZ
Köhler, E.	20 Leichte melodische progressive Lektionen, op. 93, 2 vols.	WZ
Köhler, H.-Paubon	Ecole de la velocité	Bil
Köhler, H.-Marx	6 Preludes, op. 122, 2 vols.	M&M
Krell, J.-comp.	20th Century Orchestra Studies	Sch
Kubát, A.	50 Technische Phrasierungsübungen	Art
Kucinski	Brahms Studies	SF
Kujala, W.	The Flutist's Progress	PP
Kummer, K.	Melodische Etüden, op. 110	SS
Labate, B.	10 Capricci	Spr
Langenus, G.	Practical Transposition	CF
Langey, O.	Practical Tutor	B&H
Langey, O.	Tutor	CF
Lateef, Y.	Flute Book of the Blues Number Two	FaM
Lateef, Y.	4 Etudes	FaM
LeJeune, H.	A Flutist's Manual	S-B
LeJeune, H.	Pitch and Sound Search Studies	BB
LeRoy, R.	Traité de la Flûte	EMT
Lester, L.-Terry	60 Rambles	CF

106

Linde, H.	4 Capricen	Hei
Lindpaintner, P.	50 Etudes, op. 126, 2 vols.	Bil
Link, J.	12 Caprices	FrH
List, E. (ed)	Flötenstudien im alten und neuen Stil, 3 vols.	FrH
Lorenz, J.	Fingergymnastische Studien	WZ
Lorenzo, L. de	Das "Non plus ultra" des Flötisten, op. 34, 18 Capricen, op. 34	WZ
Lorenzo, L. de	9 Grosse Künstler-Studien	WZ
Lowry, R.	Von Weber Studies	SF
Lubin	Tchaikovsky Studies	SF
Lüttmann, R.	12 Dodecaphonic Studies	ALe
MacGillavry, A.	20 Easy Studies	B&V
Mahaut, A.	Nouvelle méthode pour apprendre en peu de tems à jouer de la flûte traversière (reprint of 1759 edition)	MiR
Maquarre, A.	Daily Exercises	Sch
Michelis, V.-Vinci	24 Exercises, op. 25	Ric
Moore, E.	Daily Routine	CF
Moore, E.	The Flute & Its Daily Routine	Leb
Moore-Sieg	Preparatory Instructor for Flute	CF
Moyse, L.	7 Caprices-études	Bil
Moyse, L.	La Grande Velocité	SM
Moyse, M.	Bouquet des Tons, op. 125 by Fürstenau	ALe
Moyse, M.	De la sonorité	ALe
Moyse, M.	18 Exercises or Studies by Berbiguier	ALe
Moyse, M.	Exercises, op. 15 by Fürstenau	ALe
Moyse, M.	Exercices journaliers, new edition	ALe
Moyse, M.	50 Melodic Studies, op. 4 by Demersseman	ALe
Moyse, M.	50 Variations on the First Movement of the Sonata for Flute alone by J.S. Bach	M&M
Moyse, M.	Gammes et Arpèges	ALe
Moyse, M.	Grand Characteristic Studies by Berbiguier	ALe
Moyse, M.	Le Débutant Flutiste	ALe
Moyse, M.	Mécanisme-Chromatisme	ALe
Moyse, M.	100 Easy Graduated Studies after Cramer, 2 vols.	ALe
Moyse, M.	School of Articulation	ALe
Moyse, M.	6 Grand Studies by Fürstenau	ALe
Moyse, M.	Studies and Exercises in	

107

	Technique	ALe
Moyse, M.	12 Studies after Boehm	ALe
Moyse, M.	10 Studies after Kessler	ALe
Moyse, M.	10 Studies after Wieniawski	ALe
Moyse, M.	12 Studies in Great Virtuosity after Chopin	ALe
Moyse, M.	20 Exercises et Etudes sur les grandes Liaisons	ALe
Moyse, M.	24 Little Melodic Studies	ALe
Moyse, M.	20 Studies after Kreutzer	ALe
Moyse, M.	24 Caprice-Studies, op. 26 by Boehm	ALe
Moyse, M.	24 Daily Studies, op. 53 by Soussmann	ALe
Moyse, M.	25 Melodic Studies	ALe
Moyse, M.	25 Studies in Virtuosity after Czerny	ALe
Moyse, M.	26 Exercises, op. 107 by Fürstenau, 2 vols.	ALe
Moyse, M.	48 Studies in Virtuosity, 2 vols.	ALe
Müller, G.	Virtuose Studien	WZ
Neumann, F.	20 Spielstucke	MV
Nicolet, A.	Studies to Play New Music	HG
North, C.	Charts of Fingering	CF
Ostendorf, J.	Multiphonia	HSM
Paganini & Gavinies -Hahn	12 Etudes and Caprices	CF'
Paganini, N. -Herman	24 Caprices	ECh
Parès, G. -Hovey	Daily Exercises	B-M
Parès, G.	Daily Exercises and Scales	CF
Parès, G.	Elementary Method	B-M
Parès, G. -Whistler	Parès Scales	Rub
Patero	80 Etudes déchiffrages, 4 vols.	ALe
Patti, S.	Flute School, 2 vols.	EDS
Paubon, P.	Méthode de Flûte Traversière	GD
Pease, D.	Fundamental Method	UMI
Peetoom, A.	Concert Studies	HeE
Peichler, A. -Wummer	40 Grand Studies, 4 vols.	Int
Pellerite, J.	A Modern Guide to Fingerings	Za
Petersen, A.	Elementary Method	Rub
Petroff, I.	Scale and Arpeggio Tutor	WZ
Piazza, I. -Giampieri	Popular Method	Ric
Platonov, V. -Wummer	20 Studies	Int
Platonov, V. -Wummer	24 Studies	Int
Platonov, V. -Wummer	30 Studies	Int
Platonow, N.	20 Etüden	HSM
Platonow, N.	30 Studien	HSM
Ployhar, J.	Tunes for flute technic (Level 3)	B-M
Porret, J.	24 Déchiffrages manuscrits	EdR
Prescott, G.	Outlines of Technic	CF

Prill, E.	Method for the Boehm Flute	WZ
Prill, E.	24 Technical Studies	Sim
Reichert, M.-Caratgé	7 Exercices journaliers	ALe
Reichert, M.	7 Daily Exercises, op. 5	CF
Reichert, M.	Tägliche Übungen, op. 5	SS
Reichert, M.	6 Etudes	ALe
Reichert, M.	6 Etudes, op. 6	CF
Retiz, H.	12 Caprices, op. 4 (Studies to 20th century music)	Pet
Richter, W.	Schule	SS
Rieger-Unger	Das Querflötenspiel, 2 vols.	FrH
Riehm, R.	Gebräuchliches	HMo
Rieunier	22 Déchiffrages rythmiques instrumentaux	ALe
Rivera	Metodo	UME
Röhler, R.	Flötenschule, 2 vols.	FrH
Ruggiero, G.	16 Etudes atonales	ALe
Rusch, H. & Barto, A.	Breath Control and Tuning and Intonation Studies	CF
Rynearson, P.	11 Contemporary Etudes	Wes
Safranow	Staccato Etude	CF
Salvo, V.	243 Double and Triple Tonguing Exercises	PrA
Saunders, R.	The Flute	Nov
Schade, W.-Cavally	12 Impromptu Etudes	SM
Schade, W.	24 Caprices	CF
Schade, W.-Cavally	24 Caprices	SM
Schaeffer, B.	Annotated Fingering Tables for the Boehm Flute	RS
Schmitz, H.	Flötenlehre, 2 vols.	B&N
Schneider, H.	Neue Schule	RuE
Schwarz-Reiflingen, E. (ed)	Das Flötenbuch Friedrichs des Grossen	BrH
Shostakovitch, D.-List	Orchestral Studies	FrH
Shostakovitch, D.	Orchestra Studies from Symphonies 1-9	HSM
Shostakovitch, D.	Orchestral Excerpts from Symphonies 1-9	MCA
Siqueira, J.	Etüden	B&N
Skornicka, J. & A. Petersen	Intermediate Method	Rub
Smith, W.	Orchestral Studies, 3 vols.	UMP
Soussmann, H.-Popp	Complete Method for Flute, 3 vols.	CF
Soussmann, H.-Ehrmann	24 Etudes journalières, op. 53	Bil
Steensland, D. & J. Ployhar	Flute Student (Level 3)	B-M
Steensland, D. & F. Weber	Studies and melodious etudes (Level 1)	B-M
Steensland, D. & J. Ployhar	Studies and melodious etudes (Level 2)	B-M
Steensland, D. & J. Ployhar	Studies and melodious etudes	

	(Level 3)	B-M
Steensland, D. & F. Weber	Tunes for flute technic (Level 1)	B-M
Steensland, D. & F. Weber	Tunes for flute technic (Level 2)	B-M
Steensland, D. & J. Ployhar	Tunes for flute technic (Level 3)	B-M
Stepanow, T.	Tonleitern, Akkorde und	
	Arpeggien	WZ
Stokes & Condon	Illustrated Method	TrA
Stokes & Condon	Special Effects for Flute	TrA
Strauss, R.	Orchestra Studies from the	
	Symphonic Works	CF
Strauss, R.	Orchestral Excerpts	Int
Taffanel, P. & Gaubert, P.	Complete Flute Method, 2 vols.	ALe
Taffanel, P. & Gaubert, P.	17 Grand Daily Exercises	
	(Méthode)	ALe
Takahashi	Flute School, 2 vols.	Z-O
Tassinari, A.	Esercizi tecnici di perfeziona-	
	mento	Edi
Terschak, A.	26 Tägliche Übungen, op. 71	SS
Tomaszewski, F.	Wybór etiud, 3 vols.	AP
Torchio, B.	Orchestra Studies, 2 vols.	Ric
Torchio, B.	10 Studies	Ric
Trizno, B.	Etudes	MKE
Trizno, B.	Scales, Arpeggios and Intervals	
	for Development of Virtuoso	
	Technique	MKE
Van Bodegraven, P.	Adventures in Flute Playing,	
	2 vols.	Sta
Van Vactor, D.-Kitti	Carl Fischer Basic Method	CF
Vermeulen, G.	Easy Melodious Studies	B&V
Vester, F. (ed)	100 Klassische Studien, Vol. 1	UE
Vester, F. (ed)	50 Additional Classical Studies,	
	Vol. II	UE
Vinci, D.	12 Studies	Ric
Viola, J.	The Technique of the Flute	BPP
Vivian, A.	Scale Exercises	B&H
Vivian, A.	Scale Exercises	CF
Voxman, H. & W. Gower	Advanced Method, 2 vols.	Rub
Voxman H. (ed)	Selected Studies	Rub
Wagner, E.	Foundation to Flute Playing	CF
Wagner, E.	Table of Fingerings for the	
	Boehm Flute	CF
Wagner, R.-Schwedler	Orchesterstudien	BrH
Wagner, R.-Bartuzat	Orchestral Studies	FrH
Wagner, R.	Orchestral Excerpts	Int
Wanausek, C.	Cadenzas to Classical Flute	
	Concertos	LDo
Weber, F. & D. Steensland	Flute student (Level 1)	B-M
Webster, M.	Flute Instructor	Lud
Wood, D.	Studies for Facilitating the	
	Execution of Upper Notes	CF

Wummer, J. (ed)	Orchestral Excerpts from Classical and Modern Works, 10 vols.	Int
Wummer, J.	12 Daily Exercises	CF
Wunderlich, F.	Arpeggios (Chords)	CF
Yagudin, Y.	24 Etudes	MKE
Zachert, W.	Melodische Ubungen	SS
Zimmermann, B.	Spielanleitung	SS
Zöller, K. (ed)	Moderne Orchester–Studien, 2 vols.	SS

Oboe, English Horn, and Oboe d'amore

Oboe

Unaccompanied Solos

Adler, S.	Oboration	TP
Amy, G.	Jeux. 1970	UE
Andriessen, J.	Balocco. 1960	SD
Andriessen, L.	A Flower song II. 1964	SD
Antoniou, T.	5 Likes	B&N
Apostel, H.	Sonatine, op. 39a	UE
Arbatsky, Y.	Sonata	WZ
Arma, P.	Divertimento No. 7	TP
Arma, P.	Soliloque	Bil
Arnold, M.	Fantasie, op. 90. 1966	Fab
Bartolozzi, B.	Collage. 1968	ESZ
Bartolozzi, B.	The Hollow Man. 1968	ESZ
Bartsch, C.	4 Pieces	Mau
Ben-Haim, P.	3 Songs Without Words	AlB
Berio, L.	Sequenza VII. 1969	UE
Blume, J.	Metamorphoses	MV
Boone, C.	Vermillion	EdS
Booren, J. van den	Ballade	SD
Booren, J. van den	Chanson du printemps	SD
Bozza, E.	Suite Monodique	ALe
Braun, G.	Sonatine	WZ
Britten, B.	6 Metamorphoses after Ovid, op. 49	B&H
Camilleri, C.	Talba	JB
Castiglioni, N.	Alef. Kompositionen	SS
Chagrin, F.	Sonatina	Nov
Childs, B.	5 Soundpieces	TP
Childs, B.	Oboe Piece for Jackson MacLow	CoF

111

Childs, B.	Sonata	CoF
Cohn, J.	Baroque Suite	EdM
Colaço Osorio-Swaab, R.	Sonatine. 1959	SD
Crawford-Seeger, R.	Diaphonic Suite No. 1	AlB
Debras, L.	Sequenza II. 1968	See
Douel, J.	Pastorale	GD
Dubois, P.	Gafsa (Sonatina tunisienne)	ECh
Engelmann, H.	Variety, op. 40. 1971	HG
Exton, J.	3 Pieces	Che
Filippi, A. de	Ex Tempore	Gen
Franken, W.	Sonata. 1948	SD
Fricker, P.	Refrains, op. 49	OxU
Gaslini, G.	Segnali	UE
Glaser, W.	Ordo Meatus. 1967	STI
Globokar, V.	Atemstudie	Pet
Grahn, U.	Musik. 1968	STI
Grandis, R. de	3 Intermezzi	EdT
Hartley, W.	3 Pieces	Roc
Hartzell, E.	5 Skizzen (Monolog II). 1964	LDo
Hedwall, L.	6 Monologer. 1965	STI
Hrisanide, A.	"A la recherche de la verticale"	HG
Hudadoff, I. -arr.	50 Standard Solo Series	PrA
Hummel, B.	Suite	Sim
Jacob, G.	7 Bagatelles	OxU
Koch, R. (ed)	Solo Book, 3 vols.	Sim
Kotonski, W.	Monochrome. 1964	AP
Krek, U.	Sonatine	HG
Krenek, E.	Sonatina. 1956	B&N
Kruyf, T. de	Echoi, op. 25	B&B
Kunc, B.	Dance, op. 62	Ron
Lacour, L. De	Album de solos	Bil
Laporte, A.	Ludus fragilis. 1967	EdT
LeFanu, N.	Soliloquy	Nov
Lemeland, A.	Scansions	Bil
Lewis, R.	Monophony II	LDo
Lüttmann, R.	Méditation I, fantaisie sur un thème de plain-chant	ALe
Maderna, B.	Aulodia per Lothar. 1965	ESZ
Maderna, B.	Solo	Ric
Mengelberg, K.	Sonata. 1939	SD
Mills, C.	Chant and Hymn	CoF
Moortel, L. van de	Lente	Mau
Müller, G.	Sonata	HSM
Patterson, P.	Monologue	JoW
Persichetti, V.	Parable III, op. 109	E-V
Phillips, P.	A Lonesome Music	Bou
Presser, W.	Partita	Ten
Racol, M. -Pierlot	Les Plaintes d'Ariadne	Bil
Rainier, P.	Pastoral Triptych	S&C
Reinhardt, B.	12 mal 12	ImV

Renosto	Ar-loth (ob/ehn/ob d'amore/ musette)	Ric
Riehm, R.	Ungebräuchliches	EMo
Ruggiero, G.	Capriccio in forma di valzer	Edi
Sacco, P.	Oboe Solo	Wes
Schenker, F.	Monolog. 1968	Deu
Schibler, A.	Dithyrambus, op. 98. 1971	Eul
Schneider, W.	Sonata, op. 53	Hei
Schroeder, H.	Sonata. 1971	HG
Schwartz, E.	Sonata	Gen
Sehlbach, E.	Music, op. 87/2	MV
Sellner, J.	Album de solos	EdR
Sigtenhorst Meyer, B.	3 Rustical Miniatures, op. 24	Als
Sigtenhorst Meyer, B.	Sonatine. 1930, op. 34	Als
Sigtenhorst Meyer, B.	3 Rustical Miniatures, op. 40	Als
Sigtenhorst Meyer, B.	3 Rustical Miniatures, op. 45	Als
Singer, L.	Work	ESZ
Steffens, W.	Grande Rose. 1970, op. 21	B&B
Stein, L.	Sonata	CoF
Stockhausen, K.	Solo	UE
Stockhausen, K.	Spiral	UE
Stoker, R.	3 Pieces, op. 29	Pet
Strop, S.	Musik	MV
Strilko, A.	Music for Oboe Alone	TP
Stutschewsky, J.	Moods	See
Swain, F.	3 Whimsies	Bou
Szalonek, W.	4 Monologhi. 1966	AP
Tisné, A.	Dinos (ob/ehn)	EMT
Tomasi, H.	Evocations	ALe
Turok, P.	Partita	CCo
Waters, C.	Little Suite	HE
Weber, A.	Synecodoque	ALe
Wellesz, E.	Suite	Ron
Wildberger, J.	Pour les neuf doigts	HG
Wildberger, J.	Rondeau. 1960	EMo
Wyttenbach, J.	Solo-Sonate. 1962-72	HG
Yun, I.	Piri. 1971	B&B
Zender, H.	3 Pezzi. 1963	B&B

Oboe and Piano or Harpsichord

Contemporary French Recital Pieces	Int
Morceaux de Concours et pièces d'audition	ALe
Oboe Solos	MS
Radio Collection of National Songs & Hymns	Rub
72 Oboe Solos	B-M
Sonata, d	LDo

-Staeps, Kolz	Sonata, d	LDo
-Bouvet	Suite, F (ob, bc)	EME
-Kolz	3 Sinfonias (ob, bc)	LDo
Abaco, E. dall'-Winschermann	Concerto, C, op. 5/5	HSM
Ackermans, H.	Paysage Nordique	EMb
Ackermans, H. & J. Faulx	Vers les Cimes Neigeuses	EMb
Adams, W.	Ländliche Bilder	SS
Addison, J.	Inventions	OxU
Addison, J.	Prologue	OxU
Addison, J.	Rhapsody	OxU
Albéniz, I.-Amaz	Mallorca. Barcarola	UME
Albéniz, I.-Amaz	Puerta de tierra	UME
Albinoni, T.-Paumgartner	Concerto, op. 7/3	B&H
Albinoni, T.-Paumgartner	Concerto, op. 7/6	B&H
Albinoni, T.-Giazotto	Concerto, d, op. 9/2	Int
Albinoni, T.-Joosen	Concerto, op. 9/2	MM
Albinoni, T.	Concerto à cinque, op. 9/5	MR
Albinoni, T.-Giegling	Concerto à 5, op. 9/8	AlB
Albinoni, T.	Concerto, op. 9/8	MR
Albinoni, T.	Concerto à cinque, op. 9/11	MR
Albinoni, T.-Schäffler	Sonata, a (ob, bc)	NV
Albrechtsberger, J.-Vecsey	Concertino und Notturno	SS
Albrespic, J.	Elégy	ALe
Alessandro, R. d'	Récitatif et valse-impromptu	EMP
Aletter, W.	Rendezvous	NK
Alexander, J.	Movement	Bou
Alexeyev, M.	Suite (Chavash Melodies)	MKE
Aliabev, A.-Fortunatov	Dance (The Magic Drum)	MKE
Alpaerts, F.	Concertstuk	EMe
Alwyn, W.	Concerto	AlL
Ameller, A.	L'Anémone	HLe
Ameller, A.	Chicoutimi	ALe
Ameller, A.	Suite Concertante	ALe
Ames, W.	Rhapsody	CoF
Amirov, F.	Piece on an Azerbaijan Folk Theme	MKE
Ammann, B.	Frequences variables (ob, hpcd)	EdT
Andraud, A.-arr.	15 Grands Solos de Concert	SM
Andraud, A.-arr.	Oboists Concert Album	SM
Andriessen, H.	Ballade. 1952	SD
Anrep-Nordin, B.	Partita	STI
Arányi, G.	Romance. 1954	EMB
Arban, J.-Vanasek	Perpetual Motion	MCA
Arensky, A.-Fedulov	Dance (Egyptian Nights)	MKE
Arne, M.-Rothwell	Pastorale	Che
Arnold, J. (ed)	Oboe Solos	MS
Arnold, M.	Concerto	Pat
Arnold, M.	Sonatina	AlL
Arrieu, C.	Impromptu	ALe
Aubain, J.	Air de ballet	ALe

114

Oboe and Piano or Harpsichord

Aubain, J.	2 Etudes	ERR
Aubin, T.	Concertino dello scoiattolo	ALe
Austin, F.	Molly Brazen	B&H
Babell, W.-Tilmouth	Sonata, f	OxU
Babell, W.-Tilmouth	Sonata, g	OxU
Bach, C.P.E.-Lauschmann	Concerto, Bb, No. 1	For
Bach, C.P.E.-Kaul	Concerto, Bb	Leu
Bach, C.P.E.-Töttcher, Grebe	Concerto, Eb	HSM
Bach, C.P.E.-Walther	Sonate, g, WV 135 (ob, bc)	BrH
Bach, C.P.E.-Scheck, Ruf	Sonata, g (ob, bc)	Ric
Bach, J.C.	Air Cantabile	MM
Bach, J.C.	Andante (Sinfonia)	MM
Bach, J.C.-Marteau	Andante Cantabile	Lud
Bach, J.C.-Maunder	Concerto, F	S&C
Bach, J.C.	Concerto, F, No. 2	MR
Bach, J.C.-Johnson	Andante	B-M
Bach, J.S.-Rothwell	Adagio	Che
Bach, J.S.	4 Adagios (Cantatas)	Mit
Bach, J.S.-Butterworth	Aria (St. Matthew Passion)	Cha
Bach, J.S.	Aria, D	Dur
Bach, J.S.-Reuschel	Air de la passion selon St. Mathieu, 2nd pt. No. 48	Bil
Bach, J.S.-Gaylord	Arioso (Cantata No. 156)	CF
Bach, J.S.-Crossman	Art of the Fugue I	PMP
Bach, J.S.-Bleuzet	Bourrée (Suite, C)	ALe
Bach, J.S.	Choral	Ham
Bach, J.S.-Töttcher, Müller	Concerto, F	HSM
Bach, J.S.	Concerto, F	SS
Bach, J.S.-Radeke, Haverkampf	Concerto, g, BWV 1056	BrH
Bach, J.S.-Slavinsky	Concerto No. 2 for Violin	MKE
Bach, J.S.	Jesu, Joy of Man's Desiring	MM
Bach, J.S.-Andraud	Minuet and Famous Air	SM
Bach, J.S.-Harris	2 Minuets	Lud
Bach, J.S.-Stouffer	Musette	Ken
Bach, J.S.	Pastorale	Cor
Bach, J.S.-Tustin	Prelude in Bb Minor	Bar
Bach, J.S.-Pushechnikov	Prelude and Fughetta, d	MKE
Bach, J.S.-Bleuzet	Scherzetto	ALe
Bach, J.S.-Cazden	Siciliano, BWV 1063	Spr
Bach, J.S.-Andraud	Siciliano and Arioso	SM
Bach, J.S.-Meylan	Sonata, g, BWV 1030 (ob, bc)	Pet
Bach-Gounod-Edlefsen	Ave Maria	B-M
Bach, W.F.-Johnson	Andante	B-M
Backes, L.	Spielmusik	Hei
Badings, H.	Cavatina	SD
Bakaleinikoff, V.	Danse	B-M
Bakaleinikoff, V.	Elegy	B-M
Bakaleinikoff, V.	Pastorale	B-M

Oboe and Piano or Harpsichord

Baker, E.	Cantilena	Che
Balfe, W.-Buchtel	I Dreamt I Dwelt in Marble Halls	NK
Barab, S.	Pastorals	GaM
Barat, J.	Nostalgia	ALe
Bariller, R.	Complainte et danse maraichine	ALe
Bariller, R.	Gerberoy	ALe
Bariller, R.	Miniatures	ALe
Bariller, R.	Paysages	ALe
Bariller, R.	Russiacanto	ALe
Barlow, W.	Winter's Passed	CF
Barret, A.-Pazemis	Chansonette	Rub
Bárta, L.	4 Kompositionen. 1965	Art
Barthe, A.-Andraud	Petite Suite Pittoresque	SM
Bartók, B.-Szeszler	Bagpiper	EMB
Bartók, B.-Szeszler	3 Chansons Populaires Hongroises	EMB
Bartsch, C.	Suite	Mau
Bassi, L.-Voxman	Lamento (Nocturne)	Rub
Bassi, L.	Nocturne	CF
Baton, C.-Neate	Première Suite	S&C
Bauer, M.	Duo, op. 25	Pet
Baur, J.	Concerto Romano. 1960	BrH
Baur, J.	Fantasie. 1954	BrH
Bavicchi, J.	Sonatina	OxU
Beck, C.	Concertino	SS
Beck, C.	Sonatine	SS
Beckler, S.	Little Sonata, op. 49/3	CoA
Beethoven, L. van-Andraud	Adagio Cantabile	SM
Beethoven, L. van-Hanson	Bagatelle	Lud
Beethoven, L. van-Trinkaus	Minuet	CF
Beethoven, L. van-Bleuzet	Rondo (Sonata No. 27)	ALe
Beethoven, L. van-Katz	6 Allemandes	SF
Belinfante, C.	By the River	GD
Belinsky, I.	Oboe and English Horn Solos from the Symphonic Repertoire	MB
Bellini, V.-Meylan	Concerto	B&N
Bellini, V.-Joosen	Concerto	MM
Bellini, V.-Leskó	Concerto, Eb	Ric
Bellini, V.-Peters	Concerto, Eb	SM
Bellini, V.-Sambini	Duet (La Sonnambula)	EdS
Benary, P.	Sonatine	MV
Ben-Haim, P.	3 Lieder ohne Worte	ImV
Benjamin, A.	Divertimento on Themes by Gluck	B&H
Bennett, Richard Rodney	Concerto. 1969-70	UE
Bennett, Richard Rodney	Sonata	B-M
Benson, W.	Evening Piece	B&H
Benson, W.	Recuerdo (ob/ehn, pf)	MCA

116

Oboe and Piano or Harpsichord

Bentzon, N.	2 Pieces, op. 41	WH
Berger, J.	Sonata da Camera	BB
Berghmans, J.	The Labyrinth (Scenes from a Traveling Circus)	ALe
Berkeley, L.	Sonatina	Che
Bernaud, A.	Capriccio Rustique	ALe
Berthelot, R.	Air Pastoral	ALe
Berthelot, R.	Arioso and Rondo	GD
Berthomieu, M.	Andante et rigaudon	Bil
Besozzi, A.	Concerto, G	MR
Besozzi, A.-Rothwell	Sonata, C	Che
Besozzi, A.-Ruf	Sonata, D	SS
Best, A.-arr.	Folk Songs from Grieg	B-M
Best, A.-arr.	Organ Grinder	B-M
Bettoney-Findlay-arr.	Pearls of the Old Masters, 2 vols.	CF
Beyer, J.	3 Pieces	AMC
Beyer, J.	3 More Pieces	AMC
Beyer, J.	6 Pieces	AMC
Bialosky, M.	Sonatina	Wes
Bitsch, M.	Romanza	ALe
Bitsch, M.	Suite Française sur des thèmes du XVII siècle	ALe
Bitti, M.-Ruf	Sonatas, c, a (ob, bc)	B&N
Bitti, M.-Ruf	Sonatas, g, G (ob, bc)	B&N
Bizet, G.	Adagio (Symphony, C)	EdM
Bizet, G.-Isaac, Feldman	Aragonaise (Carmen)	CF
Bizet, G.-Johnson	Barcarolle (The Pearl Fishers)	Rub
Bizet, G.-Herman, Sabon	Carmen	ECh
Bizet, G.-Mayer	Seguidilla	B-M
Bizet, G.	Serenade Espagnole	EdM
Blank, A.	Moments in Time	See
Blatt, J.	Sonata	M&M
Blémant, L.	Sous les sapins	ALe
Boeck, A. De	Lied	ScF
Boerlin, R.	Reflections	Hel
Boisdeffre, R.	Andantino	Ham
Boisdeffre, R.	Elevation	Ham
Boisdeffre, R.	Scènes villageoises	Ham
Boisdeffre, R.	Village Scenes	SM
Boisdeffre, R.	3 Pièces	Ham
Bonelli, E.	6 Variazioni	GZ
Bonelli, E.	Variations on a Theme of Corelli	GZ
Boni, G.-Rothwell	Sonata, G	Che
Bonsel, A.	Suite (ob, hpcd)	SD
Bonzon, F.	En Ardennes	ScF
Boone, C.	Zephyrus	EdS
Bordier, J.	Habanera	Dur
Borodin, A.-Buchtel	Polovetsian Dances	NK

Borodin, A.-Walters	Polovetsian Dance (Prince Igor)	Rub
Boroff, E.	Variations and Theme	SF
Borris, S.	Sonata, op. 48/1	Hei
Borris, S.	Sonata, op. 65 (ob, hpcd)	Hei
Borris, S.	Sonatine, op. 116/4	Hei
Borris, S.	Te Deum-Lauda	S-V
Boscovich, A.	Concerto	ImV
Bossi, M.	Improvviso	Bon
Bourguignon, F. de	Andante et scherzo, op. 77. 1943	CBD
Boustad, A. & Chambers, C.	Essential Repertoire for Oboe	UE
Boutry, R.	Prelude, Pastoral and Tarantella	ALe
Boutry, R.	Sonatina	EdS
Bowen, Y.	Sonata	Che
Boyce, W.-Rothwell	Gavotte and Gigue	Che
Bozay, A.	Tetelpar (Pair of Movements)	EMB
Bozza, E.	Conte pastoral	ALe
Bozza, E.	Fantaisie Italienne	ALe
Bozza, E.	Fantaisie Pastorale	ALe
Bozza, E.	Sonata	ALe
Braga, G.	Serenata	Dur
Brahms, J.-Cacavas	A Sonnet	B-M
Brahms, J.-Andreoni	Waltz, op. 39/15	Ric
Brandon, S.	Suite. 1969	Man
Brant, H.	Colloquy	Spr
Bréville, P. de	Sonatina	EdS
Briegel, G.	Little Shepherd	GFB
Briegel, G.-arr.	2 Stephen Foster Melodies	GFB
Britain, R.	Phantasy	See
Brons, C.	Dialogen. 1962	SD
Brown, C.	Fantaisie agreste	SS
Brun, H.	Jeux Sylvestres	ALe
Bruniau, A.	Sur la montagne	Bil
Bruns, V.	Concerto, op. 28	FrH
Bruns, V.	Sonata, op. 25	FrH
Buchtel, F.	Chant d'amour	Vol
Buchtel, F.	Country Dance	NK
Buchtel, F.	Cradle Song	NK
Buchtel, F.	Crescent March	B-M
Buchtel, F.	Crown Prince	NK
Buchtel, F.	First Book of Solos for Oboe	Col
Buchtel, F.	The Flatterer	B-M
Buchtel, F.	A Gay Song	NK
Buchtel, F.	Golden Glow Waltz	B-M
Buchtel, F.-arr.	Holy City	NK
Buchtel, F.	Irene	NK
Buchtel, F.	Lucky Day	NK
Buchtel, F.	Meditation (Sonatina, F)	NK

Oboe and Piano or Harpsichord

Buchtel, F.	My Buddy	NK
Buchtel, F.	Saucy Sally	NK
Buchtel, F.	Serenade	NK
Buchtel, F.	Tango	NK
Buchtel, F.	Twilight Shadows	NK
Buchtel, F.	Valse Romantique	Vol
Buononcini, G.-Worley	Rondeau	Spr
Bush, A.	Northumbrian Impressions	Nov
Bush, G.	Concerto	Elk
Bush, G.	Dialogue	GaM
Busser, H.	Asturias, op. 84	ALe
Busser, H.	Eglogue, op. 63	ALe
Busser, H.-Andraud	Eglogue (Pastorale Poem), op. 63	SM
Busser, H.	Piece in Bb, op. 22	ALe
Cacavas, J.	Preludio	B-M
Cacavas, J.	Winterscape	B-M
Caine, E.	Andante	GaM
Caldara, A.-Cacavas	Alma del core	B-M
Camidge, M.-Joosen	Sonatine, Bb	MM
Camilleri, C.	Meditation	Wat
Camilleri, C.	Sonata Antica	Nov
Campra, A.-Boulay	Carnival of Venice	GD
Campra, A.-Bleuzet	Gavotte des bergers (Achille et Déidamie)	ALe
Campra, A.-Bleuzet	Menuet vif et Gigue (L'Europe galante)	ALe
Canal, M.	Theme and Variations	GrF
Canivez, L.	Air Varie, op. 31	T-M
Carles, M.	The Troubadour	ALe
Carse, A.	Dance Measure	GaM
Casanova, A.	Capriccio	Job
Casinière, Y. de la	Berceuse	ALe
Castelnuova-Tedesco, M.	Concerto da camera	B-M
Castérède, J.	Intermezzo	ALe
Castérède, J.	Sonata	ALe
Chagrin, F.	Barcarole and Berceuse	S&C
Chagrin, F.	4 Lyric Interludes	Nov
Chagrin, F.	Sarabande	AlL
Challan, R.	Divertissement	ALe
Challan, R.	Fantasy, F	EdS
Chandler, M.	Holiday Tunes	Nov
Chédeville, N.-Ruf	Sonata, e (ob, bc)	SS
Chédeville, N.-Favre	Sonata No. 6	ERS
Chédeville, P.-Favre	Sonatille No. 3	ERS
Chevreuille, R.	Pastorale variée, op. 75. 1960	CBD
Chopin, F.	Cavatina	NK
Chopin, F.	Nocturne, op. 37/1	Dur
Chopin, F.	Nocturne, op. 48/1	Dur
Chopin, F.	Nocturne, op. 55/1	Dur

Chopin, F.-Davis	Nocturne, op. 55/1	Wes
Christiansen, C.	Aria	EMf
Cilensek, J.	Sonata	Pet
Cima, G.-Grebe	Sonata, D, No. 2 (ob, bc)	HSM
Cimarosa, D.-Thilde	Concerto, Bb	Bil
Cimarosa, D.-Thilde	Concerto, C	Bil
Cimarosa, D.-Thilde	Concerto, G	Bil
Cimarosa, D.-Benjamin	Concerto	B&H
Cimarosa, D.-Joosen	Sonata, Bb	MM
Clarke, H.	Danza de la Muerte	AMC
Clement, F.	Silvertone Polka	Vol
Clérisse, R.	Adieu du berger	Com
Clérisse, R.	Au fil de l'eau	ALe
Clérisse, R.-Leblanc	Eglogue	Bil
Clérisse, R.	Fantaisie	ALe
Clérisse, R.-Leblanc	Pièce de concours	Bil
Clérisse, R.	Pour un soir de Noel	ALe
Clostre, A.	Concerto	EMT
Codivilla, F.	Sonata	Bon
Cohen, S.	Arioso	CF
Cohen, S.	Autumn Reverie	B-M
Cohen, S.	Piper in the Valley	B-M
Cohen, S.	Shepherd's Song	CF
Cole, H.	Dance	S&C
Cole, H.	A Slow Air	S&C
Colin, C.	Les Echos de Marnes, Pastoral	SM
Colin, C.-Bajeux	1st Competition Solo, op. 33	ALe
Colin, C.-Bajeux	2nd Competition Solo, op. 34	ALe
Colin, C.-Bajeux	3rd Competition Solo, op. 40	ALe
Colin, C.-Andraud	3rd Solo de Concert, op. 40	SM
Colin, C.-Bajeux	4th Competition Solo, op. 44	ALe
Colin, C.-Bajeux	5th Competition Solo, op. 45	ALe
Colin, C.-Bajeux	6th Competition Solo, op. 46	ALe
Colin, C.-Bajeux	7th Competition Solo	ALe
Colin, C.-Bajeux	8th Competition Solo, op. 52	ALe
Colin, C.-Cailliet	Eighth Solo	SM
Colin, C.	Grande Fantaisie Concertante, op. 47	ALe
Constant, F.	Maree, op. 61	JB
Cooke, A.	Concerto	Nov
Cooke, A.	Sonata	OxU
Coolidge, E.	Sonata	CF
Coolidge, R.	Weeping Dancer	Ken
Corbeel, R.	Alcanar	Mau
Corbeel, R.	Allegretto	Mau
Corbeel, R.	Cantilena	Mau
Corbeel, R.	Marinez	Mau
Corelli, A.	Air and Dance	EdM
Corelli, A.-Barbirolli	Concerto	B&H
Corelli, A.-Krainis	La Follia, op. 5/12	M&M
Corelli, A.	Suite, Bb	EdM

Oboe and Piano or Harpsichord

Coriolis, E. de	Gambades	ALe
Coriolis, E. de	Tarentelle	Bil
Corrette, M.-Ruf	Suite, C (ob,bc)	Ric
Coulthard, J.	Sonata. 1947	Can
Couperin, F.-Rothwell	Le Bavolet Flottant	Che
Couperin, F.-Bleuzet	Berceuse en rondeau (Pièces de clavecin)	ALe
Couperin, F.-Boulay	Concerto No. 6 (ob,bc)	EMT
Couperin, F.-Ruf	Concerto, Bb, No. 6 (ob,bc)	SS
Couperin, F.-Bleuzet	Musette of Taverny (Pièces de clavecin)	ALe
Crawford-Kent	The Army Air Corps	CF
Craxton, H.-arr.	Queen's Dance & Dance of the Jews	OxU
Craxton, H.-arr.	3 Elizabethan Pieces	OxU
Craxton, J. & A. Richardson	First Book of Oboe Solos	Fab
Craxton, J. & A. Richardson	Second Book of Oboe Solos	Fab
Croebelis, D. del	The New Dutch Playhouse	HeE
Cui, C.	Orientale, op. 50/9	CF
Cui, C.	Orientale	NK
Cumberworth, S.	5 Sketches	AMC
Cundick, R.	Turnabouts	B&H
Dalen, H. van	Romance	MM
D'Alessandro, R.	Sonate, op. 67	RuE
Dallier, T.	Fantaisie-Caprice	ALe
Dallier, T.-Andraud	Fantaisie Caprice	SM
Dandrieu, J.-Rothwell	Les Fifres	Che
Daneau, N.	Caprice	T-M
Danican-Philidor, A.-Ruf	Suite I, g (ob,bc)	SS
Darke, H.	6 Miniatures	S&C
Dautremer, M.	Air Lointain	ALe
Dearnley, C.-arr.	8 Easy Pieces by Classical Composers	Che
Dearnley, C.-arr.	More Easy Pieces by Classical Composers	Che
DeBueris, J.	Musette	CF
Debussy, C.	Air de Lia	EdM
Debussy, C.-Koepke	Clair de Lune (Suite Bergamasque)	Rub
Debussy, C.-Cazden	Clair de Lune	Spr
Debussy, C.-Stotyn	The Girl with the Flaxen Hair	MM
Debussy, C.-Stotyn	The Little Shepherd	MM
Debussy, C.-Stotyn	Petite Piece	MM
Debussy, C.-Hurrell	Sarabande	Rub
Dedrick, A.	A Tune for Christopher	Ken
Dedrick, C.	Twilight	Ken
Delalande, M.-Boulay	Air, Musette and Passepied (ob,bc)	GD
Delaunay, R.	Au fil de l'eau	Bil
Delaunay, R.	Sérénade matutinale	Bil

Delcroix, L.	Fantaisie Bucolique, op. 74	ALe
Delibes, L.-Edlefsen	Waltz	B-M
Delmas, M.	Complainte et air de ballet	Bil
Delmas, M.	Conte rose	Bil
Delmas, M.	Soir d'été	Bil
Delvaux, A.	Sonatine. 1956	CBD
Depelsenaire, J.	Danse du Chale	E-V
Depelsenaire, J.	Sur l'Albaicin	Com
Deslandres, A.	Introduction and Polonaise	ALe
Desmarets, A.-Bleuzet	Gavotte and Bourrée (Circe)	ALe
Desportes, E.	Pastorale Joyeuse	EdS
Desportes, E.	Pastorale Melanèsque	EdS
Desportes, Y.	Matin d'été	ALe
Desportes, Y.	Sérénade des oiseaux	ALe
Desprez, F.	Apaisement	Mau
Destouches, A.-Bleuzet	Pastorale and Passepied (Issé)	ALe
Devienne, F.-Pierlot	6 Sonates (2 suites)	Bil
Devreese, F.	Complainte	EMb
Diémer, L.	Légend, op. 52	ALe
Diémer, L.	2 Pièces, op. 35	Dur
Diercks, J.	Sonata	TP
Dillon, R.	Scherzo	B&H
Dindale, E.	Bucolique	EMb
Dindale, E.	Canzonetta	EMb
Dindale, E.	Danse Paysanne	EMb
Dindale, E.	Lied	EMb
Dittersdorf, K. von-Rhau	Concerto, G	BrH
Dodgson, S.	Suite, D	OxU
Dondeyne, D.	Chanson Espagnole	EMT
Donizetti, G.-Meylan	Sonata, F	Pet
Donjon, J.-Medicus	Invocation	CF
Donjon, J.	Offertory	GD
Douane, J.	Andante et danse	Com
Draeger, W.	3 Miniatures	FrH
Dranishnikova, M.	Poem	MKE
Drejsl, R.	Fête de la Moisson	Pan
Drejsl, R.	Donzinkova suita	Art
Drejsl, R.	Erntefest-Suite	Art
Drigo, R.	Andantino Idillico	CF
Drigo, R.-Damm	Serenade	CF
Dubois, P.	Ballade Médiévale	ALe
Dubois, P.	Berceuse a Gigi	ERR
Dubois, P.	Dialogues Canadiens	ALe
Dubois, P.	Gafsa sonatine	ECh
Dubois, P.	Neuf esquisses	ECh
Dubois, P.	Passepied	ALe
Dubois, P.	Promenons-nous dans l'hautbois	ALe
Dubois, P.	Sonatina	ALe
Dubois, P.	2 Paysages	ALe

Oboe and Piano or Harpsichord

Dubois, P.	Variations	ALe
Duck, L.	Impressions	OxU
Duijck, G.	Caprice	EMb
Dukas, P.-Gillet	Alla Gitana	ALe
Duke, V.	Variations on an Old Russian Chant	BB
Duport, F.	Romance	Spr
Durand, A.	1st Valse	Dur
Durand, E.	Le Biniou	EdS
Dutilleux, H.	Sonata	ALe
Duysburgh, F.	Elégie	Mau
Dvořak, A.	Largo (New World Symphony)	CF
Dvořak, A.-Isaac, Feldman	Slavonic Dance, op. 72/10	CF
Dvořak, A.	Songs My Mother Taught Me	GFB
East, R.	Siciliano	Bos
Eckard, W.-arr.	Highlights of Familiar Music	TP
Eder, H.	3 Pezzi Espressivi, op. 37. 1963	B&N
Edlefsen, B.	Allegretto	B-M
Edlefsen, B.	Caprice	B-M
Edlefsen, B.	Oboe soloist (Level 1)	B-M
Edlefsen, B.	Slow Dance	B-M
Edlefsen, B.-arr.	Sweet Nightingale	B-M
Edmondson, J.	Canzonetta	Ken
Edmondson, J.	Lament and Eulogy	Ken
Edmunds, C.	Andante	S&C
Edmunds, C.	High Summer	S&C
Edmunds, C.	Longing for Summer	S&C
Eichner, E.-Gerhardt	Concerto, Bb	FrH
Eichner, E.-Rothwell	Concerto	OxU
Elgar, E.-Trinkaus	Love's Greeting	CF
Elgar, E.-Akers	Pomp and Circumstance, op. 39/1	CF
Elgar, E.	Salut d'amour, op. 12	SS
Elliott, M.	3 Pieces	Che
Erdmann, D.	Sonata	HG
Erickson, F.-Best	Polka	B-M
Erickson, F.-Best	Prelude and Dance	B-M
Erickson, F.-Best	Sweet Dreams	B-M
Erickson, F.-Best	A Time to Remember	B-M
Etesse, E.	Sérénade	EdS
Etler, A.	Introduction and Allegro. 1952	AMP
Etler, A.	Sonata. 1952	AMP
Evans, E.	Spanish Eyes	CF
Evans, E.	Sweet and Dainty	CF
Evans, P.	Sonata	Che
Eymieu, H.	Pastorale	GD
Fargues, C.	Intermezzo	GD
Fargues, C.	Romance	GD
Fargues, C.	Souvenir	GD

Fasch, J.	Concerto, d	MV
Fasch, J.-Töttcher, Spannagel	Concerto, g	HSM
Fauré, G.	Berceuse	Ham
Fauré, G.	Pièce	ALe
Feld, J.	Burlesque	ALe
Feld, J.	3 Kompositionen	ES
Felton, W.-Curwin	Adagio and Allegro	Cha
Ferneyhough, B.	Coloratura	Pet
Ferte, A.	Fantasie on an Old Breton Air	EMT
Fesch, W. de-Kaplan	Canzonetta	Spr
Fiala, J.-Storch	Concerto, D, No. 1	B&H
Field, J.-Rothwell	Nocturne	Che
Field, J.	Notturno	MM
Fiocco, J.-Bent, O'Neill	Arioso	S&C
Fischer, J.-Carse	Concerto, C	GaM
Fischer, J.-Meylan	Konzert, Eb, No. 2	BrH
Fischer, J.-Bergmann	Divertissement (ob, bc)	S&C
Fischer, J.-Bergmann	Suite, G	S&C
Flegier, A.	Villanelle du Midi	EdM
Flemming, F.	25 Melodische Studien, 2 vols.	WZ
Flothuis, M.	Kleine suite, op. 47. 1952	SD
Flotow, F. von-Mayer	Ah! So Pure	B-M
Flowers, G.	A Plaintive Air	Nov
Foret, F.	Eglogue	Bil
Foret, F.	Grave et allegro giocoso	Bil
Foret, F.	Patres et rythmes champêtres	Bil
Foret, F.	Sonate, G	Bil
Forsman, J.	Andantino carino (Romance)	EdF
Förster, E.-Lauschmann	Concerto, e	For
Fortner, W.	Aulodie	SS
Foss, L.	Concerto	SMP
Françaix, J.	Flower Clock	EMT
Franck, C.	Pièce V	ALe
Franck, C.-Tustin	Pièce V	Spr
Francl, J.	Pastoral Suite	ES
Franco, J.	Pastorale	CoF
Fraser, S.	Prelude and Scherzino	B&H
Frensel Wegener, E.	Hobosuite. 1926	SD
Frensel Wegener, E.	Menuetto. 1929	SD
Frescobaldi, G.-Cerha	Canzonen (ob, bc)	LDo
Frešo, T.	Composition	SHF
Fricker, P.	4 Dialogues	OxU
Fried, G.	Melody, op. 22/2	MKE
Frotscher (ed)	Noels, 2 vols. (ob, bc)	Hei
Frumerie, G. de	Concertino, op. 54	CGM
Fuga, S.	Concertino	Ric
Funk, H.	Sonatina, op. 116	FrH
Fuste-Lambezat, M.	Cantilène	Com
Fuste-Lambezat, M.	Pièce en Forme de Danse	Com
Gaál, J.	Sonata. 1956	EMB

Oboe and Piano or Harpsichord

Gabaye, P.	Sonatina	ALe
Gabelles, G.	Aubade	Bil
Gabelles, G.	Cantilène	Com
Gabus, M.	Automne	HLe
Gal, H.	Sonata, op. 85	HE
Galliard, J.-Scheck, Ruf	Sonata, C, op. 1/1	Ric
Galliard, J.-Scheck, Ruf	Sonata, d, op. 1/2	Ric
Galliard, J.-Scheck, Ruf	Sonata, e, op. 1/3	Ric
Gallois-Montbrun, R.	Prélude	ALe
Gargiulio, T.	Concertino	Edi
Garimond, H.	Air suisse	Bil
Garlick, A.	Sonata da Chiesa	See
Gartenlaub, O.	Silhouette	ERR
Gaubert, P.	Intermède champêtre	ALe
Geiser, W.	Sonatine, op. 38. 1949	B&N
Geminiani, F.	Sonate, e (ob, bc)	B&N
Geminiani, F.-Vené	Sonata No. 1	Ric
Genzmer, H.	Kammerkonzert. 1957	SS
Georges, A.	Daphnis et Chloé	EdS
Geraedts, J.	Jan Klaassen-serenade. 1944	SD
Gerschefski, E.	"America" Variations for Winds, op. 45/7	CoF
Ghys, J.-Harris	Amaryllis & Country Gardens	Lud
Gibilaro, A.	4 Sizilianische Miniaturen	B&B
Gibilaro, A.-Rothwell	4 Sicilian miniatures	B-M
Gillis, D.	Courthouse Square	B&H
Girnatis, W.	Sonata	HSM
Gluck, C.-Bleuzet	Ballet (Pâris et Hélène)	ALe
Gluck, C.	Largo	Pet
Godard, B.-Trinkaus	Berceuse (Jocelyn)	CF
Godard, B.	Berceuse	NK
Godard, B.	Highlander's March	SM
Godard, B.	Légende Pastorale	Ham
Godard, B.	Légende Pastorale	SM
Godard, B.	Légende Pastorale	War
Godard, B.	Marche Highlanders	Ham
Godard, B.	Sérénade à Mabel	Ham
Godard, B.	Sérénade à Mabel	SM
Godron, H.	Suite Bucolique. 1939	SD
Goens	Scherzo	Ham
Goepfart, O.	Andante religioso, op. 22	WZ
Goeyens, A.	English Melody	HeE
Golestan, S.	Elégie et Danse rustique	Dur
Goossens, E.	Concerto in One Movement	ALe
Goossens, E.	Islamite Dance	ALe
Gorbulskis, B.	Concerto	MKE
Gorlov, W.	Suite	MKE
Gossec, F.-Johnson	Gavotte	Rub
Gounod, C.-Herman, Sabon	La Ciel a visité la terre	ECh
Gounod, C.-Herman, Sabon	Faust	ECh

Oboe and Piano or Harpsichord

Gounod, C.-Herman, Sabon	Mireille	ECh
Gounod, C.-Salter	Serenade (Le Médecin malgré lui)	OxU
Gover, G.	April Song	Che
Gow, D.	Romance, Bb	GaM
Granados, E.-Amaz	Spanish Dance No. 2. Oriental	UME
Granados, E.-Amaz	Spanish Dance No. 5. Andaluza	UME
Granados, E.-Amaz	Spanish Dance No. 6. Rondalla Aragonesa	UME
Grandval, C.	Concerto, op. 7	SM
Graun, J.-Tottcher	Concerto, c	HSM
Graves, R.	Alla Gigue	B&H
Green, H.	Berceuse	PMP
Green, H.	Elegy	Spr
Green, H.	Incantation	PMP
Green, H.	Sonata	PMP
Green, H.	Tropical Island	PMP
Gregoir, E.	Dernier pensée de Nicolo Paganini	ScF
Gretchaninoff, A.	Brimborions, op. 138	GaM
Gretchaninoff, A.	En Avant; Mazurka	GaM
Gretchaninoff, A.	La Demande; Le Soir	GaM
Gretchaninoff, A.	La Fête; Plainte	GaM
Gretchaninoff, A.	En Route!; Pastorale	GaM
Gretchaninoff, A.	Sévère Réprimande; L'Adieu	GaM
Gretchaninoff, A.	Travail du Matin; Une Journée Grise	GaM
Grétry, A.-Bleuzet	Ariette (Panurge)	ALe
Grétry, A.-Bleuzet	Duet (Le Tableau parlant)	ALe
Grétry, A.-Bleuzet	Romance (Le Huron)	ALe
Grieg, E.-Tustin	Anitra's Dance (Peer Gynt, op. 46/3)	Bar
Grieg, E.	At the Cradle, op. 68/5	Pet
Grieg, E.-Phillips	9 Norwegian Folksongs	OxU
Grieg, E.-Strauwen	Soir dans les montagnes	ScF
Grieg, E.-Johnson	Solvejg's Song	Rub
Groot, C. de	Concertino champêtre	SD
Groot, C. de	Concertino pastorale	SD
Groot, C. de	Sonatine pastorale. 1961	SD
Grovlez, G.	Sarabande et Allegro	ALe
Gruber -arr.	The Caissons Go Rolling Along	CF
Guarnieri, C.	Cançao Sertaneja	CF
Guerrini, G.	Arcadica	Edi
Guilhaud, G.	1st Concertino	Bil
Guilhaud, G.-Voxman	First Concertino	Rub
Guilhaud, G.-Andraud	1st Concertino	SM
Guilhaud, G.	4 Pièces, suite 1	Bil
Haas, J.	Ein Kränzlein Bagatellen, op. 23	SS
Haas, P.	Suite	ES
Habicht, G.	Sonatina	FrH

Haeyer, F. d'	Pastorale	EMe
Hand, C.	Aria and Giga	S&C
Hand, C.	Petite Suite Champêtre	B&H
Handel, G.-Rothwell	Air and Rondo	Che
Handel, G.-Bell	Aria	AlL
Handel, G.-Bell	Bourrée (Organ Concerto No. 7)	AlL
Handel, G.-Bell	Bourrée, G	AlL
Handel, G.	Celebrated Largo	Dur
Handel, G.-Andraud	Largo (5 Solos)	SM
Handel, G.-Hanson	Minuet and Allegretto	Lud
Handel, G.-Poston	Sleep	OxU
Handel, G.	Instrumental Concertos	SM
Handel, G.-Willner	3 Concertos, Bb, Bb, g	
	(Published separately)	B&H
Handel, G.-Bas	3 Concertos (Published	
	separately)	Bil
Handel, G.	Concerto, Bb	BrH
Handel, G.	Concerto Grosso, Bb, No. 8	SM
Handel, G.-Peters	Concerto, c	SM
Handel, G.-Stein	Concerto, Eb	Pet
Handel, G.-Bleuzet	Concerto, g	Bil
Handel, G.-Craxton, Goossens	Concerto grosso, G, No. 10	BrH
Handel, G.	Concerto, g	Int
Handel, G.-Voxman	Concerto, g	Rub
Handel, G.-Andraud	Concerto, g (5 Solos)	SM
Handel, G.-Wunderer	Concerto, g	UE
Handel, G.-Tustin	4 Sonatas	Sch
Handel, G.-Andraud	3 Sonatas (5 Solos)	SM
Handel, G.-Bleuzet	2 Sonatas	ALe
Handel, G.	Sonatas No. 1, No. 2	CF
Handel, G.-Pushechnikov	2 Sonatas	MKE
Handel, G.	Sonata, e, op. 1/1a, No. 1	BrH
Handel, G.	Sonata, e, op. 1/1b, No. 2	BrH
Handel, G.	Sonata, g, op. 1/2, No. 3	BrH
Handel, G.	Sonata, G, op. 1/5, No. 6	BrH
Handel, G.-Seiffert	Chamber Sonata, g, op. 1/6,	
	No. 7 (ob, bc)	BrH
Handel, G.-Glazer, Bodky	Chamber Sonata, c, op. 1/8,	
	No. 9 (ob, bc)	AMP
Handel, G.-Seiffert	Chamber Sonata, c, op. 1/8,	
	No. 9 (ob, bc)	BrH
Handel, G.-Seiffert	Chamber Sonata, g, op. 1/10	BrH
Handel, G.	Sonata, a, No. 17	BrH
Handel, G.-Dart, Bergmann	Sonata, Bb	S&C
Handel, G.-Stade	2 Sonatas, c, g	Pet
Handel, G.-Pierlot	Sonate, c	Bil
Handel, G.-Scheck, Ruf	Sonata, c (ob, bc)	Ric
Handel, G.	Sonata, F	EdM
Handel, G.-Pierlot	Sonata, g	Bil
Handel, G.-Scheck, Ruf	Sonata, g (ob, bc)	Ric

Handel, G.	Sonata	EdR
Handel, G.	Sonata No. 1	Spr
Hannay, R.	Lament	Roc
Hanson, H.	Pastorale, op. 38	CF
Hanus, J.	5 Impromptus, op. 45	Art
Hanus, J.	Short Story	Gen
Hanus, J.	Short Stories No. 2	Gen
Hanus, J.	Sonata, op. 61	Gen
Harris, F.	Gay Minuet	Lud
Harrison, P.	Chase a Shadow	GaM
Harty, H.	A la Campagne	GaM
Harty, H.	Chansonette	GaM
Harty, H.	Orientale	GaM
Hashagen, K.	Suite (ob, hpcd)	Hei
Hasse, J.	Canzone	EdM
Hasse, J.-Töttcher	Concerto, F	HSM
Hasse, J.-Joosen	Concerto, g	MM
Haydn, F.-Bleuzet	Adagio (Quartet No. 34)	ALe
Haydn, F.	Andante & Finale	MR
Haydn, F.	Capriccietto	Pet
Haydn, F.-Wunderer	Concerto, C	BrH
Haydn, F.-Rothwell	Concerto, C	OxU
Haydn, F.-Ruyssen	Divertissement	GD
Haydn, F.-Brearley	Larghetto	Cur
Haydn, F.-Bleuzet	Poco adagio (Quartet No. 42)	ALe
Haydn, F.	Serenade	CF
Haydn, F.-Strauwen	La 7e parole du Christ	ScF
Haydn, F.-Tustin	Trumpet Concerto	Sch
Haydn, F.-Muller	Sonatine	Mau
Head, M.	Elegiac Dance	B&H
Head, M.	Gavotte	B&H
Head, M.	Presto	B&H
Headington, C.	Sonatina	B&H
Healey, D.	Italian Notebook	Cha
Healey, D.	Partita Bizzara	Cha
Hedges, A.	Count Down	BrH
Hedwall, L.	Oboe Concerto	EMf
Heldenberg, A.	Allegro	HeE
Herbert, V.-Best	Gypsy Sweetheart	B-M
Hertel, J.-Winschermann	Partita I, C (ob, bc)	HSM
Hertel, J.-Winschermann	Partita No. 2 (ob, bc)	HSM
Hertel, J.-Winschermann	Partita No. 3 (ob, bc)	HSM
Hertel, J.	Partita, d, No. 3 (ob, hpcd)	Pet
Hervelois, C. d'	Suite	GD
Hess, W.	3 Pieces, op. 71	Pet
Hessenberg, K.	Capriccio	ALe
Hewson, R.	3 Andalusian Songs	OxU
Hidas, F.	Concerto. 1951	EMB
Hindemith, P.	Sonata. 1938	SS
Hlobil, E.	Allegro leggiero, op. 26b	Art

Hlobil, E.	Andante amabile	Art
Hlouschek, T.	Little Kaleidoskope	BrH
Hofmann, R.	10 Melodische Übungs- und	
	Vortragsstücke, op. 58	FrH
Holford, F	Dance for a Gnome	Che
Holford, F.	Pastorale and Goblin	Che
Holford, F.	Summer Madrigal	Che
Hollingsworth, S.	Sonata, op. 2	Sch
Hook, J.-Joosen	Engelse Sonate	MM
Horder, M.-Goossens	Variations on a Sussex Folk	
	Tune	HE
Horovitz, J.	Sonatina, op. 3	B-M
Hoskins, W.	Suite	CoF
Hotteterre, J.-Viollier	Sonata, D	ERS
Hotteterre, J.-Scheck, Ruf	Suite, D (ob, bc)	Ric
Houdy, P.	Prélude	ALe
Hubay, J.	Traumerei	NK
Huber, K.	Noctes intelligibilis. 1961	
	(ob, hpcd)	SS
Hudadoff & Spire-arr.	11 Classic Solos	PrA
Hudadoff, I.-arr.	15 Intermediate Solo Series	PrA
Hudadoff, I.-arr.	Marches	PrA
Hüe, G.	Petite pièce, G	ALe
Hughes-Jones, L.	Elegy and Scherzo	Che
Hugon, G.	Adagio	EMT
Hummel, J.	Adagio and Theme with	
	Variations, op. 102	Eul
Hummel, J.	Introduction, Theme and	
	Variations, op. 102	MR
Hurník, I.	Concerto	CHF
Hurrell, C.-arr.	Meadowland	Rub
Hurrell, C.	Peregrine	Rub
Hytinkoski, A.	Corn Flower	See
Ibert, J.	Escales No. 2	ALe
Ibert, J.	Symphonie Concertante	ALe
Iliff, J.	Syzygy	InM
Ilyinsky, A.	Lullaby	NK
Indy, V. d'	Fantaisie, op. 31	Dur
Ippolitov-Ivanov, M.-Isaac,		
Feldman	Excerpts (Caucasian Sketches)	CF
Istrate, M.	Sonata. 1964	EdR
Jacob, G.	Concerto No. 1	GaM
Jacob, G.	Concerto No. 2	GaM
Jacob, G.	Sonata	MR
Jacob, G.	Sonatina	OxU
Jacob, G.	10 Little Studies	OxU
Jakma, F.	Concertino	HeE
Jakma, F.	2e Concertino	T-M
Janáček, L.	Ballada	AM
Jarnefelt, A.-Pardee	Berceuse	Ken

Jeanjean, P.	Heureux temps	Bil
Jeanjean, P.	Remembrances	EdR
Jeanjean, P.	Rêverie de printemps	Bil
Jírovec, V.	Adagio	Art
Johnson, C.	Meditation	Rub
Jolivet, A.	Sérénade	Bil
Jongen, L.	Humoresque	ALe
Jordahl, R.	Lyric serenade	Ken
Kabeláč, M.	Sonatine, op. 24. 1955	Art
Kai, N.	Pastoral	ALe
Kalabis, V.	Suite. 1953	Art
Kalinnikov, V.	Chanson Triste	EdM
Kalliwoda, J.	Concertino, op. 110	MR
Kauder, H.	Sonata	SM
Kaufmann, A.	Sonatine, op. 53/4	LDo
Kay, U.	Brief Elegy	MCA
Keldorfer, R.	Concerto	LDo
Keldorfer, R.	Sonata ritmica	LDo
Kelemen, M.	Sonata	SS
Kelkel, M.	Sonatine, op. 9	HMo
Kelkel, M.	Toccata, op. 2/2	Ric
Kelly, B.	3 Bagatelles	Cha
Kelterborn, R.	Sonatina (ob, hpcd)	EMo
Kempe, H.	Serenad	STI
Kennan, K.	Scherzo, Aria and Fugato	SM
Kennaway, L.	Interrupted Serenade	HE
Kennaway, L.	Watersmeet	HE
Kersters, W.	Concertino, op. 2. 1953	CBD
Kersters, W.	Meditatie	Mau
Kesnar, M.	French Idyll	CF
Khandoshkin, I.-Soloduyev	Concerto for Viola	MKE
Kilpatrick, J.	Serenade	CoF
Kinyon, J.	Devotional Solos	War
Kinyon, J.	Recital Pieces	War
Kirkor, G.	Capriccio	MKE
Kirnberger, J.-Töttcher	Sonata, Bb	HSM
Kisielewski, S.	Suite	AP
Klemcke, L.-Voxman	Pastorale (Concerto)	Rub
Klucharev, A.	3 Pieces	MKE
Knight-Clement	Rocked in the Cradle of the Deep	Vol
Kocsar, M.	Saltus Hungaricus	B&H
Koepke, P.	On Quiet Waters	Rub
Kopelent, M.	Kleine Suite	Art
Korda, V.	Pastorale	LDo
Korda, V.	Scherzo	LDo
Korevaar, A.	Air Ancien	B&V
Kořínek, M.	Sonatina. 1960	SHF
Kořínek, M.	2 Compositions. 1953	SHF
Korn, P.	Rhapsodie	B&N

Oboe and Piano or Harpsichord

Korn, P.	Sonata, op. 7	B&H
Kossenko, V.-Cybriwsky, Tyndall	Gavotte	Spr
Kracke, H.	Sonata. 1962	BrH
Kramar-Krommer, F.	Concerto, F, op. 36	ES
Kramar-Krommer, F.-Weelink	Concerto, F, op. 37	B&V
Krebs, J.-David	Fantasie, f	BrH
Krenek, E.	Andante and Allegretto on Themes by Handel	B-M
Krenek, E.	4 Stücke. 1966	B&N
Kroeger, K.	Concerto da Camera	CoF
Kronke, E.	Suite im alten Stil, op. 160	WZ
Kropfreiter, A.	3 Stücke	LDo
Kubizek, A.	Sonate. 1955	LDo
Kuhlau, F.	Menuett	NK
Kummer, H.	Eine Handvoll Feldblumen, 7 Stücke, op. 33	WZ
Labate, B.	Barcarolle	CF
Labate, B.	Canzona	CF
Labate, B.	Concertino	Spr
Labate, B.	Dancing Doll	Spr
Labate, B.	Habanera	CF
Labate, B.	Minuetto	CF
Labate, B.	Pastorale	CF
Labate, B.	Pomposo	CF
Labate, B.	Romanesque	Spr
Labate, B.	Seguidilla	CF
Labate, B.	Strolling	CF
Labate, B.	"Sunset" and "Rondo"	Sch
Labate, B.	Tarantella	CF
Labate, B.	Villanella	CF
Labate-Findlay-arr.	Oboists Repertoire Album, 2 vols.	CF
Lacome, P.-Haring	Aubade à la Mariée	E&C
Lalliet, T.	Fantaisie Originale	Bil
Lamote de Grignon, J.-Amaz	Canço de Maria	UME
Lamote de Grignon, J.-Amaz	Rêverie (Schumanniana)	UME
Lamy, F.	Rustique	ALe
Lamy, F.	Pastorales variées	Dur
Langenus, G.-Verroust	To A Poppy	CF
Langley	Chansonette	HE
Lapis, S.-Ruf	3 Leichte Sonaten, op. 1/3, 4, 8 (ob, bc)	SS
Lara, A.	Granada	SMP
Larsson, L.	Concertino, op. 45/2	CGM
Latham, W.	Sonata No. 1	Spr
Latham, W.	Sonata No. 2	Spr
Laurischkus, M.	Studiensonate, c, op. 31	FrH
Lavigne, A.-Hillemann	Sonata, C, op. 2/1 (La Barssan) (ob, bc)	Hei

Lavigne, A.-Hillemann	Sonata, c, op. 2/2 (La d'Acut) (ob, bc)	Hei
Lavigne, A.-Hillemann	Sonata, C, op. 2/3 (La Dubois) (ob, bc)	Hei
Lavigne, A.-Hillemann	Sonata, C, op. 2/4 (La Beaumont) (ob, bc)	Hei
Lavigne, A.-Hillemann	Sonata, G, op. 2/5 (La Persan) (ob, bc)	Hei
Lavigne, A.-Hillemann	Sonata, G, op. 2/6 (La Simianne) (ob, bc)	Hei
Lawton, S.	The Young Oboist, 3 vols.	OxU
Lazarus, D.	Invention	ChM
Le Boucher, M.	Fantaisie Concertante	ALe
Leclair, J.	Sarabande and Tambourin	Pet
Leclair, J.-Redel	Concerto, C, op. 7/3	Leu
Leclair, J.-Scheck, Ruf	Concerto, C, op. 7/3	Ric
Lecuona, E.-Simon	Andalucia	EBM
Lecuona, E.-Simon	Malaguena	EBM
Leduc, J.	Concertino, op. 10. 1962	CBD
Lees, B.	Concerto	B&H
Lefèbvre, C.-Andraud	Andante and Allegro, op. 106	SM
Lefèbvre, C.	2 Pièces	Dur
Le Fleming, C.	Air and Dance	Che
Leichtling, A.	Oboe Sonata	AMC
Lely	Capricietto	GrF
Lemare, E.-Trinkaus	Andantino	CF
Lemare, E.-Long	Andantino	Vol
Lenom, C.	Canzonetta	EdS
Lenom, C.	Caprice-Mazurka	EdS
Lenom, C.-Findlay	Lullaby	CF
Lenom, C.	Musette	EdS
Lenom, C.	Musette	SM
Lentz	Kishore	Tem
Leschetizky, T.	Variations on a theme of Beethoven	SS
Lester	Romance Exotique	Wes
Lethbridge, L.-arr.	Mélodies de France	OxU
Levy, E.	Divertimento. 1952	See
Lewallen, J.	Moon Child	B-M
Lewallen, J.	Watergirl Blues	B-M
Liviabella, L.	Adagio, Pastorale e Scherzo	GZ
Liszt, F.-Balassa	Notturno, op. 1	EMB
Loeillet, J.-Rothwell	Sonata, C	Che
Loeillet, J.-Beon	Sonata, G	Int
Loeillet, J.B.-Ruf	Sonata, g (ob, bc)	SS
Loeillet, J.	Sonata, op. 5/1 (ob, bc)	MR
Loeillet, J.-Ruf	Sonata, Bb, op. 3/9 (ob, bc)	Ric
Loeillet, J.	Sonata, D, op. 3/11 (ob, bc)	ALe
Loeillet, J.	Sonata, E	HLe
Loeillet, J.	Sonata, e	MR

Oboe and Piano or Harpsichord

Loeillet, J.	Sonata, G	HLe
Lombard, M.	Cadences pour un Sylphie	ALe
Longmire, J.	Reverie	B&H
Longo, A.	Sonatina	EDS
Lorenzo, L. de	Giovalita	CF
Lovreglio, E.	Morning Call	GD
Ludewig, W.	Essay. 1968-69	B&B
Luening, O.	3 Nocturnes	CoF
Luigini, A.	Romance	GD
Lully, J.-Bleuzet	Air tendre et Courante	ALe
Lully, J.	Dances for the King	EdM
Lully, J.-Bleuzet	Pavane (Ballets du Roi)	ALe
Lully, J.-Bleuzet	Saraband and Passepied (Isis)	ALe
Maasz, G.	Concertino	HSM
MacDowell, E.-Edlefsen	To a Wild Rose	B-M
MacDowell, E.	To A Wild Rose	NK
MacDowell, E.-Hurrell	To A Wild Rose	Rub
MacMahon, D.	Northumbrian Suite	Elk
Maconchy, E.	3 Bagatelles (ob, hpcd)	OxU
Maganini, Q.	Concert Album	EdM
Maganini, Q.	4 Miniatures for Young Players	EdM
Maganini, Q.	Paris Soir	EdM
Mahy, A.	Bourrée, Cadenze e Finale	MM
Mai, P.	Concertino	FrH
Makovsky, L.	Concertino	LDo
Malipiero, G.	Impromptu Pastoral	ALe
Malipiero, R.	Sonata	ESZ
Mamlok, U.	Capriccios. 1968	See
Manziarly, M. de	Periple	Bil
Marais, M.-Kestner	Menuette (Pièces de viole)	FrH
Marais, M.-Craxton	3 Old French Dances	Che
Marcelin, E.	Andante and Musette	ALe
Marcello, A.-Vené	Concerto, c	Ric
Marcello, A.-Bonelli	Concerto, c	GZ
Marcello, A.-Lauschmann	Concerto, c	Int
Marcello, A.	Concerto, c	SM
Marcello, A.-Joosen	Concerto, c	MM
Marcello, B.-Rothwell	Largo and Allegretto	Che
Marcello, B.-Tassinari, Toma	12 Sonatas, op. 2, 2 vols. (ob, bc)	EDS
Marcello, B.-Martucci, Veggetti	4 Sonatas	EDS
Marez, Oyens, T. de	Deducties. 1964 (ob, hpcd)	SD
Margola, F.	Piccolo Concerto	Car
Marie, G.	Chant pastoral	Bil
Marie, G.	La Cinquantaine, Air dans le style ancien	Sch
Marpurg, F.-Scarmolin	Minuet	Lud
Marpurg, F.-Scarmolin	Rondo	Lud
Martelli, H.	Adagio, Cadenza & Finale,	

	op. 71	EME
Martinu, B.	Concerto	EME
Mascagni, P.-Best	Intermezzo	B-M
Massenet, J.-Edlefsen	Elegie	B-M
Massenet, J.-Trinkaus	Elegy	CF
Massenet, J.	Mélodie-Elégie des Erinnyes	Job
Massenet, J.	The Virgin's Last Slumber	CF
Matěj, J.	Sonata da camera	Art
Matthes, C.-Spannagel, Töttcher	Sonata, C	HSM
Matthus, S.	Musik fur Oboeninstrumente und Klavier (ob/ehn/ob d'amore/schalmei,pf)	Deu
Matz, A.	Sonata	Pet
Maurat, E.	Petites Inventions, op. 39/2	EME
Mazellier, J.	Thème varié languedocien	EdS
McBride, R.	Workout	CoF
McClellan, R.	Arioso	Wes
Meacham, F.-Kent	American Patrol	CF
Melant, C.	N'effrayons pas les Tourterelles	ScF
Mellnäs, A.	Sonat. 1957	STI
Mendelssohn, F.	Mosquito Dance	NK
Mendelssohn, F.-Trinkaus	Nocturno	CF
Mendelssohn, F.-Weber	On Wings of Song	B-M
Mendelssohn, F.	On Wings of Song	CF
Mendelssohn, F.	On Wings of Song	NK
Mendelssohn, F.-Zverov	Song without Words, op. 19/2	SM
Mendelssohn, F.-Bleuzet	Romances sans paroles No. 15	ALe
Mendelssohn, F.-Bleuzet	Romances sans paroles No. 19	ALe
Merkù, P.	Variations on Primož Ramovš's theme	EdD
Mersson, B.	3 Monkey Dances, op. 19	EMo
Meulemans, A.	Concerto No. 1. 1942	CBD
Meunier, G.	Andantino	Com
Meyer	Sailor's Hornpipe	B-M
Meyer, J.	Pavane Française	GD
Meyerbeer, G.-Trinkaus	Coronation March	CF
Mezzacapo, E.	Le Chant du Gondolier	EdS
Mezzacapo, E.	Tristesse	EdS
Michael, E.	Elegy	Ric
Middeleer, J. de	Recitativo e allegro. 1970	CBD
Mieg, P.	Concerto. 1957	SS
Mielenz, H.	Schelmische Amoretten	R&E
Migot, G.	Fantaisie 2	EdO
Migot, G.	La Malouve (Sonate a danser)	ALe
Milhaud, D.	Concerto	Heu
Milhaud, D.	Sonatine	Dur
Milhaud, D.	Stanford Serenade	EME
Milwid, A.	Sinfonia concertante	AP

Oboe and Piano or Harpsichord

Mitscha	Sonatina	AP
Molique, B.-Gugel	Concertino	BrH
Monfeuillard, R.	Mélopée et scherzo	Bil
Monti, V.-Roberts	Csardas	CF
Moortel, A. van de	Improvisation sur un thème de choral, op. 41	ScF
Moreau, L.	Évocations Rythmiques	ALe
Moreau, L.-Taunay	Pastorale	ALe
Morra, G.	Nocturnal Serenade	CF
Morra, G.	Romantique	CF
Mortensen, O.	Sonata	WH
Mouquet, J.	Bucolique	ALe
Mourant, W.	Air and Scherzo	AMP
Mozart, W.-Harris	Adagio (Clarinet Concerto)	CF
Mozart, W.-Rochon	Adagio, K. 411	HeE
Mozart, W.	Adagio, KV 411	MM
Mozart, W.-Andraud	Adagio Religioso	SM
Mozart, W.-Hautvast	Adagio en Romance	T-M
Mozart, W.-Scarmolin	Allegretto	Lud
Mozart, W.-Edlefsen	Allegro (Divertimento No. 3)	B-M
Mozart, W.-Hanson	Allegro	Lud
Mozart, W.-Bleuzet	Andante (Piano Sonata, C)	ALe
Mozart, W.-Isaac	Andante (Piano Sonata No. 1)	CF
Mozart, W.-Bleuzet	Andante with variations (Quartet, A)	ALe
Mozart, W.-Cole	Andantino (Divertimento No. 14)	TP
Mozart, W.-Paumgartner	Concerto, K. 314	B&H
Mozart, W.-Baudo	3 Cadenzas for the Concerto, K. 314 (285)	ALe
Mozart, W.-DeLancie	3 Cadenzas for K. 314	B&H
Mozart, W.	Concerto, Eb	CF
Mozart, W.-Bleuzet	Idyll (Les Petits Riens)	ALe
Mozart, W.-Bleuzet	Larghetto (La Clemenza di Tito)	ALe
Mozart, W.-Bleuzet	Minuet (Divertimento, D)	ALe
Mozart, W.-Voxman	Pantomime (Les Petits Riens)	Rub
Mozart, W.-Goossens	Sonata, K. 370	B&H
Mozart, W.-Rothwell, Craxton	Oboe Quartet, KV 370	Che
Mozart, W.-Hodgson	Oboe Quartet, F, K. 370	Pet
Mozart, W.-Desportes	Concertino (Oboe Quartet), K. 370	SM
Mozart, W.-Slavinsky	Sonata for Violin	MKE
Mozart, W.-Muller	Sonatine	Mau
Mozart, W.-Rothwell	2 Songs	Che
Müller, S.	Sonate, Eb, op. 52	BrH
Müller-Lampertz, R.	Kleines Konzert	PG
Mulder, H.	Sonata op. 39, No. 1. 1934	SD
Murray, D.-arr.	Oboe-Album Klassischer Stücke	S&C

135

Oboe and Piano or Harpsichord

Nagy, F.	Zigany	Lud
Naudot, J.-Favre	1re Fête Rustique	ERS
Naumann, E.	Variations-Suite	B&B
Nave, A.	The Cuckoo	CF
Nave, A.	Serenade	CF
Nemiroff, I.	Concerto	M&M
Neukomm, S.-Kaplan	Aria	Spr
Nicholas, M.	Melody	Che
Nicholas, M.	Rhapsody	Che
Nielsen, C.	Fantasy Pieces, op. 2	WH
Nielsen, C.-Andraud	Romance and Humoresque	SM
Niverd, L.	Élégie	Bil
Niverd, L.	Mélopée et danse	ALe
Niverd, L.	Musette et tambourin	EdR
Niverd, L.	Pastourelle	GD
Niverd, L.	6 Pièces brèves	Com
Niverd, R.	Concertino	GD
Noble, H.	Recitative	S&C
Norden, H.	Serenade	Ken
Novák, M.	3 Compositions	SHF
Nowak, L.	Sonata	CoF
Nuyens, H.	Souvenir de Bohême	ScF
Odegard, P.	Sonatina	M&M
Ohana, M.	Neumes	Amp
Olcott, C.	My Wild Irish Rose	NK
Organn, R.	The Brook	Reb
Organn, R.	Falling Leaves	Reb
Organn, R.	Idledale	Reb
Organn, R.	Janina	Reb
Organn, R.	Serenade	Reb
Organn, R.	Serenade et Danse	Reb
Organn, R.	Solitude	Reb
Organn, R.	Valenciennes	Reb
Ortolani, O.	More (Theme from Mondo Cane)	EBM
Ostransky, L.	Aria and Dance	Rub
Paderewski, I.-Trinkaus	Minuet a l'Antique	CF
Painter, P.	Petite Pastorale	CF
Pala, J.	Bonjour	MM
Paladilhe, E.-Voxman	Concertante	Rub
Paladilhe, E.	Solo	Heu
Pangaert d'Opdorp	Les Echos, op. 25	ScF
Paradis, H.	Pastel Menuett	NK
Paradis, H.	Sicilienne	NK
Parcham, A.-Dart	Solo	OxU
Parès, G.	Crépuscule	Bil
Parès, G.-Judy	Crépuscule (Twilight)	Rub
Parrott, I.	Minuet	S&C
Partzkhaladze, M.	2 Pieces	MKE
Pascal, A.	Theme and Variations	GD

Pascal, C.	Pièce	Dur
Pascal, C.	Sonate brève en 2 mouvements. 1966	Dur
Pasculli, A.	Le Api	M&M
Pasfield, W.	Humoresque	GaM
Passani, E.	Pastorale	Com
Pauer, J.	Capricci	ES
Pauer, J.	Konzert	Art
Paulson, G.	Ballad, op. 52b	STI
Paulson, G.	Concerto No. 1	EMf
Paulson, G.	Concerto No. 2	EMf
Paulson, G.	Divertimento, op. 119c. 1962	STI
Paulson, G.	Sonat, op. 64	STI
Payne, F.	Images I and II	Sha
Paynter, J.	3 Pieces	OxU
Pearson, W.	A Haydn Suite	Cha
Pearson, W.	Scherzando and Adagio	Cha
Pedrollo, A.	Concertino	GZ
Pepusch, J.-Ruyssen	Sonata	GD
Pergolesi, G.-Barbirolli	Concerto	OxU
Pergolesi, G.-Elkan	Se Tu M'Ami	HeE
Pergolesi, G.-Johnson	Siciliana	Rub
Perilhou, A.	Passepied	Heu
Peter, H.	Bagatelle	AMP
Peter, H.	Pastorale	AMP
Petit, A.	Doux rêve	EdS
Petit, A.	Gracieux babil	EdS
Petit, A.	Historiette	EdS
Petric, I.	Sonatina	EdD
Pfeuffer, W.	Menuett, op. 37	PG
Philidor, F.-Bleuzet	Chant d'Eglise	ALe
Philidor, P.-Boulay	Suite (ob, bc)	EMT
Phillips, I.	9 Norwegian Folk-songs	OxU
Pierné, G.	Pièce in G minor, op. 5	ALe
Pierné, G.-Edlefsen	Pièce, g	B-M
Pierné, G.	Pièce in G Minor	CF
Pierné, G.	Sérénade, op. 7	ALe
Pierné, P.	Fantaisie pastorale	Bil
Pilss, K.	Sonata, e	LDo
Pisk, P.	Arabesque, op. 102/1	CoF
Pisk, P.	Berceuse Slave	B-M
Pisk, P.	Idyll, op. 86/2	AMP
Pisk, P.	Shanty-Boy	AMP
Pisk, P.	Suite	PIC
Piston, W.	Suite	ECS
Pitfield, T.	Sonata, a	GaM
Planel, R.	Chanson Romantique	ALe
Planel, R.	Prelude and Dance	ALe
Platonov, N.	Sonata	MKE
Platti, G.-May	Concerto, G	SS

Platti, G.-Winschermann	Concerto, g	HSM
Poot, M.	Capriccio. 1928	CBD
Porpora, N.-Marx, Maynard	Sinfonia, d	M&M
Porret, J.	3e Solo de Concours	MM
Porret, J.	4e Solo de Concours	MM
Porret, J.	Concertino No. 13	EdR
Porret, J.	Concertino No. 14	EdR
Poser, H.	Sonata, op. 9	HSM
Poser, H.	Sonatina	HSM
Pcspisil, J.	2 Compositions	SHF
Poulenc, F.	Sonata	Che
Presser, W.	Sonata	TP
Prestini, G.	Concerto, d	Bon
Prowo, P.-Lauschmann	Sonata, A (ob, bc)	For
Purcell, H.	Dance Suite	EdM
Purcell, H.	Nymphs and Shepherds	NK
Purcell, H.-Edmunds	Princess of Persia Incidental Music	CF
Purcell, H.	Suite (Orpheus Britannicus)	Che
Purcell, H.-Revell	2 Pieces	B&H
Pushechnikov, I.-comp.	Anthology of Teaching Repertoire, Pt. 2, 2 vols.	MKE
Pushechnikov, I. & Krein, M.	32 Easy Pieces	MKE
Quantz, J.-Sonntag	6 Sonatas, op. 2	WMS
Quantz, J.-Hinnenthal	Sonate, D (ob, bc)	B&N
Rachyunas, A.	Sonatina	MKE
Radauer, I.	Duo concertante	EMo
Raff, J.	Tarentelle	Dur
Rakov, N.	Sonata	MKE
Ralston, A.	3 English Folk Tunes	B&H
Rameau, J.	Gavotte (Temple de la Gloire)	Pet
Rameau, J.-Burmester	Gavotte	S&C
Rameau, J.	Minuet and Passepied	Pet
Rameau, J.	Tambourin	NK
Rameau, J.-Rothwell	Les Tendres Plaintes	Che
Rameau, J.-Scarmolin	La Villageoise	Lud
Ramovs, P.	Ricercare (on Pavle Merkù's theme)	EdD
Ranger, A.-arr.	The Old Refrain	CF
Ránki, G.	Don Quijote y Dulcinea. 1961	EMB
Raphael, G.	Sonate, b, op. 32. 1931	BrH
Raphael, G.	Sonatina, op. 65/2. 1948	BrH
Raphling, S.	Pastorale	Gen
Raphling, S.	Sonata	Spr
Ravel, M.	Pavane pour une Infante Défunte	EdM
Ravel, M.-Piguet	Pavane pour une Infante défunte	EME
Ravel, M.-Hurrell	Pavane	Rub
Ravel, M.	Pavane	SS
Ravel, M.	Pièce en forme de Habanera	ALe

Rawsthorne, A.	Concerto	OxU
Reed, A.	Concertino	CF
Reger, M.-Piguet	Romanze, G	BrH
Reicha, A.	Air	M&M
Reizenstein, F.	Sonatina	AlL
Reizenstein, F.	3 Concert Pieces	B&H
Reutter, H.	Pastorale de Noël	ALe
Revel, P.	Eglogue	ECh
Reynolds, V.	3 Elegies	MCA
Richardson, A.	Aria and Allegretto	Che
Richardson, A.	French Suite	OxU
Richardson, A.	Reverie	GaM
Richardson, A.	Roundelay	OxU
Richardson, A.	Scherzino, op. 23	GaM
Richardson, L.	3 Dances	Ken
Richardson, N.	6 Oboe Solos	B&H
Riegger, W.	Duos, op. 35	TP
Rimsky-Korsakov, N.	Hummelflug	BrH
Rimsky-Korsakov, N.-Bettoney	Hymn to the Sun	CF
Rimsky-Korsakov, N.-Isaac, Feldman	Scheherezade	CF
Rimsky-Korsakov, N.-Edlefsen	Song of India	B-M
Rimsky-Korsakov, N.-Isaac	Song of India (Sadko)	CF
Rimsky-Korsakov, N.	Song of India	Rub
Rimsky-Korsakov, N.-Pierlot	Variations	Bil
Rimsky-Korsakov, N.-Hall	Variations	B&H
Rimsky-Korsakov, N.-Marx	Variations on a Theme of M. Glinka	M&M
Rivier, J.	Concerto	EMT
Rivier, J.	Improvisation and Final	ALe
Robbins, G.	Regattas	ALe
Robbins, G.	Sonatina	ALe
Robert, C.	Concerto	T-M
Rochberg, G.	La Bocca della verita	ImV
Roesgen-Champion, M.	Nocturno	ALe
Roesgen-Champion, M.	2nd Nocturno	ALe
Roland-Manuel, A.	Fantasy	EdS
Romero	Primer solo original	UME
Ropartz, G.	Adagio	EdS
Ropartz, G.	Lamento	EdS
Ropartz, G.	Pastorale and Dance	B-M
Ropartz, G.	Pastorale et Danses	E&C
Rorem, N.	Mountain Song	PIC
Rosetti, F.	Concerto, C, No. 1	MR
Rosetti, F.-Koch	Concerto, C	Pet
Rota, N.	Elegy	ALe
Rougnon, P.	Allegro Symphonique	Ham
Rougnon, P.	Rêverie	Ham
Roussel, A.	Aria	ALe
Rovics, H.	Composition (ob, hpcd)	CoF

Rowley, A.	Pavan and Dance	B&H
Roxburgh, E.	Images	JB
Roye, E. de	Canzonetta	EMe
Rubbra, E.	Sonata, C, op. 100	AlL
Rubin, M.	Sonatina. 1927	LDo
Rubinstein, A.	Romance	SF
Rubinstein, A.-Long	Romance	Vol
Rudolf, B.	Concertino	LDo
Ruyneman, D.	Sonatina. 1952	SD
Saint-Saens, C.	Le Déluge, Prélude	Dur
Saint-Saens, C.	Etienne Marcel, Pavane	Dur
Saint-Saens, C.-Edlefsen	My Heart at thy Sweet Voice	B-M
Saint-Saens, C.-Piguet	"O beaux rêves évanouis"	Dur
Saint-Saens, C.	Prosperpine, Pavane	Dur
Saint-Saens, C.	Rêverie du soir (Suite algérienne)	Dur
Saint-Saens, C.	Romance, op. 51	Dur
Saint-Saens, C.	Sonate, op. 166	Dur
Saint-Saens, C.-Isaac, Feldman	The Swan (Carnival of the Animals)	CF
Saint-Saens, C.-Langenus	The Swan	CF
Saint-Saens, C.-Trinkaus	The Swan	CF
Saint-Saens, C.	Le Cygne	Dur
Samazeuilh, G.	Esquisse d'Espagne	Dur
Sambin, V.	Duo de la Somnambule	EdS
Sammartini, G.	Concerto No. 1	Sch
Sammartini, G.-Rothwell	Sonata, G	Che
Sammartini, G.-Ruf	Sonata, G, op. 13/4 (ob, bc)	SS
Sancan, P.	Sonatine	Dur
Sandre, G.	Pastorale	Ham
Sarada	Andante Grazioso	Wat
Sarada	Ballade	Wat
Sarada	Serenade	Wat
Sauget, H.	Sonatine aux bois	ALe
Saunders, R.	Round the Clock	GaM
Scarlatti, A.-Ewerhart	2 Sonatas, G, F (ob, bc)	WMS
Scarlatti, D.-Bryan	Concerto, G, No. 1	Che
Scarlatti, D.-Bell	Tempo di Gavotta	AlL
Schaefers, A.	Concerto, op. 20. 1953	B&B
Schaffrath, C.-Ruf	Duetto, Bb (ob, hpcd)	Hei
Schibler, A.	Lyrische Musik, op. 12b. 1947-56	A&S
Schibler, A.	Lyrische Musik, op. 12c	A&S
Schickele, P.	Gardens	AlB
Schilling, H.	Suite	HMo
Schlemm, G.	Pastorale und Scherzo	WZ
Schlemm, G.	Sonatine	R&E
Schmitt, F.	Andantino	ALe
Schmutz, A.	Nocturne	B-M
Schollum, R.	Sonatine, op. 55/2	LDo

Schollum, R.	Sonatine, op. 68/1	LDo
Schollum, R.	Sonatine, op. 68/2, No. 3	LDo
Schouwman, H.	Sonatine. 1940	SD
Schouwman, H.	2nd Sonatine, op. 38. 1944	SD
Schouwman, H.	3 Oud-Nederlandse minne-liederen, op. 42	SD
Schroeder, H.	Concerto, op. 34	WMS
Schroeder, H.	Sonata	HG
Schubert, F.-Bleuzet	Ave Maria	ALe
Schubert, F.	Ave Maria	CF
Schubert, F.	Entr'act II (Rosamunde)	NK
Schubert, F.-Andreoni	Moment musical, op. 94/3	Ric
Schubert, F.-Bleuzet	Sérénade	ALe
Schubert, F.-Bleuzet	Suite de Valses, op. 9	ALe
Schubert, F.-Isaac	3 Themes	CF
Schule, B.	Spiel mit musikalischen Formen, op. 83	GBV
Schuller, G.	Sonata	M&M
Schumann, G.	Sonatine	S-V
Schumann, R.	Adagio and Allegro, op. 70	BrH
Schumann, R.-Bleuzet	Chanson du printemps (Album for the Young)	ALe
Schumann, R.	Einsame Blumen	Spr
Schumann, R.-Best	Humming Song	B-M
Schumann, R.-Edlefsen	Romance No. 1	B-M
Schumann, R.	3 Romanzen, op. 94	BrH
Schumann, R.	Romances, op. 94	GaM
Schumann, R.	3 Romances, op. 94	Pet
Schumann, R.-Schradieck	3 Romances, op. 94	Sch
Schwadron, A.	Gigue	Ken
Schwenke, C.-Lauschmann	Concerto	FrH
Scott, C.	Concerto	Elk
Sehlbach, E.	Kammermusik in 4 Sätzen, op. 105	MV
Seiber, M.	Improvisation. 1957	S&C
Seidel, J.	Concerto, No. 2. 1955	Art
Seletsky, H.	3 Pieces, op. 9. 1966	See
Semler-Collery, J.	Cantilène & Petit Divertissement	EME
Semler-Collery, J.	Récit and Scherzando	ALe
Serrette, F.	Dora, 3 Essais	EMT
Sherman, E.	Sonata, op. 39	PE
Shinohara, M.	Obsession	ALe
Shishakov, G.	2 Pieces	MKE
Sibelius, J.-Trinkaus	Valse Triste	CF
Siennicki, E.	Highland Heather	NK
Siennicki, E.	Memphis Ridge	NK
Siennicki, E.	Valse Ballet	Bar
Silva, P. de	Praeludium. 1968	B&B
Simons, N.	Facets 3	CoF

Oboe and Piano or Harpsichord

Siqueira, J.	3 Etüden	Deu
Skeat, W.	Morris Dance	B-M
Skorzeny, F.	Concerto	LDo
Slates, P.	Serenade	AMC
Slavický, K.	Suite. 1959-60	Art
Smith, D.	Sonata, op. 43	TP
Smolanoff, M.	In Memoriam	SM
Snyder, R.	Quiet Music. 1972	See
Snyder, R.	3 Miniatures	Wes
Söderlundh, L.	Concertino	EMf
Soloduyev, N.-comp.	7 Pieces by Russian Composers	MKE
Soloduyev, N.-comp.	8 Pieces by Soviet Composers	MKE
Soloduyev, N.	13 Pieces by Western Classical Composers	MKE
Soloduyev, N.	14 Easy Pieces by Western Classical Composers	MKE
Somers-Cocks, J.	Sonatina	GaM
Somers-Cocks, J.	3 Sketches	GaM
Soudère, V.	Stance & Mouvement Perpétuel	EME
Spadi, G.-Horsley, Davenport	Anchor Che Col Partire. Diminutions for a solo instrument on a Madrigal by de Rore	AMP
Spencer, W.	Adagio & Rondo	Wes
Spendiarov, A.-Stone	Chanson Elégiaque	SM
Spiréa, A.	Poem	ImV
Sporck, G.	Chanson d'Antan	EdR
Sporck, G.	Méditation	Bil
Sporck, G.	Novelette	Bil
Sporck, G.	Orientale	Bil
Sporck, G.	Rustique	Bil
Spurgin, A.	Discourse	B&H
Srámek, V.	Sonatine	ES
Stamitz, J.-Töttcher, Hartig	Concerto, C	HSM
Stamitz, K.-Schroeder	Concerto, Bb	BrH
Stamitz, K.-Wojciechowski	Concerto, Bb	Sim
Stanley, J.-Coleman	Suite	OxU
Starer, R.	Recitation	SMP
St. Clair, F.	Admiration	Vol
St. Clair, F.	Dream Time	Vol
St. Clair, F.	Golden Days	Vol
Steiner	Arab Chant	B-M
Stekke, L.	Burlesco	Bil
Still, W.	Incantation and Dance	CF
Stölzel, G.-Töttcher	Concerto, D	HSM
Stolz, R.	Shepherd's Prayer	B&H
Stolzenbach, L.	Sonata	Pet
Stone, G.	Hora Exotique	SM
Stone, M.	Little Sonnet	CoA

Oboe and Piano or Harpsichord

Stout, A.	Music	CoF
Stout, A.	Recitative	CoF
Strandsjö, G.	Concertino	EMf
Stratton, G.	Pastorale Concerto	Nov
Strauss, R. -Willner	Concerto	B&H
Strauwen, J.	Conte Pastoral	ScF
Strimer, J.	Pastorale caucasienne	Dur
Suppé, F. von -Long	Andante Maestoso (Poet and Peasant)	Vol
Švara	Fantasia	EdD
Swain, F.	Fantasy-Suite	Bou
Swain, F.	Paspy	Cha
Swain, F.	Tambourin Gai	Cha
Swinstead, F.	Pastorale	GaM
Sydeman, W.	Variations (ob, hpcd)	ECS
Sylvan, S.	Tema med variationer	STI
Szalowski, A.	Sonatina	Amp
Szeszler, T. (ed)	Album for Oboe	B-M
Szeszler, T.	Oboenmusik für Anfänger	EMB
Takács, J.	Sonata Missoulana, op. 66. 1958	LDo
Tansman, A.	Suite Concertante	EME
Tartini, G. -Ticciati	Andante Cantabile	OxU
Tartini, G. -Voxman	Andante Cantabile	Rub
Tartini, G. -Reff	Larghetto	GaM
Tartini, G. -Worley	Sarabanda	Spr
Tchaikovsky, P. -Tustin	Andante Cantabile (Quartet, op. 11)	Bar
Tchaikovsky, P. -Isaac, Feldman	Andantino (Symphony No. 4)	CF
Tchaikovsky, P. -Rothwell	The Canary	Che
Tchaikovsky, P. -Buchtel	Chanson Triste	NK
Tchaikovsky, P. -Porsch	Chant sans Parole	B&H
Tchaikovsky, P. -Hurrell	Danse Arabe (The Nutcracker Suite)	Rub
Tchaikovsky, P. -Trinkaus	Song without Words	CF
Tchaikovsky, P. -Erickson, Best	Sweet Dreams	B-M
Tchaikovsky, P. -Fote	Sweet Dreams	Ken
Tchaikovsky, P.	3 Pieces	EdM
Telemann, G. -Sirucek	Allegro	Hal
Telemann, G. -Barnes	Arie (Pimpinone)	Spr
Telemann, G. -Pätzold	Ein fröhlicher Tugendspiegel in 12 Märschen	MRL
Telemann, G. -Pätzold	Heldenmusik in 12 Märschen	MRL
Telemann, G. -Sirucek	Largo	Hal
Telemann, G. -Lauschmann	Little Chamber Music, 2 vols. (ob, bc)	Pet
Telemann, G. -Polnauer	6 Menuette (ob, bc)	SS
Telemann, G. -Stouffer	Minuet	Ken

Telemann, G.-Bergmann	Partita, G, No. 2	S&C
Telemann, G.-Andraud	4 Short Melodic Pieces	SM
Telemann, G.-Pätzold	15 Stücke (7 mal 7 und ein Menuett)	MRL
Telemann, G.-Bergmann	Wedding Divertissement	S&C
Telemann, G.	Concerto, A	Eul
Telemann, G.-Schlövogt	Concerto, c	SS
Telemann, G.-Töttcher	Concerto, d	HSM
Telemann, G.-Töttcher, Mueller	Concerto, e	HSM
Telemann, G.-Joosen	Concerto, F	MM
Telemann, G.-Stein	Concerto, f	Pet
Telemann, G.	Concerto, f	SM
Telemann, G.-Moehl	6 Partitas (ob, bc)	B&N
Telemann, G.-Harrison	Sonata, A	SM
Telemann, G.-Bleuzet	Sonata, a	ALe
Telemann, G. -Veyron-Lecroix, R.	Sonate, a	Bil
Telemann, G.-Andraud	Sonata, a	SM
Telemann, G.-Lauschmann	Sonata, Bb	HSM
Telemann, G.-Ruf	Sonata, Bb (Essercizii Musici) (ob, bc)	SS
Telemann, G.-Hinnenthal	Sonata, c (ob, bc)	BrH
Telemann, G.-Brüggen	Sonata, d	B&V
Telemann, G.-Lauschmann	Sonata, e	HSM
Telemann, G.-Ruf	Sonata, e (Essercizii Musici) (ob, bc)	SS
Telemann, G.-Brüggen	Sonata, F	B&V
Telemann, G.-Ruyssen, Bleuzet	Sonata, G	ALe
Telemann, G.-Seiffert	Sonata, g (ob, bc)	BrH
Telemann, G.-Schlövogt	Sonata, g	OxU
Telemann, G.-Bergmann	Sonata, g	S&C
Telemann, G.-Andraud	Sonata, g	SM
Telemann, G.-Töttcher, Scholz	Triosonate, Eb (ob, bc)	HSM
Templeton, A.	Scherzo Caprice	Sha
Tenaglia, A.	Aria	Pet
Thackray, R.-arr.	9 Short Pieces from Three Centuries	OxU
Thärichen, W.	Oboe Concerto, op. 46	B&B
Theophane, M.	Prelude and Allegro. 1959	Cre
Thilman, J.	Kleine Sonate	Pet
Thiry	Dialogue	MM
Thiry	Pont du Gard	MM
Thomé, F.	Simple aveu	Dur
Thomé, F.	Sous la feuillée	Dur
Ticciati, N.-Goossens	6 Pieces in Contrasting Style	OxU
Toduta, S.	Sonata	FrH
Toldrá, E.-Amaz	Ave Maria	UME

Toldrá, E.-Amaz	Dels Quatre Vents	UME
Toldrá, E.-Amaz	La Font	UME
Toldrá, E.-Amaz	Oracio al Maig	UME
Toldrá, E.-Amaz	Soneti de la Rosada	UME
Tomasi, H.	Chant Corse	ALe
Tomasi, H.	Concerto	ALe
Tomasi, H.	Danse agreste (5 danses profanes et sacrées)	ALe
Ton-That Tiét	5 Pièces	EMT
Touma, H.	"Sam'i"	Isr
Trinkaus, G.	Lament	CF
Trinkaus, G.-arr.	World's Best-Known Pieces	CF
Troubat, G.	Air Gai	Com
Trowbridge, L.	Homage to Chopin	See
Turner, R.	Sonatina. 1951	Can
Tustin, W.	Fantasia Romantica	Spr
Tustin, W.-arr.	Solos for the Oboe Player	Sch
Tuthill, B.	Sonata, op. 24	Spr
Uray, E.	Minnelied	LDo
Urbanner, E.	Concerto. 1966	LDo
Vachey, H.	Aria a variations	ALe
Vachey, H.	Cantilene and Valse	GD
Valentine, R.	3 Sonatas, d, G, g (ob,bc)	MRL
Valentine, R.-Lefkovitch, Bergmann	2 Sonatas, F, G	S&C
Vallier, A.	Sonatine	Bil
Vaughan Williams, R.	Concerto	OxU
Velde, van de	Romance	EdS
Velden, R. van der	Concerto. 1941	CBD
Vellère, L.	Dialogue	Mau
Ven, D. van der	Sonata	MM
Verdi, G.-Stone	Addio del Passato	SM
Verhaar, A.	Klein concert, op. 29. 1953	SD
Vernon, A.	Rhapsody	E-V
Verroust, S.	4th Solo de Concert	SM
Verroust, S.	Old Quebec	SM
Verroust, S.-Langenus	Premier Amour	CF
Verroust, S.-Langenus	To a Poppy	CF
Victory, G.	Esquisse	Nov
Vigneron, J.	Concertino	Mau
Vilec, M.	4 Compositions, op. 42. 1966	SHF
Vilec, M.	Summer notes. 1959	SHF
Villetard, A.	Sous les ombrages	Bil
Villette, P.	Romance	ALe
Villette, P.	Sérénade	ALe
Vincent, T.-Dawes	Sonata, D	S&C
Vivaldi, A.-Nagy, Szeszler	Concerto, a	EMB
Vivaldi, A.-Slavinsky	Concerto, a	MKE
Vivaldi, A.	Concerto, a	MR
Vivaldi, A.-Leskó	Concerto, a, F. VII, No. 5	Ric

Vivaldi, A.-Kolneder	Concerto, a	SS
Vivaldi, A.	Concerto, C	Eul
Vivaldi, A.	Concerto, C, op. 8/12	SS
Vivaldi, A.-Leskó	Concerto, D, F. VII, No. 10	Ric
Vivaldi, A.-Ephrikian	Concerto, d, F. VII, No. 1	Ric
Vivaldi, A.-Ephrikian	Concerto, F, F. VII, No. 2	Ric
Vivaldi, A.-Oubradous	Concerto, F, No. 5	EMT
Vivaldi, A.-Balla	Concerto, F, F. VII/12	Eul
Vivaldi, A.-Leskó	Concerto, F, F. VII, No. 12	Ric
Vivaldi, A.-Upmeyer	Il Pastor fido, op. 13.	
	6 Sonatas, C, C, G, A, C,	
	g (ob, bc)	B&N
Vivaldi, A.-Schlövogt	Sonata, c (ob, bc)	SS
Vivaldi, A.-Pierlot	Sonata, c, F. XV/2	Bil
Vivaldi, A.	2 Sonatas, F, d (ob, bc)	WMS
Vivaldi, A.-Brüggen	Sonate, F	B&V
Vivaldi, A.-Marx	Sonata, g	M&M
Vivaldi, A.	Rain	EdM
Vogt, G.	Concertino, F, No. 2	SM
Volkart-Schlager, K.	2 Kleine Sonatinen, g, a	WMS
Von Kreisler, A.	Sonatina	SM
Votquenne, V.	Fioriture	EMb
Voxman, H.-arr.	Concert and Contest	
	Collection	Rub
Wachs, P.	Danse bretonne	Ham
Wagner, J.	3 Pastorals	Wes
Wagner, R.-Schmeisser	Adagio	BrH
Wagner, R.	Dreams	CF
Wagner, R.-Trinkaus	Song to the Evening Star	CF
Wagner, R.-Trinkaus	Walther's Prize Song	CF
Wagner, R.-Buchtel	Walther's Prize Song	NK
Waldteufel, E.	España	E&C
Waldteufel, E.	Estudiantina	E&C
Walker, R.	2 Taureg Pieces	B-M
Wallner, L.	Elégie	ScF
Wallner, L.	3 Morceaux--Chant d'amour;	
	Mazurka; Rêverie	ScF
Walters, H.-arr.	Sakura, Sakura (Cherry	
	Blossoms)	Rub
Wanhal, J.	Concerto	OxU
Wanhal, J.-Tuthill	Sonata	M&M
Warren, D.	Meditation	Lud
Waters	Moorland Sketches	HE
Webber, C.-arr.	First Solo Album	TP
Webber, L.	The Woods at Penn	AHC
Weber, A.	Sonata	ALe
Weber, F.	Evening Shadows	B-M
Weber, F.	Sentimental Lady	B-M
Weemaels, L.	Clochettes	Mau
Weinberger, J.	Sonatine	CF

Wesly, E.	Rêverie d'automne	EdS
Westerfield, R.	Aire and Dance	Sha
Westerfield, R.	Nocturne and Dance	Sha
Wetterberg, K.	Pastorale	STI
Whettam, G.	3 Pieces	InM
Whitcomb, R.	Sonata in One Movement. 1961-62	Cre
White, C.	Basque Folk Song	B-M
Widerkehr, J.	Duo Sonata	MR
Widor, C.	Elégie	Ham
Widor, C.	Pastorale	Ham
Widor, C.	Pavane	SM
Wieniawski, H.	Romance	NK
Wiernsberger, J.	In the Boat	GD
Wigy, F.	Andante en Rondo	Mau
Wilder, A.-Diamond	Concerto	AMP
Wilder, A.	Sonata No. 1	SF
Wilhelmi, T.	Liten svit	EMf
Wilkinson, P.	Suite	Nov
Williams, S.	4 Whimsies	B&H
Willner, A.-arr.	Classical Album	B&H
Wisse, J.	Sonanze I. 1963	SD
Wohlgemuth, O.	Concertino	Pet
Wolf-Ferrari, E.	Idillio concertino, A, op. 15	Ric
Woollen, R.	Fantasy. 1962 (ob, hpcd)	CoF
Wordsworth, W.	Theme and Variations, op. 57	AIL
Wuorinen, C.	Composition	Pet
Wurmser, L.	Badinéries	Bil
Wurmser, L.	Barcarolle	Bil
Wurmser, L.	Fantasia	EMT
Wurmser, L.	Introduction et Danse	GrF
Wurmser, L.	Piècettes	Bil
Wurmser, L.	Tristesse	Com
Yakhnina, Y.	Concerto	MKE
Zach, J.-Klement	Concerto, Bb	ES
Zagwijn, H.	Pastorale. 1940	SD
Zamacois, J.	Serenada d'Hivern	UME
Zimmerman, R.-arr.	Play a Song of America	TP
Zimmerman, R.-arr.	Play a Song of Christmas	TP
Zimmermann, B.	Concerto. 1952	SS
Zipp, F.	Au clair de la lune. 1963	WMS
Zipp, F.	Concerto grosso, op. 29	WMS
Zonn, P.	Sonata	CoF
Zverev, V. (ed)	7 Pieces by Soviet Composers	MKE
Zverev, V.	Reminiscenses	MKE

Oboe and Organ

Badings, H.	Canzona	SD
Bottje, W.	Little Sonata (Version B). 1969	ACA

Brown, R.	Sonata	Wes
Hammarström, H.	Pastorale	EMf
Hovhaness, A.	Sonata	Pet
Kauffmann, G.-Gore	6 Chorales (Harmonische Seelenlust)	Con
Krebs, J.	Ausgewählte Orgelwerke, 3 Folge	Con
Krebs, J.	8 Chorale Preludes	TP
Kropfreiter, A.	2 Pieces. 1968	LDo
Pinkham, D.	Variations	Pet
Rheinberger, J.	Rhapsodie, op. 127	M&M
Rivier, J.	Aria	JB
Schroeder, H.	3 Dialoge	B&N
Verrall, J.	Serenade and Pastorale	PE
Weeks	Pastorale Morning	EdM

Oboe and Orchestra

Abaco, E. dall'-Winschermann	Concerto, C, op. 5/5	HSM
Albinoni, T.-Paumgartner	Concerto, Bb, op. 7/3	B&H
Albinoni, T.-Paumgartner	Concerto, D, op. 7/6	B&H
Albinoni, T.-Paumgartner	Concerto, F, op. 7/9	LDo
Albinoni, T.	Concerto, C, op. 7/12	LDo
Albinoni, T.	Concerto a cinque, d, op. 9/2 (ob, str)	EK
Albinoni, T.-Giazotto	Concerto, op. 9/2	ESZ
Albinoni, T.	Concerto, op. 9/2	Int
Albinoni, T.	Concerto a cinque, op. 9/5 (ob, str)	MR
Albinoni, T.-Giegling	Concerto a 5, op. 9/8 (ob, str)	AlB
Albinoni, T.	Concerto, op. 9/8 (ob, str)	MR
Albinoni, T.	Concerto a cinque, op. 9/11	MR
Albrechtsberger, J.-Kalmar	Concertino and Notturno	SS
Alessandro, R. d'	Concerto, op. 79	Pet
Alwyn, A.	Concerto	AlL
Ameller, A.	Suite Concertante (ob, str)	ALe
Amy, G.	Jeux et Formes	UE
Andriessen, H.	Concertino. 1969-70 (ob, str)	SD
Andriessen, L.	Anachronie II. 1969	SD
Arma, P.	6 Transparencies (ob, str)	Bil
Armando, G.	Concertino (ob, str)	Schu
Armando, G.	Concerto, g	Schu
Arnold, M.	Concerto (ob, str)	Pat
Bach, C.P.E.-Lauschmann	Concerto, Bb, No. 1 (ob, str)	For
Bach, C.P.E.-Kaul	Concerto, Bb	Leu
Bach, C.P.E.-Töttcher, Grebe	Concerto, Eb	HSM
Bach, J.C.	Concerto, F, No. 2	MR
Bach, J.S.-Töttcher, Müller	Concerto, F	HSM
Bach, J.S.-Radeke	Concerto, g	BrH
Baird, T.	4 Dialogues. 1964	AP
Ballou, E.	Concertino, op. 1 (ob, str)	ACA

Barlow, W.	Winter's Passed (ob, str)	CF
Baur, J.	Concerto Romano. 1960	BrH
Bažant, J.	Concerto. 1961	CHF
Becher, H.	Amourette	PG
Belfín, F.	Suite, op. la. 1943	CHF
Bellini, V.-Meylan	Concerto	Leu
Bellini, V.-Gargiulo	Concerto, Eb (ob, str)	Ric
Benguerel, X.	Music for Oboe and 13 Players	HMo
Benjamin, A.	Divertimento on Themes by Gluck	B&H
Bennett, Richard Rodney	Concerto. 1969-70 (ob, str)	UE
Bentzon, N.	Concerto, op. 74	WH
Berghmans, J.	The Labyrinth (Scenes from a Traveling Circus)	ALe
Besozzi, A.	Concerto (ob, str)	MR
Bezanson, P.	Concertino (ob, str)	ACA
Blackwood, E.	Concerto (ob, str)	Sch
Boedijn, G.	Poetische suite, op. 90. 1941	SD
Börschel, E.	Miniaturen	WZ
Bonelli, E.	6 Variazioni	GZ
Bordier, J.	Habanera	Dur
Boscovich, A.	Concerto	ImV
Bozza, E.	Fantaisie Pastorale	ALe
Brant, H.	Colloquy	Spr
Bredow, E.	Concertino	B&N
Breuer, P.	12 Bagatellen	HG
Bush, G.	Concerto (ob, str)	Elk
Busser, H.	Asturias, op. 84	ALe
Busser, H.	Piece in Bb, op. 22	ALe
Calmel, R.	Concerto (ob, str)	ECh
Casanova, A.	Capriccio	Job
Castelnuovo-Tedesco, M.	Concerto da Camera	B-M
Chagrin, F.	Sarabande (ob, str)	AlL
Cimarosa, D.-Benjamin	Concerto	B&H
Cimarosa, D.-Thilde	Concerto, Bb	Bil
Cimarosa, D.-Thilde	Concerto, C	Bil
Cimarosa, D.-Thilde	Concerto, G	Bil
Clostre, A.	Concerto	EMT
Corelli, A.-Barbirolli	Concerto	B&H
Corelli, A.	Concerto	HU
Diethelm, C.	Concertino op. 102 (ob, str)	S-V
Dittersdorf, K. von	Concerto, C	RS
Dittersdorf, K. von-Rhau	Concerto, G	BrH
Domažlický, F.	Concerto, op. 25. 1958 (ob, str)	CHF
Donizetti, G.-Hofmann	Concertino	Pet
Donizetti, G.	Concerto	B&N
Donovan, R.	Suite (ob, str)	ACA
Dresden, S.	Concerto. 1939	SD
Dubois, P.	Dialogues Canadiens	ALe
Duke, V.	Variations on an Old	

	Russian Chant	BB
Eder, H.	Concerto, op. 35	B&N
Eichner, E.-Rothwell	Concerto	OxU
Eisma, W.	Little Lane. 1973	SD
Eklund, H.	Musica da camera IV. 1970	STI
Endo, R.	Ritsu. 1966	ESZ
Faldi, A.	Concerto (ob, str)	B-M
Fasch, J.-Töttcher, Spannagel	Concerto, g	HSM
Fasch, J.	Concerto, G	HU
Felderhof, J.	Rapsodie. 1935	SD
Ferlendis, G.-Barblan	Concerto No. 1	Ric
Filippucci, E.	Elégie	E&C
Finch, R.	Concerto	OxU
Fischer, J.-Meylan	Konzert, Eb, No. 2	BrH
Fischer, J.	Concerto	GaM
Flothuis, M.	Concertino, op. 70b. 1968	SD
Foss, L.	Concerto	SMP
Fox, F.	Ternion	See
Françaix, J.	L'Horloge de flore	EMT
Friemann, W.	Concerto lirico. 1961	AP
Frigyes, H.	Concerto	EMB
Frumerie, G. de	Concertino. 1960	CGM
Fuga, S.	Concertino (ob, str)	Ric
Furer, A.	Concertino, op. 24 (ob, str)	Pel
Gibilaro, A.	4 Sizilianische Miniaturen	B&B
Gillis, D.	Courthouse Square	B&H
Glaser, W.	Concerto. 1966	STI
Godard, B.	Scènes écossaises	CF
Goeb, R.	Fantasy	AMP
Golestan, S.	Elégie et Danse rustique	Dur
Goossens, E.	Concerto in One Movement	ALe
Graun, J.-Töttcher	Concerto, c	HSM
Graupner, C.-Kreutz	Concerto, F	B&N
Grigoriu, T.	Concerto	EMU
Gyring, E.	Adagio & Rondo (Concerto)	AMC
Gyring, E.	Concerto	AMC
Hall, R.	Idylls (ob, str)	Pet
Hallnäs, H.	Momenti bucolici. 1969	STI
Handel, G.-Pfannkuch	Concerto grosso, Bb, No. 8	BrH
Handel, G.-Seiffert	Konzert, Bb (Concerto Grosso No. 8)	BrH
Handel, G.	Concerto, Bb, No. 8	M&M
Handel, G.	Concerto Grosso, Bb	MV
Handel, G.-Pfannkuch	Concerto grosso, Bb, No. 9	BrH
Handel, G.-Seiffert	Konzert, Bb (Concerto Grosso No. 9)	BrH
Handel, G.-Stein	Concerto, Eb	Pet
Handel, G.-Pfannkuch	Concerto grosso, g, No. 10	BrH
Handel, G.-Seiffert	Konzert, g (Concerto Grosso No. 10)	BrH

Oboe and Orchestra

Handel, G.	Concerto, g	MV
Handel, G.	Concerto, g	SM
Handel, G.	Concerto (ob, str)	CF
Handel, G.	Largo	Dur
Hanson, H.	Pastorale, op. 38	CF
Hasse, J.-Töttcher	Concerto, F	HSM
Haydn, F.-Wunderer	Concerto, C	BrH
Hedwall, L.	Concerto. 1956	STI
Hemel, O.	Concerto. 1955	SD
Hengeveld, G.	Musica concertante. 1968	SD
Henriques, F.	Suite, op. 12	WH
Hidas, F.	Concerto. 1951	EMB
Hobson, M.	Concertino	Che
Hoddinott, A.	Concerto	OxU
Höffer, P.	Concerto	Kis
Hofmann, W.	Concertino (ob, str)	S-V
Holzbauer, I.-Lebermann	Concerto, d	Pet
Hugon, G.	Adagio (ob, str)	EMT
Hummel, J.N.	Adagio and Theme with Variations, op. 102	Pet
Hummel, J.N.	Introduction, Theme and Variations, op. 102	MR
Hurník, I.	Concerto. 1961 (ob, str)	CHF
Ibert, J.	Escales No. 2	ALe
Ibert, J.	Symphonie Concertante	ALe
Indy, V. d'	Fantaisie, op. 31	Dur
Jacob, G.	Concerto No. 1	GaM
Jacob, G.	Concerto No. 2	GaM
Jíra, M.	Concertino. 1965 (ob, str)	CHF
Kalliwoda, J.	Concertino, op. 110	MR
Kauder, H.	Concerto. 1928 (ob, str)	See
Kay, U.	Brief Elegy	MCA
Keldorfer, R.	Concerto (ob, str)	LDo
Kelly, B.	Concerto da Camera (ob, str)	Nov
Kilpatrick, J.	Romanza (ob, str)	CF
Koch, F.	Veltin Fantasy	See
Koetsier, J.	Concertino, op. 14/1. 1936	SD
Kohs, E.	Legend	AMP
Koppel, H.	Concerto, op. 82. 1970	SPD
Kořinek, M.	2 Compositions. 1953	SHF
Kotonski, W.	Concerto	PWM
Kramar-Krommer, F.	Concerto, F, op. 52	B&N
Kramar-Krommer, F.	Concerto, F, op. 52	CHF
Krebs, J.-Winter	Concerto, b	HSM
Laderman, E.	A Single Voice (ob, str)	OxU
Lampersberg, G.	Musik für Oboe	UE
Lamy, F.	Rustique	ALe
Larsson, L.	Concertino, op. 45/2	CGM
Lavagnino, F.	Concerto	Car
Le Boucher, M.	Fantaisie Concertante	ALe

Lebrun, L.	Concerto, C, No. 4	RS
Leduc, J.	Concertino, op. 10. 1962	CBD
Lessard, J.	Cantilena (ob, str)	ACA
Loeillet, J.	Concerto	MV
Loudová, I.	Rhapsodie in black. 1966	Art
Ludewig, W.	Essay	B&B
Luft, J.	Concerto, op. 5	EdK
Lund, E.	Concertpiece	EdK
Maasz, G.	Concertino (ob, str)	HSM
MacMahon, D.	Northumbrian Suite (ob, str)	Elk
Maderna, B.	Concerto No. 2. 1967	ESZ
Maderna, B.	Concerto No. 3	EdS
Makovsky, L.	Concertino (ob, str)	LDo
Malipiero, R.	Sonata	ESZ
Marcello, B.-Bonelli	Concerto, c (ob, str)	GZ
Marcello, A.	Concerto, d	BB
Marcello, A.	Concerto, d	MV
Marcello, A.-Ruf	Concerto, d	SS
Marcello, B. [A?]	Concerto (ob, str)	SM
Margola, F.	Piccolo concerto	Car
Matěj, J.	Sonata	Art
Milhaud, D.	Concerto	Heu
Milwid, A.	Sinfonia concertante	AP
Molique, B.	Concertino	BrH
Moreau, L.-Taunay	Pastorale	ALe
Mourant, W.	The Marble Faun, An Idyll (ob, str)	ACA
Mozart, L.-Winschermann	Concerto, F	HSM
Mozart, W.-Paumgartner	Concerto, KV 314 (285d)	B&H
Mozart, W.-Baudo	3 Cadenzas for Concerto, K. 314	ALe
Mozart, W.-DeLancie	3 Cadenzas for K. 314	B&H
Natra, S.	Music. 1965 (ob, str)	Isr
Nemiroff, I.	Concerto	M&M
Novák, J.	Concerto	Art
Olli, A.	Solitude. 1972 (ob, str)	Fin
Painter, P.	Petite Pastorale	CF
Passani, E.	Concertino	EMT
Pauer, J.	Concerto	Art
Paulson, G.	Concerto, op. 57	STI
Paulson, G.	Concerto, op. 94. 1957 (ob, str)	STI
Pedrollo, A.	Concertino	GZ
Penderecki, K.	Capriccio (ob, str)	HMo
Pergolesi, G.-Barbirolli	Concerto	OxU
Pfister, H.	Aegäisches Tagebuch	Hei
Pisk, P.	Shanty Boy	AMP
Platti, G.-Lebermann	Concerto, G	SS
Platti, G.-Winschermann	Concerto, g	HSM
Pylkkänen, T.	Suite. 1946	Fin
Quantz, J.-Frotscher	Concerto, Bb	WMS

Quantz, J.-Frotscher	Concerto, d	WMS
Ránki, G.	Don Quijote y Dulcinea. 1960	EMB
Ravel, M.	Pièce en forme de Habanera	ALe
Rawsthorne, A.	Concerto	OxU
Redman, R.	Concerto (ob, str)	Pet
Řehoř, B.	Repose and movement. 1965 (ob, str)	CHF
Reicha, J.	Concerto, F	Pet
Richter, F.	Concerto, F	EBM
Richter, F.-Koch	Concerto, F	RS
Rimsky-Korsakov, N.	Variations on a Theme by Glinka	M&M
Rivier, J.	Concerto (ob, str)	EMT
Roessler, F.	Concerto	EBM
Ropartz, G.	Pastorale et danses	E&C
Rosetti, F.-Koch	Concerto, C	Lit
Rosetti, F.	Concerto, C, No. 1	MR
Rosetti, A.-Koch	Concerto, C	Pet
Roussel, A.	Aria	ALe
Rudajev, A.	Konzert. 1964 (ob, str)	CHF
Rudolf, B.	Concertino	LDo
Sainton, P.	Sérénade fantasque	Che
Salich, M.	Concerto. 1968	CHF
Sammartini, G.-Töttcher	Concerto, Eb	HSM
Sammartini, G.-Jenkins	Concerto No. 1	Sch
Scarlatti, D.	Concerto, G, No. 1	Che
Schaefers, A.	Konzert, op. 20. 1953	B&B
Schat, P.	Thema. 1970	SD
Schenker, F.	Concerto (ob, str)	Deu
Schlemm, G.	Pastorale und Scherzo (ob, str)	WZ
Schneider, W.	Concertino (ob, str)	MV
Scott, C.	Concerto (ob, str)	Elk
Sehlbach, E.	Concertino, op. 58	MV
Seidel, J.	Concerto No. 2. 1955	Art
Sinigaglia, L.-Mareczek	12 Variationen über ein Thema von Franz Schubert, op. 19	BrH
Sinigaglia, L.	12 Variazioni, op. 12	Car
Sivic, P.	Dialogues (ob, str)	DSS
Skorzeny, F.	Concerto	LDo
Söderlundh, L.	Concertino (ob, str)	STI
Spinks, C.	Dance Suite	OxU
Stadler, R.	Konzert, op. 22	BrH
Stamitz, J.-Töttcher, Hartig	Concerto, C	HSM
Stamitz, K.-Wojciechowski	Concerto, Bb	AMP
Stamitz, K.-Schroeder	Konzert, Bb	BrH
Stamitz, K.	Concerto	RS
Stibil, M.	Contemplation (ob, str)	B&N
Stölzel, G.-Töttcher	Concerto, D	HSM
Straesser, J.	Summerconcerto	EMo
Strategier, H.	3 stukken. 1937	SD

Oboe and Orchestra

Strauss, R.	Concerto	B&H
Suchý, F.	Concerto, op. 35	CHF
Sydeman, W.	Concertino	EBM
Takács, J.	Meditation, op. 66a	LDo
Tartini, G.-Ticciati	Andante Cantabile (ob, str)	OxU
Telemann, G.-Schlövogt	Concerto, c	SS
Telemann, G.-Töttcher	Concerto, d	HSM
Telemann, G.-Töttcher, Mueller	Concerto, e	HSM
Telemann, G.-Schroeder	Concerto, f	Eul
Telemann, G.-Stein	Concerto, f	Pet
Tepper	Concertino	EdK
Thärichen, W.	Concerto, op. 46	B&B
Tomasi, H.	Concerto	ALe
Tomasi, H.	Danse agreste (5 danses profanes et sacrées)	ALe
Trexler, G.	Musik	BrH
Urbanner, E.	Concerto	LDo
Vaughan Williams, R.	Concerto	OxU
Veress, S.	Passacaglia Concertante	ESZ
Vigneron, J.	Concertino	Mau
Villette, P.	Sérénade	ALe
Vivaldi, A.-Kolneder	Concerto, a	SS
Vivaldi, A.	Concerto, C, P. 41	Eul
Vivaldi, A.-Károlyi	Concerto, C, P. 44	Eul
Vivaldi, A.	Concerto, C, F. VII, No. 4	Ric
Vivaldi, A.-Braun	Concerto, D, P. 187	Pet
Vivaldi, A.-Kolneder	Concerto, D, op. 10/3	SS
Vivaldi, A.	Concerto, d	B-M
Vivaldi, A.	Concerto, d	M&M
Vivaldi, A.-Ephrikian	Concerto, d, F. VII, No. 1	Ric
Vivaldi, A.-Oubradous	Concerto, F, No. 5	EMT
Vivaldi, A.-Balla	Concerto, F, P. 318	Eul
Vivaldi, A.	Concerto, F	M&M
Vivaldi, A.-Ephrikian	Concerto, F, F. VII, No. 2	Ric
Vivaldi, A.	Concerto, F, F. VII, No. 12	Ric
Vivaldi, A.-Kolneder	Concerto, F, op. 10/1	SS
Vivaldi, A.-Kolneder	Concerto, F, op. 10/5	SS
Vivaldi, A.-Kolneder	Concerto, G, op. 10/4	SS
Vivaldi, A.-Kolneder	Concerto, G, op. 10/6	SS
Vivaldi, A.-Kolneder	Concerto, g, op. 10/2	SS
Voormolen, A.	Concerto. 1938	SD
Voormolen, A.	Pastorale. 1940 (ob, str)	SD
Vorlová, S.	Pastoral Concerto, Eb, op. 28. 1952	CHF
Wanhal, J.-Tausky	Concerto	OxU
Wieczorek, J.	Concerto-Fantasia. 1954	AP
Wigy, F.	Andante en Rondo (ob, str)	Mau
Wildberger, J.	Oboe Concerto	A&S
Wilder, A.	Air	Bou
Wilder, A.	Concerto	AMP

Wislocki, L.	Concerto. 1958	AP
Wolf-Ferrari, E.	Idillio. Concertino, A, op. 15	Ric
Wolpert, F.	Banchetto musicale, op. 24, No. 1	BrH
Zach, J.-Klement	Concerto, Bb	ES
Zipoli, D.-Salvaggi	12 a Canzone dall'organo (ob, str)	UE
Zipp, F.	Au clair de la Lune. 1963 (ob, str)	WMS
Zipp, F.	Concerto grosso, op. 29	WMS

Oboe and Band

Andrieu	Dans la forêt	EdR
Andrieu	Impressions Napolitaines	EdR
Bellini, V.-Zurmühle	Concerto	MM
Blémant, L.	Sous les sapins	ALe
Bruniau	Sur la Montagne	EdR
Dedrick, C.	Twilight	Ken
Godard, B.-Fernand	Berceuse de Jocelyn	EdR
Lefébvre, C.-Cailliet	Andante and Allegro	SM
Marcello, B.-Frison	Concerto, c	MM
Moussard	Oboe-Mazurka	EdR
Parès, G.	Message d'amour	EdR
Quéru	Loisirs d'antan	EdR
Rimsky-Korsakov, N.	Variations on a Theme By Glinka	MCA
Verrall, J.	A Pastoral Elegy	ACA

Methods and Studies

	Rubank Instrumental Chart (Conservatory System)	Rub
	Scale for Oboe (Trills)	CF
Ajosa, A.	8 Grand Etudes	Ric
Andraud, A.	Practical and Progressive Oboe Method	SM
Andraud, A.	Premier cahier d'études	ALe
Andraud, A.	Vade Mecum of the Oboist	SM
Anzalone, V.	Breeze-Easy Method, 2 vols.	War
Arcamone, B.	12 Studies	Ric
Bach, J.S.-Rothwell	105 Difficult Passages	B&H
Bach, J.S.-Faulx	20 Etudes de virtuosité	EMb
Bach, J.S.-Corroyez	22 Pièces	Bil
Bach, J.S.-Heinze	Studien, 2 vols.	BrH
Bajeux, P.-ed.	Difficult Passages	ALe
Bajeux, P.	Tablature du Hautbois et Cor Anglais	ALe
Barret, A.	Complete Method, 3 vols.	ALe
Barret, A.	Complete Method	B&H
Barret, A.-Lüttmann	Extrait de la Méthode complète, 2 vols.	ALe
Barret, A.	15 Grand Studies	B&H
Bas, L.	Method	E&C

155

Bassi, L.-Iasilli	27 Virtuoso Studies	CF
Besozzi	28 Etudes	MM
Blatt, F.	15 Entertaining Etudes	EdM
Blatt, F.	20 Exercices, op. 30	Bil
Bleuzet, F.-Pierlot	48 Etudes, op. 31	Bil
Bleuzet, L.	Oboe Technique, 3 vols.	ALe
Boerema, G.	Method	Col
Boerman, B.	Concert Studies	HeE
Bozza, E.	14 Etudes in Karnatic Modes	ALe
Bozza, E.	18 Etudes	ALe
Brandaleone, G.	6 Caprices	Ric
Brandaleone, G.	12 Studies	Ric
Brandaleone, G.	20 Studies, 2 vols.	EDS
Braun, C.-Gleissberg	18 Capricen	BrH
Brod, H.-Bajeux	8 Etudes	ALe
Brod, H.-Bajeux	Etudes et Sonates, 2 vols.	ALe
Brod, H.	20 Studies	Int
Brod, Gillet	Oboe Method	EdR
Brown, J.	370 Exercices	ALe
Bruyant, A.	25 Grandes études de Hugot, op. 13	Bil
Caillićret, A.	15 Etudes after Bach	ALe
Capelle, A.	20 Grand Studies, 2 vols.	ALe
Carey, M.	Method	CF
Cavallini, E.-Iasilli	30 Caprices, 2 vols.	CF
Corroyez, G.	22 Pièces de J.S. Bach	EdR
Crozzoli, S.	Difficult Passages and Solos from Italian Operas, 3 vols.	Ric
Cruchon, P.	Oboe Method	Bil
Davies, J.	Scales and Arpeggios	B&H
Debondue, A.	12 Studies	ALe
Debondue, A.	24 Melodic Studies	ALe
Debondue, A.	25 Etudes-déchiffrages	ALe
Debondue, A.	50 Etudes-déchiffrages	ALe
Debondue, A.	25 Studies	ALe
Debondue, A.	32 Studies	ALe
Debondue, A.	48 Etudes, op. 31	ALe
Debondue, A.	100 Exercises	ALe
Degen, J.-ed.	Orchestral Studies	FrH
Degen, J.	20 Leichte Etüden	ES
DeLancie, J.	20th Century Orchestra Studies	Sch
Dubois, P.	12 Studies	ALe
Duschenes, M.	12 Studies	Ber
Edlefsen, B. & Ployhar, J.	Oboe Student	B-M
Edlefsen, B.	Studies and melodious etudes (Level 1)	B-M
Edlefsen, B.	Studies and melodious etudes (Level 2)	B-M
Edlefsen, B. & Ployhar, J.	Studies and melodious	

	etudes (Level 3)	B-M
Edlefsen, B. & Weber, F.	Tunes for oboe technic (Level 1)	B-M
Edlefsen, B.	Tunes for oboe technic (Level 2)	B-M
Edlefsen, B.	Tunes for oboe technic (Level 3)	B-M
Ensor, C.	Baroque Studies	Spr
Faldi, A.	12 Brevi studi seriali	Ric
Faulx, J.	20 Virtuoso Studies after Bach	HeE
Ferling, W.-Pierlot	18 Etudes, op. 12	Bil
Ferling, W.-Gerlach	18 Technische Übungen, op. 12	FrH
Ferling, W.-Pierlot	48 Etudes	Bil
Ferling, W.-Bleuzet	48 Etudes	EdR
Ferling, W.-Gerlach	48 Übungen, op. 31	FrH
Ferling, W.	48 Famous Studies	SM
Ferling, W.-Pierlot	144 Préludes et études (Bks. 1, 2)	Bil
Ferling, W.-Gerlach	144 Präludien und Etüden, 2 vols.	FrH
Ferling, W.	144 Préludes and Études	MKE
Findlay, F.	Oboette Method	CF
Fitch, G.	Oboe Method	Wah
Flemming, F.	60 Progressive Etudes, 3 vols.	WZ
Freillon-Poncein, J.	La Véritable manière d'apprendre à jouer en perfection du hautbois, de la flûte et du flageolet (reprint of 1700? edition)	MiR
Froseth, J.	The Individualized Instructor, 2 vols.	GIA
Garnier, F.-Wieprecht	Oboe-Schule	JoA
Gekeler, K.-Hovey	Belwin Oboe Method, 3 vols.	B-M
Gekeler, K.	Method for Oboe, 2 vols.	B-M
Gekeler, K.	Practical Oboe Studies	B-M
Giampieri, A.	6 Daily Studies for Perfection	Ric
Giampieri, A.	Progressive Method	Ric
Gillet, F.	Conservatory System Fingering Chart	CF
Gillet, F.	Exercises for advanced oboe technique	ALe
Gillet, F.	Exercises on scales, intervals and staccato	ALe
Gillet, F.	Method for beginners	ALe
Gillet, F.	20 Minutes d'étude	ALe
Gillet, G.-Gillet, F.	Etudes pour l'enseignement supérieur	ALe
Gornston, D. & B. Paisner	Beethoven Sonatas	SF
Gornston, D. & B. Paisner	Chopin Studies	SF
Gornston, D. & B. Paisner	Playing with Chords	SF

Gornston, D.	Very First Oboe Method	Ash
Gugel, E.	Rhythmus, Technik und Vortrag, 2 vols.	PG
Handel, G.-Heinze	Studies, 4 vols.	FrH
Heinze, W.-comp.	Orchesterstudien, 2 vols.	BrH
Hendrickson, C.	Handy Manual of Fingering Charts	CF
Herfurth, P.	A Tune a Day	BM
Herfurth-Stuart	Sounds of the Winds, 2 vols.	CF
Hetzel, J.	Photographic Fingering Chart	TP
Hinke, G.-Stotijn	Practical Elementary Method	Pet
Hofmann, R.	10 Melodic Exercises and Pieces, op. 58	BrH
Holliger, H.	Studies to Play New Music	HG
Holliger, H.	Studie über Mehrklänge	HG
Hovey, N. & Davitt	Daily Exercises	B-M
Hovey, N.	Elementary Method	Rub
Karg-Elert, S.-Gerlach	Etüden-Schule, op. 41	FrH
Klosé, H.	20 Studies	SF
Koch, R.	Short Exercises	Sim
Koebner, R.-Skornicka	Master Method	B&H
Kubát, A.	50 Technische Phrasierungs-übungen	Art
Kubát & Smetácek	Schule	ES
Kucinski	Brahms Studies	SF
Labate, B.	Etudes and Scales for Advanced Oboists	CF
Labate, B.	10 Capricci	Spr
Labate, B.	16 Daily Exercises for Advanced Players	CF
Lacour, G.	100 Déchiffrages manuscrits en forme de petites études mélodiques et rythmiques, 2 vols.	Bil
Lamorlette, R.	12 Etudes	ALe
Lamotte, A.	18 Etudes	Bil
Lamotte, A.-Marx	First Book of Scale and Arpeggio Studies	M&M
Langenus, G.	Practical Transposition	CF
Langey, O.	Practical Tutor	B&H
Langey, O.	Tutor (Revised Edition)	CF
Lee, S.	20 Studies	CF
Lester, L.	50 Rambles	CF
Lore, M.	30 Escercizi progressivi	GZ
Lowry, R.	Von Weber Studies	SF
Loyon, E.	32 Etudes	Bil
Lubin	Tchaikovsky Studies	SF
Lüttmann, R.	21 Etüden über eine Zwölftonreihe	B&N
Luft, J.	24 Etudes	Bil
Luft, J.-Bleuzet	24 Etudes	EdR

158

Luft, J.-Tamme	Etudes	Pet
MacBeth	Learn to Play Oboe, 2 vols.	Alf
Mariani, G.-Giampieri	Popular Method	Ric
Marzo	Metodo	UME
Masuy, F.	10 Etudes de Force moyenne	EMb
Masuy, F.	10 Etudes Difficiles et Très Difficiles	EMb
Mayer, R.	Essentials of Oboe Playing	KMC
McDowell, P.-Hovey	Daily Exercises compiled from works of Albert and Pares	B-M
Meylan, R.	Cadenzas and ornamentation suggestions for 18th-century concertante music	Pet
Michálek, J.	Schule für Oboe	Art
Mille, K.	10 Etudes	FrH
Mille, K.	15 Etudes	FrH
Mille, K.	20 Studies	FrH
Mille, K.	25 Studies and Caprices	FrH
Moore, E.	The Oboe & Its Daily Routine	Leb
Mueller, F.	Method	Uni
Niemann, T.	Method	WZ
Niemann & Labate	Method	CF
Niverd, R.-Pierlot	Method	Bil
Organn, R.	Overtone Series Method, 2 vols.	Reb
Paessler, C.	24 Larghi	Ric
Page, R.	Méthode	ECh
Pantaleo-Iasilli	6 Virtuoso Caprices	CF
Parés, G.	Daily Exercises and Scales	CF
Parés, G.-Whistler	Parés Scales	Rub
Perreau, G.	20 Caprices after Fiorillo	Bil
Petrow, I.	Tonleiterschule	WZ
Pietzsch, G.-Gerlach	Schule	FrH
Porret, J.	24 Déchiffrages manuscrits	EdR
Prescott, G.	Outlines of Technic	CF
Prestini, G.	Collection of Studies	Ric
Prestini, G.	Daily Studies	Bon
Prestini, G.	12 Studies in Modern Style with Chromatics	Ric
Prestini, G.	12 Studies in Modern Style with Rhythmic Difficulties	Bon
Prestini, G.	30 Studies for the Execution of Embellishments	Bon
Pushechnikov, I.	Beginning School, Pt. 1	MKE
Pushechnikov, I.	Virtuoso Etudes	MKE
Rieunier, J.	22 Déchiffrages instrumentaux	ALe
Rivera	Metodo	UME
Rose, C.-Gornston	22 Selected Studies	PrA
Rothwell, E.	A Book of Scales	OxU
Rothwell, E.	Difficult Passages, 3 vols.	B&H

Rothwell, E.	The Oboist's Companion, 2 vols.	OxU
Ruggiero, G.	6 Etudes atonales	ALe
Rusch, H. & Barto, A.	Breath Control and Tuning and Intonation Studies	CF
Sabon, E.	12 Etudes	Bil
Salviani, C.	Studies from the Method, 4 vols.	Ric
Schiemann, C.	7 Characteristic Studies	EdM
Schiemann, C.	7 Karaktersitieke Oef.	MM
Scozzi, R.	Esercizi preliminari	Edi
Scozzi, R.	6 Studi fantastici	Car
Scozzi, R.	Studi	Car
Segouin, P.	25 Etudes artistiques, 2 vols.	Bil
Sellner, J.-Bleuzet	Etudes élémentaires	EdR
Sellner, J.-Bleuzet	Etudes progressives	EdR
Sellner, J.-Bleuzet	Méthode, 2 vols.	Bil
Shostakovitch, D.-Gerlach	Orchestral Studies	FrH
Singer, L. & Bartolozzi, B.	Metodo	ESZ
Singer, S.	Theoretical and Practical School, Pt. 3: Arpeggios	Ric
Singer, S.	Theoretical and Practical School, Pt. 4: 13 Studies	Ric
Singer, S.	Theoretical and Practical School, Pt. 5: 20 Studies	Ric
Singer, S.	Theoretical and Practical School, Pt. 6: 27 Studies and Caprices in All Keys	Ric
Siqueira, J.	Etüden	B&N
Skornicka, J. & Koebner	Intermediate Method	Rub
Slavinsky, L.	30 Etudes	MKE
Slavinsky, L.	65 Etudes	MKE
Small, J.	27 Melodious and Rhythmical Exercises	CF
Smetáček, V.	Tonleiteretüden	Art
Snavely, J.	Basic Technique for Oboe	Ken
Snieckowski, S.-comp.	Wybór etiud	AP
Soloduyev, N.-comp.	Orchestral Difficulties (Soviet Composers)	MKE
Sous, A.	Neue Oboenschule	Pet
Stotijn, J.	Etudes	MM
Stotijn, J.	De Kunst van het maken van Hoborieten	MM
Strauss, R.-Baumgaertel	Orchestra Studies, 2 vols.	Pet
Szeszler, T.	Oboe Tutor, 3 vols.	EMB
Tomasi, H.	3 Concert Etudes (Cadenzas from Mozart's Concerto in C)	EME
Tustin, W.	Daily Scales	SMP
Van der Hagen, A.	Méthode nouvelle et raisonée	

160

	pour le hautbois (reprint	
	of edition of ca. 1792)	MiR
Verdi, G.-Gumbert	Orchestral Studies	FrH
Verdi, G.-Kraus	Orchestral Studies	FrH
Verroust, S.	24 Etudes mélodiques, 2 vols.	Bil
Verroust, S.-Marx	24 Melodic Studies, op. 65	M&M
Votquenne, V.	Technique Moderne, 2 vols.	EMb
Voxman, H.-arr.	Selected Studies	Rub
Voxman, H. & W. Gower	Advanced Method, 2 vols.	Rub
Wagner, R.-Gerlach	Orchestral Studies, 2 vols.	FrH
Wagner, R.	Orchestral Studies	Int
Weber, F. & B. Edlefson	Oboe Student	B-M
Wiedemann, L.	45 Etüden	BrH
Wunderlich, F.	Arpeggios	CF

English Horn

Unaccompanied Solos

Bancquart, A.	Sonatine	Job
Childs, B.	4 Involutions. 1955	TP
Filippi, A. de	Equations	Gen
Glaser, W.	Solo. 1965 (ob d'amore)	STI
Mimaroglu, I.	Monologue III. 1964	See
Stockhausen, K.	Spiral	UE
Tomasi, H.	Evocations	ALe
Wagner, R.-Pierlot	Solo de Tristan	Bil

English Horn and Piano

Akimenko, T.	Eclogue	SM
Bach, J.S.	Aria, D	Dur
Bancquart, A.	Sonatine	Job
Barat, J.	Nostalgie	ALe
Bartsch, C.	Concertino	Mau
Benson, W.	Recuerdo (ob/ehn, pf)	MCA
Bentzon, N.	Sonata, op. 71	WH
Berg-Sansone	The Shepherd	SM

English Horn and Piano

Boeck, A. De	Lied	ScF
Bonson, F.	En Ardennes	ScF
Borkovec, P.	Intermezzo	Art
Botting, C.	Pastorale	Ham
Bottje, W.	Concertino	Col
Bourgault-Ducoudray, L.	Les Bergers à la crèche	EdS
Bozza, E.	Divertissement	SM
Bozza, E.	Lied	ALe
Braga, G.	Serenata	Dur
Bréville, P. de	Maneh	ALe
Buchal, H.	Sonata, Eb, op. 86	BrH
Carter, E.	Pastoral	TP
Chopin, F.	Nocturne, op. 9/2	CF
Chopin, F.	Famous Nocturne, op. 9/2	SM
Couperin, F.-Bleuzet	Berceuse en rondo (Pièces de Clavecin)	ALe
Debussy, C.	Rapsodie pour saxophone	Dur
Donizetti-Meylan	Concertino, G	Pet
Dubois, P.	La Leçon de Danse	ERR
Dubois, P.	Sonatina	ALe
Dvorak, A.-Isaac, Feldman	Largo (New World Symphony)	CF
Dvorak, A.-Johnson	Largo (New World Symphony)	CF
Elgar, E.-Akers	Pomp and Circumstance, op. 39/1	CF
Fricker, P.	Concertante, op. 13	S&C
Godard, B.	Berceuse (Jocelyn)	CF
Gottwald	Friendship	SM
Green, H.	Berceuse	PMP
Gregoir, E.	Dernière pensée, de Nicolo Paganini	ScF
Grieg, E.-Strauwen	Soir dans les montagnes	ScF
Guillou, R.	Sonatina	ALe
Handel, G.	Celebrated Largo	Dur
Handel, G.-Andraud	Concerto, c	SM
Haydn, F.-Strauwen	La 7e parole du Christ	ScF
Hill, E.	Music for English Horn & Orchestra	AMC
Hindemith, P.	Sonata. 1941	SS
Hlobil, E.	Sonata	Art
Jacob, G.-Addison	Rhapsody	GaM
Karlins, M.	Music	CoF
Kauder, H.	Sonata	SM
Kennaway, L.	Watersmeet	HE
Koechlin, C.	Pièce	EdS
Korchmarev, K.	Ovez-Djan (Turkmenian Melody)	MKE
Latham, W.	Sonata No. 2	Spr
Law, A.	Sauterne	ATL
Lucky, S.	Elegie	Art
Lully, J.-Bleuzet	Pavane (Ballets du Roi)	ALe

162

Maertens, J.	Moments tristes	Mau
Maganini, Q.	Villanella of Autumn	CF
Malipiero, G.	Canto nell' infinito	ALe
Mareczek, F.	Summer Evening on the Mountain	WZ
Mascagni, P.-Painter	Siciliana	War
Mason, F.	Berceuse en Carillon	Bra
Mason, F.	Serenade Gaie	Bra
Mason, J.	Tenuto	See
McBride, R.	Parking on the Parkway	CoF
Mills, C.	Sonata	CoF
Moore, T.	Andante	S&C
Morra, G.	Nocturnal Serenade	CF
Morra, G.	Romantique	CF
Mozart, W.	Adagio (Concerto, op. 107)	CF
Mozart, W.	Adagio Religioso	SM
Mulder, H.	Sonata, op. 79. 1950	SD
Nuyens, H.	Souvenir de Bohême	ScF
Organn, R.	Nocturne	Reb
Pangaert d'Opdorp	Les Echos, op. 25	ScF
Paulson, G.	Concerto op. 99, No. 1	EMf
Paulson, G.	Concerto op. 103, No. 2	EMf
Perina, H.	Impromptu	Art
Philidor, F.-Bleuzet	Ego dis amicum (Chant d'Eglise)	ALe
Presser, W.	Passarumbia	TP
Purcell, H.-Kaplan	Saraband	Spr
Rasse, F.	Cantabile	ALe
Ravel, M.-Kochanski	Pavane pour une Infante défunte	EME
Ravel, M.	Pavane	SS
Ravel, M.	Piece en forme de Habanera	ALe
Richardson, A.	3 Pieces	GaM
Rosetti, F.	Rondo (Concerto)	Art
Sachse, H.	Sonata, op. 64	Pet
Saint-Saens, C.	Proserpine, Pavane	Dur
Saint-Saens, C.-Isaac, Feldman	Swan (Carnival of Animals)	CF
Saint-Saens, C.	Le Cygne	Dur
Schaeffer	Spring in the Forest	CF
Scheer, L.	Lament	See
Schmitt, F.	Chant du soir	EdS
Schubert, F.-Bleuzet	Ave Maria	ALe
Schumann, R.	Einsame Blumen	Spr
Searle, H.	Gondoliera, op. 19	S&C
Shalitt-Isaac, Feldman	Eili, Eili	CF
Sibelius, J.-Johnson	Swan of Tuonella	B-M
Skroup, J.	Concerto, Bb	Art
Stevens, H.	3 Hungarian Folk Songs	GaM
Strauwen, J.	Conte pastoral	ScF
Tchaikovsky, P.	Andante Cantabile, op. 11	CF

Tchaikovsky, P.-Isaac, Feldman	Ye Who Have Yearned Alone	CF
Telemann, G.-Barnes	Arie (Pimpinone)	Spr
Thilman, J.	Kleine Sonate, op. 34. 1946	WMS
Thomé, F.	Simple aveu	Dur
Trowbridge, L.	Quietude	See
Tuthill, B.	A Little English	Ten
Wagenseil, G.-Janetzky	Concerto	WMS
Wagner, R.-Johnson	Shepherd's Song (Tristan and Isolde)	CF
Wagner, W.	10 Miniatures	SMP
Wallner, L.	Elegie	ScF
Wallner, L.	3 Morceaux--Chant d'amour; Mazurka; Rêverie	ScF
Wolf-Ferrari, E.-Strom	Concertino, op. 34. 1947	Leu

English Horn and Organ

Becher, H.	Präludium	PG
Hammarström, H.	Elegi	EMf
Koetsier, J.	Partita, op. 41/1	SD
Krol, B.	Antifona, op. 53	B&B
Lüttmann, R.	Méditation II	ALe
Sowerby, L.	Ballade	B-M

English Horn and Orchestra

Alwyn, W.	Autumn Legend (ehn, str)	AlL
Bartsch, C.	Concertino	Mau
Booren, J. van den	Suite dionysienne. 1963-64	SD
Bottje, W.	Concertino (ehn, str)	Col
Donizetti, G.-Meylan	Concertino	Pet
Fiala, J.	Concerto	Art
Fiala, J.	Concerto	CHF
Hallaste, U.	Romanza appassionata. 1935	Fin
Jacob, G.	Rhapsody	GaM
Klami, U.	Intermezzo. 1937	Fin
Koetsier, J.	Vision Pastorale, op. 15/1. 1937	SD
Mourant, W.	Elm St., Fairbury, Ill.	AMC
Paulson, G.	Concerto op. 99, No. 1. 1958	STI
Paulson, G.	Concerto op. 103, No. 2. 1959	STI
Powell, M.	Cantilena Concertante	Sha
Punttila, A.	A Day at Sea. 1956	Fin
Ravel, M.	Pièce en forme de Habanera	ALe
Stockmeier, W.	Sonata (ehn, str)	MV
Stout, A.	Intermezzo, op. 4	Pet

Methods and Studies

Blatt, F.	20 Exercices, op. 30	Bil
Ferling, F.-Gerlach	18 Technique Studies, op. 12	FrH

Karg-Elert, S.	Etüden-Schule, op. 41	FrH
Wagner, R.-Schultz	Orchestral Studies	FrH

Oboe d'amore

Oboe and Piano or Harpsichord

Borris, S.	Sonata (ob d'amore, hpcd)	Hei
McCabe, J.	Dance-Prelude	Nov
Mulder, H.	Fantasie, op. 118. 1960	SD
Redel, M.	Dialoge. 1970 (ob d'amore, hpcd)	B&B
Telemann, G.	Concerto, A	Pet
Telemann, G.-Schroeder	Concerto, D	Leu
Telemann, G.-Töttcher, Spannagel	Concerto, G	HSM

Oboe d'amore and Orchestra

Armando, G.	Suite (ob d'amore, str)	Schu
Bach, J.S.	Concerto, A, BWV 1055	Deu
Dittersdorf, C. von	Concerto, A	EBM
Glaser, W.	3 Satser	STI
Graupner, C.-Koch	Concerto, C	WMS
McCabe, J.	Concerto	Nov
Stranz, U.	Déjà vu	B&N
Telemann, G.-Schroeder	Concerto, A	Eul
Telemann, G.-Schroeder	Concerto, D	Leu
Telemann, G.-Töttcher, Spannagel	Concerto, G	HSM
Telemann, G.	Concerto	M&M

Eb Clarinet, Bb and A Soprano Clarinet, Alto Clarinet, Basset Horn, Bass Clarinet, and Contrabass Clarinet

Eb Clarinet

Eb Clarinet and Piano

Aubert, J.	Gigue	EdM
Barat, J.-Voxman	Chant Slave	Rub
Cavallini, E.	Carnevale di Venezia	MRL
Corelli, A.-Voxman	Sarabande and Gigue	Rub
Déré, J.-Voxman	Andante and Scherzo	Rub
Escudié, L.	3e Fantaisie	MM
Forestier, J.	Solo	MM
Garlick, A.	Sonata	See
Gee, H.	Ballade	PrA
Johnson, C.	Scene Sylvan	Rub
Koepke, P.	Arietta and Scherzo	Rub
Lecail, G.-Voxman	Fantaisie Concertante	Rub
Mann, G.-van Leeuwen	Concertstuk	MM
Marcello, B.-Voxman	Andante and Allegro (Sonata, G)	Rub
Massenet, J.	Valse des Esprits	EdM
Ostransky, L.	Praeludium	Rub
Platti, G.-Hervig	Pastorale (Sonata No. 5)	Rub
Rabaud, H.	Solo de Concours	EdM
Reed, A.	Hoe-Down	EBM
Reed, A.	March Variations	EBM
Shishov	Grotesque Dance	EdM
Tchaikovsky, P.-Hurrell	2 Dances (The Nutcracker Suite)	Rub

Eb Clarinet and Band

Bléger	Les Echos de Barcelone	EdR
Mozart, W.-Dias	Larghetto (Quintet, op. 108)	EdR

Bb and A Soprano Clarinet

Unaccompanied Solos

	Album of Famous Pieces	EdK
	Clarinet Classics, 3 vols.	CF
	Favorites through the Years	SF
	L'Idéal du clarinettiste, 2 vols.	Dur
	Master Folio	CF
Adler, S.	Clarinon	TP

Adler, S.	Harobed	SM
Ahlberg, G.	Miniature I. 1966	E–V
Aitken, H.	Suite	E–V
Antoniou, T.	3 Likes. 1973	B&N
Apostel, H.	Sonatine, op. 19/2	UE
Arma, P.	Petite Suite	HLe
Arnold, M.	Fantasie, op. 87. 1966	Fab
Avni, T.	Echoes from the Past. 1970	Isr
Bach, J.S.-Simon	Bach for the clarinet, Pt. II	Sch
Bach, J.S.-Langenus	Chaconne (Sonata No. 4)	CF
Bach, J.S.-Langenus	Chromatic Fantasia	CF
Bach, J.S.-Simon	3 Pieces	PIC
Ballif, C.	Solfeggietto No. 5	EMT
Barati, G.	Pastorale. 1947	CoF
Bartolozzi, B.	The Hollow Man. 1968	ESZ
Baur, J.	6 Bagatellen. 1964	BrH
Bavicchi, J.	Sonata	OxU
Bavicchi, J.	Sonata No. 2	OxU
Becucci	A pouffer de rire	Dur
Ben-Haim, P.	3 Songs Without Words	AlB
Benjamin, T.	Articulations. 1971	Man
Bentzon, J.	Theme and Variations	WH
Bettinelli, B.	Studio da concerto	Ric
Beyer, J.	Suite	AMC
Binet, F.	Chanson de Louisette	Dur
Bischof, R.	Sonatina, op. 1	LDo
Bois, R. du	Une Danse pour Sonia	SD
Boone, C.	Not Now	EdS
Bornyi, L.	1983	Wat
Boulez, P.	Domaines. 1968–69	UE
Braun, Y.	3 Movements for Clarinet	Isr
Brindle, R.	Sikel	B&H
Brons, C.	Monolog III. 1968	SD
Bucchi, V.	Concerto (Carte fiorentine, No. 2)	Ric
Bucht, G.	Klarinettstudie – 59	EMf
Cage, J.	Sonata	Pet
Cahuzac, L.	Arlequin	Bil
Camilleri, C.	3 Visions for an Imaginary Dancer	Nov
Cantor, M.	Suite	TP
Carbonnier, C.	Marche des poupées	Dur
Chagrin, F.	Improvisation and Toccatina	GaM
Cheslock, L.	Descant	OxU
Childs, B.	Sonata. 1951	TP
Colaço Osorio-Swaab, R.	Sonatine. 1946	SD
Cope, D.	3 Pieces	CoA
Croley, R.	Trittico. 1967	TP
Deák, C.	Sonatina	Nor
Debras, L.	Sequenza III. 1968	See

DeLacour, L.	Album de solos	Bil
Denissow, E.	Sonata. 1972	HG
De Sica, M.	Voice. 1971	Ric
Diamond, A.	Composition	TP
Doran, M.	7 Pieces	Wes
Drummond, D.	Suite	Wes
Dubois, P.	Sonata breve	ALe
Durand, A.	Pomponnette	Dur
Dure, R.	3 Episodes	AMC
Eaton, J.	Concert Music	Sha
Eitler, E.	Ansias	TP
Eklund, H.	4 Pezzi brevi. 1963	STI
Escher, P.	Pièce pour clarinette seule, op. 84	EK
Evans, R.	Suite Bizarre. 1967	Can
Ferritto, J.	Addio C.M.	CoF
Fine, A.	Solo for Clarinet	AMC
Focheux, J.	Dormez mignonne	Dur
Franco, J.	Little Suite. 1937	CoF
Frohne, V.	Study for Clarinet Solo, op. 17	B&B
Geispieler, F.-arr.	Clarino, Collection of Master Works, 2 vols.	GD
Gelbrun, A.	Partita for Clarinet. 1969	Isr
Genzmer, H.	Fantasie	Pet
Godard, B.	1st Gavotte	Dur
Goehr, A.	Paraphrase on the dramatic madrigal Il Combattimento de Tancred e Clorinda by Claudio Monteverdi	S&C
Goldberg, L.	Galante conversation	Dur
Goode, D.	Circular Thoughts	TP
Guiraud, E.	Piccolino	Dur
Gyring, E.	Scherzando	HeE
Hartley, W.	2 Little Pieces	Cre
Hartley, W.	2 Studies	Cre
Hartzell, E.	Sonatine (Monolog I). 1957	LDo
Haselbach, J.	"Zeilen"	S-V
Hedwall, L.	Sonatin. 1958	STI
Heider, W.	Inventio II	A&S
Heininen, P.	Discantus II, Sonatine	EdF
Hekster, W.	Play	SD
Heussenstamm, G.	Die Jugend, op. 10	See
Hitz, F.	Bonjour bluette	Dur
Hovhaness, A.	Lament	Pet
Hudadoff, I.-arr.	50 Standard Solo Series	PrA
Hummel, B.	Suite	Sim
Ioannidis, Y.	Versi	HG
Ivey, J.	Sonatina	AMC
Jacob, G.	5 Pieces	OxU
Jenni, D.	Musica Della Primavera	AMP

Jensen, J.	3 Pieces	CoA
Jettel, R.	5 Grotesques	Pet
Johannes, J.	Solo-sonatine	EdH
Jolivet, A.	Ascèses	Bil
Kardos, I.	Solo Sonata	Gen
Karg-Elert, S.	Sonata, op. 110	WZ
Karlins, M.	Solo Piece with Passacaglia	AE
Kempe, H.	3 Rapsodiska stycken	STI
Konietzny, H.	Les Trois reliefs	OJ
Kotschoubey, L.	Oh! dites-lui	Dur
Krenek, E.	Monologue. 1956	Ron
Krenz, J.	Musica	PWM
Kunc, B.	Pastoral Fantasy, op. 59	Ron
Kupferman, M.	5 Singles	Gen
Kurtz, S.	Fantasy	SF
Lachenmann, H.	Dal Niente. 1970	HG
Laderman, E.	Serenade	Ron
Lambert, C.	Tunes for Bb Clarinet	KPM
Láng, I.	Monodia. 1965	EMB
Lanzi, A.	Ele Affar. 1969	ESZ
Latham, W.	5 Atonal Studies	Spr
La Violette, W.	Suite	Wes
Lefort, A.	Chanson villageoise	Dur
Lehmann, H.	Mosaik. 1964	HG
Lewis, R.	Monophony III	LDo
Linke, N.	Fantasia und Zortico	HG
Lorenzo, L. de	Suite Mythologique, op. 38	WZ
Lourié, A.	The Mime	Ron
Lovano, M.	2 Moments musicaux	Com
Lowthian, C.	Venetia	Dur
Mamlok, U.	Poliphony. 1968	See
Marbe, M.	Incantatio. 1965	HG
Martin, R.	En fanant	Dur
Martino, D.	B,A,B,B,I,T,T	Sch
Martino, D.	A Set for Clarinet	M&M
Massenet, J.	Andante	Dur
Mather, B.	Etude. 1962	Can
Mayer, J.	Raga Music	AlL
Mayer, W.	Two Moods	TP
McBride, R.	Rhumba Study	CoF
McBride, R.	Show Business Study	CoF
Milano, R.	4 Arabesques	TP
Mills, C.	Sonata Fantasia	CoF
Mimaroglu, I.	Monologue I. 1958	See
Moore, M.	Ragtime and Variations on an Irish Theme	Wes
Morhange, E.	Marquis et marquisette	Dur
Morley, C.	Les Bluets	Dur
Mouton, H.	Recueillement	Dur
Mozart, W.	Sérénade (Don Juan)	Dur

169

Nemiroff, I.	3 Pieces	M&M
Olah, T.	Sonata. 1964	EdS
Osborne, W.	Rhapsody	Pet
Paganini, N.	Moto Perpetuo, op. 11/6	EdK
Pauer, J.	Alltägliche Monologe, 7 Stücke	Art
Perle, G.	3 Sonatas	TP
Persichetti, V.	Parable XIII, op. 126	E-V
Pfeiffer, H.-Kroll	Musik für eine unbegleitete A-Klarinette	MRL
Pfister, H.	Suite	Hei
Pfister, H.	Vignetten	Eul
Pinkham, D.	Etude	ECS
Pousseur, H.	Madrigal I	UE
Presser, W.	Partita	TP
Prunty, W.	Sketches	Acc
Przybylski, B.	Saggio di suonare	PWM
Purdy, W.	Ixohoxi. 1962	Can
Raff, J.	Cavatine	Dur
Reiner, K.	4 Stücke	CHF
Reinhardt, B.	12 mal 12	IMP
Rivier, J.	Les Trois "S"	EMT
Rosenberg, H.	Sonat. 1960	ESu
Rózsa, M.	Sonatina, op. 27	Ron
Rubbra, E.	5 Sonnets	GaM
Russell, R.	Metamorphoses	Gen
Russo, J.	4 Pieces	CoA
Ruyneman, D.	Divertimento	AMC
Ruzicka, P.	3 Szenen	HSM
Rychlík, J.	Burleskni suita	Art
Sacco, P.	The Cold Mountain	Wes
Saguer, L.	Quatre essais	Job
Saint-Saens, C.	Danse macabre	Dur
Sandström, S.	Changes. 1970	STI
Sandström, S.	Combinations. 1969	STI
Sári, J.	Stati. 1968	EMB
Saucier, G.	3 Pieces	Sch
Schinstine, W.	Solitary Sequence	SM
Schneider, W.	Partita	MV
Schroeder, H.	Sonata. 1971	HG
Schwadron, A.-arr.	Teacher's Choice of 26 Clarinet Solos	Alf
Smith, W.	5 Pieces	UE
Smith, W.	Variants	UE
Snow, M.	5 Monodies	LP
Souffriau, A.	Sonate	Mau
Spooner, I.	Chalumeau Sonata	HE
Stearns, P.	Invention	CoF
Steffens, W.	Hommage II, op. 16	B&B
Steffens, W.	Rose Ouest, op. 19. 1970	B&B
Stein, L.	Sonata	CoF

Clarinet — Unaccompanied Solos

Stewart, D.	Suite	CoF
Stockhausen, K.	Plus Minus	UE
Stockhausen, K.	Solo	UE
Stockhausen, K.	Spiral	UE
Stout, A.	Construction	CoF
Stravinsky, I.	3 Pieces	Che
Stravinsky, I.	3 Pieces	EdK
Stravinsky, I.	3 Pieces	Int
Stravinsky, I.	3 Pieces	SF
Stutschewsky, J.	Monologue	See
Sutermeister, H.	Capriccio. 1947	SS
Swain, F.	3 Whimsies	Bou
Sydeman, W.	Sonata	Pet
Tailleferre, G.	Sonata	Ron
Tanenbaum, E.	Sonatina	CoF
Terzakis, D.	Stixis II	HG
Tisné, A.	Invocations pour Ellora	Bil
Tomasi, H.	Sonatine attique	ALe
Tuthill, B.	2 Snacks for a Lonesome Clarinet	SM
Vandermaesbrugge, M.	Introduction et Danse, op. 33	JB
Verrall, J.	Brief Elegy	CoF
Wachs, P.	Pendant la cueillette	Dur
Wagner, R.	Choeur des fiançailles	Dur
Wagner, R.	Duo (Lohengrin)	Dur
Wagner, R.	Prière (Rienzi)	Dur
Wagner, R.	Romance de l'étoile (Tannhauser)	Dur
Wagner, R.	Le Vaisseau Fantôme	Dur
Waldteufel, E.	Bella bocca	Dur
Waldteufel, E.	Dolores	Dur
Waldteufel, E.	Pluie de diamants	Dur
Waldteufel, E.	Pomone	Dur
Waldteufel, E.	Souviens-toi	Dur
Waldteufel, E.	A toi	Dur
Waldteufel, E.	Toujours ou jamais	Dur
Waldteufel, E.	Tout ou rien	Dur
Waldteufel, E.	Très jolie	Dur
Waldteufel, E.	Tric trac	Dur
Waldteufel, E.	Vergissmeinnicht	Dur
Waldteufel, E.	Les Violettes	Dur
Waters, C.	Little Cycle	HE
Welander, S.	Praeludium	STI
Wellesz, E.	Suite	Ron
Whittenberg, C.	3 Pieces, op. 29	M&M
Zonn, P.	Revolutions	MeP
Zonn, P.	Stray Puffs	CoF

Clarinet and Piano

	Artist Solo Album	Wat

Clarinet and Piano

—Lester	Auld lang syne	B-M
	Bläsers Lieblinge	WZ
	Broadway Showcase	War
	Caissons Go Rolling Along	NK
	Clarinet Album No. 1	HE
	Clarinet Album No. 2	HE
	Clarinet Hour	Rub
	Clarinetist's Concert Album	CF
	Clarinetist's Melody Album	Rub
	Clarinette Selection	GD
	Contemporary French Recital Pieces, 2 vols.	Int
—Bettoney	Dark Eyes	CF
	Deep River	CF
	Devotional Solos	War
	Easy Does It, 3 vols.	War
	Easy to Play Pieces	Ash
	Elementary Clarinet Solos	MS
	Encore Folio	Rub
—Klosé, Jeanjean	Fantasia on Carnival in Venice	ALe
	59 Masterpieces	B-M
	The First Pete Fountain Folio	MCA
	First Solo Album	TP
—Schaposchnikow	5 Pieces by Russian Composers	HSM
	40 Hits of Our Times	MCA
	40 More Hits of Our Times	MCA
	Fox Album of Clarinet Solos, 3 vols.	SF
	Great Themes from Chamber Music	Smo
	Intermediate Pieces	Ash
	The Joy of Clarinet	MS
	Londonderry Air	MM
	Merry Makers Gavotte	NK
	Morceaux de Concours et pièces d'audition	ALe
	More Easy Clarinet Solos	MS
—Hovey, Leonard	Le Petite Rien	B-M
—Lester	Pop Goes the Weasel	B-M
	Radio Collection of National Songs & Hymns	Rub
	Sacred Solos	Rub
	Selected Clarinet Solos	MS
	Soloist Folio	Rub
—Bettoney	Song of the Volga Boatmen	CF
—Land	Zigeunerweisen (Gypsy airs)	B-M
Abbis, R.	Andante et allegro	Mau

Clarinet and Piano

Absil, J.	Fantaisie humoresque	ALe
Absil, J.	5 Easy Pieces	HLe
Ackermans, H.	Humoresque	EMe
Ackermans, H.	Paysage Nordique	EMb
Adam, A.-Claus	Cavatina (Giralda)	CF
Adam, A.-Klosé, Jeanjean	Fantasia on Si J'étais Roi	ALe
Adam, A.	O Holy Night	Rub
Adams, S.-Glenn	Holy City	B&H
Adams, S.	Holy City	B-M
Adams, S.	The Holy City	HeE
Adams, S.-Buchtel	The Holy City	NK
Adams, S.-DeLamater	The Holy City	Rub
Adolphus, M.	Opus 93	CoF
Adolphus, M.	Opus 99	CoF
Aerts, F.	Fantaisie Variée	T-M
Aeschbacher, W.	Adagio	Eul
Albéniz, I.	Chant d'amour	ALe
Albéniz, I.-Amaz	Mallorca. Barcarola	UME
Albéniz, I.-Amaz	Puerta de tierra	UME
Albéniz, I.	Tango, op. 165/2	CF
Albéniz, I.-Frank	2 Spanish Pieces	OxU
Albinoni, T.	Adagio	Com
Albinoni, T.	Adagio, g	GD
Albinoni, T.-Joosen	Concerto, Bb	MM
Alessandro, R. d'	Sonatina giocosa	HG
Aletter, W.	Rendezvous	NK
Alexander, J.	Sonata	Gen
Alexeyev, M.	Poem	MKE
Alwyn, W.	Sonata	B&H
Amani, M.-Hite	Ancient Menuet	SM
Ameller, A.	Andantino	HLe
Ameller, A.	Burlesque	ALe
Ameller, A.	Cantilena	ALe
Ameller, A.	Dolbeau	ALe
Ameller, A.	La Violette	HLe
Ameller, A.	Promenade en Bourgogne	ALe
Anderberg, C.	4 Seriosa capricer. 1956	STI
Andersen, J.-Waln	Scherzino	B-M
Anderson, L.	Belle of the Ball	B-M
Anderson, L.-Edwards	Blue Tango	B-M
Anderson, L.	Fiddle-faddle	B-M
André, F.	Improvisation	EMb
Andriessen, H.	Sonata	SD
Andrieu, F.	Divertissement	Bil
Andrieu, F.	Rossignol d'amour	Bil
Antufeyev, B.-Grigorian	2 Pieces (Melody-Lesginka)	MKE
Arányi, G.	Rhapsodia. 1961	EMB
Arban, J.	Oberto, Air Varie	MM
Arban, J.-Vanasek	Perpetual Motion	MCA
Archer, V.	Sonata. 1970	Can

Clarinet and Piano

Arditi, L.	Il Bacio (The Kiss)	Cen
Arensky, A.-Fedulov	Dance (Egyptian Nights)	MKE
Arensky, A.-Semyonov	2 Pieces	MKE
Arlen, H.-Sears	Blues in the Night	War
Arma, P.	Divertimento No. 6	HLe
Armato, B.-ed.	Recital Clarinetist	CF
Armitage, I.	Dance Suite	B&H
Arndt, F.	Nola	SF
Arne, T.	Drink to Me Only	MM
Arne, T.-Kaplan	Minuet and Gigue	Spr
Arne, T.-Craxton	Sonata, Bb	OxU
Arnell, R.	8 Clarinet Pieces	HE
Arnič, B.	Tales	EdD
Arnold, J.-ed.	Clarinet Solos	MS
Arnold, J.	Easy Clarinet Solos	MS
Arnold, M.	Clarinet Concerto	AlL
Arnold, M.	Sonatina	AlL
Atayan, R.	Poem	MKE
Aubert, J.-Waln	Aria and Presto	NK
Aubert, J.	Gigue	EdM
Aubert, P.	1st Solo de concours	Bil
Aubin, T.	Le Calme de la mer (Suite éolienne)	ALe
Aubin, T.	Divertimento dell' incertezza	ALe
Auric, G.	Imaginées	EdS
Austin, L.	Current	CPE
Avon, E.	Danse Joyeuse	CF
Avon, E.	Divertissement	CF
Avon, E.	Fantaisie de concert	Bil
Avon, E.	Prelude and Rigaudon	EdS
Avon, E.	Rondo	CF
Avon, E.	La Traviata, Fantaisie	EdS
Avshalomov, J.	Evocations	CoF
Avshalomoff, J.	Sonatine. 1945	TP
Avshalomoff, J.	2 Bagatelles	TP
Babcock, E.	In Modo Triste	CF
Bacewicz, G.	Easy Pieces	PWM
Bach, E.-Gallo	Spring's Awakening	CF
Bach, J.C. & W. Mozart -Ettlinger	Concerto, Eb	B&H
Bach, J.S.	Adagio (Organ Concerto No. 3) (cl in A)	Int
Bach, J.S.-Setaccioli	Adagio (Organ Sonata No. 3)	Ric
Bach, J.S.	Andante (Sinfonia)	MM
Bach, J.S.	Aria, D	Dur
Bach, J.S.-Kent	Arioso	CF
Bach, J.S.-Crossman	Art of the Fugue I	PMP
Bach-Gounod	Ave Maria	CF
Bach, J.S.-Gounod	Ave Maria	HeE

174

Clarinet and Piano

Bach–Gounod	Ave Maria	MM
Bach, J.S.–Simon	Bach for the Clarinet	Sch
Bach, J.S.	Bist Du Bei Mir	GD
Bach, J.S.–Hite	Bourrée	SM
Bach, J.S.–Tomei	Concerto (Violin Concerto No. 1)	PrA
Bach, J.S.	My Heart Ever Faithful (Pentecost Cantata No. 68)	GD
Bach, J.S.	Pastorale	Cor
Bach, J.S.–Périer	Sarabande (Suite in G)	ALe
Bach, J.S.–Buchtel	Siciliano	NK
Bach, J.S.–Cazden	Siciliano (BWV 1063)	Spr
Bach, J.S.–Menéndez	Sonata, f, No. 1	UME
Bach, J.S.–Menéndez	Sonata, g, No. 2	UME
Bach, J.S.–Gateau	Sonate No. 2	Bil
Bach, J.S.–Menéndez	Sonata, b, No. 3	UME
Bach, J.S.–Gee	Sonata No. 4	SM
Bach, J.S.–Menéndez	Sonata, F, No. 4	UME
Bach, J.S.–Menéndez	Sonata, G, No. 5	UME
Bach, J.S.–Menéndez	Sonata, D, No. 6	UME
Bach, J.S.–Bellison	Sonata, G	CF
Bach, J.S.–Benoy-Bryce	2 Slow Airs	OxU
Bach, J.S.–Tomei	Wachet Auf	Bar
Bacon, E.	Okefenokee	Ron
Bäck, S.	Elegy	Nor
Baermann, C.	Longing, op. 84/1	CF
Baermann, C.	Menuetto	NK
Baermann, C.	On the Lake, op. 85/5	CF
Baermann, C.	Pastorale, op. 84/3	CF
Baermann, C.	Serenade, op. 85/4	CF
Baermann, C.	Souvenirs de Bellini, op. 52	CF
Baermann, C.	24 Studies, op. 63	PWM
Baermann, H.–Schmeisser	Adagio (attributed to R. Wagner)	BrH
Baermann, H.	Adagio	EdK
Baeyens, H.	Adagio et Animato	EMb
Baeyens, H.	Canzonetta	EMb
Baeyens, H.	Pastorale	EMb
Bagdassarian, E.	Sonata	MKE
Baimgartner	Noch sind die Tagen der Rosen	MM
Baird, T.	2 Caprices	PWM
Baker, E.	Cantilena	Che
Baklanova, N.–Stark	8 Leichte Stücke	FrH
Baklanova, N.–Stark	8 Easy Pieces	MKE
Balay, G.	Monge–Czardas	EdS
Bal Y Gay, J.	Sonata	SMP
Banks, D.	Prologue, Night Piece and Blues for Two	S&C
Barat, J.–Voxman	Berceuse	Rub
Barat, J.	Chant Slave	ALe
Barat, J.	Fantaisie Romantique	ALe

Clarinet and Piano

Barat, J.	Pièce, g	ALe
Barat, J.	Solo de Concours	ALe
Barbi, C.	Carnival of Venice	CF
Barbier, R.	Allegro Brillante	EMb
Barbier, R.	Poco Adagio	EMb
Bariller, R.	Arlequinada	ALe
Bark, J.	Serenad. 1958	STI
Barlow, W.	Lyrical Piece	CF
Barnard, G.	Gloriana	CF
Barnard, G.	Merriment Polka	CF
Barnard, G.	Merriment Polka	Wat
Barnard, G.	Moana Waltz	Bar
Barnard, G.	Punch and Judy	Bar
Barnes	Arioso and Caprice	Big
Barnes	Valse Impromptu	Big
Barnett, D.	Fantasy on a Popular Song	EdS
Barraine, E.	Sérénade	GrF
Barret, A.-Pazemis	Chansonette	Rub
Barret, A.-Toll	5 Pleasing Airs	CF
Bárta, L.	4 Kompositionen. 1965	Art
Bárta, L.	Sonate	Art
Bartelt, E.	Meditation	PrA
Bartlett, J.-Hummel	A Dream	Rub
Bartók, B.-Suchoff	11 Easy Pieces	MCA
Bartók, B.-Harris	Evening in the Country	Lud
Bartók, B.-Váczy	An Evening in the Village	EMB
Bartók, B.-Balassa	Sonatina	EMB
Bartók, B.-Balassa	3 Chansons Populaires Hongroises	EMB
Bartók, B.-Stevens	3 Hungarian Folksongs	GaM
Bartsch, C.	Introduction et allegro	Mau
Bassi, L.	Fantasia on Airs (Il Trovatore)	CF
Bassi, L.	Fantasie (Rigoletto)	CF
Bassi, L.-Voxman	Lamento	Rub
Bassi, L.	Nocturne	CF
Bassi, L.-Voxman	Nocturne	Rub
Bauer, J.	Toccatina	PWM
Bauer, M.	Sonata	TP
Baur, J.	Ballata Romana. 1960	BrH
Bautista, J.	Fantasia Española, op. 17	Ba
Bavicchi, J.	Concerto	OxU
Bax, A.	Sonata	Cha
Bayly, T.	Long, Long Ago, op. 12	CF
Bazelaire-Londeix	Suite Française, op. 114	ScF
Beaucamp, A.	Complainte	ALe
Beaumont, P.	Con Amore	Cen
Becher, H.	Rhapsodie	PG
Beck, C.	Concerto	SS
Beck, C.	Legend	ALe
Beck, J.	Ornamente. 5 kleine Stücke	Hei

Becker, A.-Allendorff	Romance	CF
Becker, J.-Voxman	Romance, op. 3	Rub
Beechey, G.-arr.	5 Romantic Pieces	OxU
Beeckman, N.	Rapsodie flamande	ScF
Beeckman, N.	Souvenir du château de Miramar, op. 21	ScF
Beeler, W.-arr.	Christman Favorites	Sch
Beer, J.-Kratochvíl	Concerto, Bb, op. 1	MR
Beethoven, L. van -Langenus	Adagio	B&H
Beethoven, L. van	Adagio (Piano Sonata, op. 27/2)	CF
Beethoven, L. van -Bettoney	Adagio (Sonata Pathetique)	CF
Beethoven, L. van -Stouffer	Adagio Cantabile, op. 13	Ken
Beethoven, L. van -Andraud	Adagio Cantabile, (Sonata Pathetique)	SM
Beethoven, L. van	Adelaide	CF
Beethoven, L. van	Allegro (Sonata Pathetique)	CF
Beethoven, L. van - Frank, Forbes	A Beethoven Suite	OxU
Beethoven, L. van -Périer	Cantilena	ALe
Beethoven, L. van -Giampieri	Concerto, Bb (Violin Concerto, D)	Ric
Beethoven, L. van -Périer	Melody	ALe
Beethoven, L. van -Langenus	Menuetto (Piano Sonata, op. 22)	B&H
Beethoven, L. van -Trinkaus	Minuet	CF
Beethoven, L. van	Minuetto	MM
Beethoven, L. van -Delcampe	Romance en Fa	EMb
Beethoven, L. van	Sonata, op. 17	CF
Beethoven, L. van	Theme varie (Serenade)	MM
Beethoven, L. van -Bellison	Variations on a Theme of Mozart (Don Juan)	CF
Beez, J.	Sonatina	FrH
Bellini, V.-Joosen	Concerto	MM
Bellini, V.-Sambin	Duet (La Sonnambula)	EdS
Bellini, V.-Bassi	Fantasia (I Puritani)	CF
Bellini, V.-Lazarus	Fantasia on Airs (I Puritani)	CF
Bellini, V.-Davis	La Sonnambula	Rub
Benda	Introduction and Dance	EdM
Benda, F.	Sonata, F	EdM
Bender, V.	Concertino	ScF
Benguerel, X.	Duo. 1963	See
Ben-Haim, P.	Pastorale variée	ImV
Ben-Haim, P.	3 Lieder ohne Worte	IMP
Benjamin, A.-Kell	Jamaican Rumba	B&H
Benjamin, A.	Le Tombeau de Ravel	B&H
Bennett, D.	Clarinet Royale	CF
Benoy, A. & A. Bryce -arr.	First Pieces for Clarinet, 2 vols.	OxU
Benoy, A. & A. Bryce -arr.	2 Romantic Pieces	OxU

Benson, W.	Gentle Song	B&H
Bent, R.	Swiss Boy	CF
Bentzon, J.	Chamber Concerto op. 39, No. 3. 1941	SPD
Berg, A.	4 Pieces, op. 5	UE
Berghmans, J.	The Tight-rope Walker (Scenes from a Travelling Circus)	ALe
Bergman, E.	3 Fantasias, op. 42	EdF
Bergson, M.	Concert Aria	CF
Bergson, M.	In the North--In the South	CF
Bergson, M.	Scene and Air, op. 82	CF
Bergson, M.	Scene und Arie (Luisa di Montfort), op. 82	JoA
Bergson, M.	Louise de Montfoort--Scène et Air	MM
Bergson, M.-Voxman	Scene and Air (Luisa de Montfort)	Rub
Berkes, K.-arr.	Little Concert Pieces, 2 vols.	EMB
Berkes, K.-arr.	Works for Clarinet by Hungarian Composers	EMB
Berlioz, G.-Blachet	Pièce brève	Bil
Berlioz, H.	Suite (The Trojans) (cl in A)	S&C
Bernaud, A.	Concerto lyrique	ALe
Bernaud, A.	Phantasmes	ERR
Bernaud, A.	Recitative and Air	ALe
Bernier, R.	Reverdies	ALe
Bernstein, L.	Sonata	War
Berr, F.-Schütte	Instruktive Variationen nach dem "Air varie"	FrH
Berry	Fantasy in Five Statements	CF
Berthelot, R.	Ouled Nail	ALe
Bertouille, F.	Concertino	JB
Bettoney & Findlay-arr.	Pearls of the Old Masters, 2 vols.	CF
Beugniot, J.	Concertino	EMT
Beyer, E.	Divertissement	CF
Beyer, J.	Sonata	AMC
Bezanson, P.	Sonatina	CoF
Billault	Grand solo de concert	EdR
Birtwistle, H.	Linoi I. 1968	UE
Birtwistle, H.	Verses	UE
Bitsch, M.	Romantic Piece	ALe
Bizet, G.	Adagio (Symphony, C)	EdM
Bizet, G.	Agnus Dei (L'Arlésienne)	EdM
Bizet, G.	Agnus Dei	MM
Bizet, G.-Routier	Carmen Fantaisie	ECh
Bizet, G.	Entr'acte (Carmen)	EdM
Bizet, G.-O'Neill	Intermezzo (L'Arlésienne Suite No. 2)	Wat

Clarinet and Piano

Bizet, G. -Brooke	Minuet de l'Arlésienne	CF
Bizet, G.	Menuet de L'Arlésienne	MM
Bizet, G.	Serenade Espagnole	EdM
Bjelinski, B.	Sonata. 1966	HG
Blaauw, L.	2 Eenvoudige voordrachts stukken	T-M
Blake -Haring	Memories of You	ShB
Blatný, P.	Sonata	Art
Blavet, M. -Joosen	Sonatine, f	MM
Blazevich, V. -Schuman	Etude No. 86	Spr
Blazevich, V. -Schuman	Etude No. 92	Spr
Bléger, A.	Souvenir de Valence	MM
Blémant, L.	Boléro	ALe
Blémant, L.	8 Easy Pieces	EdS
Blémant, L.	4 Grands Solos	EdS
Bloch, A.	Denneriana	GrF
Bloch, W.	Concerto. 1955	LDo
Blok, V.	Sonatina	MKE
Blume, J.	Dispositionen	MV
Boccalari, E.	Fantasia di Concerto	CF
Boccherini, L.	Menuet	CF
Boccherini, L.	Menuet	MM
Boccherini, L.	Celebrated Minuet	NK
Boccherini, L. -O'Neill	Menuet	Wat
Bochsa, C.	Thème et variations	EdO
Boda, J.	Sonatina	Ken
Boeck, A. de	Impromptu	ScF
Boehm, T. -Bettoney	Souvenir des Alpes, op. 27/1	CF
Böhlmann, E.	Scherzo	FrH
Boéllmann, L. -Lucas	Menuet gothique	Dur
Boéllmann, L. -Lucas	Prière à Notre-Dame	Dur
Bohm, C. -Isaac	Perpetual Motion (Suite No. 3/6)	CF
Boieldieu, F. & Gambaro -Tuthill	Sonata	M&M
Boieldieu, F. -Wojciechowski	Sonata, Eb	Sim
Bois, R. du	Rounds	SD
Boisdeffre, R. de	Sonata op. 12, No. 1	Ham
Boisdeffre, R. de	3 Pièces	E&C
Boisdeffre, R. de	3 Pièces	Ham
Bonade, D. -arr.	16 Grand Solos de Concert	SM
Bonneau, P.	Suite	ALe
Bordogni, G. -Collis	4 Canzone	B&H
Bordogni, G. -Clark	20 Solo Studies	SM
Borodin, A. -Walters	Polovtsian Dance (Prince Igor)	Rub
Borodin, A. & Liadov, A. -Semyonov	3 Pieces	MKE
Borowski, F. -Harris	Valsette	Lud
Borris, S.	Rhapsodie und Capriccio,	

	op. 94	Hei
Bottje, W.	Modules. 1972	ACA
Boucard, M.	Andante cantabile	Bil
Bouillon, P.-Smith	Shower of Gold	CF
Bouillon, P.	La Pluie d'Or	MM
Bouny, J.	Andante de Concours	Bil
Bourguignon, F. de	Andante et Allegro	EMb
Bournonville, A.	Fantaisie-impromptu	Bil
Bousquet, F.	Solo de Concours	Com
Bousquet, F.	Solo de Concours	EdK
Bousquet, N.	Golden Robin Polka	CF
Boustad, A. & Chambers, C.	Essential Repertoire	UE
Bowman-Haring	12th Street Rag	ShB
Boyton, C.	Scherzo	B&H
Božič, D.	2nd Sonata in cool	EdD
Bozza, E.	Aria	ALe
Bozza, E.	Bucolique	ALe
Bozza, E.	Caprice-Improvisation	ALe
Bozza, E.	Claribel	ALe
Bozza, E.	Concerto	ALe
Bozza, E.-Hite	Divertissement	SM
Bozza, E.	Épithalame	Bil
Bozza, E.	Fantaisie Italienne	ALe
Bozza, E.	Idylle	ALe
Bozza, E.	Prélude et Divertissement	ALe
Bozza, E.	Pulcinella	ALe
Bozza, E.	Suite	ALe
Braga, G.-Clark	Angel's Serenade	CF
Braga, G.	Serenata	Dur
Brahe, M.-Glenn	Bless This House	B&H
Brahe, M.-Glenn	I Passed By Your Window	B&H
Brahms, J.-Langenus	Adagio (Violin Concerto, op. 77)	CF
Brahms, J.	Allegretto Grazioso	CF
Brahms, J.	Allegro Amabile	CF
Brahms, J.	Allegro Appassionato	CF
Brahms, J.	Andante con Moto	CF
Brahms, J.	Andante un poco Adagio	CF
Brahms, J.-Frank, Forbes	A Brahms Suite	OxU
Brahms, J.-Weston	Clarinet Quintet, op. 115	AlB
Brahms, J.-Harris	The Famous Waltz	CF
Brahms, J.	Hungarian Dance No. 5	CF
Brahms, J.	Hungarian Dance No. 6	CF
Brahms, J.	Lullaby (Cradle Song)	CF
Brahms, J.-Langrish	Romance, F	Nov
Brahms, J.	2 Sonatas, op. 120	Pet
Brahms, J.	Sonata, f, op. 120/1	AlL
Brahms, J.	Sonata, f, op. 120/1	B&H
Brahms, J.	Sonate, f, op. 120/1	BrH
Brahms, J.	Sonata, f, op. 120/1	CF

Brahms, J.	Sonata, f, op. 120/1	EdK
Brahms, J.	Sonata, f, op. 120/1	GaM
Brahms, J.	Sonata, f, op. 120/1	Int
Brahms, J.-Giampieri	Sonata, f, op. 120/1	Ric
Brahms, J.-Simon	Sonata, f, op. 120/1	Sch
Brahms, J.	Sonata, f, op. 120/1	Sim
Brahms, J.-Cavally	Sonata No. 1	SM
Brahms, J.-Müller, Michaels, Seiler	Sonata, f, op. 120/1	UE
Brahms, J.	Sonata, Eb, op. 120/2	AlL
Brahms, J.	Sonata, Eb, op. 120/2	B&H
Brahms, J.	Sonate, Eb, op. 120/2	BrH
Brahms, J.	Sonata, Eb, op. 120/2	CF
Brahms, J.	Sonata, Eb, op. 120/2	GaM
Brahms, J.	Sonata, Eb, op. 120/2	Int
Brahms, J.-Simon	Sonata, Eb, op. 120/2	Sch
Brahms, J.-Giampieri	Sonata, Eb, op. 120/2	Ric
Brahms, J.	Sonata, Eb, op. 120/2	Sim
Brahms, J.-Müller, Michaels, Seiler	Sonata, Eb, op. 120/2	UE
Brahms, J.-Scholtes	Waltz, Ab	Wat
Brandmüller, T.	Aphorismen. 1972	B&B
Brandt	Air Varie	T-M
Brant, H.	Colloquy	Spr
Braun, R.	Spirituals	YM
Brepsant, E.	5th Air Varie	CF
Brepsant, E.	Air varié No. 5	EdS
Brepsant, E.	Air varié No. 6	EdS
Brepsant, E.	8th Air Varie (Grand Fantasy)	CF
Brepsant, E.	Air varié No. 8	EdS
Bresgen, C.	Studies II, III, 2 vols.	LDo
Briegel, G.	Staccato-Legato	GFB
Briegel-Tucker	Triplets	GFB
Bright, W.	Enchantment (Andante and Polacca)	B-M
Brings, A.	Sonata	AMC
Brown, C.	2 Pieces	GD
Brown, R.	Double Fugue	Wes
Bruch, M.-de Smet	Kol Nidre, op. 47	Pet
Bruch, M.-Cheyette	Kol Nidre	SF
Bruniau, A.	Fantaisie tyrolienne	Bil
Bruniau, A.	Fantaisie variée	Bil
Bruniau, A.	Grande introduction et polonaise	Bil
Bruniau, A.	Sur la montagne	Bil
Bruns, V.	Concerto, op. 26	FrH
Bruns, V.	4 Stücke, op. 44	BrH
Bruns, V.	Sonate, op. 22	PrM
Brunt	Dapper Donkey	B-M
Brusselmans, N.	Recitative and Aria	EdS

Buchtel, F.	At the Ball	NK
Buchtel, F.	Chant d'amour	Vol
Buchtel, F.-arr.	Cielito Lindo	NK
Buchtel, F.	Dancing Shoes	NK
Buchtel, F.	Dutch Dance	NK
Buchtel, F.	The Flatterer	B-M
Buchtel, F.	Fun and Frolic	NK
Buchtel, F.	Gay Nineties Waltz	NK
Buchtel, F.	Golden Dreams Waltz	NK
Buchtel, F.	Golden Glow Waltz	B-M
Buchtel, F.	Happy Prince	NK
Buchtel, F.	Janus Waltz	NK
Buchtel, F.	King's Jester Waltz	NK
Buchtel, F.	Laughing Boy	NK
Buchtel, F.-arr.	Marines Hymn	NK
Buchtel, F.	Novelette	NK
Buchtel, F.	Pixies Waltz	NK
Buchtel, F.	Princess Helene	NK
Buchtel, F.	Serenade	NK
Buchtel, F.	Silhouette	NK
Buchtel, F.	Tango	NK
Buchtel, F.	Tarantelle	NK
Buchtel, F.	Valse Romantique	Vol
Buchtel, F.	Waltz Medley	NK
Buchtel, F.-arr.	When the Saints Go Marching In	NK
Buononcini, G.-Worley	Rondeau	Spr
Burger, J.	Dans van de Sultan	MM
Burger, J.	Herdersdans	MM
Burger, J.	Illusie	MM
Burgmueller, N.	Duo, op. 15	M&M
Burgmüller, N.-Michaels	Duo, op. 15	Sim
Burgmüller, N.-Lebermann	Duo, Eb, op. 15. 1834	SS
Burgstahler, E.	Chalumeau Caper	PrA
Burgstahler, E.	Clarion Caper	PrA
Burgstahler, E.	4 Clarinet Solos	PrA
Burgstahler, E.	Over the Break	PrA
Burnett, M.	Prelude, Song & Dance	Ric
Burt, F.	Duo	UE
Bush, G.	Rhapsody	Elk
Busoni, F.-Taubmann	Concertino, op. 48	BrH
Busoni, F.	Elegie	BrH
Busser, H.	Aragon, op. 91	ALe
Busser, H.	Cantegril, op. 72	ALe
Busser, H.	Pastoral, op. 46	ALe
Busser, H.	Pastorale, op. 46	Int
Buys, P.	Adagio and Tarantella	B-M
Buzzi-Peccia-Andreoni	Lolita	Ric
Byrne, A.	Suite	HE
Byrne, A.	2 Pieces	HE
Cabus, P.	Andante cantabile	Mau

Clarinet and Piano

Cacavas–McCathren	Air and Dance	SHM
Cacavas–McCathren	Clarantique	SHM
Cahuzac, L.	Cantilène	Bil
Cahuzac, L.	Fantaisie Variée	Bil
Cahuzac, L.	Pastorale Cévenole	Bil
Cahuzac, L.	Variations sur un air du pays d'oc	ALe
Cailliet, L.	Caprice Sentimental	SM
Cailliet, L.	Fantaisie	SM
Calmel, J.	Blues et Variation	Com
Calmel, R.	Concerto	EMT
Calmel, R.	Suite	Mau
Camidge, M.–Joosen	Sonatine, Bb	MM
Camilleri, C.	Divertimento No. 2	B–M
Camilleri, C.	Picolla Suita	Wat
Campagnoli, B.–Périer	7 Divertissements	Bil
Campo, F.	Kinesis	Wes
Campra, A.–Périer	Quick menuet and Gigue (L'Europe galante)	ALe
Canives, L.	Air Varie, op. 31	T–M
Canning, T.	3 Pieces	CoF
Caplet, A.	Improvisations	Dur
Capua, E. di	O Sole Mio (My Sunshine)	Cen
Capua, E. di	O Sole Mio	CF
Cardew, P.	The Lazy Faun	B&H
Cardew, P.	Scherzo	B&H
Cardillo–Andreoni	Core'ngrato	Ric
Carion, F.	Elégie	EMb
Carissimi, G.–Barnes	Heart Victorious	Spr
Carmichael, J.	Fêtes Champêtres	GaM
Carol, H.	Melodie	GaM
Carpentier, A.	La Parisienne	EdR
Carr, E.	Aubade	Ric
Carse, A.	Happy Tune	GaM
Carse, A.	Reverie	GaM
Carter, E.	Pastoral (cl in A)	TP
Castéréae, J.	Sonata	ALe
Carter, T.–Bettoney	Boston Commandery March (Onward Christian Soldiers)	CF
Casanova, A.	Ballade	Ric
Cattolica, G.	Duo	Ric
Cavallini, E.	Adagio e Tarantella	CF
Cavallini, E.–Waln	Adagio-Tarantella	NK
Cavallini, E.–Giampieri	Adagio and Tarantella	Ric
Cavallini, E.	Concert Fantasia (La Sonnambula)	CF
Cavallini, E.–Giampieri	Fiori Rossiniani	Ric
Cavallini, E.–Giampieri	Serenata	Ric
Cechvala, A.	Carnival Polka	PrA
Ceremuga, J.	4 Bilder (cl, accordion)	ES

Clarinet and Piano

Cerfontaine, M.	Andante and Allegro de Concert	MM
Ceulemans, I.	Sonatine	Mau
Chaban, F.	Library of the Student Clarinetist, 2 vols.	MKE
Chabrier, E.	Larghetto	EdS
Challan, R.	Pièce de Concours	ECh
Chambers, S.	Fragments & Things	AMC
Chambers, S.	Prelude	AMC
Chaminade, C.	Callirhoe (Air de Ballet)	Cen
Chaminade, C.-Paquot	La Chaise à porteurs	E&C
Chaminade, C.	The Flatterer	Cen
Chaminade, C.	Pastorale Enfantine, op. 12	CF
Chaminade, C.	Scarf Dance	Cen
Chapelle	Une Serenade	CF
Chavarri, E.	Fantasia	UME
Chenette, E.	Beauty and Joy	B-M
Chevreuille, R.	Récit et air gai, op. 46. 1950	CBD
Chiaffarelli, A.	Polonaise	CF
Chiapparin, T.	Prélude et Scherzo	ECh
Chopin, F.-Langenus	Etude, op. 10/3	CF
Chopin, F.-Galladoro	Fantasy ("Fantaisie Impromptu")	B-M
Chopin, F.-Bellison	Mazurka, op. 67/4	B-M
Chopin, F.-Gallodoro	Minute Waltz	B-M
Chopin, F.-Langenus	Minute Valse, op. 64/1	CF
Chopin, F.	Minute Waltz, op. 64/1	GFB
Chopin, F.-McCathren	Minute Waltz	SHM
Chopin, F.-York	Nocturne	BM
Chopin, F.-Schmutz	Nocturne	SHM
Chopin, F.-Forrest	Nocturne, No. 20	HeE
Chopin, F.	Nocturne, op. 9/2	CF
Chopin, F.-Delcampe	Nocturne, op. 9/2	EMb
Chopin, F.-Harris	Nocturne, op. 15/2	CF
Chopin, F.-Lalliet	Nocturne, op. 37/1	Dur
Chopin, F.-Lalliet	Nocturne, op. 48/1	Dur
Chopin, F.-Lalliet	Nocturne, op. 55/1	Dur
Chopin, F.-Jolliff	Ode to Music	Rub
Chopin, F.-Edwards	Polonaise	B-M
Chopin, F.-Carol	Polonaise, A	GD
Chopin, F.-Martin	Tristesse	EdR
Chopin, F.-Tesson	Tristesse	GD
Chopin, F.-Andreoni	Tristezza, op. 10/3	Ric
Chopin, F.-Mayeur	Valse, Db	CF
Chopin, F.-Delcampe	Valse, op. 64/1	EMb
Chopin, F.-Bellison	Waltz, op. 64/2	B-M
Chopin, F.-Gallodoro	Valse, op. 64/2	B-M
Christmann, A.-arr.	Baroque Music for the Clarinet	Sch
Christmann, A.-arr.	The Clarinet Recital	Sch
Christmann, A.-arr.	Solos for the Clarinet Player	Sch

Clarinet and Piano

Chruszch, R.	Duo	CoA
Chuikov, M.	Variations on "Not One Path in the Field"	MKE
Cimarosa, D.-Benjamin	Concerto	B&H
Cimarosa, D.-Joosen	Sonata, Bb	MM
Cirri, G.	Arioso	EdM
Clarke, Henry	Dialogue	AMC
Clarke, Herbert	Bride of the Waves	War
Clarke, Herbert	Southern Cross	War
Classens. H.	Chanson Anglaise	Com
Classens, H. & J. Lancelot -arr.	The Classic Clarinet, 4 vols.	Com
Classens, H.	Humoresque	Com
Classens, H.	Le Printemps	Com
Clement, F.	Marching thro' Georgia	CF
Clement, F.	Silvertone Polka	Vol
Clérisse, R.	Cadence de concours	ALe
Clérisse, R.	Préambule et danse	ALe
Clérisse, R.	Prélude et musette	Bil
Clérisse, R.	Promenade	ALe
Clérisse, R.	Récit et allegro	Bil
Clérisse, R.	Sylphide	Com
Clérisse, R.	Vielle chanson	ALe
Cockshott, G.	3 Pieces on Appalachian Folk-Tunes	Nov
Cohen, S.	Prelude and Tarantella	B-M
Colaço Osorio-Swaab, R.	Sonatine. 1958	SD
Collery, J.	Méditation	Bil
Collery, J.	Romance	GrF
Collis, J.	Festival Solo	B&H
Collis, J.	Little Concerto No. 1	Han
Collis, J.	Little Concerto No. 2	Han
Collis, J.	Tom Sawyer Suite	B&H
Collis, J.	Your First Clarinet Solos	Bou
Combelle, F.	1st Solo de concert	Bil
Confrey, Z.-Lang	Dizzy Fingers	B-M
Conley, L.	Summer Nocturne	Ken
Constant	Dialogue	ScF
Cooke, A.	Alla Marcia	OxU
Cooke, A.	Concerto	Nov
Cooke, A.	Sonata, Bb	Nov
Coolidge, R.	Visions of Things Past	Ken
Coolidge, R.	Weeping Dancer	Ken
Copland, A.	Concerto	B&H
Coquard, A.	Mélodie et scherzetto, op. 68	ALe
Coquard, A.	Mélodie et Scherzetto, op. 68	CF
Corbeel, R.	Moderato	Mau
Corbin, A.	Deauville	MM
Corelli, A.-Hite	Adagio and Gigue	SM
Corelli, A.	Air and Dance	EdM

185

Corelli, A.	Gavotte and Gigue	EdM
Corelli, A.	Gigue	EdM
Corelli, A.-Kell	Gigue	Int
Corelli, A.	Grave	GD
Corelli, A.-Hanson	Sonata	Lud
Corelli, A.	Suite, Bb	EdM
Corghi	Jeux	Ric
Coriolis, E. de	Sarabande et Tambourin	ALe
Corniot, R.	Sérénade-Tarantelle	ECh
Cosacchi, S.	Berceuse, op. 5d	HG
Cowell, H.	6 Casual Developments	TP
Cox, D.	Shalemy Dance	OxU
Crawford, R.-Kent	The Army Air Corps	CF
Creston, P.	Suite	Sha
Crooke, S.	Caprice	Sim
Cruft, A.	Concertino	GaM
Crusell, B.-Michaels	Concerto, f, op. 5	HSM
Cui, C.	Cantabile	CF
Cui, C.	En partant	ALe
Cui, C.	Orientale, op. 50/9	CF
Cundick, R.	Turnabouts	B&H
Cundy, W.	Fascinating Polka	CF
Custer, A.	Bagatelle	B-M
Dahl, I.	Sonata da Camera	AlB
Dahm, P.-arr.	Concert Album	EdM
Dahm, P.-arr.	Paris Soir	EdM
Dalen, H. van	Romance	HeE
Dancla, C.	Air Varié sur un Thème de Donizetti	MM
Dancla, C.	Andante et Mazurka	MM
Dancla, C.	Ballade et Air de Ballet	MM
Dancla, C.	Petite Etude et Polonaise	MM
Dancla, C.	Romance et Valse	MM
Daneau, N.	Caprice	T-M
Danks, H.	Silver Threads Among the Gold	CF
Danks, H.-De Rooij	Silver Threads Among the Gold	HeE
Dankworth, J.	Amusements	InM
Danzi, F.-Rimmer	Larghetto	OxU
Danzi, F.	Sonata, Bb	Sim
Dapogny, J.	6 Variations	MeP
Daquin, C.-Langenus	The Cuckoo	CF
Darcy, R.	Impromptu	EMb
Dautremer, H.	Gavottina	HLe
Dautremer, H.	Premier Souffle	HLe
Dautremer, M.	Page en Contraste	HLe
Dautremer, M.	Récit et impromptu	ALe
Davidson, J.	Sea Song Fantasy	PMP
Davies, P.	Hymnos	B&H

Clarinet and Piano

Davis, H. -arr.	Carnival of Venice	Rub
Davis, T. -Ayres	Sonata, g	Sha
Dearnley, C. -arr.	8 Easy Pieces by Classical Composers	Che
Dearnley, C. -arr.	More Easy Pieces by Classical Composers	Che
DeBeriot, C. -Rocereto	Adagio (Scene de Ballet)	Vol
De Bueris, J.	Gavotte Caprice	CF
De Bueris, J.	Miami Moon	CF
De Bueris, J.	Miami Shore	CF
De Bueris, J.	Musette	CF
Debussy, C.	Air de Lia	EdM
Debussy, C. -Piguet	Arabesque No. 1	Dur
Debussy, C. -Piguet	Arabesque No. 2	Dur
Debussy, C. -Roelens	Clair de Lune	Job
Debussy, C. -Cazden	Clair de Lune	Spr
Debussy, C. -Lucas	La Fille aux cheveux de lin	Dur
Debussy, C.	4 Pieces	MR
Debussy, C.	The Little Negro	ALe
Debussy, C.	Mandoline	EdM
Debussy, C.	Petite Pièce	Dur
Debussy, C.	Petite Pièce	Pet
Debussy, C.	Première Rapsodie	Dur
Debussy, C.	Première Rhapsodie	Pet
De Caprio, A.	Chant D'Orient	Rub
De Caprio, A. -Pierkot	Impressions	Rub
De Caprio, D.	Gypsy Aria	NK
De Caprio, D.	Toccatina, c	NK
De Costa, L.	Clarinette Dansant	B-M
DeCrepy, B.	Répliques	EMT
Deemer, C.	April Morning	B-M
Deemer, C.	Polka Tot	B-M
Deemer, C.	Sea Breezes	B-M
Defossez, R.	Sonatine	EMe
DeLacour, L. -arr.	Album de solos	Bil
DeLamater, E. -arr.	Adeste Fidelis	Rub
DeLamater, E.	Christmas Festival	Rub
Delaunay, R.	Au fil de l'eau	Bil
Delaunay, R.	Sérénade matutinale	Bil
Delbecq, L.	Enfantillage	MM
Delbecq, L.	Flanerie	MM
Delbecq, L.	Gemini	MM
Delbecq, L.	Juliana	MM
Delbecq, L.	Mélodia	EdR
De Leva -Andreoni	'E spingole frangese	Ric
Delhaye, A.	Silver Threads air varie	MM
Delibes, L. -Koff	Lakmé	Kof
Delibes, L. -Brooke	Le Pas des Fleurs	CF
Dello Joio, N.	Concertante	CF
Dello Joio, N.	3 Essays	B-M

Clarinet and Piano

Delmas, M.	Clair de lune	Bil
Delmas, M.	Fantaisie italienne	Bil
Delmas, M.	Promenade	Bil
Delmas, M.	Promenade	CF
Delmas, M.	Soir d'été	Bil
Delmas, M.	Variation tendre	Bil
DeLuca, J.	Thoughts of Gold	CF
Delvaux, A.	Pièce. 1967	CBD
Demersseman, J.	In Arcadie	MM
Demersseman, J.	Morceau de concert, op. 31	Bil
Denza, L.-Andreoni	Funiculì-funiculà	Ric
Depelsenaire, J.	Baroque	GD
Depelsenaire, J.	Concertino	Com
Depelsenaire, J.	Concertino da camera	EMT
Depelsenaire, J.	Concertino Melodico- Rhythmique	GrF
Depelsenaire, J.	Déploration	HLe
Depelsenaire, J.	Fièvre	Com
Depelsenaire, J.	Forlane	Bil
Depelsenaire, J.	Funambules	EMT
Depelsenaire, J.	Méditation	ECh
Depelsenaire, J.	Petite suite zoologique	Com
Depelsenaire, J.	Prélude et Divertissement	ECh
Depelsenaire, J.	Prélude et Scherzetto	ECh
Depelsenaire, J.	Recitative and Air	GD
Depelsenaire, J.	Sonatine, f	Com
Depelsenaire, J.	Spirals (Volutes)	GD
Depelsenaire, J.	Sur l'Albaicin; Souvenir d'Espagne	HLe
Déré, J.-Hite	Andante and Scherzo	SM
Dervaux, P.	Badinerie	ALe
Dervaux, P.	Complainte	ALe
De Schrijver, K.	Adagio en rondo capriccioso	Mau
Desenclos, A.	D'un troubadour	ALe
Desprez, F.	Apaisement	Mau
Desprez, F.	Esquisse poétique	Mau
Desprez, F.	Loryette	Mau
Dessau, P.	Variationen über ein nord- amerikanisches Volkslied	Pet
De Taeye, A.	Chant Élégiaque	ECh
Devienne, F.-Lancelot	First Sonata	EMT
DeVille, P.-Goldman	Blue Bells of Scotland	CF
DeVille, P.	Swiss Boy	Wat
Dewanger, A.	Ballad	ALe
Diabelli, A.-Hite	Introduction and Rondo	SM
Dias, J.	Petit fantaisie sur "Le Carnival de vénise"	Bil
Diaz, P.-Clement	The Carnival of Venice	CF
Dillon, R.	Tarantella	B&H
Dimler, A.-Balassa, Fodor	Concerto, Bb	Eul

Clarinet and Piano

Dindale, E.	Bucolique	EMb
Dindale, E.	Canzonetta	EMb
Dindale, E.	Danse Paysanne	EMb
Dindale, E.	Lied	EMb
Dinicu-Heifetz	Hora Staccato	CF
Dittersdorf, K. von -Hanson	Scherzo	Lud
Dobrzynski, I.-Kurkiewicz	Concerto	PWM
Dobrzynski, I.	Duo	PWM
Dodd, R.	Prelude, Air and Scherzo	OxU
Domazlicky, F.	Romance	HU
Donahue, R.	Divertimento	Bar
Donato, A.	Sonata	SM
Dondeyne, D.	Concertino	ALe
Dondeyne, D.	Romance	ALe
Donington, M.	Gavotte	GaM
Donington, M.	Prelude	GaM
Donizetti, G.-Päuler	Concertino	Eul
Donizetti -Meylan	Concertino, Bb	Pet
Donizetti, G.-Bassi	Divertissement on Airs from La Favorita	CF
Donizetti, G.-Menéndez	Fantasy on a theme from Lucrecia Borgia	UME
Donizetti, G.-Andreoni	Una Furtiva lagrima (L'Elisir d'amore)	Ric
Donizetti, G.	Sextette (Lucia di Lammermoor)	CF
Donizetti, G.-Lowry	Themes from Lucia di Lammermoor	B-M
Donjon, J.-Whiting	Invocation (Morceau pour Elévation)	CF
Donjon, J.-Whiting	Offertoire, op. 12	CF
Doppler, F.-Homer	Souvenir du Rigi	CF
Doran, M.	Sonata	Wes
Doren, T. van	Feuille d'Album	EMe
Dorsselaer, W. van	Andantino (d'après Lavignac)	HLe
Dorsselaer, W. van	Bella venezia	Bil
Dorsselaer, W. van	Féerie sur glace	Bil
Dorsselaer, W. van	Feux Follets	MM
Dorsselaer, W. van	Invocation et danse	Bil
Dorward, D.	Holiday Suite	GaM
Douliez, V.	Esquisse Pastorale	EMb
Douliez, V.	Feuille d'album	Mau
Drdla, F.-Damm	Souvenir	CF
Drdla, R.-Fischer	Souvenir	CF
Dressel, E.	Konzert	R&E
Dressel, E.	Partita	R&E
Driessler, J.	5 Stücke, op. 24/3a. 1952	B&N
Drigo, R.-Damm	Serenade	CF
Drigo, R.-Hofmann	Serenade	CF
Drucker, S.-ed.	Easy Original Clarinet Solos	MS

Dubensky, L.	Theme & Variations	CF
Dubois, P.	Beaugency-Concerto	ALe
Dubois, P.	Epitaphe	ERR
Dubois, P.	Menuet de Beaugency	ALe
Dubois, P.	9 Impromptus	ALe
Dubois, P.	Les Premiers pas du clarinet- tiste	ECh
Dubois, P.	Rhapsody	ALe
Dubois, P.	Romance	ALe
Dubois, P.	Sonatina	ALe
Dubois, P.	Virginie	ERR
Ducat, A.	Esquisse	Mau
Duijck, G.	Sonatine	T-M
Dukas, P.-Paquot	Alla Gitana	ALe
Dumortier, G.	3 Esquisses	Mau
Dunhill, T.	Phantasy Suite, op. 91	B&H
Duport, J.	Romance	Spr
Durand, A.-Hovey, Leonard	Chaconne	B-M
Durand, A.-Lucas	Chacone	Dur
Durand, A.	1st Valse	CF
Durand, A.	1st Valse	Dur
Durand, E.	Le Biniou	EdS
Durand, J.-Lucas	Rêverie	Dur
Dury, M.	Sérénade, op. 6	EMb
Dussek, F.-Pisk	Sonatina	TP
Duysburg, F.	Prélude et Danse	EMb
Dvořak, A.	Humoresque	Cen
Dvořak, A.-Sargent	Humoreske	CF
Dvořak, A.	Humoreske	NK
Dvořak, A.	Humoresque	MM
Dvořak, A.	Larghetto	NK
Dvořak, A.	Largo (New World Symphony)	CF
Dvořak, A.-Davis	Largo	Rub
Dvořak, A.-Simon	Sonatina	Bou
Dvořak, A.	Songs My Mother Taught Me	CF
Dyck, V.	Invocation à Euterpe	EdS
Dzerbashian, S.	Prélude-Dance	MKE
Eagles, M.	2 Sketches	Cha
Eckard -arr.	Highlights of Familiar Music	TP
Eckhardt-Gramatte, S.	"Ruck-Ruck" Sonate. 1947, rev. 1962	Can
Eddleman, D.	Diversions	MeP
Edelson, E.	Autumn Sunset	PrA
Edelson, E.	The Cuckoo Clarinet	Ken
Edelson, E.	The Forsaken Troubadour	PrA
Eder, H.	Sonatine, op. 34/5	LDo
Edmunds, C.	Gay Hornpipe	S&C
Edmunds, C.	Highland Croon	S&C
Edmunds, C.	Lament	S&C
Effinger, C.	Dialogue	TP

Clarinet and Piano

Effinger, C.	Melody	TP
Elgar, E.-Langenus	La Capricieuse	CF
Elgar, E.-Trinkaus	Love's Greeting (Salut d'amour)	CF
Elgar, E.	Salut d'amour, op. 12	SS
Elgar, E.	Pomp and Circumstance	B&H
Elgar, E.-Akers	Pomp and Circumstance	CF
Elgar, E.	Romance, op. 62	Nov
Ellstein, A.	Chassidic Dance	B-M
Emch, W.	Rondino	CF
End, J.	Idyl	Ken
End, J.	Introspection	Ken
End, J.	March of the Dwarfs	Ken
End, J.	Reverie	Ken
End, J.	Valse Cantabile	Ken
Endresen, R.	The Bumble Bee	CF
Endresen, R.	Caminando	Rub
Endresen, R.	Chief Eagle Feather	CF
Endresen, R.	Duke and the Cottontail	CF
Endresen, R.	Indispensable Folio	Rub
Endresen, R.	Over the Hills	CF
Endresen, R.	Pepperino	Rub
Endresen, R.	Rhapsody, g	B-M
Endresen, R.	U.S.A. Military March	CF
Endresen, R.	The Virtuoso	CF
Enesco, G.-Simon	First Roumanian Rhapsody	Bou
Enesco, G.-Goehr	Roumanian Rhapsody	EBM
Engelmann, H.	Melody of Love	TP
Engelmann, H.	Mobile II, op. 35	A&S
Erdmann, D.	Notturni. 1971	HG
Erdna	6 Swing Pieces	EdS
Escudié, H.-Seymour	Third Fantasia, op. 46	CF
Escudié, H.	3e Fantasie	MM
Escudié, H.	4e Fantasie	MM
Eshpai, A.	3 Mari Melodies	MKE
Esposito, E.	3 Momenti musicali	Edi
Etler, A.	Sonata. 1952	AMP
Evans, E.	Spanish Eyes	CF
Evans, E.	Sweet and Dainty	CF
Evans, L.	Nocturne	B-M
Evans, T.	Lady of Spain	SF
Evlakhov, O.	2 Pieces	MKE
Excoffier	Rapsodie provençale	Com
Eymann	Pastoral Portrait	B-M
Fabre, C.	Second Air Varie	Bil
Fabre, C.	Second Reverie	CF
Farkas, F.	Rumänische Volkstänze aus Belá Bartóks Sammlung aus dem Komitat Bihar	EMB
Fauconnier, B.	Fantaisie de salon sur un thème original	ScF

Clarinet and Piano

Faulx, J.	Bagatelle	EMb
Faulx, J.	Petite Pièce	EMb
Faulx, J.	Pièce de Concert	EMb
Faulx, J.	Romance	EMb
Fauré, G.	Berceuse	Ham
Fauré, G.	En Prière	EdM
Fauré, J.-Akers	The Palms	CF
Feld, J.	Instruktive Suite. 1960	Art
Feld, J.	Scherzino	ALe
Feld, J.	Sonatina	JB
Feld, J.	3 Kompositionen	ES
Felix-arr.	3 Canzonettas of the 17th Century	EdM
Felix, V.	Fantasia, op. 9	Art
Ferguson, H.	4 Short Pieces	B&H
Ferling, W.-Lefèbvre, Petiot	Adagio	ALe
Ferling, W.-Jeanjean	Andante de Concert	SM
Fernandez, C.-Jolliff	Cielito Lindo	Rub
Fernström, J.	Concerto	EMf
Fesch, W. de-Kaplan	Canzonetta	Spr
Fibich, Z.	Idylle, op. 16	Art
Fibich, Z.	Pastorale, op. 16	MKE
Fibich, Z.	Poem (Romance)	Cen
Fibich, Z.	Poem	NK
Fibich, Z.	Selanka	Lud
Field, J.	Notturno	MM
Fievet, L.	Chant Lyrique	GD
Fievet, P.	Minuetto	Bil
Filas, T.	Design for Clarinet	Big
Filas, T.	Elegy for Clarinet	Big
Filas, T.	Scherzo for Clarinet	Big
Filas, T.	Serenade for Clarinet	Big
Filas, T.	Tarantelle for Clarinet	Big
Filas, T.	Velocity	CF
Fillmore, H.	Lightning Fingers	CF
Finch, R.	Romanza	Che
Fink, M.	Caprices	Wes
Finke, F.	Sonate. 1950	BrH
Finlayson, W.	Curious Game	TP
Finlayson, W.	Teen's Parade	TP
Finzi, G.	Carol (5 Bagatelles)	B&H
Finzi, G.-Perry	Concerto	B&H
Finzi, G.	5 Bagatelles	B&H
Fiocco, J.-Balbo	Allegro (Première Suite)	SF
Fischer, C.	Nellie Gray	CF
Fischer, C.	Old Uncle Ned	CF
Fischer, J.	Concerto. 1965	Art
Flegier, A.	Villanelle du Midi	EdM
Fletcher, G.	Sonata	AMC
Flosman, O.	Rebellensonatine	Art

Clarinet and Piano

Flothuis, M.	Kleine suite, op. 47. 1952	SD
Flotow, F. Von-De Rooij	Tenor Aria (Martha)	HeE
Fomin, Y.-Fortunatov	Arioso (Orpheus)	MKE
Fontyn, J.	Mosaiques	Job
Forst	Homage to Ravel	EdM
Foster, I.	Evening Song	S&C
Foster, S.	Beautiful Dreamer	Cen
Foster, S.	Beautiful Dreamer	MM
Foster, S.	Jeanie with the Light Brown Hair	MM
Foster, S.	Massa's in the Cold, Cold Ground	CF
Foster, S.-Fisher	My Old Kentucky Home	CF
Foster, S.-Goldman	My Old Kentucky Home	CF
Foster, S.-Smith, Holmes	Old Black Joe	CF
Foster, S.-Lester	Old Folks at Home	B-M
Foster, S.	Sweetly She Sleeps	HeE
Frackenpohl, A.	Sonatina	Sch
Françaix, J.	Concerto	SS
Franck, C.-O'Neill	O Lord Most Holy	Wat
Francl, J.	Pastoral Suite	ES
Francl, J.	3 Instruktive Kompositionen	ES
Franco, J.	Introduction and Scherzo	PE
Francoeur, F.-Hite	Sonata, F	SM
Frangkiser, C.	Capricious Imp	B-M
Frangkiser, C.	Elegance	B-M
Frangkiser, C.	Joyeuse	B-M
Frangkiser, C.	Remembrance	B-M
Frangkiser, C.	Song of the Seine	B-M
Frank, A. & A. Forbes-arr.	Easy Classics for Clarinet	OxU
Frank, M.	Clownish Clarinet	B-M
Frank, M.	Concertino	B-M
Frank, M.	Evening Piece	CF
Frank, M.	Moment Musicale	SF
Frank, M.-McCathren	Serenade Classique	Bou
Frank-McCathren	Dance Humoresque	SHM
Franken, W.	Sonata. rev. 1972	SD
Frešo, T.	Composition	SHF
Frey, H.-arr.	Anchors Aweigh	Big
Frid, G.	Rhapsody on Dutch Folk Songs	SMP
Friedrichs, G.	Hommage à Anton Webern	B&B
Friemann, W.-Kurkiewicz	Quasi una sonata	PWM
Friml, R.-Simon	The Donkey Serenade	Sch
Frolich, O.	Vision	E-V
Frumerie, G. de	Concerto. 1958	CGM
Fürst, P.	Anti-Konzert, op. 52	LDo
Fulton, N.	3 Movements	GaM
Gabaye, P.	Sonatine	ALe
Gabelles, G.	Andante appassionato	Bil
Gabriel-Marie	La Cinquantaine	CF

Clarinet and Piano

Gabucci, A.	Concerto, Eb	Car
Gabucci, A.	Preludio all'Antica	Car
Gabucci, A.	7 Pezzi	Car
Gabus, M.	Sans-Souci	HLe
Gade, N.	Fantasiestücke	GaM
Gade, N.	Fantasy Pieces	WH
Gäfvert, H.	Fantasi	STI
Gagnebin, H.	Andante et allegro	ALe
Gagnebin, H.	Fantasy	ALe
Gal, H.	Sonata, op. 84	HE
Gallet, J.	Mini marche	Bil
Gallois-Montbrun, R.	Concertstück	ALe
Gallois-Montbrun, R.	Humoresque	ALe
Gallois-Montbrun, R.	6 Pièces musicales d'étude	ALe
Gamaliya	Concert Intermezzo	MKE
Gambaro, J.-Prendiville	Third Air Varie	CF
Ganne, L.-Paquot	Air de ballet	E&C
Ganne, L.-Hovey	La Czarine	B-M
Ganne, L.	La Czarine	E&C
Ganne, L.-Paquot	Danse Persane et Danse Egyptienne	E&C
Ganne, L.-Herman	Marche des Saltimbanques	ECh
Garant, S.	Asymetries No. 2. 1959	Can
Garden, E.	2 Contrasting Sketches	Bos
Gárdonyi, Z.	Sonatina. 1959	EMB
Gargiulo, T.	Serenata	Edi
Garland-Haring	In the Mood	ShB
Garlick, A.	Concert Piece	See
Garlick, A.	Sonata	See
Gastyne, S. de	Abstract	Fer
Gatti-Morra-Morra	Concertino, Bb	CF
Gaubert, P.	Allegretto	ALe
Gaubert, P.	Allegretto	CF
Gaubert, P.	Fantaisie	CF
Gaubert, P.	Fantaisie	Heu
Gaubert, P.-DeCaprio	Fantaisie	War
Gaubert, P.	Romance	ALe
Gaubert, P.	Romance	CF
Gautier, L.	Le Secret	CF
Gautier, L.-Davis	Le Secret	Rub
Gee, H.	Ballade	PrA
Gee, H.-ed.	12 Progressive Pieces	SM
Geissler, F.	Sonate. 1954	BrH
Geist, C.	Andante Pastorale	CF
Genzmer, H.	Concertino	Pet
Genzmer, H.	Sonatina	Pet
German, E.	Pastoral Dance	CF
German, E.	Valse Gracieuse	CF
Gerschefski, E.	"America" Variations for Winds, op. 44/7	CoF

Gerschefski, E.	"America" Variations for Winds, op. 45/5	CoF
Gerschefski, E.	March	CoF
Gerschefski, E.	Second March, op. 29/2	CoF
Gerschefski, E.	Sonatine	CoF
Gershwin, G.	Andante and Finale (Rhapsody in Blue)	War
Gershwin, G.-Sears	Blues (An American in Paris)	War
Gershwin, G.-Wood	Fascinating Rhythm	War
Geszler, G.	Recruiting Dance of 1848. 1948	EMB
Ghys, H.-Harris	Amaryllis & Country Gardens	Lud
Ghys, H.-Jolliff	Amaryllis	Rub
Giampieri, A.	Capriccio variato on "Carnival of Venice"	Ric
Giampieri, A.	Fantasia	Ric
Giazotto-Albinoni-Orsomando	Adagio, g	Ric
Gibbs, C.	3 Pieces	OxU
Giggy, F.	Rhapsody	CoA
Gilbert, A.	Spell Respell, op. 14 (cl in A/electric basset clarinet)	JB
Gillet, E.-Paquot	La Lettre de Manon	E&C
Gillis, D.	From a Winter's Dream	B&H
Gilmore, C.	Martinello	Rub
Giordani, G.	Caro mio ben	ScF
Giordani, G.	An 18th Century Air	EdM
Gipps, R.	Kelpie of Corrievreckan	HE
Glick, S.	Suite Hébraïque. 1961	B&H
Glière, R.-Jolliff	Russian Sailors Dance	Rub
Glière, R.	Valse Triste, op. 35/1	CF
Glinka, M.-Gurewich	The Lark--Romance	CF
Glinka, M.	Romance Melody	Spr
Glover, S.	Rose of Tralee	MM
Gluck, C.-Périer	Chorus and Aria (Pâris et Hélène)	ALe
Gluck, C.-Elkan	O Del Mio Dolce Ardor	HeE
Gluck, C.-Périer	Hymn (Iphigénie en Tauride)	ALe
Gluck, C.	Largo	For
Gluck, C.-Périer	Minuet (Orphée)	ALe
Gluck, C.-Brooke	Minuet and Dance of the Blessed Spirits	CF
Gluck, C.-Périer	Monastic March (Alceste)	ALe
Gluck, C.-Périer	The Naiad's Echo (Armide)	ALe
Gluck, C.-Davis	Spirit Dance	Rub
Godard, B.-Isaac	Adagio Pathetique, op. 128/3	CF
Godard, B.	Allegretto, op. 116	CF
Godard, B.-Lalliet	Allegretto, op. 116	Dur
Godard, B.-Roberts	Berceuse	CF
Godard, B.-Trinkaus	Berceuse	CF
Godard, B.	Berceuse de Jocelyn	ECh
Godard, B.	Berceuse (Jocelyn)	MM

Godard, B.	Berceuse	NK
Godard, B.-Herald	Canzonetta	CF
Godard, B.-Bettoney	The Idylle	CF
Godard, B.-Bettoney	Valse (Suite, op. 116/3)	CF
Goeb, R.	Concertant IVc	CoF
Goeb, R.	Homage à Debussy	CoF
Goedicke, A.-Simon	Etude, op. 28/2	Int
Goedicke, A.	Nocturne, op. 28/1	MKE
Goehr, A.	Fantasias, op. 3 (cl in A)	S&C
Goepfart, O.	Andante religioso, op. 22	WZ
Goeyens, A.	Berceuse	EMb
Goeyens, A.	Mélodie Anglaise	EMb
Goeyens, F.	Arioso	EMe
Goeyens, F.	Chant moresque	EMe
Goeyens, F.	Prélude et Allegro	EMb
Goeyens, F.	Rêverie	EMb
Goldman, E.-Tobani	Italian Fantasia	CF
Goldman, E.-Tobani	Tramp, Tramp, Tramp	CF
Goldman, E.	When You and I Were Young	CF
Goldmark, K.-Isaac	Adagio Pathetique, op. 128/3	CF
Goldmark, K.-Fain, Isaac	Bridal Song (Rustic Wedding, op. 26)	CF
Golestan, S.	Eglogue	EdS
Gonez-Freed	Hora Legato	Bou
Goodman, B.-Sauter	Clarinet à la King	B&H
Gordon, P.	Sonatina	TP
Gossec, F.-Weber	Gavotte	B-M
Gossec, F.	Gavotte	NK
Gossec, F.	Sonata	MM
Gossiaux, A.	Peter Pan	Mau
Gotkovsky, I.	Concerto	EMT
Gould, M.	Guajira	Cha
Gounod, C.	Adagio and Valse Lento (Faust)	CF
Gounod, C.-Marteau	Aria (Mireille)	Lud
Gounod, C.-Vachey	Ave Maria	GD
Gounod, C.-Alder	Ballet de Faust	ECh
Gounod, C.	Fantasia on "Faust" Themes	EdM
Gounod, C.-Routier	Faust Fantaisie	ECh
Gounod, C.-Brooke	Helen's Dance and Maiden's Entry (Faust)	CF
Gounod, C.-O'Neill	Madrigal and Arietta (Romeo and Juliet)	Wat
Gounod, C.-Walters	March of a Marionette	Rub
Gounod, C.-Routier	Mireille Fantaisie	ECh
Gow, D.	3 Miniatures	GaM
Graaf, de	Sonatine	MM
Granados, E.-Amaz	Spanish Dance No. 2. Oriental	UME
Granados, E.-Amaz	Spanish Dance No. 5. Andaluza	UME
Granados, E.-Amaz	Spanish Dance No. 6. Rondalla	

	Aragonesa	UME
Grebenshchikov, O.	3 Greek Dances	MKE
Green, H.	Phantom Ship	PMP
Gretchaninov, A.	Au foyer (Miniature Suite)	ALe
Gretchaninov, A.	Miniature Suite--Au Foyer	CF
Gretchaninov, A.	Bal champêtre (Miniature Suite)	ALe
Gretchaninov, A.	Brimborions, op. 138	GaM
Gretchaninov, A.	Chant d'artisan (Miniature Suite)	ALe
Gretchaninov, A.	Chanson d'aurore (Miniature Suite)	ALe
Gretchaninov, A.	La Demande; Le Soir	GaM
Gretchaninov, A.	En Avant; Mazurka	GaM
Gretchaninov, A.	En Route!; Pastorale	GaM
Gretchaninov, A.	Fanfare des coquelicots (Miniature Suite)	ALe
Gretchaninov, A.-Voxman	Fanfare of the Poppies	Rub
Gretchaninov, A.	La Fête; Plainte	GaM
Gretchaninov, A.-Voxman	Homeward	Rub
Gretchaninov, A.	Humoresque (Miniature Suite)	ALe
Gretchaninov, A.	Phantasm (Miniature Suite)	ALe
Gretchaninov, A.	Sévère Réprimande; L'Adieu	GaM
Gretchaninov, A.	Sonata, op. 172, No. 2	MKE
Gretchaninov, A.-Voxman	Song of the Dawn	Rub
Gretchaninov, A.	Souvenir de l'ami lointain (Miniature Suite)	ALe
Gretchaninov, A.-Voxman	Suite Miniature	Rub
Gretchaninov, A.	3 Easy Pieces, op. 145	EdK
Gretchaninov, A.	Travail du Matin; Une Journée Grise	GaM
Gretchaninov, A.	Valse dans le soir	ALe
Gretchaninov, A.	Vers la maison (Miniature Suite) (cl in A)	ALe
Grétry, A.-Périer	Arietta (Panurge)	ALe
Grétry, A.-Périer	Romance (Le Huron)	ALe
Grétry, A.-Périer	Sérénade (L'Amant jaloux)	ALe
Grieg, E.	Album	HE
Grieg, E.	Berceuse	CF
Grieg, E.-Phillips	4 Lyric Pieces	OxU
Grieg, E.	Ich Liebe Dich	MM
Grieg, E.	I Love Thee, op. 41/3	Pet
Grieg, E.	Letzter Frühling	MM
Grieg, E.	Norwegian Dance	CF
Grieg, E.	Poème Erotique	MM
Grieg, E.	Solvejg's Song op. 52/4	Cen
Grieg, E.-Goldman	Solvejg's Song	CF
Grieg, E.	Solvejgs Lied	MM
Grieg, E.-Schad	Sonata, F, op. 8	B-M
Grieg, E.	Watchman's Song, op. 12/3	Cen

Grillaert, O.	Fantaisie Varie	HeE
Grooms, C.-arr.	Dark Eyes (Russian Song)	Cen
Grooms, C.-arr.	Two Guitars (Russian Song)	Cen
Grovlez, G.	Concertino	Com
Grovlez, G.	Lamento et Tarentelle	ALe
Grovlez, G.	Sarabande et Allegro	ALe
Gruber-Kent	The Caissons Go Rolling Along	CF
Grudzinski, C.	Variations	PWM
Grundman, C.	Pipe Dream	B&H
Guarnieri, C.	Cançao Sertaneja	CF
Guenther, F.	Viennese Popular Melody	CF
Guide, R. de	Suite	ALe
Guilhaud, G.-Paquot	First Concertino	CF
Guilhaud, G.-Voxman	First Concertino	CF
Guilhaud, G.-Bennett	First Concertino	SF
Guilhaud, G.-DeCaprio	First Concertino	War
Guillaume, M.	Capriccietto, Canzona,	
Guillaume, E.	Introduction et Valse	EMb
Guillaume, M.	Capriccietto, Canzona,	
Gyring, E.	Saltarello	EMb
Gyring, E.	Little Serenade	HeE
Gyring, E.	Sonata No. 1	CoF
Gyring, E.	Waltz	HeE
Haass, H.	Mixtura	HG
Haddad, D.	Andante & Allegro	Sha
Haeyer, F. d'	Andante cantabile	EMe
Hagen-Haring	Harlem Nocturne	ShB
Hahn, R.	Sarabande et Thème Variée	CF
Hahn, R.	Sarabande et Thème Variée	Heu
Hahn, R.-Bonade	Sarabande et Thème Variée	SM
Hajdu, M.	Capriccio all ongarese	EMB
Hajdu, M.	Hungarian Shepherd's Song 1953	EMB
Halévy, J.-Balogh	Serenata	Lud
Halvorsen, J.-Forrest	Entrance March of the Boyards	HeE
Hamilton, I.	Sonata, op. 22	S&C
Hamilton, I.	3 Nocturnes, op. 6 (cl in A)	S&C
Handel, G.-Lalliet	Air Varié (L'Harmonieux Forgeron)	Dur
Handel, G.-Lucas	Air Varié	Dur
Handel, G.-Périer	Aria (Rinaldo)	ALe
Handel, G.	Cantilena	NK
Handel, G.-Brisset	Célébre largo (Air de Xerxes)	Bil
Handel, G.-Lucas	Celebrated Largo	Dur
Handel, G.-Barbirolli	Concerto	OxU
Handel, G.-Waln	Concerto, g	NK
Handel, G.-Voxman	Concerto, g	Rub
Handel, G.-Andraud	Oboe Concerto, g	SM
Handel, G.-Périer	Larghetto (2nd Organ Concerto)	
Handel, G.	Largo	CF

Handel, G.-Tesson	Largo	GD
Handel, G.	Largo	MM
Handel, G.	Largo	Wat
Handel, G.-Kaplan	Largo and Gigue	Spr
Handel, G.-Périer	Little March	ALe
Handel, G.-Hovey, Leonard	Sarabande and bourée	B-M
Handel, G.-Stiévenard	Sonate	ALe
Handel, G.	Sonata, F	EdM
Handel, G.	3e Sonata	MM
Handel, G.-Lurie	Sonata	Wes
Handel, G.-Glazer, Bodky	Sonata, op. 1/8	AMP
Handel, G.-Menéndez	6 Sonatas	UME
Handel, G.-Barnes	Sound an Alarm	Spr
Handel, G.	3 Dances and an Air	EdM
Handel, G.-Kell	3 Pieces	Int
Hanisch, E.	Sonata	S-V
Hannay, R.	2 Sketches	Roc
Hansen, T.	Nocturne	CoA
Hanus, J.	5 Impromptus, op. 45	Art
Hanus, J.	Short Stories No. 3	Gen
Harris, A.	A Kerry Tune	CF
Harris, F.	Andante & Gavotte	Lud
Harris, F.	Ballroom Echoes	Lud
Harris, F.	Charming Ballerina	Bar
Harris, F.	Clarinet Solo Collection	Lud
Harris, F.	Gay Minuet	Lud
Harris, F.	Marilee	Bar
Harris, F.	A Rendezvous in the Forest	Bar
Harris, F.	Sherilee Waltzes Nos. 1, 2	Lud
Harris, F.	2 Marionettes	Lud
Hartig, H.	Sonate, op. 7	B&B
Hartmann, J.	Longing for Home	CF
Hartmann, J.	The Return	MM
Has, S.	Concertino	PWM
Hasse, J.	Canzone	EdM
Hasse, J.-Joosen	Concerto, g	MM
Hasseneier	Dernière Pensée de Weber	T-M
Haubiel, C.	Gray Skies	B-M
Hauck, F.	Concertino	HG
Haufrecht, H.	Caprice	Bou
Haugland, A.	Stevjing (Duo)	Col
Haworth, F.	Shepherd's Purse Suite. 1958	Can
Hawthorne, A.	Whispering Hope	GFB
Haydn, F.-Kaplan	Allegro Grazioso	Spr
Haydn, F.	Andante (Concerto)	Spr
Haydn, F.	Capriccietto	For
Haydn, F.-Simon	Concerto, Bb	B&H
Haydn, F.	Concerto	MM
Haydn, F.-DeCaprio	Concerto (Cello Concerto)	War
Haydn, F.-Speets	Fragment uit de Harmonie-	

	Messe	T-M
Haydn, F.-Speets	Gratias	T-M
Haydn, F.-Brearley	Larghetto	Cur
Haydn, F.-Buchtel	Minuet (Militaire Symphony)	NK
Haydn, F.	Serenade	CF
Haydn, F.	Serenade	MM
Haydn, F.-Wienandt	Serenade	SM
Haydn, F.-Willaman	Serenade, op. 76/5	Spr
Haydn, F.-O'Neill	Serenade	Wat
Haydn, F.-Strauwen	La 7e parole du Christ	ScF
Haydn, F.	Theme con Variazione	MM
Haydn, F.-Kaplan	Theme and Variations	Spr
Head, M.	Echo Valley	B&H
Heaton-Smith, R.	Concerto	MR
Hedges, A.	Count Down	BrH
Heiden, B.	Sonatina	AMP
Heider, W.	Dialogue No. 1	Pet
Heine, S.-Merriman	Sonata	SM
Hekster, W.	Fluxions No. 2	SD
Heldenberg, A.	Allegro	MM
Heldenberg, A.	Esquisse	Mau
Heldenberg, A.	Improvisata	Mau
Heldenberg, A.	Tarantella	Mau
Heller, S.	L'Avalanche	NK
Helm, E.	3 Epigrams	AMC
Hemel, O. van	Capriccio. 1960	SD
Henderson -Sears	The Birth of the Blues	War
Henneberg, A.	Concertino	EMf
Henried, R.	Chinese Love Song	CF
Herberigs, R.	Sonatine. 1939	CBD
Herbert, V.	Czardas	NK
Herbert, V.	Gypsy Love Song	NK
Hermann, R.	Clarinet on the Town	CF
Hervig, R.	Sonata	AMC
Hess, W.	7 Recital Pieces, 2 vols.	HE
Hessenberg, K.	Variations	ALe
Heuberger, R.-Kreisler, Langenus	Midnight Bells	CFo
Heuberger, R.-Kreisler, Leidzen	Midnight Bells	CFo
Hewitt-Jones, T.	Capriccio	Nov
Hidas, F.	Concerto. 1951	EMB
Hidas, F.	Phantasy. 1964	EMB
Higuet, N.	Pièce pour concours No. 2	Mau
Hildemann, W.	Sonata	Hei
Hill, M.	Come Summer	B&H
Hindemith, P.	Sonata. 1939	SS
Hindemith, P.	Concerto. 1947 (cl in A)	SS
Hite, D.-arr.	18 Short Concert Pieces	SM
Hittler, L.	Country Gardens	Spr

Hlobil, E.	Rapsodie, op. 51	Art
Hoddinott, A.	Concerto	OxU
Hoffmann, A.	Alborada	B&H
Hoffmann, A.	Jota Aragonesa	B&H
Hoffmann, N.	Feu d'Artifice	EMb
Hoffmeister, F.-Stofer	Duo, A	SS
Hoffmeister, F.	Sonata (cl in A)	MR
Hofmann, R.-Waln	Polonaise	NK
Holewa, H.	Lyriska dialoger. 1964	STI
Holm, P.	Concertino	WH
Holmes, A.	Fantasy	ALe
Holmes, A.	Fantasie	CF
Holmes, A.	Fantasy	SM
Holmes, G.	Auld Lang Syne	CF
Homs, J.	2 Inventions. 1963	See
Honegger, A.	Sonatina	EdS
Hooghe, C. d'	Ballade	EMe
Hook, J.-Joosen	Engelse Sonate	MM
Hopkins, A.	Fantasy	Che
Horder, M.	Theme with 6 Short Variations	HE
Horder, M.	Variations on a Sussex Folk Tune	HE
Horký, K.	Sonatina	Art
Horovitz, J.	Concertante	Che
Horovitz, J.	Concerto, op. 7	B-M
Horovitz, J.	2 Majorcan Pieces	B-M
Hoskins, W.	2 Romances	CoF
Hosmer, L.-Waln	Romanza	NK
Houdy, P.	Elegy	ALe
Hovey-Leonard	Andante & Waltz	B-M
Hovey-Leonard	Aria Cantando	B-M
Hovey-Leonard	Arioso	B-M
Hovey-Leonard	Bagatelle	B-M
Hovey-Leonard	Berceuse	B-M
Hovey-Leonard	Caprice	B-M
Hovey-Leonard-arr.	Carnival of Venice	B-M
Hovey-Leonard	Chanson Moderne	B-M
Hovey-Leonard	Clouds in Summer	B-M
Hovey-Leonard	Concert Piece	B-M
Hovey-Leonard	Contra Danse	B-M
Hovey-Leonard	Gypsy Moods	B-M
Hovey-Leonard	In Minor Mood	B-M
Hovey-Leonard	Minuetto	B-M
Hovey-Leonard	Pergola	B-M
Hovey-Leonard	Il Primo Canto	B-M
Hovey-Leonard	Reflections	B-M
Hovey-Leonard	Scottish Air	B-M
Hovey-Leonard	Solo Semplice	B-M
Hovey-Leonard	Song of Spring	B-M

Clarinet and Piano

Hovey-Leonard	Theme and Variations	B-M
Hovey-Leonard	Valse Grazioso	B-M
Hovey-Leonard	Waltz Miniature	B-M
Howard	Still Waters	EdM
Howell	Rustic Dance	Cen
Howland, R.	Slumber Hour	CF
Howland, R.	Valse Teniral	CF
Hrisanide, A.	Sonate. 1960-62	HG
Hrisanide, A.	Sonata. 1964	EdR
Hubbell, F.	Typical Waltz	Ken
Hubeau, J.	Air tendre et varié	Dur
Huber, H.-Collis	Concertino, F	HeE
Hubert, R.	Un Soir	EdR
Hubschmann, W.	Fantasia	FrH
Hudadoff & Spire	11 Classic Solos	PrA
Hudadoff, I.-arr.	15 Intermediate Solo Series	PrA
Hudadoff, I.-arr.	Marches	PrA
Hughes-Pelz	Moods and Contrasts	SF
Hugon, G.	Scherzo	Bil
Humel, G.	Sonata. 1960	B&B
Hummel, B.	5 Miniatures	RS
Hummel, H.-arr.	Clarinet Polka	Rub
Humperdinck, E.-Lowry	Song & Prayer (Hansel & Gretel)	B-M
Hunt, R.	Meditation	B&H
Hurrell, C.	Bingo	GFB
Hurrell, C.	Dark Distance	CF
Hurrell, C.	The Lonely Birch Tree	Rub
Hurrell, C.	Tango Gitano	CF
Hyman, D.	Clarineta	B-M
Ibert, J.	Aria (cl in A)	ALe
Iliev, I.	Sonata, op. 36	MKE
Ilyinsky, A.	Lullaby	NK
Indy, V. d'-Piguet	Choral varié, op. 55	Dur
Ireland, J.	Fantasy Sonata	B&H
Isaac, M. & Lillya, C.	Album of Favorite Concert Clarinet Solos	Col
Isaac, M. & Lillya, C.	Album of Favorite Clarinet Solos	Col
Ištvan, M.	Sonata	Art
Ivanovici, J.-Davis	Waves of the Danube	Rub
Jacob, G.	Sonatina	Nov
Jacque-Dupont	Soir	ALe
Jahrl	Frolic of the Keys	GFB
Jakma, F.	1e Concertino	T-M
Jakma, F.	2e Concertino	T-M
Jakma, F.	Sancta Lucia air varié	MM
Jakma, H.	Romance	T-M
Jakma, H.	Starlight Dream	T-M
Jarnefelt, A.-Lowry	Prelude	B-M

Clarinet and Piano

Jeanjean, P.-Bonade	Andantino	SM
Jeanjean, P.	2nd Andantino	Bil
Jeanjean, P.	Arabesques	Bil
Jeanjean, P.	Au clair de la lune	Bil
Jeanjean, P.	Carnival of Venice	CF
Jeanjean, P.	Variations on "Carnival of Venice"	EdS
Jeanjean, P.	Clair Matin, Idylle	Bil
Jeanjean, P.	Heureux temps	Bil
Jeanjean, P.	Prelude and Scherzo	ALe
Jeanjean, P.	Rêverie de printemps	Bil
Jeanjean, P.	Scherzo Brillante	CF
Jeanjean, P.-Bonade	Scherzo Brillante	SM
Jessel, L.-Miller	Parade of the Wooden Soldiers	EBM
Jettel, R.	Concertino	Pet
Jettel, R.	4 Concert Etudes (Accomplished Clarinettist, vol. 3)	AlB
Jettel, R.	Introduktion und Variationen	JKM
Jettel, R.	9 Leichte Vortragsstücke	Wel
Jettel, R.	Sonata	FrH
Jettel, R.	10 Kleine Übungsstücke	LDo
Jettel, R.	3 Caprices	Pet
Johnson, C.	Bel Canto	Rub
Jolivet, A.	Meditation	Int
Jolliff, A.-arr.	Home on the Range (Cowboy Song)	Rub
Jolliff, A.-arr.	I've Been Workin' on de Railroad	Rub
Jonák, Z.	Serenade	ES
Jones, R.	Sonatina	Sha
Jongen, L.	Pastorale et Gigue	EMb
Jordan, E.	La Brilliante	CF
Juchelka, M.	Sonatine	Art
Kabalevsky, D.-Seay	Waltz (The Comedians)	Spr
Kalabis, V.	Sonate, op. 30. 1968-69	Art
Kalinnikov, V.	Chanson Triste	EdM
Kalliwoda, J.-Bellison	Morceau de Salon	CF
Kaplan, D.-arr.	Gotham Collection	Spr
Kardos, I.	Poema	Gen
Karg-Elert, S.	Sonata, op. 139b, No. 2 (cl in A)	WZ
Karkoff, M.	Notturno, op. 81. 1966	STI
Károlyi, P.	Meditazione. 1967	EMB
Kauder, H.	Sonata	SM
Kauffmann, G.-Gore	6 Chorales (Harmonische Seelenlust)	Con
Kaufmann, A.	Schipot, op. 48	LDo
Kaufmann, A.	Sonatine, op. 53	LDo

Clarinet and Piano

Kelly, B.	3 Bagatelles	Cha
Kelly, B.	2 Concert Pieces	Nov
Kelterborn, R.	4 Pieces. 1970	B&B
Kempe, H.	Trikolon; serenad	STI
Kendell, I.	Episode	Che
Kenins, T.	Divertimento. 1960	B&H
Kennaway, L.	Caprice	S&C
Kennedy, A.-Hummel	Star of the East	Rub
Kennedy, H.	Star of Hope (Reverie)	Cen
Kent -arr.	Let Us Have Music for Clarinet	CF
Kesnar, M.	Canzonetta	CF
Kesnar, M.	Clown Festival	CF
Kesnar, M.	Mood of the Hills	CF
Kesnar, M.	Serenade	CF
Ketelbey, A.-Teague	In a Monastery Garden	War
Ketelbey, A.	In a Persian Market	Bos
Keys, I.	Concerto	Nov
Khachaturian, A.-Stark	Andante (Gayane)	MKE
Khachaturian, A.-Schöebel	Sabre Dance	MCA
Khagagortian, E.	Concerto	MKE
Kindermann, J.-Stubbins	Old Suite	Uni
King -Garrison	Song of the Islands	EBM
King, K.	Night in June	Bar
Kinyon, J.	Program Pieces	War
Kinyon, J.	Recital Pieces	War
Kirkor, G.	Meditation, op. 16/1	MKE
Kisielewski, S.	Intermezzo	PWM
Kitazume, Y.	Sonatine	Bil
Klauss, N.	Masquerade	PrA
Klauss, N.-McCathren	Moonlight Melody	Ken
Kleinsinger, G.	Street Corner Concerto	Cha
Klosé, H.-Jeanjean	2nd Air varié	ALe
Klosé, H.-Jeanjean	7th Air varié	ALe
Klosé, H.-Jeanjean	8th Air varié	ALe
Klosé, H.-Jeanjean	Concertino	ALe
Klosé, H.-Jeanjean	Pensées musicales, L'Aube	ALe
Klosé, H.-Jeanjean	2nd Solo	ALe
Klosé, H.-Langenus	9th Solo	CF
Klosé, H.-Jeanjean	12th Solo	ALe
Klosé, H.-Gatley	12th Solo	CF
Knight, J.-Clement	Rocked in the Cradle of the Deep	Vol
Knipper, L.	Meadowlands	CF
Koch, E.	Spielbuch, 2 vols.	Deu
Koehler, E.	Sonatina, op. 15	CoF
Koepke, P.	Rhapsody	Rub
Kohn, K.	Song for Clarinet	CF
Kohs, E.	Sonata	TP

204

Clarinet and Piano

Kókai, R.	4 Hungarian Dances. 1951	EMB
Koll, A.	Rendezvous	FrH
Komarovsky, A.	5 Pieces	MKE
Koppel, H.	Variations	ALe
Korchmarev, K.	2 Pieces on Turkmenian Themes	MKE
Korda, V.	Novelette	LDo
Kořínek, M.	Concerto	SHF
Kořínek, M.	Sonatine	Art
Kornauth, E.	Violasonate, op. 3	LDo
Kossenko, V.-Cybriwsky, Tyndall	Gavotte	Spr
Kostlan, I.	2 Etudes	MKE
Kouguell, A.	Song without Words	SF
Koutzen, B.	Melody with Variations	Gen
Koutzen, B.	Pastorale and Dance	BM
Kovařiček, F.	Concerto	Art
Koželuh, J.-Kratochvíl	Concerto, Eb	ES
Kozlovsky, O.-Fortunatov	2 Pieces (Fingal)	MKE
Kraft, L.	Ballad	TP
Kraft, L.	5 Pieces	Gen
Kratochvíl, J.	Kleine Suite	Art
Kratochvíl, J. (ed)	Selected Compositions, 2 vols.	Art
Krebs, W.	Tête à Tête	B-M
Krein, A.	2 Pieces	MCA
Kreisler, F.-Langenus	Andantino	CFo
Kreisler, F.-Langenus	Caprice Viennois	CFo
Kreisler, F.-Langenus	Liebesfreud	CFo
Kreisler, F.-Leidzen	Liebesfreud	CFo
Kreisler, F.-Langenus	Liebeslied	CFo
Kreisler, F.-Leidzen	Miniature Viennese March	CFo
Kreisler, F.-Langenus	The Old Refrain	CFo
Kreisler, F.-Ranger	The Old Refrain	CF
Kreisler, F.-Langenus	Praeludium & Allegro	CFo
Kreisler, F.-Leidzen	Rondino on a theme of Beethoven	CFo
Kreisler, F.-Langenus	Schön Rosmarin	CFo
Kreisler, F.-Leidzen	Schön Rosmarin	CFo
Kreisler, F.-Leidzen	Tambourin Chinois	CFo
Krenek, E.	Kleine Suite, op. 28. 1924	B&N
Krenek, E.	Suite. 1955	Ron
Krieger, J.-Stubbins	Old Suite	Uni
Kriukov, V.	Concertino	MKE
Kroepsch, F.-Sargent	Down in a Deep Cellar	CF
Krommer, F.-Kratochvíl	Concerto, Eb, op. 36	Art
Kropfreiter, A.	Aphorismen	LDo
Kubik, G.	Sonatina	MCA
Kubín, R.	Concerto	Art
Kubizek, A.	Concerto, op. 9	LDo
Kubizek, A.	Sonatine, op. 5a	LDo

Clarinet and Piano

Kuhlau, F.	Menuett	NK
Kummer, H.	Eine Handvoll Feldblumen, op. 33	WZ
Kupferman, M.	Four on a Row. 1965	Gen
Kurpinski, K.-Madeja	Concerto	PWM
Kurtz, S.	Notturno	SF
Kuszing, J. (ed)	Klarinettenmusik für Anfänger	EMB
Kutsch, B.	Bläsers Lieblinge	WZ
Labate, B.	Dancing Doll	Spr
Labate, B.	Habanera	CF
Labate, B.	Intermezzo--Polka	CF
Labate, B.	Villanella	CF
Labitzky, A.	Dream of the Shepherdess	Cen
Labitzsky, A.	The Herd Girl's Dream	CF
Labole	Papillon d'azur	EdR
Lachowska, S.	Liryki	PWM
Lachowska, S.-Wyczynski	Sonatina	PWM
Lacome, P.	Rigaudon	SM
Laderman, E.	Sonata	OxU
Ladmirault, P.	Sonate	ALe
Lake, M.	Annie Laurie	CF
Lake, M.	Naida	Lud
Lalinov, M.	Armenian Dance	MKE
Lalo, E.-Langenus	Andante (Symphonie Espagnole)	CF
Lalo, E.-Langenus	Scherzando (Symphonie Espagnole, op. 21)	CF
Lalo, E.	Le Roi d'Ys	MM
Lamote de Grignon, J.-Amaz	Canço de Maria	UME
Lamote de Grignon, J.-Amaz	Rêverie (Schumanniana)	UME
Lancelot, J.-arr.	La Clarinette classique, 4 vols.	Com
Lancen, S.	Espièglerie	HeE
Lancen, S.	Intimité	.MM
Lancen, S.	Introduction et Allegro Giocoso	MM
Lancen, S.	Introduction et rondo	Bil
Lancen, S.	Pastorale	HeE
Lancen, S.	Romance	HeE
Lancen, S.	3 Pièces	MM
Lancen, S.	Vacances et rondo	Bil
Landré, G.	Concerto	SD
Lange, G.	Blumenlied (Flower Song)	CF
Langenus, G.	Chrysalis	CF
Langenus, G.	Commuters' Express	CF
Langenus, G.	Donkey-Ride	CF
Langenus, G.	Examinations	CF
Langenus, G.	In Cowboy Land	CF
Langenus, G.	In The Forest	CF
Langenus, G.	Indian Mother Song	CF
Langenus, G.	Irish Serenade	CF

Clarinet and Piano

Langenus, G.-arr.	Langenus Clarinet Repertoire	CF
Langenus, G.	Lullaby	CF
Langenus, G.	Mount Vernon Menuet	CF
Langenus, G.	Old New Orleans	CF
Langenus, G.	Scale Waltz	CF
Langlois, T.	Nocturne et Finale	EMb
Langlois, T.	Pastorale	Mau
Langlois, T.	Sonatine	Mau
Lannoy, J. de	Introduction et thème varié	ScF
Lannoy, J. de	Le Lever de l'Aurore ou le Réveil des Oiseaux	ScF
Laparra, R.	Prélude valse et Irish reel	ALe
Lara, A.	Granada	SMP
Larsson, L.	Concertino, op. 45/3	B&H
Laube, P.	Alsatian Dance	CF
Law, A.	Burgundy	ATL
Lawton, S.-arr.	Clarinetist's Book of Carols	OxU
Lawton, S.	Fugue on a Nursery Theme	B&H
Lawton, S.-arr.	The Young Clarinetist, 3 vols.	OxU
Lebierre	Airs Bohemiens	T-M
Lebierre	Variations Concertantes sur un Air Suisse	T-M
Le Boucher, M.	Ballade	Bil
Le Boucher, M.	Fantaisie Concertante	ALe
Leclair, J.	Dance Provençale	EdM
Leclair, J.-Simm	Dance Provençale	GaM
Leclair, J.	Musette and Scherzo	NK
Leclair, J.	Sarabande and Tambourin	For
Leclerc, M.	Contrasts	Mau
Leclercq, E.	Intimité	EMb
Leclercq, E.	Moment heureux	EMb
Lecuona, E.-Simon	Andalucia	EBM
Lecuona, E.-Simon	Malaguéña	EBM
Lederer, D.-Paquot	Poème hongrois	E&C
Leduc, J.	Ballade	ALe
Leduc, J.	Dialogue, op. 39	JB
Leduc, J.	Fantaisie sur La Folia	Mau
Leeuwen, A. van	Andante	MM
Lefèbvre, C.-Cailliet	Andante and Allegro	SM
Lefèbvre, C.	Fantaisie-Caprice, op. 118	ALe
Lefèvre, C.	Fantaisie Caprice, op. 118	CF
Lefèbvre, C.-Bonade	Fantaisie Caprice, op. 118	SM
Lefèvre, J.X.-Dobrée	Sonata, Bb, op. 12/1	OxU
Lefèvre, X.-Borrel	Sonata No. 2 (cl, bc)	ERS
Lefèvre, J.X.-Borrel	Sonata op. 12, No. 3	ERS
Lefèvre, X.-Viollier	Sonata No. 5	ERS
Lefèvre, X.-Robert	Sonata No. 7	GD
Legley, V.	Sonate, op. 40/3. 1952	CBD
Lehar, F.-Klickmann	Frasquita Serenade	EBM
Lemaire, F.	3 Chants	Bil

Clarinet and Piano

Lemare, E.-Trinkaus	Andantino	CF
Lemare, E.-Long	Andantino	Vol
Lemare, E.	Cathedral Meditation	Cen
Lenom, C.	Caprice-Mazurka	EdS
Lenom, C.-Findlay	Lullaby	CF
Leoni, C.	Idyl	B-M
Leoni, C.	Ode to Autumn	B-M
Leroux, F.	Une Soirée près du Lac	Heu
Lester, L.	Crimson Blushes	Cen
Letellier & Lecomte	Ballade	EdR
LeThière, C.	Alvanian	CF
LeThière, C.	Andante and Polonaise	B&H
Levy, E.	Divertimento. 1952	See
Levy, E.	Sonata	AMC
Levy, F.	Sonata. 1968	See
Lewis, E.	2 Lyric Pieces	TP
Lewis, F.	Sonata	CoA
Liddle, S.-Glenn	How Lovely Are Thy Dwellings	B&H
Lieurance, T.	The Brides Maid	CF
Liliuokalani (Queen)	Aloha Oe	CF
Lillo, G.-Marteau	Osteria Bolero	Lud
Lincke, P.-Miller	Glow-Worm	EBM
Lincke, P.	Glow Worm	NK
Lincke, P.-Walters	The Glowworm	Rub
Linglin	Andante et Allegro	GrF
Linke, N.	5 Stücke	Hei
Lisenko, M. & Shchurovsky, Y.	Elegy-Romance	MKE
Liszt, F.	Love Dreams (Liebestraum)	Cen
Liszt, F.-Bettoney	Liebestraume (Dreams of Love)	CF
Liszt, F.-Tesson	Liebestraum	GD
Liszt, F.-Balassa	Notturno No. 1	EMB
Liszt, F.-Balassa	Première Valse Oubliée	EMB
Liszt, F.-Balassa	Romance Oubliée	EMB
Litaize, G.	Récitatif et thème varié	ALe
Litolff, H.-Richardson	Scherzo (Concerto Symphonique No. 4)	B&H
Llewellyn, E.-MacLean	My Regards	War
Lloyd, C.	Suite in the old style	B&H
Locatelli, P.	Aria	EdM
Loeillet, J.	Courante	EdM
Loeillet, J.-Kaplan	Minuetto	Spr
Loeillet, J.	Sonata, Eb	Sha
Loevendie, T.	10 Easy Sketches	SD
Loewe, C.	Scottish Scenes	M&M
Lolli, A.-Stubbins	Grave and Allegro	CF
Lonque, A.	Introduction et Danse Rustique	EMb
Lonque, A.	Tema e variazioni	Mau
Lonque, A.	3 Pièces de Fantaisie	EMb
Lopez, C.	Fantasia	UME
Lorenzo, L. de -Labate	Giovialita (Valse di Concerto)	CF

Clarinet and Piano

Lotti, A.	Arietta	EdM
Lotzenheiser, G.	Minuet Miniature	B-M
Loumey	Shadows on the Water	Cen
Lovelock, W.	Sonatina	Cha
Lovelock, W.	2 Pieces	B&H
Lowry, R. & F. Weber	Clarinet Soloist (Level 1)	B-M
Lowry, R.	Festival Fantasia	B-M
Lowry, R.	Sioux Song & Dance	B-M
Lowry, R.	Valse & Volante	B-M
Lucas, E.	Divertissement	Dur
Luening, O.	Fantasia brevis	TP
Lully, J.-Kaplan	Air and Courante	Spr
Lully, J.-Périer	Ariette en rondeau (Les Ballets du Roy)	ALe
Lully, J.	Dances for the King	EdM
Lully, J.-Périer	Minuet and Bourrée (Phaeton)	ALe
Lully, J.-Périer	Religious March and Minuet (Bellérophon)	ALe
Lully, J.-Périer	Saraband and gavotte	ALe
Lully, & Bach, J.S.-Semyonov	3 Pieces	MKE
Lunden, L.	Canzonetta. 1959	STI
Lurie & Neufeld-arr.	Classics for Clarinet	CF
Luscomb, F.	My Old Kentucky Home	Bar
Lutoslawski, W.	Préludes de Danse	AP
Lutyens, E.	5 Little Pieces, op. 14/1. 1945	S&C
Luysterburg	Bagatelle	T-M
Macbeth, A.	Intermezzo "Forget Me Not"	CF
MacDonald	Cuban Rondo	B-M
MacDowell, E.-Isaac	To A Wild Rose	CF
MacDowell, E.	To A Wild Rose	MM
MacDowell, E.	To A Wild Rose	NK
MacDowell, E.-Dahl, Roussakis	3 Pieces	JB
Maddox, E.	Coordinates for Clarinet and Piano	Ken
Maganini, Q.	Peaceful Land	EdM
Magnani, A.	Concert Solo	ALe
Magnani, A.	1st Divertimento	ALe
Magnani, A.	2nd Divertimento	ALe
Magnani, A.	Mazurka-caprice	ALe
Magnani, A.-Arnold	Mazurka Caprice	CF
Mahy, A.	Bourrée, Cadenze e Finale	MM
Mahy, A.	Serenade voor Klarinet	MM
Maillot, J.	Impromptu	Com
Mallord, J.	Five, Six, Seven	Sch
Malotte, A.-Lake	The Lord's Prayer	Sch
Manevich, A.-Drucker	Concerto	Int
Manevich, A.-Rosenthal	Concerto	MCA
Maniet, R.	Prélude et Allegro	Mau
Maniet, R.	Romance I	Mau
Maniet, R.	Romance II	Mau

Clarinet and Piano

Marcello, B.-Joosen	Concerto, c	MM
Marcello, B.-de Smet	Sonata, Bb, No. 6	Pet
Marchetti, F.-Hurrell	Fascination	Rub
Marco, T.	Jetztzeit. 1971	HMo
Margola, F.	3 Studi da concerto	GZ
Marie, G.	Sérénade badine	Bil
Marie, G.	Serenade "Badine"	CF
Marie, G.	La Cinquantaine	Bil
Martelli, H.	Préambule et scherzo	Bil
Martini, G.	Canzona	MM
Martini, P.	Plaisir d'Amour	EdM
Martini, P.-Overveld	Plaisir d'Amour	T-M
Martinon, J.	Sonatine	Bil
Martinu, B.	Sonatina	ALe
Marttinen, T.	Delta. 1962	MT
Marty, G.	1st Fantasy	ALe
Marty, G.	Première Fantasy	CF
Marty, G.-Bonade	First Fantaisie	SM
Mascagni, P.-Lowry	Intermezzo (Cavalleria Rusticana)	B-M
Mascagni, P.	Intermezzo	CF
Mascagni, P.	Intermezzo Sinfonico	CF
Mascagni, P.-Davis	Intermezzo	Rub
Mascagni, P.-Schaefer	Siciliana	War
Mason, J.	Tenuto	See
Massenet, J.	Andante	CF
Massenet, J.	Elegie (Melody)	Cen
Massenet, J.-Trinkaus	Elegy	CF
Massenet, J.-Isaac	Meditation (Thais)	CF
Massenet, J.-Taffanel	Meditation (Thais)	CF
Massenet, J.	The Virgin's Last Slumber	CF
Maugue, J.	Bucolique	Bil
Maurat, E.	Petites Inventions, op. 39/3	EME
Maury, L.	Song Without Words	Wes
Mayerus, A.	Cadenza et Divertimento	EMb
Mayeur, L.	Caprice Polka	CF
Mayeur, L.-Brooke	Valse Caprice	CF
Mazas, J.-Paulson	Musette	PrA
Mazellier, J.	Fantasy-Ballet	ALe
Mazellier, J.-Waln	Fantasy Ballet	NK
Mazellier, J.	Fantasy-Ballet	SM
McBride, R.	Hot-Shot Divertimento	CoF
McBride, R.	The World Is Ours	CoF
McCabe, J.	3 Pieces. 1964	Nov
McCathren, D.	Premier Waltz	Hal
McCoy-Stuart	Trio (Lights Out March)	CF
McKay, F.	Buckboard Blues	Bar
McKay, F.	Dream Waltz	Bar
McKay, F.	Hallowe'en Time	Bar
McKay, F.	Hernando's Holiday	Bar

Clarinet and Piano

McKay, F.	Jig for Jeanine	Bar
McKay, F.	The Powdered Wig	Bar
McKay, F.	Ye Traveling Troubador	Bar
McKay, G.	Arietta and Capriccio	BM
McKay, G.	Concert Solo Sonatine	BM
McKay, G.	Moods	TP
McKay, G.	Moonlight Over the Jungle	CCo
McKay, G.	2 Dance Scenes	TP
Meacham, F.	American Patrol	Cen
Meacham, F.-Kent	American Patrol	CF
Meacham, F.-Hummel	American Patrol	Rub
Meister, G.-Langenus	Erwinn Fantasia	CF
Meister, G.	Erwinn Fantasie	MM
Mellnäs, A.	Concerto	EMf
Mendelssohn, F.-Hermann	Allegro (Violin Concerto)	Pod
Mendelssohn, F.-Kohl	Andante (Sonate. 1824)	B&B
Mendelssohn, F.-Davis	Andante and Finale (Concerto, op. 64)	Rub
Mendelssohn, F.	Frühlingslied	MM
Mendelssohn, F.-Davis	Nocturne	Rub
Mendelssohn, F.-Trinkaus	Nocturno	CF
Mendelssohn, F.-Bettoney	On Wings of Song	CF
Mendelssohn, F.-Trinkaus	On Wings of Song	CF
Mendelssohn, F.-Périer	Romances sans paroles, No. 22	ALe
Mendelssohn, F.	Soldiers March	NK
Mendelssohn, F.	Sonata	MCA
Mendelssohn, F.-Bellison	Song without Words	Ric
Mendelssohn, F.-Gruenwald	Spring Song	CF
Mendelssohn, F.-Schreiner	Spring Song	CF
Mendelssohn, F.	Spring Song	Wat
Mendelssohn, F. & Schumann, R.	2 Pieces	MKE
Mendelssohn, F.-Benoy-Bryce-	2 Songs without Words (Bk. 8, Nos. 44, 46)	OxU
Mendelssohn, F.-Bellison	Venetian Boat Song, op. 30/6	B-M
Mendelssohn, F.-Koff	Violin Concerto	Kof
Menéndez, J.	Contemplation	ALe
Menéndez, J.	8 Studies	UME
Menéndez, J.	Introduction, Andante and Dance	UME
Menéndez, J.-ed.	12 Classical Sonatas, 2 vols.	UME
Merkel, G.	In the Lovely Month of May	CF
Merkel, G.	In the Lovely Month of May	Wat
Merkù, P.	Concerto Lirico	ESZ
Merlet, M.	Diptyque	ALe
Merlet, M.	Stabile	ALe
Messager, A.	Solo de Concours	ALe
Messager, A.	Solo de Concours	B-M
Messager, A.	Morceau de Concours	CF
Messager, A.-Snavely	Solo de Concours	Ken

211

Clarinet and Piano

Messager, A.-Bonade	Solo de Concours	SM
Mestres-Quadreny, J.	Duo para Manolo. 1964	See
Metcalf, L.	Carino	CF
Metcalf, L.	Tarantella	B-M
Metcalf, L.	Thana	CF
Meulemans, A.	Sonata concertante. 1948	CBD
Mever, van	Fantasie	MM
Meyer	Redonnelle	ALe
Meyer, J.	Arioso	HLe
Meyerbeer, G.-Trinkaus	Coronation March	CF
Mezzacapo, E.	Le Chant du Gondolier	EdS
Mezzacapo, E.	Tristesse	EdS
Michel, P.	Sonatina	JB
Michiels, G.-Paquot	Eljen-Czardas	E&C
Middeleer, J. de	Recitativo e allegro. 1970	CBD
Mignion, R.	Historiettes	Bil
Mignion, R.	Méditation et pastorale	Bil
Migot, G.	Fantaisie 3	EdO
Mihalovici, M.	Dialogues, op. 92	Heu
Mihalovici, M.	Musique Nocturne	ALe
Mihalovici, M.	Sonata	Heu
Milford, R.	Lyrical Movement	OxU
Milhaud, D.	Caprice	Int
Milhaud, D.	Concerto	E-V
Milhaud, D.	Duo Concertant	Heu
Milhaud, D.	Scaramouche	EdS
Milhaud, D.	Sonatine	Dur
Mimaroglu, I.	Deformations. 1961	See
Mimaroglu, I.	3 Pieces. 1954	See
Mirandolle, L.	Sonata	ALe
Mirandolle, L.	Sonatina	ALe
Mirandolle, W.	2 Epigrammen	B&V
Mirouze, M.	Humoresque	ALe
Missud, J.-Catlin	Magnolia Serenade	CF
Missud, J.-Laube	Serenade and Polonaise	CF
Moerenhout, J.	Pièce	EMb
Möschinger, A.	Sonatine	B&H
Mohr, J.	Second Air Varie	CF
Molique, B.-Michaels	Concertino, f	B&N
Molloy, J.-Jolliff	Love's Old Sweet Song	Rub
Molter, J.-Weston	Concerto No. 3	S&C
Monti, V.-Andreoni	Aubade d'amour	Ric
Monti, V.	Csardas	CF
Monti, V.-Parola	Czardas No. 1	Ric
Monti, V.-Parola	Czardas No. 2	Ric
Montsalvatge, X.	Self-parafrasis	UME
Moore, C.	Sonata	CoA
Mopper, I.	7 Short Pieces	BM
Moritz, E.	Pavane	WZ
Morra, G.	Nocturnal Serenade	CF

212

Clarinet and Piano

Morra, G.	Romantique	CF
Morrissey, J.-MacLean	Interlude	War
Morrissey, J.	Nightfall	EBM
Mostras, K.	Etude on a Theme of Rimsky-Korsakov	MKE
Moszkowsky, M.-Waln	Etude Caprice	B-M
Moszkowski, M.	Serenade, op. 15/1	CF
Moszkowski, M.-McCathren	Serenade	Ken
Moszkowski, M.	Serenade	NK
Moszkowski, M.	Spanish Dance No. 1	CF
Moszkowski, M.	Spanish Dance No. 2	Cen
Moszkowski, M.-Heald	Spanish Dance No. 2	CF
Moszkowski, M.-Buchtel	Spanish Dance	NK
Moszkowski, M.	Spanish Dance No. 5	Cen
Moszumanska-Nazar, K.	3 Miniatures	PWM
Moulaert, R.	Rhapsodie écossaise. 1940	CBD
Mouquet, J.	Solo de Concours	ALe
Moussorgsky, M.-Barbera	Old Castle (Pictures at an Exhibition)	B-M
Mozart, W.	Adagio (Adagio, E)	CF
Mozart, W.-Harris	Adagio (Concerto, op. 107)	CF
Mozart, W.-Brearley	Adagio (K. 576)	Cur
Mozart, W.	Adagio	EdK
Mozart, W.	Adagio (Clarinet Concerto)	MM
Mozart, W.-Rochon	Adagio, KV 411	MM
Mozart, W.-Voxman	Adagio (Concerto, K. 622)	Rub
Mozart, W.-Voxman	Adagio and Menuetto	Rub
Mozart, W.-Hautvast	Adagio en Romance	T-M
Mozart, W.-Andraud	Adagio Religioso	SM
Mozart, W.-Wilson	Allegro (Sonata, e, No. 4)	War
Mozart, W.-Voxman	Alleluja	Rub
Mozart, W.	Andante	CF
Mozart, W.-Bettoney	Andante, F	CF
Mozart, W.-Isaac	Andante (Piano Sonata No. 1)	CF
Mozart, W.-Ayres	Aria and Menuetto	Bar
Mozart, W.-Benoy-Bryce	2 Arias	OxU
Mozart, W.-Périer	Arietta (Cosi fan tutte)	ALe
Mozart, W.-Hunt	Berühmte Stücke	SS
Mozart, W.-Bartholomew	Clarinet Quintet, 1st Movement	B-M
Mozart, W.-Bartholomew	Clarinet Quintet, 4th Movement	B-M
Mozart, W.-Catelinet	Clarinet Quintet, K. 581 (cl in A/Bb)	Pet
Mozart, W.-Thurston	Concerto K. 622	B&H
Mozart, W.-Cahuzac	Concerto	Bil
Mozart, W.-Kling	Concerto, A, KV 622	BrH
Mozart, W.	Clarinet Concerto, K. 622	CF
Mozart, W.-Bellison	Concerto, op. 107, K. 622	CF
Mozart, W.	Concerto, K. 622	EdK

213

Mozart, W.	Concerto, K. 191	EdM
Mozart, W.-Kell	Concerto, A, K. 622	
	(cl in A/Bb)	Int
Mozart, W.-Samyonov	Concerto, A	MKE
Mozart, W.	Clarinet Concerto	MM
Mozart, W.-Sliwinski	Concerto, A, K. 622	PWM
Mozart, W.-Giampieri	Concerto, A, K. 622	
	(cl in A/Bb)	Ric
Mozart, W.-Simon	Concerto, K. 622	Sch
Mozart, W.-Hacker	Concerto A, K. 622	
	(cl in A/basset cl)	SS
Mozart, W.-Delécluse	Concerto, A. Cadenzas by	
	Ibert (cl in A)	ALe
Mozart, W.	Concert Rondo, Bb	CF
Mozart, W.-Bellison	Divertimento, Bb	Ric
Mozart, W.-Giampieri	Divertimento, Bb, K. 581	Ric
Mozart, W.-Bellison	Divertimento, F	Ric
Mozart, W.-Simon	Duo	Bou
Mozart, W.-Périer	Invocation (Die Zauberflöte)	ALe
Mozart, W.-Périer	Larghetto (La Clemenza di	
	Tito)	ALe
Mozart, W.-Richardson	Larghetto, K. 581	B&H
Mozart, W.-Joosen	Larghetto (Quintet)	MM
Mozart, W.-Voxman	Larghetto (Clarinet Quintet)	Rub
Mozart, W.-Hautvast	Larghetto, KV 581	T-M
Mozart, W.-Langenus	Minuet (Divertimento No. 17)	CF
Mozart, W.-Lucas	Menuet	Dur
Mozart, W.-Dupont	Menuetto du Divertissement, D	GrF
Mozart, W.-Voxman	Menuet (Divertimento, D)	Rub
Mozart, W.-Wilson	Menuetto (Sonata, e, No. 4)	War
Mozart, W.-Buchtel	Merry Minuet	NK
Mozart, W.-Périer	Minuet (Don Giovanni)	ALe
Mozart, W.-Benoy-Bryce	Minuet (Violin Sonata No. 5)	OxU
Mozart, W.-Douglas	Minuet and Trio	OxU
Mozart, W.-Frank	Minuet with Country Dance	OxU
Mozart, W.-Buchtel	Mozart Adagio	NK
Mozart, W.-Frank-Forbes	Mozart Suite	OxU
Mozart, W.-Barnes	Per Questa Bello Mano	Spr
Mozart, W.-Cochrane	Quintet, K. 581	CF
Mozart, W.-Heald	Romance (Concerto No. 2)	CF
Mozart, W.-Willaman	Solo (String Quartet, K. 465)	Spr
Mozart, W.-Simon	Sonata (Violin Sonata, K. 304)	B&H
Mozart, W.-Gabucci	6 Sonate	Car
Mozart, W.-Muller	Sonatine	Mau
Mozart, W.-Bellison	Suite, F, No. 1	CF
Mozart, W.-Waln	Waltz Fantasy	NK
Müntzing, A.	Variationer. 1958	STI
Mulder, H.	Sonata op. 41, No. 3. 1943	SD
Muller, J.	Ondes courtes	Mau
Murrill, H.	Prelude, Cadenza and Fugue	OxU

Clarinet and Piano

Myers, T.	Sonata	CoA
Nagel	Morceau de concert	GrF
Napoli, C.	"Hommages"	Edi
Nardini, P.	Shepherd's Pipes	EdM
Negrea, M.	Suite. 1962	EdR
Nelhybel, V.	Concert Etude	BM
Nemescu, O.	Sonata. 1971	EdR
Neubauer, F.	Poetische Studien, op. 10	FrH
Neukomm, S. -Kaplan	Aria	Spr
Nevin, E. -Hummel	Mighty Lak' A Rose	Rub
Nevin, E. -Hummel	Narcissus	Rub
Niculescu, S.	Inventions	EdS
Niculescu, S.	Sonata. 1963	EdR
Nielsen, C.	Concerto, op. 57 (cl in A)	SPD
Nielsen, R.	7 Aforismi (cl in A)	Bon
Niverd, L.	Insouciance	EdR
Niverd, L.	Pièce romantique	Bil
Niverd, L.	Recueillement	EdR
Niverd, L.	6 Pièces brèves (Published separately)	Com
Niverd, L.	6 Romances sans paroles	GrF
Niziurski, M.	Children's Suite	PWM
Noble, H.	Burlesca	ALe
Norden, H.	Jolly Elf	Hal
Norden, H.	Jolly Viking	CF
Norden, H. -McCathren	Midnight Serenade	SHM
Nordgren, E.	Clarinet Concerto	EMf
North, A.	Pastime Suite in 5 Movements	B-M
North, R.	Sonata	Che
Novák, M.	Sonatina. 1959	SHF
Nowak, L.	2 Dialogues	PE
Nowka, D.	Sonatine	Lit
Nux, P. de la	Morceau de concours	E&C
Offenbach, J.	Barcarolle	CF
Offenbach, J. -Davis	Barcarolle	Rub
Offenbach, J.	La Musette	CF
Offenbach, J.	La Musette	EdK
Offenbach, J.	Waltz "LaPerichole"	NK
O'Hagan	Nocturne	Tem
Olcott, C.	My Wild Irish Rose	NK
Olcott, C. -Hummel	My Wild Irish Rose	Rub
Ollone, d' M.	Fantaisie Orientale	ALe
Orelli, D.	Air varié No. 1	EdS
Orelli, D.	Air varié No. 2	EdS
Orelli, D.	Air varié No. 3	EdS
Organn, R.	The Brook	Reb
Organn, R.	L'Etoile du Nord	Reb
Ornstein, L.	Nocturne	E-V
Ortolani, O.	More (Theme from Mondo Cane)	EBM

Clarinet and Piano

Osieck, H.	Sonatine. 1932	SD
Oubradous, F.	Cadence et Divertissement	
	sur un air populaire	EdL
Owings, J.	Clarinet Holiday	CF
Owings, J.	Intermezzo	B&H
Owings, J.	Modern Moods No. 1	CF
Owings, J.	Modern Moods No. 2	CF
Owings, J.	The New Horizon	B-M
Owings, J.	Scherzo	B-M
Owings, J.	Surprise Caprice	CF
Ozi, E.	Adagio et Rondo	Spr
Pachelbel, J.-Stubbins	Old Suite	Uni
Paciorkiewicz, T.	Divertimento	PWM
Paciorkiewicz, T.	4 Caprices (quasi una sonata)	PWM
Paderewski, I.-Lowry	Melody	B-M
Paderewski, I.-Laube	Minuet, op. 14/1	CF
Paderewski, I.	Minuet a l'Antique	CF
Paderewski, I.	Romance, Song of the Voyager	CF
Paganini, N.-Reisfeld	Caprice XXIV	B&H
Painparé, H.	Morceau de Salon	MM
Pala, J.	Bonjour	MM
Paleniček, J.	Mala suita	Art
Parès, G.	Crépuscle	Bil
Paris Kerjullou	Divertissement	EdR
Parme, F.	Serenade	CF
Parrott, I.	Aquarelle	Che
Pascal, C.	Sicilenne and Allegro	Com
Pascal, C.	6 Pièces variées	Dur
Pascal, C.	3 Légendes	Dur
Pasfield, W.	5 Contrasts	Bos
Paudert, E.	Berühmte Variationen No. 1	RuE
Pauer, J.	Capricci	Art
Paul, G.	Estilian Caprice	Rub
Paul, G.	To April	Rub
Paulson, G.	Clarinet Concerto op. 100	CF
	No. 1	EMf
Paulson, G.	Clarinet Concerto op. 104,	
	No. 2	EMf
Paulson, J.	Concertino	B-M
Paulson, J.	Concerto No. 1	CF
Paulson, J.	Concerto No. 2	CF
Paulson, J.	Danse Fantastique	B-M
Paulson, J.	June Caprice	CF
Paz, J.	3 Compositions in the 12 Tones	TP
Pease, D.	Classic Miniatures	UMI
Pelemans, W.	Concertstuk	Mau
Pelemans, W.	Sonate	Mau
Pelemans, W.	Sonatine	Mau
Pellegrin	Evelyne	T-M
Pelz, W.	Nocturnal Interlude	B-M

Clarinet and Piano

Pelz, W.	School Chimes	B-M
Penderecki, K.	3 Miniatures	PWM
Pennequin, J.	Cantilène et Danse	ALe
Perfect, A.	Two Little Chums	CF
Pergolesi, G.-Hovey, Leonard	Andante	B-M
Pergolesi, G.-Barnes	Canzona	Spr
Pergolesi, G.-Elkan	Se Tu M'Ami	HeE
Pergolesi, G.	Sonata No. 12	EdM
Perilhou, A.	Passepied	Heu
Perkowski, P.	Sonata	PWM
Perle, G.	Sonata quasi una fantasia	TP
Perminov, L.	Ballade	MCA
Perrier, M.	Thème varié et presto	ALe
Pessard, E.	Andalouse	NK
Pestalozza, A.	Ciribiribin	Cen
Pestalozza, A.	Ciribiribin	CF
Pestalozza, A.	Ciribiribin	NK
Peters, C.-Jolliff	Jolly Coppersmith	Rub
Petit, A.	Doux rêve	EdS
Petit, A.	1st Etude de Concours	Bil
Petit, A.-Laube	Première Etude de Concours	CF
Petit, A.	Gracieux babil	EdS
Petit, A.	Historiette	EdS
Petrić, I.	Sonata	EdD
Pettis -Schoebel	Bugle Call Rag	B-M
Philiba, N.	Concerto da camera	Bil
Philidor -Périer	Arietta (L'Amant déguisé)	ALe
Phillips, D.	Swinging Clarinet	B-M
Phillips, G.	Air	AsM
Picheran, E.	Rêverie	Bil
Pierné, G.	Andante con eleganza	Heu
Pierné, G.	Canzonetta, op. 19	ALe
Pierné, G.-Grisez	Canzonetta, op. 19	CF
Pierné, G.-Voxman	Canzonetta, op. 19	Rub
Pierné, G.	Canzonetta, op. 19	SM
Pierné, G.-Bettoney	March of the Little Tin Soldiers, op. 14/6	CF
Pierné, G.	March of the Tin Soldiers	NK
Pierné, G.-Paquot	Pièce	ALe
Pierné, G.	Pièce in G Minor	SM
Pierné, G.	Sérénade, op. 7	ALe
Pierné, G.-McCathren	Sérénade	Sha
Pierné, P.	Andante et scherzo	Bil
Pierné, P.	Bucolique	Bil
Piggot, P.	Fantasia, Eb	ALe
Pillin, B.	Sonata	Wes
Pinard, A.	Darling	CF
Pinard, A.	Just a Little Song of Love	CF
Pinard, A.	Yearning	CF
Pinkham, D.	Sonata	CoF

Clarinet and Piano

Pipkov, L.	Concerto	MKE
Pirani, M.	Idyll	GaM
Pisk, P.	Clarinet Sonata No. 1	CoF
Pisk, P.	Dialogue, op. 102/2	CoF
Pisk, P.	Intermezzo	CoF
Pisk, P.	Shanty-Boy	AMP
Piston, W.	Concerto. 1967	AMP
Pitfield, T.	Conversation Piece	OxU
Pitfield, T.	Graceful Dance	OxU
Pitfield, T.	Sonatina	Elk
Platti, G.-Rousseau	Sonata, G	EQM
Pleyel, I.	Clarinet Concerto	MR
Pobjoy, V.	4 Stücke	S&C
Podkovirov, P.	Sonata	MKE
Pokorny, F.-Becker	Konzert, Bb	BrH
Pokorny, F.-Becker	Konzert, Eb	BrH
Poldini, E.-Hovey	Coppelia Waltz	B-M
Poot, M.	Arabesque	ALe
Poot, M.	Sonatina	ALe
Popa, A.	2 Piese. 1963	EdR
Porpora, N.-Hanson	Allegretto	Lud
Porret, J.	Concertino No. 15	EdR
Porret, J.	Concertino No. 16	EdR
Porret, J.	Concertino No. 25	EdR
Porret, J.	Concertino No. 26	EdR
Porret, J.	5e Solo de Concours	MM
Porret, J.	6e Solo de Concours	MM
Porret, J.	19e Solo de Concours	MM
Porret, J.	20e Solo de Concours	MM
Porter, C.-Gossette	Begin the Beguine	War
Poulain, S.	Mélodie	EMb
Poulenc, F.	Sonata	Che
Praag, H. van	Elégie. 1960	SD
Presser, W.	Fantasy	TP
Pressman, A.-arr.	11 Easy Pieces by Soviet Composers	MKE
Price, B.	Catriona's Scottish Airs	OxU
Prince, F.	Caprice Moderne	CF
Prokofiev, S.	Kije's Wedding (Lt. Kije)	EdM
Prokofiev, S.	Romance	EdM
Pryor, A.-Stuart	Whistler and His Dog	CF
Puccini, G.-Andreoni	Un Bel di vedremo (Madama Butterfly)	Ric
Puccini, G.-Andreoni	Che gelida manina (La Bohème)	Ric
Puccini, G.	E lucevan le stelle (Tosca)	Ric
Puccini, G.-Andreoni	O mio babbino caro (Gianni Schicchi)	Ric
Puccini, G.-Andreoni	Non piangere, Liù (Turandot)	Ric
Purcell, H.-Edmunds	Amphitryon (Incidental Music)	CF

Clarinet and Piano

Purcell, H.	Dance Suite	EdM
Purcell, H.-Worley	Little Serenade	Spr
Purcell, H.-Kaplan	Little Suite	Spr
Purcell, H.-Edmunds	The Princess of Persia	CF
Purcell, H.-Kaplan	Saraband	Spr
Purcell, H.	Sonata, g	EdM
Purcell, H.-Tesson	Trumpet Tune	GD
Pustilnik, I.	Scherzo	MKE
Pyle, F.	Sonata	Wes
Quet, L.	Petite Pièce	Bil
Quet, L.	Petite Pièce	SM
Quinet, M.	Ballade. 1961	CBD
Rabaud, H.-Hite	Etude	SM
Rabaud, H.	Solo de Concours, op. 10	ALe
Rabaud, H.	Solo de Concours, op. 10	EdK
Rabaud, H.	Solo de Concours, op. 10	EdM
Rabaud, H.-Drucker	Contest Piece, op. 10	Int
Rabaud, H.	Solo de Concours, op. 10	SM
Rachmaninoff, S.	Polka Italienne	EdM
Rachmaninoff, S.	Vocalise	EdM
Rachmaninoff, S.-Drucker	Vocalise, op. 34/14	Int
Raff, J.	Cavatina	CF
Rafter, L.	5 Pieces	Bos
Rafter, L.	5 Satires (Suite)	Bos
Rainier, P.	Suite (cl in A)	S&C
Rajna, T.	Dialogues	ALe
Rakov, N.	Sonata	HSM
Rakov, N.	Sonatina	EdK
Rakov, N.	Sonatina	MKE
Ralston, A.	3 English Folk Tunes	B&H
Rameau, J.	Gavotte (Temple de la Gloire)	For
Rameau, J.	Minuet and Passepied	For
Rameau, J.	Rigodon de Dardanus	Dur
Rameau, J.	Rigodon de Dardanus	EdM
Rameau, J.-Ettlinger	Suite	B&H
Rameau, J.-Hovey, Leonard	Le Tambourin	B-M
Rameau, J.	Tambourin	NK
Rameau, J.-Scarmolin	La Villageoise	Lud
Ramovš, P.	Sonata	EdD
Ramovš, P.	Sonatina	EdD
Ranger, A.-arr.	Country Gardens	CF
Ranger, A.-comp.	Repertoire for Clarinetists	CF
Ranger, A.	A Wreath of Holly	CF
Ranish, J.-Ayres	Sonata, F	Sha
Raphael, G.	Sonatine, op. 65/3	BrH
Raphling, S.	Lyric Prelude	EdM
Raphling, S.	Square Dance	EdM
Ratez, A.	Pièce romantique	GrF
Ratez, E.	Sonatine	GrF
Rautavaara, E.	Sonetto. 1969	MT
Ravel, M.-Bettoney	Pavane	CF

219

Ravel, M.	Pavane	EdM
Ravel, M.-Piguet	Pavane pour une Infante défunte	EME
Ravel, M.-Walters	Pavane	Rub
Ravel, M.	Pavane	SS
Ravel, M.	Pièce en forme de Habanera	ALe
Rawsthorne, A.	Concerto	OxU
Raybould, C.	Wistful Shepherd	B&H
Raymond, L.	Design	Wes
Raymond, W.	La Militaire	B-M
Read, E.	Song without Words	GaM
Rebikov, V.	A Little Girl Rocking her Doll	EdM
Redouté, J.	Mélodie	EMb
Reed, A.	Hora	EBM
Reed, A.	Pastorale	EBM
Reed, A.	Rahoon	EBM
Reed, A.	Serenade	SM
Reed, H.	Scherzo	B-M
Reger, M.	Albumblatt-Tarantella	OJ
Reger, M.-Piguet	Romanze, G	BrH
Reger, M.	Sonate, op. 49/1	UE
Reger, M.	Sonata, op. 49/2	UE
Reger, M.	Sonate, Bb, op. 107	B&B
Reger, M.-Simon	2 Pieces (Album Leaf & Tarantella)	Int
Reinecke, C.	Introduction and Allegro Appassionato, op. 256	CF
Reinecke, C.-Kaplan	Lullaby and Moderato	Spr
Reinecke, C.-Kaplan	Romanza and Allegro	Spr
Reinecke, C.	Sonata "Undine," op. 167	EdK
Reinecke, C.	Sonata "Undine," op. 167	Int
Reissiger, C.-Bellison	Fantasie	CF
Reissiger, C.	Studienkonzert (Concertino)	FrH
Reiter, A.	Concerto	LDo
Reiter, A.	Sonatine	LDo
Rema	Gentille Sérénade	Mau
Rema	Impromptu et allegro	Mau
Resch, J.	Salut au printemps	Ham
Reutter, H.	Mélodie	ALe
Revel, P.	Fantaisie	ALe
Reyloff, E.	Introduction and Bolero	B&H
Reynaud, J.	Ah! vous dirai-je Maman?	EdS
Rheinberger, J.-Stephan	Sonata, op. 105a	SS
Ricci, L.-Hume	Preludio and Balletto	B&H
Rice, T.	Fantasy	See
Richards, J.	Sunbeams	Bar
Richards, J.	Villetta	Bar
Richardson, A.	Roundelay	OxU
Richardson, A.	3 Pieces	GaM
Richardson, N.-arr.	Clarinettist's Book of Classics	B&H

Clarinet and Piano

Richardson, N.-arr.	6 Clarinet Solos	B&H
Richardson, N.	Sonatina	B&H
Richens, J.	Prelude and Dance	Ken
Richter, C.-arr.	20 Classic Favorites	CF
Richter, M.	Clarinet Sonata	AMC
Rickstal, J. van	Improvisatie	EMe
Ridout, A.	Sonatina	S&C
Rieding, O.-Collis	Introduction & Allegro	HeE
Ries, F.-Schmitz	Sonata, Eb, op. 169	B&N
Ries, F.	Sonate Sentimentale, op. 169	MR
Ries, F.	Sonata, g	B&N
Ries, F.-Lebermann	Sonata, g, op. 29	SS
Riethmueller, H.	Sonata, op. 36	Pet
Rimbout, P.	Nocturne	Mau
Rimmer, H.	Autumn Even Song	HeE
Rimsky-Korsakov, N.-Perry	Concerto	B&H
Rimsky-Korsakov, N.	Concerto	CF
Rimsky-Korsakov, N.-Simon	Concerto	Int
Rimsky-Korsakov, N.-Fitelberg	Concerto	SF
Rimsky-Korsakov, N.	Hummelflug	BrH
Rimsky-Korsakov, N.-Bettoney	Flight of the Bumble Bee	CF
Rimsky-Korsakov, N.-Iasilli	Flight of the Bumble Bee	CF
Rimsky-Korsakov, N.-Langenus	Flight of the Bumble Bee	CF
Rimsky-Korsakov, N.	Flight of the Bumble-Bee	GFB
Rimsky-Korsakov, N.-Koff	Flight of the Bumble Bee	Kof
Rimsky-Korsakov, N.-Davis	Flight of the Bumblebee	Rub
Rimsky-Korsakov, N.-Bonade	The Flight of the Bumble Bee	SM
Rimsky-Korsakov, N.-Bettoney	Hymn to the Sun	CF
Rimsky-Korsakov, N. -Depelsenaire	Hymn to the Sun	GD
Rimsky-Korsakov, N.-Colby	Hymn to the Sun	Rub
Rimsky-Korsakov, N.-Bellison	Intermezzo (Tsar's Bride)	CF
Rimsky-Korsakov, N.-Bellison	Introduction and Hymn to the Sun (The Golden Cockerel)	CF
Rimsky-Korsakov, N.-Bellison	Oriental Song	CF
Rimsky-Korsakov, N. -Depelsenaire	The Rose and the Nightingale	GD
Rimsky-Korsakov, N.-Davis	Scheherazade	Rub
Rimsky-Korsakov, N.-Bellison	Song-Dance of the Shepherd Lehl (Snow Maiden)	CF
Rimsky-Korsakov, N.	Song of India	Cen
Rimsky-Korsakov, N.-Bellison	Song of India	CF
Rimsky-Korsakov, N.-Vachey	Song of India	GD
Rimsky-Korsakov, N.	Song of India	NK
Rimsky-Korsakov, N.-Voxman	Song of India	Rub
Riotte, P.-Michaels	Concerto, Bb	HSM
Risinger, K.	Marionette Suite	Art
Ritter, R.	Long Long Ago, op. 12	CF
Ritter, R.	Long Ago air varie	MM
Rivier, J.	Concerto	EMT

Clarinet and Piano

Robert, C.	Concerto	T-M
Rochberg, G.	Dialogues	TP
Rode, P.-Bellison	Air Varie, op. 10	CF
Rodriguez, G.-Goehr	La Cumparsita	EBM
Roeck, G. de	Serenade Galante	T-M
Röntgen, J.	Sonatine. 1961	SD
Rohwer, J.	Sonate	MV
Rollinson, T.	Grand Fantasia on Home Sweet Home	CF
Rollinson, T.	Rocked in the Cradle of the Deep	CF
Rollinson, T.	Tramp, Tramp, Tramp (Grand Fantasia)	CF
Romero, A.-Menéndez	Primer solo de concierto	UME
Rooij, P. de	Greensleeves	HeE
Roos, R. de	Capriccio. 1952	SD
Rosas, J.	Over the Waves	Cen
Rosetti, F.	Concerto, Eb	EdK
Rössler, F.-Voxman, Hervig	Concerto, Eb	Rub
Ross, B.	The Magic Horn	MCA
Rosseau, N.	Sonatine, op. 59. 1956	CBD
Rossini, G.-Apodaca	Air Varie on William Tell	CF
Rossini, G.	Cavatina (Barber of Seville)	EdS
Rossini, G.-Klosé, Jeanjean	Fantasia on The Barber of Seville	ALe
Rossini, G.-Zappatini	Fantasia	ESZ
Rossini, G.-Lancelot	Variations	EMT
Rossini, G.-Omizzolo	Variazioni	GZ
Rossini, G.-Russo	Variations for Clarinet	HeE
Rossini, G.-Michaels	Introduction, Theme and Variations	HSM
Rossini, G.-Glazer-Hermann	Introduction, Theme, and Variations	OxU
Rossini, G.-Neufeld	Variations for Clarinet	Wes
Rossini, G.-Benoy-Bryce	Mazurka	OxU
Rosza, M.-Huffnagle	Lydia	SF
Roubanis-Edwards	Misirlou	B-M
Rougnon, P.	1st Solo, op. 128	ALe
Rougnon, P.	Prière	GrF
Round, H.	Zenobia	MM
Roussakis, N.	3 Epigrams	PE
Roussel, A.	Aria	ALe
Rubinstein, A.	Melodie in F	CF
Rubinstein, A.	Mélodie	MM
Rubinstein, A.	Melody in F	NK
Rubinstein, A.	Romance	SF
Rubinstein, A.-Long	Romance	Vol
Rudolph, A.-Voxman	Sonata	MR
Rudzinski, W.	Burlesque	PWM
Rueff, J.	Concertino, op. 15	ALe

Rugolo, P.	Petite Suite	Wes
Rulst –Rema	Allegro Rondo	Mau
Rulst –Rema	Canzonetta	Mau
Rulst –Rema	Carezzevole	Mau
Rulst –Rema	Con gentillezza	Mau
Rulst –Rema	Gavotte et musette	Mau
Rulst –Rema	Grazioso	Mau
Rulst –Rema	Image	Mau
Rulst –Rema	Minuetto	Mau
Rungis, R.	Aria	HLe
Rungis, R.	Barcarolle	HLe
Rungis, R.	Elégie	HLe
Rungis, R.	Menuet	HLe
Rungis, R.	Romance	HLe
Rungis, R.	Rondo	HLe
Rungis, R.	Valse	HLe
Russell, R.	Scherzo	Gen
Rusu, L.	Sonata. 1958	EdR
Ruyneman, D.	Sonata. 1936	SD
Ryelandt, J.	Fantaisie, op. 40. 1904	CBD
Ryelandt, J.	Trois morceaux, op. 17. 1897	CBD
Rytel, P.	Romance, op. 26	PWM
Rytel, P.	Variations on a Theme by Schumann	PWM
Sabatini, G.	Puppet Waltz	Cor
Sacco, P.	Romance	Wes
Säfbom, G.	Clarinet Polka	Nor
Saeys, E.	Légende	Mau
Saeys, E.	Romance	Mau
Saeys, E.	Suite	Mau
Saint-Saens, C.-Whear	Amour viens aider	Lud
Saint-Saens, C.-Langenus	Le Cygne	CF
Saint-Saens, C.-Trinkaus	Le Cygne	CF
Saint-Saens, C.	Le Cygne	Dur
Saint-Saens, C.	Danse Macabre	CF
Saint-Saens, C.-Lucas	Le Déluge, Prélude	Dur
Saint-Saens, C.-Brooke	L'Eléphant	Dur
Saint-Saens, C.-Goldman	My Heart At Thy Sweet Voice	CF
Saint-Saens, C.-Lucas	My Heart At Thy Sweet Voice	CF
Saint-Saens, C.-Piguet	Mon coeur s'ouvre	Dur
Saint-Saens, C.-Lalliet	"O beaux rêves évanouis"	Dur
Saint-Saens, C.	Pavane (Etienne Marcel)	Dur
Saint-Saens, C.	Printemps qui commence	Dur
Saint-Saens, C.-Lucas	Pavane (Proserpine)	Dur
Saint-Saens, C.	Rêverie du soir (Suite algérienne)	Dur
Saint-Saens, C.-Piguet	Romance	EdM
Saint-Saens, C.-Piguet	Romance, op. 37	Dur
Saint-Saens, C.-Mimart	Romance, op. 51	Dur
	Samson et Dalila	Dur

Clarinet and Piano

Saint-Saens, C.	Sonate, op. 167	Dur
Saint-Saens, C. -Zimmermann	Sonata	Pet
Saint-Saens, C.	2 Pavanes	EdM
Samazeuilh, G.	Luciole	Dur
Sambin, V.	Air varié No. 1	EdS
Sambin, V.	Air varié No. 2	EdS
Sambin, V.	Cavatine du Barbier de Seville	EdS
Sammartini, G.	Canto Amoroso	MM
Sancan, P.	Sonatine	Dur
Sanders, R.	The Imp	CF
Sanke, C.	Rhapsodie	PrM
Sarasate, P. de -Rogers	Zigeunerweisen	CF
Sarasate, P. de -Koff	Zigeunerweisen	Kof
Sáry, L.	Variations. 1966	EMB
Sauter, E.	Clarinet a la King	B&H
Saveliev, B.	Concerto	MKE
Saygun, A.	Horon	SMP
Scarlatti, A. -Barnes	Aria (Tigraine)	Spr
Scarlatti, D. -Drucker	4 Sonatas	Int
Scarlatti -Bacon	3 Sonatas	Sch
Scarmolin, L.	Introduction and Tarantella	PrA
Scarmolin, L.	Nocturne	PrA
Schaefer, A.	Ladder of Fame	CF
Schaefer, A.	The Showman	CF
Schaefer, A.	The Soloist	CF
Schaeffer, D.	Licorice and Lollipops	PrA
Scharres, C.	Cadence et Allegro Appassionato	EMb
Schibler, A.	Anspielungen	Eul
Schibler, A.	Concertino, op. 49	Pet
Schindler, G.	Libussa	Bos
Schmid, H.	Allegretto, op. 34/2	SS
Schmid, R.	7 Miniaturen	LDo
Schmidek, K.	Sonatine, op. 30	LDo
Schmidt, W.	Rhapsody No. 1	Wes
Schmidt, W.	Sonatina	Wes
Schmit, C.	Prélude	ALe
Schmitt, F.	Andantino	ALe
Schmutz, A.	Poeme Rapsodie	B-M
Schneider	Air Varié No. 5	EdS
Schneider-Bergen -arr.	Klassische Vortragsstücke	SS
Schneider -arr.	Kleine Spielstücke	SS
Schoeck, O.	Andante	Hug
Schoenberg, A. -Greissle	Sonata (Wind Quintet, op. 26)	UE
Schönberg, S.	Partita, "Den lille batsmannen"	STI
Schollum, R.	Sonata, op. 42/1. 1950	LDo
Schollum, R.	Sonatine, op. 55/4	LDo
Schollum, R.	3 Stücke, op. 71b. 1966	GBV
Scholtens	Claus Fantasie	T-M

Clarinet and Piano

Scholtens	Concertino	T-M
Scholtes	Anishka	Wat
Schorer	Poitus	MM
Schouwman, H.	Aubade en Barcarolle, op. 37/1. 1944	SD
Schreiner, A.-Howard	Immer Kleiner	Lud
Schrijver, K. de	6 Simple Pieces	T-M
Schroeven, L.	Concerto-Miniature	EMb
Schubert, F.-Langenus	Bee--L'Abeille	B&H
Schubert, F.-Webb	Allegro Molto	Ken
Schubert, F.-Worley	Allegro Vivace (Sonatina, op. 137/1)	Spr
Schubert, F.-Roth	Andante (Octet, op. 166)	B&H
Schubert, F.-Traxler	Ave Maria	B-M
Schubert, F.	Ave Maria	CF
Schubert, F.-Vachey	Ave Maria	GD
Schubert, F.-De Rooij	Ave Maria	HeE
Schubert, F.-Ruggiero	Canzone dalla "Bella molinara"	Edi
Schubert, F.-Overveld	Du bist die Ruh'	T-M
Schubert, F.	Entr'act II (Rosamunde)	NK
Schubert, F.-Périer	Impromptu, op. 90/3	ALe
Schubert, F.-Bellison	Introduction, Theme and Variations (Sehnsuchts-Walzer)	CF
Schubert, F.-Simon	Master Songs	B&H
Schubert, F.	Moment Musical	CF
Schubert, F.-Andreoni	Moment musical, op. 94/3	Ric
Schubert, F.-Cochrane	The Post, op. 89/13	CF
Schubert, F.	Rosamunde	MM
Schubert, F.	Rosamunde	NK
Schubert, F.-Benoy-Bryce	A Schubert Suite	OxU
Schubert, F.	Sie Mir Gegrüsst	MM
Schubert, F.-Bockmuhl	Serenade, op. 6/1	CF
Schubert, F.-Loverani	Serenade	CF
Schubert, F.-Depelsenaire	Sérénade	GD
Schubert, F.-Andreoni	Serenade	Ric
Schubert, F.-Overveld	Ständchen (Serenade)	T-M
Schubert, F.-Bellison	Sonata-Concerto, g, Arpeggione	CF
Schubert, F.-Simon	Sonatina (Violin Sonatina, op. 137/1)	B&H
Schubert, F.-Hite	Sonatina	SM
Schubert, F.-Isaac	3 Themes	CF
Schubert, F.-Phillips	2 Minuets	OxU
Schubert, F.-Davis	Unfinished Symphony	Rub
Schumann, R.-Périer	L'Auberge (Scènes de la Forêt)	ALe
Schumann, R.-Périer	Berceuse (Feuilles d'Album)	ALe
Schumann, R.-Périer	Choral et Cantabile (Pièces pour la Jeunesse)	ALe
Schumann, R.-Lancelot	Pièces de Fantaisie	Bil

Clarinet and Piano

Schumann, R.	Fantasy Pieces, op. 73	Int
Schumann, R.-de Smet	Fantasy Pieces, op. 73	
	(cl in A/Bb)	Pet
Schumann, R.-Voxman	Fantasy Piece op. 73/1	Rub
Schumann, R.-Schradieck	Fantasiestücke, op. 73	
	(cl in A)	Sch
Schumann, R.-Heine	Fantasie-Stücke, op. 73	Sim
Schumann, R.-Merriman	Folk Song	SM
Schumann, R.-Davis	Melody, op. 68/1	Rub
Schumann, R.-Périer	Rêverie (Scènes d'enfants)	ALe
Schumann, R.	Rêverie	Dur
Schumann, R.-Wenner	Rêverie	EdR
Schumann, R.	Romance	CF
Schumann, R.-Gee	Romance No. 3	SM
Schumann, R.	Romances, op. 94	GaM
Schumann, R.	3 Romances, op. 94	Pet
Schumann, R.-Schradieck	3 Romances, op. 94 (cl in A)	Sch
Schumann, R.	Traumerei	CF
Schumann, R.-Depelsenaire	Traumerei	GD
Schumann, R.-Andreoni	Traeumerei, op. 15/7	Ric
Schumann, R.-Kaplan	2 Pieces	Spr
Schwadron, A.	Adagio	PMP
Schwadron, A.	Etude	PMP
Schwadron, A.	Gigue	Ken
Schwarenka, X.	Polish Dance	CF
Sciortino, E.	Charmer de serpents	Bil
Sclater, J.	Suite	Wes
Scott, C.-Brose	Danse Nègre, op. 58/5	Elk
Scott, C.	Danse Nègre	GaM
Searle, H.	Suite, op. 32	S&C
Seelenne, T.	Berceuse	EMb
Sehlbach, E.	Kleine Lyrik, op. 102/2	MV
Sehlbach, E.	Sonata, op. 116	MV
Seiber, M.	Andantino Pastorale	S&C
Seiber, M.-Wurzburger	Concertino	S&C
Seitz, F.-Hite	Concert Piece	SM
Seleski, L.	Interlude Romantique	Ken
Semegen, D.	Changes	CoA
Semler-Collery, A.	Cantabile et allegro	Bil
Semler-Collery, J.	Etudes de Concert	EME
Semler-Collery, J.	Fantaisie et danse en forme	
	de gigue	ALe
Semler-Collery, J.	Lied & Final	EME
Semler-Collery, J.	Mélodie Expressive	EME
Semler-Collery, J.	Rêverie et Scherzo	ALe
Semler-Collery, J.	Sur un Thème Picard	MM
Semyonov, A.-arr.	3 Pieces from Borodin,	
	Liadov, & Rebikov	MKE
Semyonov, A.-arr.	3 Pieces by Zipoli, Mozart,	
	Beethoven	MKE

Clarinet and Piano

Semyonov, A. -arr.	5 Pieces by Goedicke, Glière, & Narimanidze	MKE
Semyonov, A. -ed.	5 Pieces by Soviet Composers	MKE
Semyonov, A. -arr.	6 Classical Pieces	MKE
Semyonov, A. -arr. -Stark	6 Pieces by Russian Composers	MKE
Semyonov, A. -arr.	6 Pieces by Soviet Composers	MKE
Semyonov, A. -arr.	7 Pieces by Russian Composers	MKE
Semyonov, A. -comp. -Stark	8 Pieces by Soviet Composers	MKE
Senaille, J. -de Smet	Introduction and Allegro Spiritoso	BrH
Sermon, E.	Petite pièce	EMb
Serocki, K.	Concerto	PWM
Serocki, K.	A Dance	PWM
Serventi, V.	Variations	ALe
Setaccioli, G.	Sonata, Eb, op. 31	Ric
Seter, M.	Elegy. 1954	Isr
Seymer, W.	Svit	STI
Shaposhnikov -arr.	5 Pieces	MKE
Shaw, A.	Concerto	HG
Shaw, C.	Sonata	Nov
Shchedrin, R. -Myulberg	Basso-Ostinato	MKE
Shchedrin, R.	Suite	MCA
Sherman, E.	Sonata Lyrica	CoF
Shmelev, V. -comp.	5 Pieces	MKE
Shostakovich, D.	Danse Fantastique	EdM
Shostakovich, D.	Polka (The Age of Gold)	EdM
Shostakovich, D.	Satirical Dance (The Bolt)	EdM
Shostakovich, D.	3 Pieces	ChM
Shostakovich, D. -Stark	3 Pieces	MCA
Shulman, A.	High voltage	BVC
Shulman, A.	Mood in question	BVC
Shulman, A.	Rendezvous	BVC
Sibelius, J. -Trinkaus	Valse Triste (Kuolema)	CF
Siccardi, H.	Preludio y Fuga	SMP
Siegel, A.	Pasquinade	See
Siegl, O.	Floriani-Sonate	LDo
Siegmeister, E.	Concerto	SF
Siennicki, E.	Ballade	E-V
Signorelli	Blues Serenade	B-M
Sikorski, K.	Concerto. 1947	PWM
Simeonov, B.	Monody	Wat
Simon, A. -Stark	Concert Pieces, op. 31	MKE
Simon, A. -Bellison	Serenade (The Stars)	AMP
Simon, E. -arr.	First Classics for the Clarinet	Sch
Simon, E. -arr.	First Solos for the Clarinet Player	Sch
Simon, E. -arr.	Master Songs, 2 vols.	B&H
Simon, E. -ed.	Masterworks for Clarinet and Piano	Sch
Simon, E. -arr.	Mozart for the Clarinet	Sch

227

Clarinet and Piano

Simon, L.	Eppes Yiddish	EdM
Simonis, J.	Sequences, op. 19. 1969	CBD
Singelée, J.	Fantasie Pastorale	MM
Singelée, J.	4e Solo de Concert	MM
Singer	Marionettes Modernes	CF
Siqueira, J.	3 Etüden	Deu
Skerl, D.	Sonatina	HG
Skolnik, W.	Intermezzo (Clarinet Concerto)	EdM
Smetana, B.-Harris	Polka (Bartered Bride)	Lud
Smith, C.	From Day to Day	CF
Smith, C.	Life's Lighter Hours	Bar
Smith, C.	On Pleasure Bent	CF
Smith, C.	The Spirit of Joy	CF
Smith & Holmes	Drink To Me Only With Thine Eyes	CF
Smith & Holmes	Through Shadowed Vales	Bar
Sobeck, J.-Langenus	Concert Piece	CF
Sodomka, K.	Partita semplice	Art
Söderlundh, L.	Liten svit	STI
Soler, A.-Worley	Sonata, Eb	Spr
Sosen, E. van	Arioso	Pet
Soukup, V.	Sonata	Art
Sousa, J.-Jolliff	High School Cadets	Rub
Sousa, J.	Stars and Stripes Forever	NK
Sousa, J.-Walters	The Stars and Stripes Forever	Rub
Sousa, J.-Page	Stars and Stripes Forever	TP
Spasokukotsky, L.	Song-Scherzo	MKE
Speaks, O.-Leidzen	Sylvia	BM
Spencer, W.	Silvatones	CF
Spendiarov, A.-Goldstein	Romance	MKE
Spies, L.	Kleine Suite	Pet
Spinner, L.	Suite, op. 10	B&H
Spisak, M.	Concertino	PWM
Spohr, L.-Leinert	Concerto, c, op. 26, No. 1	B&N
Spohr, L.	Concerto, c, op. 26, No. 1	CF
Spohr, L.-Drucker	Concerto, c, op. 26, No. 1	Int
Spohr, L.	Concerto, c, op. 26, No. 1	Pet
Spohr, L.	Concerto, Eb, op. 57, No. 2	CF
Spohr, L.-Drucker	Concerto, Eb, op. 57, No. 2	Int
Spohr, L.	Concerto, Eb, op. 57, No. 2	Pet
Spohr, L.-Rundnagel	Concerto, f, No. 3	BrH
Spohr, L.	Concerto, f, No. 3	EdK
Spohr, L.-Drucker	Concerto, f, No. 3	Int
Spohr, L.-Rundnagel	Concerto, e, No. 4 (cl in A)	BrH
Spohr, L.	Concerto, e, No. 4 (cl in A)	EdK
Spohr, L.-Drucker	Concerto, e, No. 4 (cl in A)	Int
Spohr, L.-Powell	Potpourri on Themes by Winter, op. 80	MR
Spohr, L.-Voxman	Variations on a theme (Alruna)	MR
Sporck, G.	Allegro de concert	Bil

Clarinet and Piano

Sporck, G.	Chanson d'Antan	Bil
Sporck, G.	Concert	Bil
Sporck, G.	Légende	Bil
Sporck, G.	Méditation	Bil
Sporck, G.	Novelette	Bil
Sporck, G.	Orientale	Bil
Srámek, V.	Sonatine	ES
Staigers, D.	Hazel	CF
Stamitz, J.-Gradenwitz	Concerto, Bb	MCA
Stamitz, J.-Lebermann	Concerto, Bb	SS
Stamitz, K.-Boese	Concerto, Eb ("Darmstadt")	FrH
Stamitz, K.-Wojciechowski	Concerto, Eb	HSM
Stamitz, K.-Christmann	Concerto, Eb	Sch
Stamitz, K.	Concerto, F	Pet
Stamitz, K.-Balassa, Nagy	Concerto, F, No. 1	EMB
Stamitz, K.-Lebermann, May	Concerto, F, No. 1	SS
Stamitz, K.-Drucker	Concerto, Bb, No. 3	Int
Stamitz, K.	Concerto, Bb, No. 3	Pet
Stamitz, K.-Michaels	Concerto, Bb, No. 10	HSM
Stanford, C.	Sonata, op. 129	GaM
Starer, R.	Dialogues	MCA
Starer, R.	Recitation	SMP
Stark, R.	Canzone, op. 41	CF
Stark, R.	Concerto, op. 50	CF
Starokadomsky, M.	5 Pieces	MCA
Starokadomsky & Fried	6 Pieces	MKE
Stastny, V.	Concertino	Art
St. Clair, F.	Admiration	Vol
St. Clair, F.	Dream Time	Vol
St. Clair, F.	Golden Days	Vol
Stearns, P.	Fantasy	CoF
Stearns, P.	3 Pieces	CoF
Steele, C.	Sonatina	Nov
Steenhuis, F.	Sonatine, op. 3. 1945	SD
Steffens, W.	Hommage à Béla Bartók, op. 5. 1953	BrH
Steiner-Schoenfeld	Tara Theme	War
Steiner, G.	Fantasy. 1964	See
Steinert, A.	Rhapsody	Sch
Stekke, L.	Andante Appassionata	HeE
Stekke, L.	Cadence et Allegro Appassionato	EMb
Stekke, L.	Prélude et danse, op. 12	Bil
Stempnevsky, S.	Bilina	MKE
Stempnevsky, S.	2 Pieces	MKE
Stevens, H.	Andante	CoF
Stevens, H.	Concerto	PIC
Stevens, H.	4 Folksongs of Touraine	CoF
Stevens, H.	4 Pieces	Cor
Stevens, H.	Suite	Pet

Clarinet and Piano

Stevens, H.	3 Hungarian Folk Songs	GaM
Stewart	La Petite Suite	Ken
Stocks –Bonade	Wessex Pastorale	SM
Stolk	Sonatine	MM
Stolz, R.	Shepherd's Prayer, op. 74	B&H
Storm, S.	Duodecimo	PrA
Storp, S.	Concerto	MV
Stouffer, P.	Recitation	HeE
Stoutamire, A.	Twilight Tune	PrA
Stradella, A.	Air d'église	Com
Strauss, J.–Jolliff	Artist's Life	Rub
Strauss, J.–Bettoney	Blue Danube Waltz	CF
Strauss, J.–Spink	4 Waltzes	OxU
Strauss, J.–Bettoney	Tales from the Vienna Woods	CF
Strauss, J.	Waltz (The Gypsy Baron)	NK
Strauss, O.–Harris	A Waltz Dream	Lud
Strauss, R.–Buchtel	Andante (Violin Concerto)	NK
Strauss, R.	Tomorrow	EdM
Strauss, R.	Zueignung	EdM
Strauwen, J.	Andante Varié	EMb
Strauwen, J.	Cantilène	EMb
Strauwen, J.	Conte pastoral	ScF
Stravinsky, I.	Berceuse (Firebird)	EdM
Stravinsky, I.	Dance of the Ballerina	EdM
Stravinsky, I.	Dance of the Princesses	EdM
Stravinsky, I.	Pastorale	EdM
Strimer, J.	Pastorale Caucasienne	Dur
Stuart, H.–arr.	BMCO Famous Clarinet Favorites	BM
Stuart, H.	Concertino	CF
Stuart, H.	Serenata	BM
Stubbins, W.–ed.	First Recital Repertoire	Uni
Stubbins, W.–ed.	Recital Literature, 5 vols.	Uni
Stürmer, B.	Sonate, op. 73	WMS
Stuhec, I.	7 Anecdotes	EdD
Stults, R.–Hummel	The Sweetest Story Ever Told	Rub
Stutschewsky, J.	Concertino	IMP
Sullivan, A.	The Lost Chord	CF
Sumbatian, I.	Improvisation and Scherzo	MKE
Sumerlin, M.	Shindig	B-M
Sumerlin, M.	Waltz Caprice	B-M
Suppé, F. von –Long	Andante Maestoso (Poet and Peasant)	Vol
Suppé, F. von –Gruenwald	Poet and Peasant Overture	CF
Swain, F.	Derry Down	GaM
Swain, F.	Heather Hill	GaM
Swain, F.	Rhapsody	Bou
Swider, J.	Caprice	PWM
Sydeman, W.	Duo	SMP

Clarinet and Piano

Szabó, F.	Sonata alla Rapsodia. 1964	EMB
Szalowski, A.-Bellison	Sonatina	SF
Szelényi, I.	Air. 1953	EMB
Szervánsky, E.	Concerto	EMB
Szervánsky, E.	Serenade. 1950	EMB
Szwed, J.	5 Caprices	PWM
Takács, J.	Essays in Sound, op. 84	B-M
Takács, J.	Fantastic, op. 88a (cl in A)	LDo
Talma, L.	3 Duologues	EdM
Taneyev, S.	Canzona	MKE
Tardos, B.	Improvisations. 1960	EMB
Tartini, G.-Jacob	Concertino, F	B&H
Tartini, G.-Worley	Sarabanda	Spr
Tartini, G.-Hite	Sonata, g	SM
Taubert, K.	French Sketches	Sim
Taylor, C.	Shepherd's Dream	Rub
Tchaikovsky, B.	Clarinet Concerto	HSM
Tchaikovsky, P.-Davis	Andante	Rub
Tchaikovsky, P.	Andante Cantabile	CF
Tchaikovsky, P.-Gurewich	Andante Cantabile (Quartet, D)	CF
Tchaikovsky, P.-Emch	Autumn Song	CF
Tchaikovsky, P.	Barcarolle	Cen
Tchaikovsky, P.-Phillips	Barcarolle, Nocturne and Russian Dance	OxU
Tchaikovsky, P.-Bellison	June Barcarolle	Ric
Tchaikovsky, P.-Langenus	Canzonetta (Violin Concerto, op. 35)	CF
Tchaikovsky, P.-Schinstine	Canzonetta (Violin Concerto)	SM
Tchaikovsky, P.-Stark	Capriccio, op. 62	MKE
Tchaikovsky, P.	Chanson Triste	CF
Tchaikovsky, P.	Chanson Triste	MM
Tchaikovsky, P.-Buchtel	Chanson Triste	NK
Tchaikovsky, P.-Bettoney	Chant sans Paroles	CF
Tchaikovsky, P.-Trinkaus	Chant sans Paroles	CF
Tchaikovsky, P.	Chant sans Paroles	MM
Tchaikovsky, P.-Lemarc	Chant sans Paroles	T-M
Tchaikovsky, P.-Hummel	Concerto, Bb Minor	Rub
Tchaikovsky, P.-Davis	Danse des Mirlitons	Rub
Tchaikovsky, P.-Langenus	Finale (Violin Concerto, op. 35)	CF
Tchaikovsky, P.-Cailliet	Finale (Violin Concerto)	SM
Tchaikovsky, P.	Lied ohne Worte	MM
Tchaikovsky, P.	Mélodie, op. 42/3	EdR
Tchaikovsky, P.-Elsenaar	Mélodie, op. 42	T-M
Tchaikovsky, P.-Laube	Mignon's Lament	CF
Tchaikovsky, P.-Rozanov	Nocturne, op. 19/4	MKE
Tchaikovsky, P.	Nocturne	MM
Tchaikovsky, P.-Rozanov	Nocturne-Romance-Mazurka	MKE
Tchaikovsky, P.-Eckstein	None But the Lonely Heart	CF
Tchaikovsky, P.-Bellison	Russian Dance (Swan Lake)	CF

Tchaikovsky, P.-Stark	Scherzo, op. 42/2	MKE
Tchaikovsky, P.-Bettoney	The Sleeping Beauty Waltz	CF
Tchaikovsky, P.-Davis	Sleeping Beauty	Rub
Tchaikovsky, P.-Seay	Song of April, op. 37/4	Spr
Tchaikovsky, P.-Bellison	Song of the Lark, op. 37/3	AMP
Tchaikovksy, P.	Song Without Words	Cen
Tchaikovsky, P.-Rozanov	Song Without Words, op. 2/3	MKE
Tchaikovsky, P.-Benoy-Bryce	A Tchaikovsky Suite	OxU
Tchaikovsky, P.	3 Pieces (Album for Children)	EdM
Tchaikovsky, P.-Rozanov	3 Pieces	MKE
Tchaikovsky, P.-Harris	Waltz	Lud
Tcherepnin, N.-Bellison	Esquisse, op. 45/6	AMP
Telemann, G.-Barnes	Arie (Pimpinone)	Spr
Telemann, G.-Joosen	Concerto, f	HeE
Telemann, G.	Concerto, F	MM
Telemann, G.	Heldenmusik	MRL
Telemann, G.-Dominik	Partita No. 5	Reb
Telemann, G.-Voxman	Sonata, c	Rub
Templeton, A.	Elegie	MCA
Templeton, A.	Pocket Size Sonata	MCA
Templeton, A.	Pocket Size Sonata No. 2	Sha
Tenaglia, A.	Aria	For
Tenaglia, A.	Aria Antica	EdM
Thärichen, W.	Concerto, op. 51	B&B
Thiriet, A.	Cantilène	ALe
Thiriet, A.	Fantaisie, op. 162	GrF
Thiry	Dialogue	MM
Thiry	Dimanche Matin	MM
Thiry	Promenade	MM
Thomas, A.	Gavotte (Mignon)	CF
Thomas, A.	Polonaise (Mignon)	CF
Thomé, F.	Simple Aveu	CF
Thomé, F.	Simple Aveu	Dur
Thomé, F.-Piguet	Sous la feuillée	Dur
Thorarinsson, J.	Sonata	HeE
Thorne, F.	3 Dance Movements	AMC
Thornton, E.	Second Air Varie	CF
Thornton, E.	5th Air Varie	CF
Thornton, E.	8th Air Varie	CF
Thornton, E.	Columbus	CF
Thornton, E.-arr.	Comin' thro' the Rye	CF
Thornton, E.	Une Pensée Lointaine	CF
Thornton, E.	Sonnambula	CF
Timokha, N.-comp.	Easy Pieces, Bk. 1	MKE
Tisné, A.	Croquis, op. 32/2	ALe
Titl, A.	Serenade	CF
Toldrá, E.-Amaz	Ave Maria	UME
Toldrá, E.-Amaz	Dels Quatre Vents	UME
Toldrá, E.-Amaz	La Font	UME
Toldrá, E.-Amaz	Oracio al Maig	UME

232

Toldrá, E. -Amaz	Soneti de la Rosada	UME
Toll, R.	Duettino	CF
Toll, R.	Legerete	CF
Toll, R.	Lullaby	CF
Toll, R.	Miniature Suite	CF
Tomasi, H.	Allegro giocoso (Concerto)	ALe
Tomasi, H.	Chant Corse	ALe
Tomasi, H.	Complainte de jeune Indien	ALe
Tomasi, H.	Concerto	ALe
Tomasi, H.	Danse nuptiale (5 danses profanes et sacrées)	ALe
Tomasi, H.	Introduction et danse	ALe
Tomasi & Albinoni -Joosen	Concerto, d, op. 9/2	MM
Tosti, F. -Andreoni	Ideale	Ric
Tournier, F.	Complainte et rondo	EDo
Tournier, F.	Sur les pointes	ERR
Trafford, E.	Introduction and Allegro	TP
Tremblay, L.	Clarinet Waltz	NK
Tremblay, L.	Country Dance	NK
Tremblay, L.	Pahokee Polka	NK
Tremblay, L.	Petite Polonaise	NK
Tremblay, L.	Rebecca	NK
Tremblot de la Croix, F.	Le Dejeuner de Chantecler	ALe
Tribukh, M. -arr.	5 Pieces by Russian Classical Composers	MKE
Trier, S. & A. Boustead	Essential Repertoire	UE
Trinkaus, G.	Lament	CF
Trinkaus, G. -arr.	World's Best-Known Pieces	CF
Troje-Miller, N.	Andante, Cantabile and Scherzando	B-M
Troje-Miller, N.	Divertissement	B-M
Troje-Miller, N.	The Magic Fountain	B-M
Troje-Miller, N.	Mazas Etude No. 7	PrA
Troje-Miller, N.	Sicilienne and Tarantelle	B-M
Troshin, B.	Concertino	MKE
Troshin, B.	3 Pieces, op. 3	MKE
Trowbridge, L.	Homage to Chopin	See
Trowbridge, L.	In Retrospect	See
Trowbridge, L.	Organum Metamorphoses	See
Trowbridge, L.	Quietude	See
Tuthill, B.	Concerto	E-V
Tuthill, B.	Fantasy Sonata, op. 3	CF
Tuthill, B.	2 Snacks for a Lonesome Clarinet	SM
Ungureanu, D. (ed)	Album de mici piese	EdR
Uray, E.	Minnelied	LDo
Vachey, H.	Concerto Bref	GD
Vachey, H.	Elegy and Dance	ALe
Vachey, H.	Thème varié	ALe
Vačkář, D.	Clarinet Concerto. 1965	Art

Válek, J.	Sonata Eroica	Pan
Vallier, J.	Andante	Com
Van de Moortel, A.	Nocturne	Mau
Van de Vate, N.	Variations	AMC
Van Doren, T.	Feuille d'Album	EMe
Van Horne, H.	Cortège Féerique	B-M
Van Moer, J.	Solo No. 1	EMb
Van Rossum, F.	Petite pièce	Mau
Van Vlijman, J.	Dialogue	SD
Vartanian, E.	Etude	MKE
Vasilenko, S.-Stark	Concerto, op. 135	MKE
Vasilenko, S.	Oriental Dance	MKE
Vasilenko, S.-Kurkiewicz	Oriental Dance, op. 47	PWM
Vasilenko, S.	Rhapsodie Orientale	EdM
Vaughan Williams, R.	6 Studies in English Folk Song	GaM
Vazzana, A.	2 Pieces	Wes
Veale, J.	Concerto	OxU
Vellère, L.	Sérénité	Mau
Verdi, G.-Andreoni	Addio, del passato (La Traviata)	Ric
Verdi, G.-Amato	Andante (La Forza del Destino)	CF
Verdi, G.-Andreoni	Deserto sulla terra (Il Trovatore)	Ric
Verdi, G.-Andreoni	Di quella pira (Il Trovatore)	Ric
Verdi, G.-Andreoni	La Donna è mobile (Rigoletto)	Ric
Verdi, G.-O'Neill	I'll Fulfill the Round of Pleasure	Wat
Verdi, G.-Andreoni	Libiam ne' lieti calici (La Traviata)	Ric
Verdi, G.-Andreoni	Questa o quella (Rigoletto)	Ric
Verdi, G.-Bassi	Rigoletto	CF
Verdi, G.-Schmidt, Bassi	Fantasia from Rigoletto	CF
Verdi, G.-Bassi, Giampieri	Rigoletto Concert Fantasy	Ric
Verdi, G.-Andreoni	Stride la vampa (Il Trovatore)	Ric
Verdi, G.	La Traviata	CF
Verdi, G.-Andreoni	Tutte le feste al tempio (Rigoletto)	Ric
Verdi, G.-Andreoni	Va, pensiero (Nabucco)	Ric
Veretti, A.	Fantasia	ALe
Vergnault	Premiers bourgeons	Com
Verhey, T.-Voxman	Nocturne	Rub
Verrall, J.-arr.	Clarinet Music the Whole World Loves	BM
Verrall, J.	Nocturne	Cre
Verroust, S.-Langenus	Premier Amour	CF
Verroust, S.-Langenus	To a Poppy	CF
Verroust, S.	12e Solo	MM
Victory, G.	Suite Rustique	ALe
Victory, G.	3 Contes de fée	ALe
Vigneron, J.	Duo rapsodique	Mau

Clarinet and Piano

Vilec, M.	Rast (Zyklus Sommernotizen)	Pan
Vilec, M.	Le Repos	Pan
Vilec, M.	Summer notes. 1959	SHF
Villa-Lobos, H.-Goehr	Song of the Black Swan	EBM
Villalonga	Babillerie	EdR
Villette, P.	Poème	ALe
Villette, P.	Romance	ALe
Vinci, L.-Waln	Sonata No. 1	NK
Vinter, G.-Perry	Concertino	B&H
Vito, B. de -Delvaux	Divertissement	EMb
Vito, B. di -Delvaux	3 Pièces	EMb
Vivaldi, A.	Giga	EdM
Vivaldi, A.-Decaprio	Giga	War
Vives Molas, J.	Canto de Sirena. Melody in F	UME
Vives Molas, J.	Mozartianas, Divertimento on Themes of Mozart	UME
Vives Molas, J.	Recuerdos juveniles de Beethoven	UME
Vlad, R.	Improvvisazione su di una melodia	Ric
Vlag, H.	Ballade (cl in A)	EdH
Vlasov, V.	Poem-Dance	MKE
Volleman, A.	Improvisatie en allegro	Mau
Von Kreisler, A.	Berceuse	SM
Von Kreisler, A.	Serenata	SM
Vostřak, Z.	Burleske	Art
Votquenne, V.	Barcarolle	EMb
Votquenne, V.	Fioriture	EMb
Voxman, H. (ed)	Concert and Contest Collection	Rub
Vránek, G.	3 Melodies	Art
Waart, J. van	Clarinet Concerto	MM
Waddington	An Evening Song	Wat
Waddington	Tone Song	Wat
Wagner, Josef Franz -Jolliff	Under the Double Eagle	Rub
Wagner, Joseph Frederick	Rhapsody	B&H
Wagner, Joseph Frederick	Sonatina	B&H
Wagner, R.-Bellison	Adagio (actually by Baermann)	B-M
Wagner, R.-Roberts	Song to the Evening Star	CF
Wagner, R.-Trinkaus	Song to the Evening Star	CF
Wagner, R.-Stone	Träume, Studie zu "Tristan und Isolde"	B&H
Wagner, R.	Träume (Dreams)	CF
Wagner, R.-Trinkaus	Walther's Prize Song	CF
Wahren, K.	Concerto. 1968	B&B
Waldteufel, E.	España	E&C
Waldteufel, E.	Estudiantian	E&C
Waldteufel, E.-Jolliff	Skater's Waltz	Rub
Walker -McCathren	Boutade	SHM
Walker, E.	Romance	GaM
Walker, G.	Perimeters	Gen

Clarinet and Piano

Walker, R.	Moment Musical	TP
Walker, R.	Persian Caprice	B-M
Wallace, J.	Top 'n' Tail, Divertissement	B&H
Walter, F.	Märchen und Tanzszene, 2 Fantasiestücke	WZ
Walters, D.	Episode	SM
Walters, H.-arr.	Amazing Grace	Rub
Walters, H.	Capricious Aloysius	Rub
Walters, H.-arr.	Fat Boy Polka	Rub
Walters, H.-arr.	Sakura, Sakura (Cherry Blossoms)	Rub
Walters, H.	Shindig (Folk song Fantasy)	Rub
Walters, H.-arr.	When the Saints Go Marching In	Rub
Wanhal, J.	Concerto	EMB
Wanhal, J.	Sonata	M&M
Wanhal, J.-Merriman	Sonata No. 2	SM
Wanhal, J.-Dobrée	Sonata, Bb (originally C)	AlB
Wanhal, J.-Simon	Sonata, Bb	Int
Wanhal, J.	Sonata, Bb	MR
Wanhal, J.-Stofer	Sonata, Eb	SS
Warland, D.	Notturno	Wes
Warren, D.	Cumberland	Lud
Warren, D.	Grenadilla Caprice	Lud
Warren, D.	Sonatina	Lud
Watelle, J.	Andante et polonaise	Bil
Waters, C.	Arabesque	HE
Webber, C.-arr.	First Solo Album	TP
Webber, L.	Frensham Pond	AHC
Webber, R.	Romany Caprice	TP
Weber -arr.	7 Melodic Pieces by Russian Composers	MCA
Weber, A.	Andantino	ALe
Weber, A.	Mélopée	ALe
Weber, C.M. von	Air & Variations	B-M
Weber, C.M. von -Rose, Lefèbvre	Concertino, op. 26	ALe
Weber, C.M. von -Simon	Concertino, op. 26	B&H
Weber, C.M. von	Concertino, Eb, op. 26	Bil
Weber, C.M. von -Hausswald	Concertino, op. 26	BrH
Weber, C.M. von -Schreinicke	Concertino, Eb, op. 26	BrH
Weber, C.M. von	Concertino, op. 26	CF
Weber, C.M. von -Strasser	Concertino, op. 26	CF
Weber, C.M. von	Concertino, op. 26	EdK
Weber, C.M. von	Concertino, op. 26	ES
Weber, C.M. von -Kell	Concertino, Eb, op. 26	Int
Weber, C.M. von -Frank, McCathren	Concertino, op. 26	Ken
Weber, C.M. -Wlach	Concertino, op. 26	LDo
Weber, C.M. von	Concertino, op. 26	MRL
Weber, C.M. von -Waln	Concertino, op. 26	NK

236

Weber, C. M. von –Giampieri	Concertino, op. 26	Ric
Weber, C. M. von –Davis	Concertino, op. 26	Rub
Weber, C. M. von –Christmann	Concertino, op. 26	Sch
Weber, C. M. von –Bonade, Hite	Concertino, op. 26	SM
Weber, C. M. von –Delécluse	Concertino No. 1, f, op. 73	ALe
Weber, C. M. von –Simon	Concerto No. 1, op. 73	B&H
Weber, C. M. von –Lancelot	Concerto No. 1, f, op. 73	Bil
Weber, C. M. von –Hausswald	Concerto No. 1, f, op. 73	BrH
Weber, C. M. von –Schreinicke	Concerto No. 1, f, op. 73	BrH
Weber, C. M. von	Concerto No. 1, op. 73	CF
Weber, C. M. von	Concerto No. 1, op. 73	EdK
Weber, C. M. von –Kell	Concerto No. 1, f, op. 73	Int
Weber, C. M. von	Concerto No. 1, op. 73	MRL
Weber, C. M. von –Madeja	Concerto No. 1, f, op. 73	PWM
Weber, C. M. von –Giampieri	Concerto No. 1, f, op. 73	Ric
Weber, C. M. von –Bennett	Concerto No. 1, f, op. 73	SF
Weber, C. M. von –Cavally	Concerto No. 1, op. 73	SM
Weber, C. M. von –Amaz	Concerto No. 1, op. 73	UME
Weber, C. M. von –Delécluse	Concerto No. 2, Eb, op. 74 Cadenza by Ibert	ALe
Weber, C. M. von –Simon	Concerto No. 2, op. 74	B&H
Weber, C. M. von –Rose	Concerto No. 2, Eb, op. 74	Bil
Weber, C. M. von –Hausswald	Concerto No. 2, Eb, op. 74	BrH
Weber, C. M. von –Schreinicke	Concerto No. 2, Eb, op. 74	BrH
Weber, C. M. von	Concerto No. 2, op. 74	CF
Weber, C. M. von	Concerto No. 2, op. 74	EdK
Weber, C. M. von –Kell	Concerto No. 2, Eb, op. 74	Int
Weber, C. M. von –Semyonov	Concerto No. 2, op. 74	MKE
Weber, C. M. von	Concerto No. 2, op. 74	MRL
Weber, C. M. von –Giampieri	Concerto No. 2, Eb, op. 74	Ric
Weber, C. M. von –Klosé, Jeanjean	Dernière Pensée	ALe
Weber, C. M. von –Laube	Excerpt from Quintet, op. 34	CF
Weber, C. M. von –Klosé, Jeanjean	Fantasia on Der Freischütz	ALe
Weber, C. M. von –Kroepsch, Bellison	Fantasie (Der Freischütz), op. 6	CF
Weber, C. M. von –Klosé, Jeanjean	Fantasia on Oberon	ALe
Weber, C. M. von –Rose, Lefèbvre	Fantasia and Rondo, op. 34	ALe
Weber, C. M. von –Langenus	Fantasia and Rondo, op. 34	CF
Weber, C. M. von –Snavely	Fantasia and Rondo, op. 34	Ken
Weber, C. M. von –Roth	Grand Duo Concertant, op. 48	B&H
Weber, C. M. von –Lancelot	Grand duo concertant, op. 48	Bil
Weber, C. M. von	Grand Duo Concertante, op. 48	CF
Weber, C. M. von	Grand Duo Concertant, op. 48	EdK
Weber, C. M. von –Kell	Grand Duo Concertant, op. 48	Int
Weber, C. M. von –Baermann	Grand Duo Concertant, op. 48	MRL

Weber, C. M. von –Hofmann	Grand Duo Concertant, op. 48	Pet
Weber, C. M. von –Simon	Grand Duo Concertant, op. 48	Sch
Weber, C. M. von –Baermann	Quintet, op. 34	MRL
Weber, C. M. von –Davis	Hunter's Chorus	Rub
Weber, C. M. von –Kohl	Introduktion, Thema und Variationen	B&B
Weber, C. M. von –Drucker	Introduction, Theme and Variations	Int
Weber, C. M. von –Kohl	Introduction, Theme and Variations	MRL
Weber, C. M. von –Klosé, Jeanjean	Invitation to the Dance	ALe
Weber, C. M. von	Invitation to the Waltz	CF
Weber, C. M. von –Harris	Minuet (Quintet, op. 34)	CF
Weber, C. M. von –Rose	Récit et polonaise, op. 74	Bil
Weber, C. M. von –Voxman	Recitative and Polacca	Rub
Weber, C. M. von	Romance, Recitative and Polacca (Concerto, op. 74)	EdK
Weber, C. M. von	Romance, Recitative and Polacca, op. 74	SM
Weber, C. M. von –Laube	Romanza Appassionata	CF
Weber, C. M. von –Phillips	Rondo	OxU
Weber, C. M. von –Rose, Lefèbvre	Solo on Der Freischütz	ALe
Weber, C. M. von –Hendrickson, Johnson	Sonatina	CF
Weber, C. M. von	Variations concertantes, op. 33	Bil
Weber, C. M. von	Variations, op. 33	CF
Weber, C. M. von	Variations, op. 33	EdK
Weber, C. M. von –Drucker	Variations, Bb, op. 33	Int
Weber, C. M. von	Variations, op. 33	MRL
Weber, C. M. von –Hodgson	Variations, op. 33	Pet
Weber, F.	Bluebird Waltz	B-M
Weber, F.	Sentimental Lady	B-M
Weinberger, J.	Sonatine	CF
Weiner, L.	Ballad, op. 8. 1911	EMB
Weiner, L.	Recruiting Dance from Pereg. 1951	EMB
Weiner, S. –Lancelot	Sonata	Bil
Weis, F.	Sonate. 1931 (cl in A)	SPD
Wellesz, E.	2 Stücke, op. 34	UE
Werkmeister	Souvenir de Sfax	EdR
Wesly, E.	Confidences	EdS
Wesly, E.	Fiançailles	EdS
Wesly, E.	Hyménée	EdS
Wesly, E.	Joyeux ébats	EdS
Wesly, E.	Rêverie d'Automne	EdS
Weston, P. –arr.	Clarinet Albums, 4 vols.	S&C
Weston, P. & W. Bergmann –arr.	12 English Country Dances	S&C

Clarinet and Piano

Wettge, G.	Fantasie Varié	MM
Wheeler, C.	Meditation	Vol
Whetstone	Andante Moderato	Wat
Whettam, G.	Sonatina	B-M
White, C.	Basque Folk Song	B-M
White, J.	Conte	ALe
White, J.	Variations	GaM
Whitney, M.	Clarinata	Spr
Whitney, M.	Gigue	Bou
Whitney, M.	Melancholy	Spr
Whitney, M.	Roaming River	Bou
Widor, C. M.	Introduction and Rondo, op. 72	Heu
Widor, C.-Bonade	Introduction and Rondo, op. 72	SM
Wieniawski, H.	Romance (Concerto No. 2)	CF
Wigy, Fr.	Recitativo en allegro	Mau
Wilber, R.	Allegro-Ballad-Allegro	Ken
Wilber, R.	Clarinet Impromptu	CF
Wilder, A.	Sonata	SF
Wildgans, F.	Concerto No. 2	LDo
Wildgans, F.	Sonatine. 1959	LDo
Wildgans, F.	3 Vortragsstücke, op. 14	UE
Williamson, M.	Pas de deux	B&H
Willner, A.-arr.	Classical Album	B&H
Wilson, T.	Sonatina	S&C
Winter, P. von	Concertino, Eb	HSM
Wirth, H.	Sonata	HSM
Wissmer, P.	Concerto	Ric
Woldring, M.	Ballade	T-M
Wolf, J. De	Sonatina	HeE
Wood, W.	Let 'Er Go	Cen
Woodworth	The Old Oaken Bucket	CF
Wordsworth, W.	Prelude and Scherzo, op. 52	AlL
Wuille, H.-Bellison	Fantasie	Ric
Wurmser, L.	Aria	Com
Wurmser, L.	Badinéries	Bil
Wurmser, L.	Barcarolle	Bil
Wurmser, L.	Fantasia	EMT
Wurmser, L.	Tristesse	Com
Wyner, Y.	Sonata	CoF
Wyczynski, I.-arr.	Collection of Easy Pieces	PWM
Yakhnina, Y.-Stark	4 Pieces	MKE
Yost, M.-Michaels	Concerto, Bb, No. 9	RS
Yun, I.	Riul. 1968	B&B
Yuste, M.	Capricho pintoresco	UME
Yuste, M.	Solo de concurso, op. 39	UME
Zachara, F.	Sonata	SM
Zamacois, J.-Amaz	Serenada d'Hivern	UME
Zambarano, A.	Neopolitan Tarantella	Sha
Zamecnik, J.	Polly	SF
Zanettovich, D.	Suite	ALe

239

Clarinet and Piano

Zaninelli, L.	Canto	E-V
Zathey, J.	Jocose Suite	PWM
Zeisl	Shepherd's Melody	B-M
Zieritz, G.	Musik	WZ
Zimmerman, R.	Play a Song of America	TP
Zimmerman -arr.	Play a Song of Christmas	TP
Zindars, E.	Sonata	AMC
Zipp, F.	Au clair de la lune	WMS
Zipp, F.	Sonatine	OHN
Zonn, P.	Sonatine. 1956	CoF
Zuckert, L.	Doina. 1967 (revised 1970)	Can

Clarinet and Organ

Brown, R.	Sonata	Wes

Clarinet and Orchestra

Absil, J.	Fantaisie humoresque	ALe
Ameller, A.	Cantilena	ALe
Anderson, T.	6 Pieces	ACA
Andriessen, J.	Symphonie No. 5 (Time-- Spirit). 1970	SD
Arnold, M.	Clarinet Concerto	AlL
Aubin, T.	Le Calme de la mer (Suite éolienne)	ALe
Aubin, T.	Divertimento dell' incertezza	ALe
Avshalomoff, J.	Evocations	ACA
Bach, J.C.-Mozart, W. -Ettlinger	Concerto, Eb (cl, str)	B&H
Baermann, H.	Adagio (formerly attributed to R. Wagner)	BrH
Barlow, W.	Lyrical Piece (cl, str)	CF
Baur, J.	Concerto. 1970	BrH
Bavicchi, J.	Concerto	OxU
Beck, C.	Concerto	SS
Becker, G.	Correspondances I. 1966 (Eb clar/cl/bcl, O)	HG
Beer, J.	Concerto, Bb, op. 1	MR
Bemers, P.	Divertimento	SS
Ben-Haim, P.	Pastorale Variée	MCA
Berghmans, J.	The Tight-rope Walker (Scenes from a Traveling Circus)	ALe
Bergson, M.	Scene und Arie (Luisa di Montfort), op. 82	JoA
Berio, L.	Concertino. 1950	UE
Bernaud, A.	Concerto lyrique	ALe
Bernier, R.	Reverdies	ALe
Bialas, G.	Concerto	B&N
Blacher, B.	Concerto. 1971	B&B
Bloch, W.	Concerto	LDo
Boesmans, P.	Corrélations	Job

Bonneau, P.	Suite	ALe
Bonsel, A.	Concerto. 1950	SD
Boulez, P.	Domaines. 1968-69	UE
Bozza, E.	Concerto	ALe
Brant, H.	Colloquy	Spr
Breuer, K.	Atonalyse I (cl, str)	HSM
Bush, G.	Rhapsody	Elk
Busoni, F.	Concertino, op. 48	BrH
Busser, H.	Aragon	ALe
Busser, H.	Pastorale, op. 46	ALe
Cahuzac, L.	Cantilène	Bil
Cahuzac, L.	Pastorale Cévenole	Bil
Cahuzac, L.	Variations sur un air du pays d'oc	ALe
Casanova, A.	Ballade	Ric
Chabrier, E.	Larghetto	EdS
Chopin, F.	Minute Waltz	GFB
Cimarosa, D.-Benjamin	Concerto for Oboe (cl, str)	B&H
Copland, A.	Concerto	B&H
Cordero, R.	Mensaje Funebre (cl, str)	PIC
Corniot, R.	Sérénade-Tarantelle (cl, pf)	ECh
Cossetto, E.	Concerto	DSS
Cruft, A.	Concertino	GaM
Crusell, B.	Concerto, Eb, No. 1	MT
Crusell, B.-Michaels	Concerto, f, op. 5	HSM
Crusell, B.	Concerto, f, No. 2	MT
Crusell, B.	Concerto, Bb, No. 3	MT
Debussy, C.	Première Rhapsodie	CF
Debussy, C.	Première Rapsody	Dur
Debussy, C.	Rhapsody No. 1	Eul
Di Biase, E.	Fantasia	TP
Dimler, A.-Balassa, Fodor	Concerto, Bb	Eul
Donizetti, G.-Päuler	Concertino	Eul
Donizetti, G.-Meylan	Concertino, Bb	Pet
Dresden, S.	Symphonietta. 1938	SD
Dressel, E.	Konzert	R&E
Dubois, P.	Beaugency-Concerto (cl, str)	ALe
Ducat, A.	Esquisse	Mau
Ellstein, A.	Chassidic Dance	B-M
Felix, V.	Fantasie	Art
Fernström, J.	Concerto, op. 30	STI
Fibich, Z.	Idylle, op. 16	Art
Finch, R.	Romanze	Che
Fischer, J.	Concerto. 1965	Art
Flosman, O.	Concerto. 1954	CHF
Flothuis, M.	Concerto, op. 58. 1957	SD
Françaix, J.	Concerto	EMT
Frid, G.	Concerto, op. 82. 1972	SD
Friemann, W.	Concerto No. 1. 1960	AP
Frohlich, O.	Vision (cl, str)	BB

Frumerie, G. de	Clarinet Concerto. 1957-58	CGM
Fuchs, G.	Concerto, Bb	EMB
Fussan, W.	Concertino	SS
Gagnebin, H.	Andante et allegro	ALe
Gagnebin, H.	Fantasy	ALe
Genzmer, H.	Concertino	Pet
Glaser, W.	Concertino. 1962	STI
Globokar, V.	Ausstrahlungen	Pet
Gmeindl, W.	Sinfonisches Konzert, op. 24	UE
Groot, H. de	Concertino	SD
Gross, P.	Concerto	I-V
Grosskopf, E.	Flecktreue, Raritätenkunst P. 1969	B&B
Haapalainen, V.	Solitude	Fin
Hamilton, I.	Concerto op. 7. 1949	SS
Handel, G.-Barbirolli	Concerto	OxU
Hasquenoph, P.	Concertino (cl, str)	Heu
Heaton-Smith, R.	Concerto (cl, str)	MR
Heider, W.	Strophen	Eul
Henneberg, A.	Concertino	STI
Hindemith, P.	Concerto. 1947 (cl in A)	SS
Hindemith, P.	Plöner Musiktag: D--Abend-konzert IV. Variations	SS
Hlobil, E.	Rapsodie, op. 51. 1955	Art
Hobson, M.	Concerto	Che
Hoddinott, A.	Concerto	OxU
Hofmann, W.	Concerto	S-V
Holm, P.	Concertino	WH
Holmboe, V.	Concerto No. 3	WH
Horký, K.	Concerto. 1967	CHF
Horovitz, J.	Concerto	B-M
Horovitz, J.	Concertante	Che
Hovhaness, A.	Processional and Fugue (cl, str)	Eul
Hummel, J.F.	Berceuse und Tarantelle	BrH
Hummel, J.F.	Concerto, Eb, No. 1	BrH
Hummel, J.F.	Concerto, f, No. 2	BrH
Indy, V. d'-Piguet	Choral varié, op. 55	Dur
Karkoff, M.	Concerto, op. 44. 1959	STI
Keller, H.	Serenade (cl, str)	CF
Ketting, P.	Concertino. 1973	SD
Klebe, G.	Raskolnikows Traum, op. 23	B&B
Klosé, H.	First Air Varie	EdK
Kořinek, M.	Concerto	SHF
Kovaříček, F.	Klarinettenkonzert. 1965	Art
Koželuch, J.	Concerto, Eb	CHF
Kramář-Krommer, F.	Concerto, Eb, op. 36	CHF
Kratochvíl, J.	Concerto No. 1. 1962	CHF
Krenek, E.	Suite	B&N
Kubín, R.	Concerto	Art
Kubizek, A.	Concerto, op. 9	LDo

Kügerl, H.	Serenade and Tarantella	LK
Kurpinski, K.-Wilczak	Concerto	AP
Landré, G.	Concerto. 1957–58	SD
Landré, G.	4 Miniatures. 1950	SD
Larsson, L.	Concertino, op. 45/3	CGM
Leclerc, M.	Contrasts	Mau
Loevendie, T.	Scaramuccia. 1969	SD
Louvrier	3 Atmospheres	ALe
Lucas, L.	Concerto	Che
Lundkvist, P.	Pärldiademet	STI
Lutoslawski, W.	5 Dance Preludes. 1955	AP
Malige, F.	Concerto	BrH
Manevich, A.-Rosenthal	Concerto	MCA
Manevich, A.	Concerto	MKE
Martelli, C.	Concerto (cl, str)	AlL
McBride, R.	The World Is Ours	ACA
Melillo, P.	Concerto	AMC
Mellnäs, A.	Concerto. 1957	STI
Meulemans, A.	Sonata concertante. 1948	CBD
Meyer, E.	Kleine Eröffnungsmusik	BrH
Meyer-Tormin, W.	Concerto	For
Mihalovici, M.	Musique Nocturne	ALe
Mihule, J.	Concerto, op. 23. 1953	CHF
Milhaud, D.	Concerto	E-V
Milhaud, D.	Scaramouche	EdS
Milveden, I.	Concerto al fresco. 1970	STI
Mirouze, L.	Humoresque	ALe
Molter, J.-Becker	Concerto, A, No. 1	BrH
Molter, J.-Becker	Concerto, D, No. 2	BrH
Molter, J.-Becker	Concerto, G, No. 3	BrH
Molter, J.-Becker	Concerto, D, No. 4	BrH
Mourant, W.	Blue Haze	AMC
Mourant, W.	Concertino	ACA
Mozart, W.-Busoni	Adagio (Concerto, K. 622)	BrH
Mozart, W.	Concerto, A, K. 622	BrH
Mozart, W.	Concerto op. 107 (K. 622)	CF
Mozart, W.	Clarinet Concerto K. 622	EdK
Mozart, W.	Concerto, A	SM
Mozart, W.	Larghetto (Quintet)	Dur
Mozart, W.-Intravaia	Rondo (Clarinet Concerto)	CF
Nielsen, C.	Concerto op. 57	Kis
Nielsen, C.	Concerto for Clarinet op. 57. 1928	SPD
Nordgren, E.	Concerto op. 26	STI
Nordgren, P.	Concerto. 1970	Fin
Pacius, F.	Adagio. 1859 (cl, str)	Fin
Páleníček, J.	Concertino da camera. 1957	CHF
Patachich, I.	3 Pieces	EMB
Pauer, J.	Concertino for quarter-tone clarinet	CHF

Paulson, G.	Concerto op. 100. 1958	STI
Peaslee, R.	Night Songs (cl, str)	JB
Perry, H.	Concertino for Violin	B&H
Petrič, I.	Concerto	EdD
Philiba, N.	Concerto da Camera	Bil
Pierné, G.	Canzonetta	ALe
Pierné, G.	Canzonetta	SM
Pisk, P.	Shanty Boy	AMP
Pleyel, I.-Michaels	Concerto, Bb	HSM
Pleyel, I.-Dobrée	Clarinet Concerto	MR
Pokorny, F.-Becker	Concerto, Bb	BrH
Pokorny, F.-Becker	Concerto, Eb	BrH
Quinet, M.	Ballade. 1961	CBD
Ranta, S.	The Even. 1932	Fin
Ravanello, O.	Meditazione, op. 118/3 (cl, str)	GZ
Ravel, M.	Pièce en forme de Habanera	ALe
Rawsthorne, A.	Concerto (cl, str)	OxU
Reed, A.	Serenade	SM
Reiner, K.	Divertimento. 1947	
	(4 concertante compositions)	CHF
Reiter, A.	Concerto	LDo
Rimsky-Korsakov, N.	Flight of the Bumble Bee	GFB
Riotte, P.-Michaels	Concerto, Bb	HSM
Rivier, J.	Concerto (cl, str)	EMT
Rogers, B.	Pastoral Mistico (cl, str)	GaM
Rosetti, A.	Concerto, Eb	Pet
Rossini, G.-Peruzzi	Variations	GZ
Rossini, G.-Michaels	Introduction, Theme and Variations	HSM
Rossini, G.	Variations	M&M
Roussel, A.	Aria	ALe
Rueff, J.	Concertino, op. 15	ALe
Saikkola, L.	Concerto. 1969	Fin
Sárközy, I.	Sinfonia Concertante. 1963	EMB
Schibler, A.	Concertino, op. 49 (cl, str)	Eul
Schönherr, M.	Hans im Glück	LK
Schollum, R.	Concerto grosso, op. 34	UE
Schouwman, H.	5 Schetsen, op. 22. 1942	SD
Seiber, M.	Concertino. 1951 (cl, str)	SS
Semler-Collery, J.	Fantaisie et danse en forme de gigue	ALe
Seter, M.	Elegy. 1954 (cl, str)	Isr
Shaw, A.	Concerto	B-M
Siegmeister, E.	Concerto	AMC
Siennicki, E.	Ballade	E-V
Sikorski, K.	Concerto. 1947	AP
Simeone, H.	Creole Clarinet	Sha
Skerjanc, L.	Concerto	EdD
Skerl, D.	5 Compositions (cl, str)	EdD
Spohr, L.-Voxman	Variations on a theme (Alruna)	MR

Spohr, L.-Leinert	Concerto, c, op. 26, No. 1	B&N
Spohr, L.	Clarinet Concerto, op. 26,	
	No. 1	EdK
Spohr, L.-Rischko	Concerto, e, No. 4	BrH
Stamitz, J.-Gradenwitz	Concerto, Bb	MCA
Stamitz, J.-Lebermann	Concerto, Bb	SS
Stamitz, K.-Wojciechowski	Concerto, Bb, No. 3	Pet
Stamitz, K.-Balassa	Concerto No. 4 (cl, str)	EMB
Stamitz, K.-Michaels	Concerto, Bb, No. 10	HSM
Stamitz, K.-Wojciechowski	Concerto, Eb	HSM
Stamitz, K.	Concerto, F	Eul
Stamitz, K.-Lebermann	Concerto, F, No. 1	SS
Stevens, H.	Concerto (cl, str)	PIC
Storp, S.	Concerto	MV
Strategier, H.	Concertino. 1950	SD
Stutschewsky, J.	Concertino	ImV
Swisher, G.	Concerto	Roc
Szajna-Lewandowska, J.	Capriccio. 1960	AP
Szeligowski, T.	Concerto. 1932	AP
Szervánsky, E.	Serenade. 1950	EMB
Tartini, G.-Jacob	Concertino	B&H
Thärichen, W.	Concerto op. 51	B&B
Tomasi, H.	Concerto	ALe
Tomasi, H.	Danse nuptiale (5 danses pro-	
	fanes et sacrées)	ALe
Tomasi, H.	Introduction et danse	ALe
Tuček, V.	Concerto, Bb	Art
Uhl, A.	Konzertante Sinfonie	UE
Vačkař, D.	Concerto. 1965	CHF
Van de Moortel, A.	Nocturne	Mau
Veale, J.	Concerto	OxU
Veretti, A.	Fantasia	ALe
Vorlová, S.	Concerto, d, op. 41. 1957	CHF
Wagner, J.	Rhapsody	B&H
Wagner, R. [H. Baermann]	Adagio (cl, str)	EdK
Wanhal, J.-Balassa, Berlasz	Concerto, C (cl, str)	EMB
Weber, C.M. von-Hausswald	Concertino, Eb, op. 26	BrH
Weber, C.M. von	Concertino op. 26	EdK
Weber, C.M. von-Hausswald	Concerto, f, No. 1, op. 73	BrH
Weber, C.M. von	Concerto, f, No. 1, op. 73	CF
Weber, C.M. von	Concerto No. 1, op. 73	EdK
Weber, C.M. von-Hausswald	Concerto, Eb, No. 2, op. 74	BrH
Weber, C.M. von	Concerto, Eb, No. 2, op. 74	CF
Weber, C.M. von	Concerto No. 2, op. 74	EdK
Weiner, L.	Ballad. 1949	EMB
Wildgans, F.	Concerto No. 2	LDo
Winter, P. von	Concertino, Eb	HSM
Wiszniewski, Z.	Concerto	PWM
Yost, M.	Concerto No. 4	M&M
Ziems, H.	Chamber Concerto. 1962	BrH

Clarinet and Orchestra
Zipoli, D.-Salvaggi | 12 a Canzone dall'organo (cl, str) | UE

Clarinet and Band

Adams, S.	Holy City	Rub
Arndt, F.	Nola	Vol
Atkinson	Taste of Licorice	CFC
Barat, J.	Chant Slave	ALe
Bauderuc	L'Étoile des solistes	EdR
Bauderuc	La Gondole Vénitienne	EdR
Bauderuc	L'Hirondelle fugitive	EdR
Bellini, V.-Zurmühle	Concerto	MM
Bennett, D.	Clarinet Royale	CF
Bergson, M.-Veenendaal	Louise de Montfoort	MM
Bernstein, L.	Prelude, Fugue and Riffs (cl, jazz band)	Sch
Blémant, L.	Bolero	ALe
Boccalari, E.-Kent, Akers	Fantasia di Concerto	CF
Boisson	Une Soirée à Alger	EdR
Bouillon, P.-Mol	La Pluie d'Or	MM
Bouillon, P.-Bennett	Shower of Gold	TP
Bruniau, A.	Fantaisie tyrolienne	EdR
Bruniau, A.	Fantaisie variée	EdR
Bruniau, A.	Grande introduction et polonaise	EdR
Bruniau, A.	Sur la montagne	EdR
Cahuzac, L.	Variations sur un air du pays d'oc	ALe
Cardew, P.-Jarman	Scherzo	B&H
Cavallini, E.-Waln	Adagio & Tarantella	CFC
Chopin, F.-Beeler	Minute Waltz	CF
Chopin, F.	Minute Waltz	GFB
Chopin, F.-Martin	Tristesse	EdR
Corbin, A.	Deauville	EdR
Crusell, B.-Lang	Concerto, f, op. 5	Lan
Cunningham, M.	Coffee-Cake Walk	CoA
Davis, A.	Ballade and Beguine	Ken
DeVille, P.	Swiss Boy	CF
Elgar, E.-Luckhardt	Land of Hope and Glory	B&H
Endresen, R.	Pepperino	Rub
Endresen, R.	Technician	Rub
Endresen, R.	Victor	Rub
Everaarts, M.	Klarinetten Twist	T-M
Filas, T.	Velocity	CF
Fillmore, H.	Lightning Fingers	CF
Frank, M.	Clownish Clarinet	B-M
Frank, M.	Concertino	B-M
Godard, B.-Fernand	Berceuse de Jocelyn	EdR
Goldman, E.	Tramp, Tramp, Tramp	CF
Groot, de	Tyrolienne	MM

Clarinet and Band

Grundman, C.	Pipe Dream	B&H
Guilhaud, G.-Bennett	First Concerto	Vol
Hermann, R.	Clarinet on the Town	CF
Kepner, F.	The Princess	Sch
Labole	Papillon d'azur	EdR
Lake, M.	Naida	Lud
Lefèbvre, C.-Cailliet	Andante and Allegro	SM
Llewellyn, E.	My Regards	Vol
Logan, R.	Presto Chango	TP
Loué	Mignonette	EdR
Magnani, A.	Mazurka-caprice	ALe
Mainzer-Jaroc	Lustige Musikanten	MM
Maltby, R.	Ballad	B-M
Maltby, R.	Moon over the Mesa	PrA
Marcello, A.-Frison	Concerto, c	MM
Marsal, E.	Grande fantaisie polka	EdR
Marsal, E.	L'Hirondelle	EdR
Mellin-Bilk	Stranger on the Shore	Vol
Mendelssohn, F.-Hermann	Allegro (Violin Concerto)	Pod
Messager, A.	Solo de Concours	ALe
Messager, A.-Snavely	Solo de Concours	Ken
Metehen	Giselle	EdR
Morrissey, J.	Interlude	War
Morrissey, J.	Nightfall	EBM
Mozart, W.-Zurmühle	Clarinet Concerto, Movement I	MM
Mozart, W.-Zurmühle	Clarinet Concerto, Movements II & III	MM
Mozart, W.-Jasper	Concerto for Clarinet	PrA
Mozart, W.-Gesse	Larghetto (Quintet)	EdR
Murray, L.	Collage	Wes
Pierné, G.-Reed, McCathren	Serenade	Vol
Planel, R.	Fantaisie rondo	EdR
Rabaud, H.-Gee	Solo de Concours	SM
Reed, A.	5 Dances for Five Clarinets	EBM
Reed, A.	Rahoon	EBM
Reed, A.	Serenade	SM
Richens, J.	Prelude and Dance	Ken
Rimsky-Korsakov, N.	Clarinet Concerto	HeE
Rimsky-Korsakov, N.-Perry	Concerto	MCA
Rimsky-Korsakov, N.-Landheer	Concerto	T-M
Rimsky-Korsakov, N.	Flight of the Bumble Bee	GFB
Rossini, G.-Glazer, Hermann	Introduction, Theme and Variations	OxU
Rossini, G.-Neufeld	Variations for Clarinet	Wes
Schorer	Clarinet Capriolen	MM
Schorer	Poitus	MM
Schreiner, A.-Howard	Immer Kleiner	Lud
Seleski, L.	Interlude Romantique	Ken
Simeone, H.	Creole Clarinet	Sha

Smith, C. & G. Holmes	Friends	Rub
Spohr, L.-Lang	Concerto No. 3, Movement I	Lan
Strategier, H.	Triptiek	MM
Tchaikovsky, P.-Schinstine	Canzonetta	SM
Titl, A.	Serenade	CF
Walters, H.	Capricious Aloysius	Rub
Watelle, J.	Andante et polonaise	EdR
Weber, C.M. von-Rose, Lefèbvre	Concertino op. 26	ALe
Weber, C.M. von-Brown	Concertino op. 26	B&H
Weber, C.M. von-Lake	Concertino op. 26	CF
Weber, C.M. von-Reed	Concertino op. 26	CFC
Weber, C.M. von-McCathren	Concertino op. 26	Ken
Weber, C.M. von-Lhomme	Concertino op. 26	MM
Weber, C.M. von-Davis	Concertino op. 26	Rub
Weber, C.M. von-Brown	Clarinet Concerto No. 2	B&H
Weber, C.M. von-Reed, McCathren	Concerto No. 2	Vol
Weber, C.M. von-Snavely	Fantasia and Rondo	Ken
Werkmeister	Souvenir de Sfax	EdR
Wichers	Clarinet Polka	MM

Methods and Studies

	Bandman's Clarinet Repertoire, 2 vols.	CF
	Military Band Studies, 3 vols.	CF
	Bandman's Studio for Clarinet, vols. III & V	CF
	Complete Scale for Clarinet	CF
	Fingering Chart	ALe
	Fun with Clarinet	War
	Jazz Studies	Han
	Phrasing Modern Melodies	McK
	Pro Art Clarinet Method, 2 vols.	PrA
	Rubank Instrumental Chart (Boehm & Albert Systems)	Rub
Albert, J.	24 Varied Scales and Exercises	CF
Albert, J. & Parès, G.-Hovey	Daily Exercises	B-M
Alessio, F.	8 Grand Etudes	EdS
Anzalone, V.	Breeze-Easy Method, 2 vols.	War
Arfine, L.	Comprehensive Choral Etudes	McK
Armato, B. (ed)	The Opera Clarinetist	CF
Arnold, J.	15 Daily Klosé Exercises	ShB
Arnold, J.	Modern Fingering System	ShB
Arnold, J.	The Very First Clarinet Method	Han
Ayres, T.	Intermediate Method, 2 vols.	S-B
Bach, J.S.-Delécluse	15 Etudes	ALe

Bach, J. S. -Delécluse	6 Suites	ALe
Bach, J. S. -Giampieri	21 Pieces	Ric
Baermann, C. -Bettoney	Clarinet Method op. 63, 5 vols. Piano accompaniments are available for vols. II & IV	CF
Baermann, C. -Langenus	Celebrated Clarinet Method op. 63, 3 vols. Published separately	CF
Baermann, C.	Vollständige Clarinetten Schule op. 63, 3 vols.	JoA
Baermann, C. -Christoffersen	Tägliche Studien (Method, op. 63)	FrH
Baermann, C.	Fortsetzung und Schluss des praktischen Teils bis zur hochsten Ausbildung, op. 64	JoA
Baermann, C. -Savina	16 Grand Concert Studies, op. 64	Ric
Baermann, H.	12 Exercices amusants, op. 30	Bil
Baermann, H. -Tenney	12 Amusing Exercises, op. 30	CF
Baermann, H. -Savina	12 Exercises, op. 30	Ric
Balassa, G. & Berkes, K.	Clarinet Tutor, 2 vols.	EMB
Balassa, G.	Collection of Studies	EMB
Beeler, W.	Play Away!	Sch
Bellison, S.	Scales and Chords	CF
Bender, H. -Jettel	Skalen-Übungen	LDo
Bernards, B.	Rhythmische Etüden	WZ
Berr, F. -Lefèbvre, Mimart	Méthode complète	ALe
Berr, F. -Berger	Méthode complète, 2 vols.	Com
Bianchini, G. -Giampieri	Popular Method	Ric
Biilmann-Petersen, C.	Klarinet I, Musicaskole	WH
Bitsch, M. -Delécluse	12 Studies in Rhythm	ALe
Blancou, V. -Delécluse	40 Studies, 2 vols.	ALe
Blancou, V.	40 Etudes (2 suites)	Bil
Blancou, V.	40 Studies from the Works of Mazas, 2 vols.	CF
Blasius, F.	Nouvelle méthode de clarinette et raisonnement des instruments (reprint of 18th-century edition)	MiR
Blatt, F. -Giampieri	12 Caprices in the Form of Studies	Ric
Blatt, F.	12 Etudes	Bil
Blatt, F. -Giampieri	24 Technical Exercises	Ric
Blazevich, V. -Hicks	Rhythmical Sequences	SF
Blémant, L.	Practical Method, 3 vols.	EdS
Blémant, L.	20 Melodious Etudes	EdS
Boehm, T. -McDevitt	Master Method	Pax
Bon, F.	12 Studies	B&V
Bonade, D.	Bonade Orchestral Studies	Leb
Bonade, D.	Clarinetist's Compendium	Leb

Bonade, D.	16 Etudes	Leb
Bonade, D.	16 Phrasing Studies	Leb
Bonnard, G.	15 Studies, 2 vols.	EDS
Bouillon, P.	Méthode élémentaire pour clarinette à 8 et 13 clés	EdR
Bozza, E.	11 Studies in Karnatic modes	ALe
Bozza, E.	12 Etudes	ALe
Bozza, E.	14 Etudes de mécanisme	ALe
Brahms, J.	First Clarinet Parts to Johannes Brahms' Major Orchestral Works	WMI
Brahms, J.-Heyneck	Orchestral Studies	FrH
Brauwer, G. de	Progressive Finger Exercises	ScF
Brauwer, G. de	Studies in Scales, Thirds and Arpeggios	ScF
Bucht, G.	Klarinettstudie--59, op. 28. 1959	STI
Cailliet, L.	Clarinet Studies	B-M
Cailliet, L.	Elementary Clarinet Method	Leb
Cailliet, L.-comp.	Orchestra Passages from the Modern French Repertoire	Dur
Calmel, J.	Le Clarinettiste	Com
Calvist y Serrano, E.	24 Estudios recreativos	EMM
Capelle, F.	20 Grand Studies, 2 vols.	ALe
Carbone, E.	Metodo Teorico-pratico	Car
Carney, G.	Orchestra Studies, 3 vols.	CF
Carr, H.	10 Famous Caprices	CF
Cavallini, E.-Delécluse	30 Caprices, 2 vols.	ALe
Cavallini, E.	30 Caprices	CF
Cavallini, E.	Caprices	FrH
Cavallini, E.-Drucker	30 Caprices	Int
Cavallini, E.	30 Caprices	MM
Cavallini, E.-Giampieri	30 Caprices	Ric
Cavallini, E.	36 Caprices	EdK
Cioffi, G.	Clarinet Virtuoso Studies, 2 vols.	CCo
Collis, J.	Modern Course for the Clarinet, 6 vols, supplement	HeE
Collis, J.	Scales and Arpeggios	HeE
Coriolis, E. de	Préambule	ALe
Costes, L.	60 Etudes, 3 vols.	Bil
Couf, H.	Let's Play Clarinet	Cha
Coward, G.	The Secret to Rapid Tongue and Finger Technic	CF
Dalby, M.	All Melody Method, 2 vols.	PrA
Daneels, F.	The Budding Clarinettist	ScF
Davies, J.	Scales and Arpeggios	B&H
DeCaprio, A.	Clarinet Method, vol. II	War

250

DeCaprio, A.	New Approach to the Clarinet	McK
DeCaprio, A.	Trill Chart	War
DeFranco, B.	Clarinet Studies	Leb
Delbecq, L. & R. Gilet	Méthode nouvelle et progressive	EdR
Delbecq, L. & R. Gilet	Tablature	EdR
Delécluse, U.	14 Grand Studies	ALe
Delécluse, U.	20 Etudes faciles	ALe
Del Giudice	40 Exercises for Perfection	Ric
D'Elia, A.	12 Grand Studies for Virtuoso Technique	Ric
Demnitz, F.	Clarinet Method	Pet
Demnitz, F.	Fundamental Scale and Chord Studies	Sch
Didier, Y.	Etude des gammes et principaux accords	HLe
Dies, W.	Anleitung zur Improvisation	SS
Dikov, B.	37 Etudes	MKE
Dolezal, A. -Etlík	Etüden	ES
Dolezal, A.	24 Leichte Etüden	ES
Draper, G.	Introduction to the Clarinet	OxU
Druart, H.	11 Modern Etudes	Leb
Drucker, S. (ed)	Orchestral Excerpts, vols. V-VIII	Int
Dubois, P.	12 Etudes	ALe
Dupont, A.	Méthode rapide	ALe
Eisenhauer & Gouse	Clarinet Method, Bk. 2	Alf
Eisenhauer, W.	Elementary Supplement Series	Alf
Elsenaar, E.	Grepen, hulpgrepen en trillergrepen	T-M
Endresen, R.	Clarinet Etudes and Solos	Col
Endresen, R.	Clarinet Method	BM
Endresen, R.	Supplementary Studies	Rub
Ensor, C. -arr.	Clarinet Studies from Baroque Period	Spr
Eriksson, G.	Klarinettskola	Nor
Etlík, M.	Studies	Art
Faulx, J.	20 Virtuoso Studies after Bach	HeE
Ferling, W. -Vacellier	16 Etudes	ALe
Ferling, W. -Collis	60 Cadenzas and Studies	Bou
Ferrando, R.	Gammes et Exercises	GD
Fontana, L.	6 Caprices	Bon
Fritsche, O.	Chart for Boehm System Clarinets	CF
Fritsche, O.	Fingered Scales for Boehm System Clarinet	CF
Fritsche, O.	Studies and Exercises, Pt. III	CF
Froseth, J.	The Individualized Instructor, 4 vols.	GIA
Gabler, M. -Schreinicke	Theoretisch-praktische	

	Klarinettenschule	BrH
Gabucci, A.	Breve Metodo	Car
Gabucci, A.	10 Etudes modernes de grande difficulté	ALe
Gabucci, A.	10 Fantasies	Ric
Gabucci, A.	12 Studi Brillanti	Car
Gabucci, A.	20 Intermediate Studies	Ric
Gabucci, A.	26 Cadenzas in the Form of Preludes	ALe
Gabucci, A.	28 Grandi Studi Tecnici e Melodici	Car
Gabucci, A.	60 Divertimenti	Ric
Galper, A.	Clarinet for Beginners	B&H
Gambaro, J.-Drucker	10 Caprices, op. 9	Int
Gambaro, G.	10 Caprices, op. 9	LDo
Gambaro, J.	12 Capricien, op. 18, 2 vols.	EdH
Gambaro, J.-Simon	12 Caprices, op. 18	Int
Gambaro, G.-Giampieri	12 Caprices	Ric
Gambaro, G.-Delécluse	20 Caprices	ALe
Gambaro, G.-Giampieri	22 Progressive Studies	Ric
Gambaro, V.-Giampieri	21 Caprices	Ric
Gay, E.	Etudes-recapitulation de technique journalière	ALe
Gay, E.	Grande méthode progressive et complète pour l'étude de la clarinette, 2 vols.	Bil
Gay, E.	24 Etudes de style	Bil
Gay, E.	30 Etudes de style	Bil
Gee, H.	Intermediate Style Etudes and Technical Exercises	SM
Gee, H.	Style Etudes and Technical Exercises	SM
Geispieler, F.	Etude rationnelle des gammes, Bk. 1	Bil
Gekeler, K.-Hovey	Belwin Clarinet Method, 3 vols.	B-M
Giampieri, A.	Collection of Exercises and Studies	Ric
Giampieri, A.	Daily Technical Exercises	Ric
Giampieri, A.-comp.	Orchestra Studies, 2 vols.	Ric
Giampieri, A.	Progressive Method, 2 vols.	Ric
Giampieri, A.	6 Caprices	Ric
Giampieri, A.	6 Fantastic Studies	Ric
Giampieri, A.	12 Modern Studies	Ric
Giampieri, A.	16 Daily Studies for Perfection	Ric
Giampieri, A.	18 Studies-Caprices	Ric
Giampieri, A.	Studies for the Week	Ric
Gibbons, A.	First Step Series--Clarinet (Simple System)	KPM
Gillet, F.	Exercices pour la technique superieure	ALe

Gillet, F.	Exercices sur les gammes, les intervalles et le staccato, 3 vols.	ALe
Glaser, W.	12 Capricci. 1969	STI
Goodman, B.	Clarinet Method	HG
Goodman, B.	Metodo per clarinetto jazz	Ric
Gornston, D.	Advanced Method	Ash
Gornston, D. & B. Paisner	Beethoven Sonatas	SF
Gornston, D. & B. Paisner	Chopin Studies	SF
Gornston, D.	Clarinet Mechanisms	MCA
Gornston, D.	Fun with Scales	MCA
Gornston, D.	Intermediate Method	Ash
Gornston, D. -arr.	Paganini Caprices for Clarinet	B-M
Gornston, D. & B. Paisner	Playing with Chords	SF
Gornston, D.	Velocity Series	SF
Gornston, D.	Very First Clarinet Method	Ash
Gower & Voxman	Modern Clarinet Method	EbM
Hamelin, G.	Gammes et Exercices	ALe
Hartmann, W.	Rhythmisch-stilistische Studien, Vol. I (Jazz studies)	Deu
Heim, N.	The Clarinet Instructor	Ken
Heim, N.	A Handbook for Clarinet Performance	Ken
Heine, A.	Solobook for Clarinet, 3 vols.	Sim
Hejda, T.	Clarinet Course, Pts. I & II	PWM
Hendrickson, C.	Handy Manual of Fingering Charts	CF
Hendrickson, C.	Method for Clarinet, 2 vols.	B-M
Herfurth & Stuart	Sounds of the Winds, 2 vols.	CF
Herfurth, P.	A Tune A Day, 3 vols.	BM
Hering	Progressing Clarinetist	CF
Hetzel, J.	Photographic Fingering Chart	TP
Hetzel, J.	Visual Method for Clarinet	TP
Hinze, F.	Orchestra Studies, 2 vols.	CF
Hite, D.	Melodious and Progressive Studies, 3 vols.	SM
Houppermans	Concert Studies	HeE
Hovey, N.	Elementary Method	Rub
Hovey, N.	Famous Clarinet Cadenzas	B-M
Hovey, N.	Practical Clarinet Studies, 2 vols.	B-M
Hovey, N.	Section Studies for Clarinet	B-M
Iasilli, G.	Daily Interval and Chord Exercises	CF
Jacobs, F.	Clarinet Method	Alf
James, M.	James Clarinet Method	PrA
Jeanjean, P.	Etudes progressives et mélodiques, 3 vols.	ALe
Jeanjean, P.	16 Etudes modernes	ALe

Jeanjean, P.	18 Etudes	Alf
Jeanjean, P.	18 Etudes de perfectionnement	Bil
Jeanjean, P.	25 Technical Melodic Studies, 2 vols.	ALe
Jeanjean, P.	Le "Vade-Mecum" du Clarinettiste	ALe
Jettel, R.	Klarinetten-Schule, 3 vols.	LDo
Jettel, R.	Modern Clarinet Practice, 3 vols.	JoW
Jettel, R.	Special Studies for the attainment of modern technique, 2 vols.	JoW
Jettel, R.	10 Etudes	FrH
Jettel, R.	18 Etudes	FrH
Jettel, R.	Der volkommene Klarinettist, 3 vols.	JoW
Jettel, R.	Vorstudien zu Der vollkommene Klarinettist, 3 vols.	JoW
Jones, E.	13 Basic Exercises	CF
Jones, M.	Virtuoso Studies	Leb
Kaplan, N. & L. Sobol	18 Concert Etudes	PrA
Kell, R.	Clarinet Method, 3 vols.	B&H
Kell, R.	Clarinet Staccato	B&H
Kell, R.	17 Staccato Studies	Int
Kell, R.	30 Interpretative Studies	Int
Kellner, F.	Méthode élémentaire	ALe
Kellner, F.-Lefèbvre	Méthode, 2 vols.	ALe
Kietzer, R.-Buyzer	Méthode, 2 vols.	MM
Kietzer, R.	Method for Clarinet, op. 79	WZ
Kietzer, R.	Der Forschritt im Klarinetten-spiel, op. 91, 3 vols.	WZ
Kliment, J.	Anfängerschule für Klarinette	JKM
Kliment, J.	Klarinetten-Schule für Fortgeschrittene	JKM
Klosé, H.-Jeanjean	Etudes caracteristiques	ALe
Klosé, H.	Characteristic Studies	CF
Klosé, H.	Etudes Characteristiques	EdK
Klosé, H.-Drucker	20 Characteristic Studies	Int
Klosé, H.-Giampieri	20 Characteristic Studies	Ric
Klosé, H.	Studies in Style and Technique	CF
Klosé, H.	Etudes de Genre et de Mécanisme	EdK
Klose, H.-Giampieri	20 Studi di genere e di meccanismo	Ric
Klosé, H.	6 Melodious Studies, op. 22	CF
Klosé, H.-Delécluse	14 Etudes	ALe
Klosé, H.	14 Studies, op. 18	CF
Klosé, H.	14 Technical Studies	EdM
Klosé, H.-Bellison	20 Studies	CF

Klosé, H.	20 Studies	SF
Klosé, H. –Jeanjean	20 Etudes d'après Kreutzer et Fiorillo	ALe
Klosé, H.	20 Studies from Kreutzer and Fiorillo	CF
Klosé, H.	20 Etudes after Kreutzer and Fiorillo	EdK
Klosé, H. -Drucker	20 Technical Studies	Int
Klosé, H.	20 Studies in Style and Technique	Ric
Klosé, H. -Jeanjean	30 Etudes d'après Aumont	ALe
Klosé, H.	30 Studies from the Works of Aumont	CF
Klosé, H.	30 Etudes after H. Aumont	EdK
Klosé, H. -Jeanjean	Exercices Journaliers	ALe
Klosé, H.	Daily Exercises	CF
Klosé, H.	Exercises Journaliers	EdK
Klosé, H. -Jeanjean	45 Exercices d'articulation (Méthode)	ALe
Klosé, H.	Diatonic Scales, Major and Minor	CF
Klosé, H. -Lefebvre	Méthode (Méthode Complète d'après Berr)	ALe
Klosé, H.	Méthode complète, 2 vols.	ALe
Klosé, H. -Draper	Complete Method	B&H
Klosé, H. -Bellison	Celebrated Method, 2 vols.	CF
Klosé, H. -Williams	Celebrated Method, 2 vols.	CF
Klosé, H. -Giampieri	Complete Method	Ric
Klosé & Lazarus -Whistler	Famous Method	Rub
Klosé, H. -Brownell	Celebrated Method, Pt. I	TP
Klosé, H.	209 Tone and Finger Exercises	SF
Klosé & Prescott	First and Second Year	CF
Koch, E.	Clarinet Tutor, 2 vols.	Deu
Kovar, S.	24 Daily Exercises	Kov
Kratochvíl, J.	Schule für Klarinette	Art
Kripper, F.	100 Stilistische Übungen	Wel
Krivin, M.	A Phrasing Book for the Young Clarinetist	SF
Kroepsch, F. -Bellison	416 Progressive Daily Studies, 4 vols.	CF
Kroepsch, F. -Simon	416 Studies, 4 vols.	Int
Krtička, S.	Volksschule	ES
Kubat, A.	50 Technische Phrasierungs- übungen	Art
Kucinski	Brahms Studies	SF
Kurkiewicz, L.	Selected Studies and Exercises, 4 vols.	PWM
Labanchi, G. -Pirolo	Progressive Method, Vol. 2	CF
Labanchi, G. -Micozzi	12 Studi Melodici	Edi

Lacour, G.	100 Déchiffrages manuscrits, 2 vols.	Bil
Lambert, C.	First Step Series--Clarinet (Boehm System)	KPM
Lancelot, J.	15 Etudes	EMT
Lancelot, J.	26 Etudes élémentaires	EMT
Lancelot, J.	20 Etudes faciles	Bil
Lancelot, J.	33 Etudes assez-faciles	EMT
Lange, H.	Schule, 2 vols.	FrH
Langenus, G.	Boehm System Fingering Chart	CF
Langenus, G.	Clarinet Cadenzas	CF
Langenus, G.	Complete Method, 3 vols.	CF
Langenus, G.	Fingered Scale Studies	CF
Langenus, G.	Practical Transposition	CF
Langenus, G.	27 Original Studies	CF
Langey, O.	Practical Tutor	B&H
Langey, O.	Tutor, Revised Edition	CF
Lazarus, H.-Bellison	Method for Clarinet, 3 vols.	CF
Lazarus, H.-Langenus	Modern Method, 3 vols.	CF
Lefèbvre & Goffin	De la Technique du son dans les Instruments à anche battante simple	ALe
Lefèvre, J.X.-Giampieri	Method, 3 vols	Ric
Lefèvre, J.X.-Giampieri	Popular Method	Ric
Lefèvre, J.X.-Savina	20 Melodious Studies	Ric
Lefèvre, J.X.-Giampieri	60 Exercises	Ric
Lester, L.	Advancing Clarinetist	CF
Lester, L.	Melodious Studies	HeE
Lester, L.	The Progressing Clarinetist	CF
Lester, L.	60 Rambles	CF
Lic & Leslaw	A Popular Course for Clarinet	PWM
Liegl, L.	Carl Fischer Basic Method	CF
Lindeman, B.	Clarinet Made Easy, 2 vols.	CCo
Lindeman, B.	Melodious Fundamentals, 2 vols.	CCo
Lockwood, A.	Guide journalier de travail	Com
Lowry, R. & F. Weber	Bb Clarinet Soloist (Level 1)	B-M
Lowry, R. & J. Ployhar	Bb Clarinet Student (Level 3)	B-M
Lowry, R. & F. Weber	Studies and Melodious Etudes (Level 1)	B-M
Lowry, R. & J. Ployhar	Studies and Melodious Etudes (Level 2)	B-M
Lowry, R. & J. Ployhra	Studies and Melodious Etudes (Level 3)	B-M
Lowry, R. & F. Weber	Tunes for Bb Clarinet Technic (Level 1)	B-M
Lowry, R. & J. Ployhar	Tunes for Clarinet Technic (Level 3)	B-M
Lowry, R.	Von Weber Studies	SF
Lubin	Tchaikovsky Studies	SF

Madeja, J.	Techniczna Szkola	PWM
Magnani, A.	Complete Method, 2 vols.	ALe
Magnani, A.-Giampieri	10 Etudes-caprices de grande difficulté	ALe
Manevich, A.-Drucker	10 Studies	Int
Marasco, G.-Giampieri	10 Studies for Perfection	Ric
Martorella	Daily Exercises	Ric
McCarty, K.	Methods for New Music, 2 vols.	LP
McGinnis, D. & E. Siennicki	Etudes for the Advanced Clarinetist	Sha
McGinnis, R. (ed)	Orchestral Excerpts, 4 vols.	Int
Melotte, H.	Neue theoretisch-praktische Klarinettenschule, 3 vols.	Pet
Menéndez, J.	18 Characteristic Studies. 1959	UME
Menéndez, J.	24 Studies	UME
Miller	Modern Method	EBM
Miller, R.-Skornicka	The Master Method	B&H
Miluccio, G.	8 Grandes études de technique mélodique	ALe
Mimart, P.	Méthode	E&C
Mimart, P.-Lancelot	20 Etudes, 2 vols.	Bil
Mohr, H.	8 Grand Etudes	EdS
Mohr, J.	25 Grand Studies	CF
Moore, E.	The Clarinet & Its Daily Routine	Leb
Moore-Sieg	Preparatory Instructor, 2 vols.	CF
Müller, F.-Hofmann	10 Etudes	Sim
Müller, I.-Wlach	21 Etüden	LDo
Müller, I.	22 Etüden mit einem Anhang moderner Studien, 2 vols.	EdH
Mueller, I.-Simon	22 Easy Studies, 2 vols.	Int
Mueller, I.	30 Studies in All Keys	Ric
Murphy, L.	Modern Harmonic Patterns, 3 vols.	Wes
Nagel	Speed Studies	SF
Naumann, R.	Schule	Hug
Nehammer, P.	Klarinetskole	WH
Nelson, R.	Method for Clarinet, Vol. I	PDS
Noferini, G.	6 Studi di tecnica seriale	Ric
Opperman, K.	Modern Daily Studies, 2 vols.	MB
Orsi, R.-Giampieri	Metodo popolare	Ric
Owen, H.	12 Concert Etudes	Wes
Paganini-Gornston	Caprices for Clarinet	B-M
Paganini, N.-Delécluse	17 Caprices et Mouvement perpetuel	ALe
Paganini, N.	14 Caprices, op. 1	EdK
Paganini, N.-Giampieri	14 Caprices, op. 1; Moto perpetuo, op. 11/6	Ric
Pantaleo-Iasilli	6 Virtuoso Caprices	CF

Parès, G.	Daily Exercises and Scales	CF
Parès, G.-Whistler	Parès Scales	Rub
Parès, G.	Elementary Method	B-M
Parès, D.	Universal's Fundamental Method	UMI
Pease, D.	Follow-Up Method	UMI
Périer, A.	Le Debutant Clarinettiste	ALe
Périer, A.	Etudes de Genre et d'Interpretation, 2 vols.	ALe
Périer, A.	Recueil de Sonates, 3 vols.	ALe
Périer, A.	20 Etudes faciles et progressives	ALe
Périer, A.	20 Etudes de virtuosité	ALe
Périer, A.	22 Etudes modernes	ALe
Périer, A.	30 Etudes	ALe
Périer, A.	331 Exercices journaliers de mécanisme	ALe
Périer, A.	Traits difficiles, 2 vols.	ALe
Petit, A.	1st étude de concours	Bil
Phillips, H.	The Clarinet Class	S-B
Polatschek, V.	Advanced Studies for the Clarinet	Sch
Polatschek, V.	12 Etudes	EBM
Polatschek, V.	24 Clarinet Studies for Beginners	EBM
Porret, J.	24 Déchiffrages manuscrits	EdR
Porret, J.	25 Déchiffrages manuscrits	EdR
Porter, G., Lowry & J. Ployhar	Studies and melodious etudes (Level 2)	B-M
Porter, G. & F. Weber	Tunes for clarinet technic (Level 2)	B-M
Prescott, G.	Outlines of Lesson Plans, 2 vols.	CF
Prisco, A.	Le Basi della tecnica	Edi
Prisco, A.	Esercizi giornalieri	Edi
Prisco, A.	Tavola delle posizioni	Edi
Prokofiev, S.	Orchestral Difficulties	MKE
Pursglove, A.	Crossing the Register	B-M
Regi, A.	24 Etudes	MKE
Reinecke, C.	Foundation to Clarinet Playing	CF
Reipsch, H.	Chorus-Etüden	FrH
Rieunier	22 Déchiffrages instrumentaux	ALe
Rigin, S.	Fingering Etudes	MKE
Rivera, S.	Método elemental	UME
Rode, P.-Carr	10 Famous Caprices	CF
Roeser, V.	Essai d'instruction a l'usage de ceux qui composent pour la clarinette et le cor (reprint of 1764 edition)	MiR

Roesler, E.	Clarinet Method	Col
Romero, A.-Menéndez	Método completo, 5 vols.	UME
Rook, K. de	24 Melodische Etudes	MM
Rose, C.	Descriptive Table for the Boehm Clarinet	CF
Rose, C.	Gammes majeures et mineures	ALe
Rose, C.	Scale for the Clarinet	CF
Rose, C.-Bonade	16 Grand Etudes	Leb
Rose, C.-Bonade	16 Phrasing Studies	Leb
Rose, C.-Lefèbvre	20 Etudes d'après Mazas et Kreutzer	ALe
Rose, C.	20 Grandes études	Bil
Rose, C.	20 Studies from the Works of Rode	CF
Rose, C.-Drucker	20 Grand Studies	Int
Rose, C.-Lefèbvre	26 Studies after Mazas and Kreutzer	ALe
Rose, C.-Blachet	26 Etudes	Bil
Rose, C.-Lancelot	26 Etudes	Bil
Rose, C.-Lefèbvre	32 Etudes d'après Ferling	ALe
Rose, C.-Blachet	32 Etudes pour clarinette d'après Ferling	Bil
Rose, C.	32 Etudes	CF
Rose, C.-Cochrane	32 Studies	CF
Rose, C.-Drucker	32 Studies	Int
Rose, C.-Lancelot	36 Etudes	Bil
Rose, C.-Lancelot	40 Etudes, 2 vols.	Bil
Rose, C.	40 Studies, 2 vols.	CF
Rose, C.	40 Studies	Han
Rose, C.-Drucker	40 Studies, 2 vols.	Int
Rozanov, S.	School, 2 vols.	MKE
Rueff, J.	15 Studies	ALe
Ruggiero, G.	Scales and 6 Melodic Exercises	GZ
Ruggiero, G.	6 Caprices	GZ
Ruggiero, G.	6 Difficult Modern Studies	ALe
Ruggiero, G.	8 Etudes atonales	ALe
Ruggiero, G.	10 Grandes études atonales	ALe
Ruggiero, G.	10 Technical Studies	GZ
Ruggiero, G.	12 Studies in Modern Technique	GZ
Ruggiero, G.	16 Studi di virtuosita	Edi
Ruggiero, G.	20 Divertimenti	GZ
Ruggiero, G.	30 Studi	GZ
Rusch, H. & A. Barto	Breath Control and Tuning and Intonation Studies	CF
Russo, J.	20 Modern Studies	HeE
Sallustio, E.	Invitation to the Clarinet	BrH
Sambin, V.	20 Etudes, 2 vols.	EdS
Sarlit, H.	25 Etudes de virtuosité, 2 vols.	ALe

Savina, L.	Studies on Scales and Intervals, 3 vols.	Ric
Savina, L.	10 Grand Studies	Ric
Schaeffer, D.	Reading Rhythms	PrA
Schneider, W.	Erstes Klarinettenspiel	SS
Schneider, W.	Schule	SS
Schreinicke	Orchestral Studies, 3 vols.	FrH
Scotese, T.	Nuovi originali studi di perfezionamento	Car
Semler-Collery, J.	Etudes de concert	EME
Shaw, A.	Clarinet Method	Edi
Shostakovitch, D.-Roscher	Orchestral Studies	FrH
Sigel, A.	The Twentieth Century Clarinetist	B-M
Siqueira, J.	3 Etüden	B&N
Skornicka & Miller	Intermediate Method	Rub
Snavely, J.	Clarinet Method for Beginning Students, 2 vols.	Leb
Snavely, J.	Clarinet Studies on the Intermediate Level	Ken
Speets, D.	Technische Oefeningen, 3 vols.	T-M
Sperti	Sperti Elementary Method	PrA
Staats, C.	New Imperial Method	TP
Stark, A.	5 Virtuoso Etudes	MKE
Stark, A.	24 Orchestral Etudes	MKE
Stark, A.	36 Easy Etudes	MKE
Stark, A.	40 Etudes	MKE
Stark, R.	Arpeggio Studies, op. 39	Int
Stark, R.	The Art of Transposition, op. 28, Vol. I	Sim
Stark, R.	The Art of Transposition, op. 29, Vol. II	Sim
Stark, R.	Daily Staccato Exercises, op. 46	Sim
Stark, R.	Daily Studies	CF
Stark, R.	Practical Staccato School, 3 vols.	Sim
Stark, R.	Die Schwierigkeiten des Clarinettenspiels, op. 40	RuE
Stark, R.	24 Studies, op. 49	CF
Stark, R.	24 Studies	Int
Stark, R.	24 Grand Virtuoso Studies, op. 51, 2 vols.	CF
Stark, R.-Simon	24 Grand Virtuoso Studies, op. 51, 2 vols.	Int
Sternberg, F.	Moderne Klarinettentechnik	FrH
Stevens, H.	12 Melodic Studies	PIC
Stievenard, E.	Practical Study of the Scales	Sch
Štolc, E.	Schule für Klarinette	Art
Strauss, R.	Death and Transfiguration	SF

Strauss, R.	First Clarinet Parts of Famous Tone Poems	SF
Strauss, R.	Orchestra Studies from the Symphonic Works, 3 vols.	CF
Strauss, R.	Orchestral Excerpts, 3 vols.	Int
Strauss, R.-Bartholomey	Orchestra Studies, 3 vols.	Pet
Stubbins, W.	Essentials of Technical Dexterity	Wah
Stubbins, W.	The Study of the Clarinet	Wah
Sundberg, S.	Klarinettspelets ABC	Nor
Temple-Savage, R.	Difficult Passages, 3 vols.	B&H
Thurston, F. & A. Frank	The Clarinet--A Comprehensive Tutor	B&H
Thurston, F.	Passage Studies, 3 vols.	B&H
Tschaikov, B.	First Tunes and Studies	SS
Tschaikov, B.	Play the Clarinet	Cha
Uhl, A.	48 Etudes, 2 vols.	SS
Váczy, G.	Practical Finger Exercises	EMB
Váczy, G.	Scale Studies	EMB
Váczy, G.	Technical Studies	EMB
Van Bodegraven, P.	Adventures in Clarinet Playing, 2 vols.	Sta
Van Bodegraven, P.	Clarinet Method for Grade Schools	CF
Van der Hagen, A.	Nouvelle méthode de clarinette (reprint of 1785? edition)	MiR
Van de Velde	Méthode élémentaire	EdR
Verdi, G.-Schreinicke	Orchestral Studies	FrH
Voxman & Gower	Advanced Method, 2 vols.	Rub
Voxman, H. (ed)	Classical Studies	Rub
Voxman, H. (ed)	Selected Studies	Rub
Wagner, R.	Orchestral Excerpts	Int
Wahls, H.	Preparatory Studies, 2 vols.	FrH
Waln, G.	Clarinet Excerpts from Orchestral Literature	B-M
Waln, G.	Elementary Clarinet Method	B-M
Waterson, J.	Grand Studies	CF
Weber, F. & R. Lowry	Bb Clarinet Student (Level 1)	B-M
Weber, F. & R. Lowry	Bb Clarinet Student (Level 2)	B-M
Weber, F. & R. Lowry	Tunes for Clarinet Technic (Level 1)	B-M
Weber, F. & R. Lowry	Tunes for Clarinet Technic (Level 2)	B-M
Webster, M.	Clarinet Instructor	Lud
Westlund, T.	Klarinettskola	Nor
Weston, P.	23 Steps for Young Clarinettists	Fab
White	Clarinet Method	Col
Wiedemann, L.	Praktische und theoretische Studien, 12 vols.	BrH
Wiedemann, L.	Clarinet Studies, 12 vols.	EdK

Wiedemann, L.	21 Etudes	MKE
Wiedemann, L.-Kurkiewicz, Kosieradzki	Studies, Vols. V & VI	PWM
Wiedemann, L.-Simon	32 Clarinet Studies	Sch
Wiedemann, L.-Tenney	33 Characteristic Sketches, 2 vols.	CF
Wildgans, F.	Nichttonale Skalen- und Akkord-studien	LDo
Wildgans, F.	Technische Studien, 3 vols.	LDo
Wunderlich, F.	Arpeggios (Chords)	CF
Wyczynski, I. (ed)	Orchestral Studies, Vol. I	PWM
Zitek, F.-Voxman	16 Modern Etudes and Studies, op. 14	Rub

Alto Clarinet

Alto Clarinet and Piano

	Caissons Go Rolling Along	NK
	Concert Album	EdM
-Goldberg	Tum Balalaika	B-M
-Goldberg	Welsh Air	B-M
Aubert, J.	Gigue	EdM
Bach, J.C.-Marteau	Andante Cantabile	Lud
Bach, J.S.-Schmidt	Allegro (Viola da gamba Sonata No. 1)	Wes
Barat, J.-Voxman	Chant Slave	Rub
Barnard, G.	Panda Dance	B-M
Beethoven, L. van-Porter	Rondo	B-M
Bennett, D.	Darkwood	CF
Bergson, M.	Scene and Air (Luisa di Montfort)	CF
Bohm, C.-Leonard	Still As the Night	B-M
Borodin, A.-Walters	Polovtsian Dance (Prince Igor)	Rub
Buchtel, F.	Crown Prince	NK
Buchtel, F.	Golden Glow Waltz	B-M
Buchtel, F.	High Stepper's March	B-M
Buchtel, F.	King's Jester	NK
Buchtel, F.	Song of the Sea	NK
Buck, L.	Reflections	NK
Cacavas, J.	Valsette	CF
Chapelle	Une Sérénade	CF
Clement, F.	Marching Through Georgia	CF
Dallin, L.	Prelude to Midnight	B-M
Debussy, C.-Cazden	Clair de Lune	Spr
Debussy, C.-Porter	Reverie	B-M
Di Chira, V.	La Spagnola	B-M

Durand–Medicus	First Valse	CF
Dvořak, A.-Leonard	Slavonic Dance	B-M
Escudie, H.-Prendiville	Third Fantasia, op. 46	CF
Fauré, G.-Judy	Sicilienne	Rub
Fesch, W. de -Kaplan	Canzonetta	Spr
Fischer, C.	Nellie Gray	CF
Fischer, C.	Old Uncle Ned	CF
Foster, S.	Massa's In the Cold, Cold Ground	CF
Foster, S.-Smith, Holmes	Old Black Joe	CF
Frangkiser, C.	Evening	B-M
Galliard, J.-Gee	Hornpipe and Allegro	SM
Giordani, G.-Goldberg	Caro Mio Ben	B-M
Gluck, C. von -Goldberg	Andante	B-M
Goldberg, N.	City Lights	B-M
Goldberg, N.-arr.	Country Dance	B-M
Goldberg, N.	German Band	B-M
Goldberg, N.	Lonesome Pup	B-M
Goldberg, N.	Sweet Betsy	B-M
Goldberg, N.	Swingin' Along	B-M
Goldberg, N.	Tarantelle	B-M
Goldberg, N.	Walking the Dog	B-M
Handel, G.-Barr	Allegro (Concerto, f)	Lud
Handel, G.-Barr	Sarabande (Concerto, f)	Lud
Hartman, J.	Longing for Home	CF
Haydn, F.-Leonard	Hidin' Haydn	B-M
Haydn, F.-Stouffer	Vivace	Ken
Herbert, V.-Goldberg	In Old New York	B-M
Hoffman, A.	Alborada	B&H
Holmes, G.	Auld Lang Syne	CF
Hudadoff, I.-arr.	15 Intermediate Solo Series	PrA
Hudadoff, I.-arr.	Marches	PrA
Hurrell, C.	Dark Distance	CF
Hurrell, C.	Legend of the Plains	Rub
Hurrell, C.	Tango Gitano	CF
Jarnefelt, A.-Pardee	Berceuse	Ken
Johnson, C.	Scene Rustical	Rub
Kesnar, M.	Mood of the Hills	CF
Koepke, P.	Mummery	Rub
Lacome, P.	Rigaudon	SM
Laurendeau, L.	Flow Gently Sweet Afton	CF
Leonard, B.	Melodie	B-M
Leonard, B.	On Glider Wings	B-M
Leonard, B.	Tandem Jaunt	B-M
Leoni, C.	Leonora	PrA
MacDowell, E.-Goldberg	To a Wild Rose	B-M
Maganini, Q.	Concert Album	EdM
Maganini, Q.	Song of the Sage-Brush Hills	CF
Marpurg, F.-Marple	Rondeau	SM
Mascagni, P.-Schaefer	Siciliana	War

Alto Clarinet and Piano

McCathren, D.	Dolphin Dance	Hal
Mendelssohn, F.	On Wings of Song	NK
Mendelssohn, F.	Romance sans Paroles	CF
Miller, R.	Evening Fantasy	B-M
Monti, V.-Roberts	Csardas	CF
Moszkowski, M.-Porter	Spanish Dance	B-M
Mozart, W.-Porter	Adagio (Concerto)	B-M
Mozart, W.	Adagio (Clarinet Concerto, op. 107)	CF
Mozart, W.-Voxman	Adagio (Concerto for Clarinet, K. 622)	Rub
Mozart, W.-Sansone	Concert Rondo	SM
Mozart, W.-Voxman	Menuetto (Divertimento No. 1)	Rub
Mozart, W.	Solo (String Quartet, K. 465)	Spr
Neukomm, S.-Kaplan	Aria	Spr
Norden, H.	Puppet Parade	Hal
Organn, R.	Falling Leaves	Reb
Ostransky, L.	Concerto Petite	Rub
Ostransky, L.	Lyric Piece	Rub
Parès, G.-Judy	Crépuscule (Twilight)	Rub
Perfect, A.	Two Little Chums	CF
Pergolesi, G.-Ephross	Nina	SM
Petit, R.-Findlay	Première Etude de Concours	CF
Petrie, H.	Asleep in the Deep	NK
Porter, G. & F. Weber	Alto Clarinet Soloist (Level 1)	B-M
Prokofiev, S.-Porter	Kije's Wedding	B-M
Purcell, H.-Kaplan	Saraband	Spr
Ravel, M.-Bettoney	Pavane	CF
Reed, A.	Intermezzo	CF
Reed, A.	Sarabande	EBM
Reed, A.	Serenata	EBM
Regi, A.-Voxman	Ancient Melody	Rub
Rimsky-Korsakov, N.	Song of India	NK
Rodriguez, G.-Porter	La Cumparsita	B-M
Schaefer, A.	Spring in the Forest	CF
Schmidt, W.	Variations on a Whaling Song	Wes
Schmutz, A.	Praeludium	CF
Schubert, F.-Buchtel	My Sweet Repose	NK
Schubert, F.-Leonard	Who Is Sylvia?	B-M
Schumann, R.	Einsame Blumen	Spr
Schumann, R.-Merriman	Folk Song	SM
Schumann, R.-Merriman	Märchenbilder No. 4	SM
Schwartz, G.	International Folk Suite	SM
Senaille, J.-Gee	Allegro Spiritoso	SM
Severn, A.	Valse Scintilla	B-M
Smith, C.-Holmes	Drink To Me Only With Thine Eyes	CF
Smith, C.	The Spirit of Joy	CF
Spencer, W.	Silvatones	CF
Strauss, O.-Harris	A Waltz Dream	Lud

Alto Clarinet and Piano

Sullivan, A.-Leonard	The Lost Chord	B-M
Suppé, F. von-Porter	Polka	B-M
Tchaikovsky, P.-Ephross	Chanson Triste	SM
Tchaikovsky, P.-Hurrell	Danse Arabe (The Nutcracker Suite)	Rub
Tchaikovsky, P.-Weber	March Slav	B-M
Titl, A.	Serenade	CF
Toselli, E.-Goldberg	Serenade	B-M
Trowbridge, L.	Album Leaf	See
Veach, D.	Wind Currents	CF
Verdi, G.	Grand Air (The Masked Ball)	EdM
Warren, D.	Cumberland	Lud
Weber, C.M. von-Porter	Excerpts from Concertino	B-M
Weber, C.M. von-Sterrett	Concertino	CF
Weber, C.M. von-Frank, McCathren	Concertino	Ken
Weber, F.	Bluebird Waltz	B-M
Weber, F.	Elephant Dance	B-M
Whitney, M.	Clarinata	Spr
Whitney, M.	Melancholy	Spr
Woodworth	The Old Oaken Bucket	CF

Methods and Studies

	Fingering Chart	ALe
Hendrickson, C.	Handy Manual of Fingering Charts	CF
Langenus, G.	Boehm System Fingering Chart	CF
Mimart, P.	Method for Alto and Bass Clarinets and Sarrusophones	CF
Porter, G. & F. Weber	Alto Clarinet Soloist (Level 1)	B-M
Porter, G., R. Lowry, & J. Ployhar	Alto Clarinet Student (Level 3)	B-M
Porter, G. & R. Lowry	Studies and Melodious Etudes (Level 1)	B-M
Porter, G., R. Lowry, & J. Ployhar	Studies and Melodious Etudes (Level 2)	B-M
Porter, G., R. Lowry, & J. Ployhar	Studies and Melodious Etudes (Level 3)	B-M
Porter, G. & F. Weber	Tunes for Alto Clarinet Technic (Level 1)	B-M
Porter, G. & F. Weber	Tunes for Alto Clarinet Technic (Level 2)	B-M
Porter, G., R. Lowry, & J. Ployhar	Tunes for Alto Clarinet Technic (Level 3)	B-M
Rhoads, W.	Advanced Studies for Alto	

265

	and Bass Clarinet	SM
Rhoads, W.	Baermann for the Alto and Bass Clarinets (The 3rd Division)	SM
Rhoads, W.	Etudes for Technical Facility for Alto and Bass Clarinets)	SM
Rhoads, W.	18 Selected Etudes for the Alto and Bass Clarinet	SM
Rhoads, W.	21 Foundation Studies for Alto and Bass Clarinet	SM
Rhoads, W.	35 Technical Studies for Alto and Bass Clarinet	SM
Voxman, H.	Introducing the Alto and Bass Clarinet	Rub
Weber, F. & G. Porter	Alto Clarinet Student (Level 1)	B-M
Weber, F. & G. Porter	Alto Clarinet Student (Level 2)	B-M
Weissenborn, J.-Rhoads	Advanced Studies	SM

Basset Horn

Basset Horn and Orchestra

Roeth, P.	Concertino	EBM

Bass Clarinet

Unaccompanied Solos

Arrigo, G.	"Par un jour d'automne.."	Ric
Bois, R. du	Chemin	SD
Gipps, R.	Prelude	GaM
Kunst, J.	Solo Identity I	SD
Kupkovic, L.	"..."	UE
Lang, R.	Concert Piece	Lan
Leichtling, A.	Fantasy Piece No. 1	See
Martino, D.	Strata	WLP
Planzer, E.	Solo	EMo
Porcelijn, D.	Pole II. 1973	SD
Regt, H. de	Musica, op. 23. 1973	SD
Wasson, S.	2 Pieces	Smo

Bass Clarinet and Piano

-Goldberg	Forest Green	B-M
-Goldberg	Jacob's Ladder	B-M

Alschausky, J.	Walzer-Arie No. 2	CF
Ammann, B.	Metaphories	EdT
Bach, J.S.-Cazden	Siciliano (BWV 1063)	Spr
Bartók, B.-Porter	2 Hungarian Songs	B-M
Bassi, L.-Voxman	Lamento	Rub
Bassi, L.	Nocturne	CF
Bennett, D.	Deepwood	CF
Bergh, H.	Praeludium	Wes
Beyer, J.	Suite	AMC
Blazevich, V.-Schuman	Etude No. 86	Spr
Blazevich, V.-Schuman	Etude No. 92	Spr
Bois, R. du	Fusion pour deux	SD
Boni, P.-Voxman	Largo and Allegro	Rub
Bozza, E.	Ballade	SM
Brahms, J.-Porter	Allegretto	B-M
Briegel, G.	Basso Profundo	GFB
Briegel, G.	Mulberry Street Tarantella	GFB
Briegel, G.	Staccato-Legato	GFB
Brown, R.	Prelude and Rughetta	Wes
Buchtel, F.	Attila	NK
Buchtel, F.	The Flatterer	B-M
Buchtel, F.	Hercules	NK
Buchtel, F.-arr.	Marines Hymn	NK
Buck, L.	Enchantment	NK
Buck, L.	Woodland Glade	NK
Cailliet, L.	Le Pionnier	SM
Carissimi, G.-Barnes	Heart Victorious	Spr
Chopin, F.-Davis	Etude	Wes
Chopin, F.-Meyer-Tormin	Etude, op. 25/7	For
Cirri, G.	Arioso	EdM
Cui, C.-Leonard	Orientale	B-M
Dankner, S.	3 Pieces	See
Desportes, Y.	Andante and Allegro	SM
Diethe, F.	Romanze	CF
Dvořak, A.-Goldberg	Largo	B-M
Eccles, H.-Goldberg	Sonata, g	B-M
Erickson, F.-Goldberg	Novelette	B-M
Fasch, J.-Kreiselman	Sonata, C	M&M
Feldsher	Adagio and Allegro	Spr
Fesch, W. de -Kaplan	Canzonetta	Spr
Fischer, L.-Leonard	In Cellar Cool	B-M
Galliard, J.-Merriman	Adagio and Allegro	SM
Galliard, J.-Kreiselman	6 Sonatas, 2 vols.	M&M
Garlick, A.	Colloquy	See
Geib	In the Deep Forest	GFB
German, E.-Voxman	Pastorale and Bourree	Rub
Glinka, M.	Romance Melody	Spr
Goldberg, N.	Boogie Bass	B-M
Goldberg, N.	Brahms with Variations	B-M
Goldberg, N.	Buggy Ride	B-M

Goldberg, N.	Concert Theme	B-M
Goldberg, N.	Down the Trail	B-M
Goldberg, N.	Israeli Melody	B-M
Goldberg, N.-arr.	Medley "H. M. S. Pinafore"	B-M
Goldberg, N.	Novelette	B-M
Gounod, C.-Leonard	Funeral March of a Marionette	B-M
Gounod, C.-Walters	March of a Marionette	Rub
Graham, O.	Neptune	CF
Grieg, E.-Porter	Norwegian Dance	B-M
Grieg, E.	Norwegian Dance	CF
Grieg, E.-Leonard	Solvejg's Song	B-M
Handel, G.-Barr	Allegro (Concerto, f)	Lud
Handel, G.-Ayres	Andante and Bourree	Bar
Handel, G.-Barr	Sarabande (Concerto, f)	Lud
Harris, F.	A Rendezvous in the Forest	Bar
Harris, F.	Sherilee Waltzes Nos. 1, 2	Lud
Harrison, P.	Faggot Dance	Cha
Hartzell, D.	Egotistical Elephant	Sha
Hasse, J.-Ayres	Bourree and Minuet	Bar
Haydn, F.	Andante (Concerto)	Spr
Haydn, F.-Kaplan	Arietta and Minuet	Spr
Hermann, R.	Punchinello	Pod
Hoffmann, A.	Alborada	B&H
Hoffmann, A.	Jota Aragonesa	B&H
Hoffmann, A.	Serenade Basque	B-M
Hummel, H.-arr.	The Foggy Dew	Rub
Indy, V. d'-Piguet	Choral varié, op. 55	Dur
Ivanovici, J.-Jolliff	Waves of the Danube	Rub
Johnson, C.	Woody Contrasts	Rub
Karel, L.	Aquamarine	B&H
Kay, F.	Night Wind	PrA
Kesnar, M.	Clown Festival	CF
Knight, J.	Rocked in the Cradle of the Deep	NK
Koepke, P.	The Buffoon	Rub
Koepke, P.	Vignette	Rub
Kučera, V.	Duodramma. 1967	Art
Kunst, J.	No time at all. 1973	SD
Lenom, C.-Findlay	Lullaby	CF
Leonard, B.	Arabesque	B-M
Leonard, B.	Dream World	B-M
Leonard, B.	Rhino Romp	B-M
Leonard, B.-arr.	Two Guitars	B-M
Loevendie, T.	Music	SD
Long, N.	Undercurrent	Rub
Lully, J.-Kaplan	Sarabande and Gigue	Spr
Macbeth, A.	Forget Me Not	CF
MacKay	Sonatina	Wes
Maganini, Q.	Afternoon of a Lady Crocodile	CF
Maganini, Q.	Paris Soir	EdM

Bass Clarinet and Piano

Maganini, Q.	Serenade Derivative	CF
Marcello, B.-Houston	Largo	SP
Marcello, B.-Hite	Sonata, a	SM
Marty, G.	Première Fantasy	CF
Marty, G.	First Fantasy	SM
Massenet, J.-Goldbert	Elegie	B-M
Massenet, J.-Taffanel	Meditation (Thais)	CF
McCathren, D.	Premier Waltz	Hal
McKay, G.	Moonlight Over the Jungle	CCo
Michel, P.	Délitation I	CBD
Mitscha, A.	Romance	PWM
Molloy, J.-Porter	Kerry Dance	B-M
Monroe, M.-Isaac	In the Garden	CF
Monti, V.-Roberts	Csardas	CF
Moussorgsky, M.-Goldberg	The Old Castle	B-M
Mozart, W.-Andraud	Adagio Religioso	SM
Mozart, W.	Concerto K. 191	EdM
Mozart, W.-Goldberg	If I Were King	B-M
Mozart, W.-Goldberg	Magic Flute	B-M
Mozart, W.-Barnes	Per Questa Bella Mano	Spr
Mozart, W.-Willaman	Solo (String Quartet, K. 465)	Spr
Nedbal, M.	Sonatine	LDo
Neukomm, S.-Kaplan	Aria	Spr
Norden, H.-McCathren	Danse Baroque	CF
Norden, H.	The Happy Woodsman	Hal
Offenbach, J.	Barcarolle	CF
Offenbach, J.	La Musette	CF
Orlamunder, J.	Romance	CF
Ostransky, L.	Autumn Song	Rub
Ostransky, L.	Marche Comique	Rub
Parris, H.	Nocturne and Burlesca	HeE
Petrie, H.	Asleep in the Deep	NK
Petrie, H.-Walters	Asleep in the Deep	Rub
Phillips, G.	Recitative and Slow Dance	S&C
Porter, G. & F. Weber	Bass Clarinet Soloist (Level 1)	B-M
Porter, G.	The Happy Hippo	B-M
Prokofiev, S.-Hummel	Romance and Troika	Rub
Purcell, H.-Kaplan	Saraband	Spr
Raphling, S.	Lyric Prelude	EdM
Rarig	Introduction & March	Wes
Rasse	Lied	ALe
Rathaus, K.	In Ancient Style	B-M
Reed, A.	Guaracha	EBM
Reed, A.	Haitian Dance	EBM
Regt, H. de	Musica, op. 24. 1973	SD
Reiner, K.	Concerto. 1965	Art
Rhoads, W.-arr.	10 Solos	SM
Rimsky-Korsakov, N.	Song of India	NK
Rodriguez, G.-Leonard	La Cumparsita	B-M
Satie, E.-Porter	Gymnopédie No. 3	B-M

Schmutz, A.	Rondino	CF
Schoeck, O.-Reinhardt	Sonata, op. 41	BrH
Schwartz, G.	International Folk Suite	SM
Scriabine, A.-Meyer-Tormin	Etude, op. 2/1	For
Senaille, J.-de Smet	Introduction and Allegro Spiritoso	BrH
Singer	Marionettes Modernes	CF
Skolnik, W.	Paris Soir	EdM
Soukup, V.	Sonety	Art
Spohr, L.-Ayres	Adagio (Concerto No. 1)	Bar
Suppé, F. von-Porter	Polka	B-M
Tchaikovsky, P.-Goldberg	Chanson russe	B-M
Tchaikovsky, P.-Davis	Sleeping Beauty	Rub
Telemann, G.-Ayres	Siciliana	Bar
Thilman, J.	Gestalten (3 Pieces)	Pet
Thornton, E.	Une Pensée Lointaine	CF
Titl, A.	Serenade	CF
Trowbridge, L.	Barcarolle	See
Veach, D.	Wind Currents	CF
Verrall, J.	Nocturne	Cre
Vivaldi, A.-Ayres	Sonata No. 6	Bar
Von Kreisler, A.	Canzone	SM
Vorlova, S.	Miniatury, op. 55	Art
Voxman, H.-arr.	Concert and Contest Collection	Rub
Wahlberg, R.	Concerto	EMf
Weber, C.M. von-Frank, McCathren	Concertino	Ken
Weber, F.	Bluebird Waltz	B-M
Weber, F.-arr.	Deep River	B-M
Weber, F.	Elephant Dance	B-M
Weissenborn, J.-Ayres	Capriccio	Bar
Whitney, M.	Clarinata	Spr
Wiggins, A.	Song and Dance Man	Ken
Winslowe, T.	Sonatine	B-M
Wolf, J.	Litania	EMo
Zaninelli, L.	Peg Leg Pete	B&H

Bass Clarinet and Orchestra

Heller, J.	Symphony-Concerto	CoA
Hermann, R.	Punchinello (bcl, str)	Pod
Indy, V. d'-Piguet	Choral varié, op. 55	Dur
Landré, G.	Concertante. 1961	SD
Linde, B.	Pezzo concertante, op. 41. 1970	STI
Reiner, K.	Concerto. 1965 (bcl, str)	Art
Soukup, V.	Sonnets. 1964	CHF
Wahlberg, R.	Concerto. 1961	STI

Bass Clarinet and Band

Bennett, D.	Basswood	S-B

Bass Clarinet and Band

Briegel, G.	Basso Profundo	GFB
Hartzell, D.	Egotistical Elephant	Sha
Hermann, R.	Punchinello	Pod
Wiggins, A.	Song & Dance Man	Ken
Zaninelli, L.	Peg Leg Pete, Burlesca	B&H

Methods and Studies

Hendrickson, C.	Handy Manual of Fingering Charts	CF
Langenus, G.	Boehm System Fingering Chart	CF
Mimart, P.	Method for Alto and Bass Clarinets and Sarrusophones	CF
Porter, G. & F. Weber	Bass Clarinet Student (Level 1)	B-M
Porter, G., R. Lowry, & J. Ployhar	Bass Clarinet Student (Level 3)	B-M
Porter, G. & R. Lowry	Studies and Melodious Etudes (Level 1)	B-M
Porter, G., R. Lowry, & J. Ployhar	Studies and Melodious Etudes (Level 2)	B-M
Porter, G. & F. Weber	Tunes for Bass Clarinet Technic (Level 1)	B-M
Porter, G. & F. Weber	Tunes for Bass Clarinet Technic (Level 2)	B-M
Porter, G., R. Lowry, & J. Ployhar	Tunes for Bass Clarinet Technic (Level 3)	B-M
Reddie, B.	8 Etudes	SM
Rhoads, W.	Advanced Studies for Alto and Bass Clarinet	SM
Rhoads, W.	Baermann for the Alto and Bass Clarinets (3rd Division)	SM
Rhoads, W.	Etudes for Technical Facility for Alto and Bass Clarinets	SM
Rhoads, W.	18 Selected Etudes for the Alto and Bass Clarinet	SM
Rhoads, W.	21 Foundation Studies for Alto and Bass Clarinets	SM
Rhoads, W.	35 Technical Studies for Alto and Bass Clarinet	SM
Saunders, R. & E. Siennicki	Understanding the Low Clarinets	Sha
Voxman, H.	Introducing the Alto and Bass Clarinet	Rub
Weber, F. & G. Porter	Bass Clarinet Student (Level 2)	B-M
Weissenborn, J. -Rhoads	Advanced Studies	SM

Contrabass Clarinet

Contrabass Clarinet and Piano

Migot, G.	Prélude	ALe
Reed, A.	Afro	EBM
Reed, A.	Scherzo Fantastique	EBM
Von Kreisler, A.	Rondo (Bb instrument)	SM
Von Kreisler, A.	Rondo (Eb instrument)	SM
Zaninelli, L.	Peg Leg Pete	B&H

Contrabass Clarinet and Orchestra

Landré, G.	Concertante. 1959	SD

Bassoon

Unaccompanied Solos

Acker, D.	Monodie	HG
Adler, S.	Bassoonery	TP
Aitken, H.	Montages	OxU
Apostel, H.	Sonatine, op. 19/3	UE
Arma, P.	4 Resonances	Bil
Arnold, M.	Fantasy, op. 86	Fab

272

Bach, C.P.E.	Sonata, c	EdM
Bach, J.S.-Cammarota	2 Suites	Sch
Bartolozzi, B.	Collage. 1969	ESZ
Bartolozzi, B.	The Hollow Man. 1968	ESZ
Börtz, D.	Monologhi II. 1966	STI
Bon, W.	Sonata op. 32	SD
Borris, S.	Musik für Fagott, op. 119	Hei
Bozza, E.	Pièces brèves	ALe
Chagrin, F.	2 Pieces	Nov
Cope, D.	3 Pieces	See
Debras, L.	Sequenza IV. 1968	See
Dhérin, G.	16 Variations	EME
Formaček, J. & O. Tvrdy	Schule des mehrfachen Stakkatos	Art
Ganzoinat	Préambule	ALe
Gelbrun, A.	Miniature for Bassoon	Isr
Gyring, E.	Arabesque	HeE
Hába, A.	Suite	CHF
Hartzell, E.	Divertimento (Monolog III). 1964	LDo
Henning, E.	Divertimento	AMC
Hudadoff, I.-arr.	50 Standard Solo Series	PrA
Jacob, G.	Partita	OxU
Kunc, B.	Buffoonery, op. 63	Ron
Leichtling, A.	Serenade-Etude, op. 37	See
Lewis, R.	Monophony IV	LDo
Lovano	2 Pièces brèves	Com
Organn, R.	Fantasia	Reb
Osborne, W.	Rhapsody	Pet
Perle, G.	3 Inventions	TP
Persichetti, V.	Parable IV, op. 110	E-V
Presser, W.	Partita. 1967	TP
Raphael, G.	Sonate, op. 46/9. 1954	WMS
Reinhardt, B.	12 mal 12	ImV
Reuter, F.	Suite, op. 23 (trombone)	WZ
Ruggiero, G.	3 Pezzi	Edi
Sacco, P.	Bassoon Solo	Wes
Schroeder, H.	Music for Bassoon Solo	MRL
Schroeder, H.	Sonata. 1971	HG
Solomon, M.	Etudes to Spring	AP
Stockhausen, K.	Plus Minus	UE
Stockhausen, K.	Solo	UE
Stockhausen, K.	Spiral	UE
Stutschewsky, J.	3 Pieces. 1963	Isr
Tcherepnin, N.	Esquisse, op. 45/7a	SF
Tcherepnin, N.	Esquisse, op. 7a	Spr
Tisné, A.	Soliloques	ECh
Weiner, S.	Sonata op. 32	MCA
Wellesz, E.	Suite op. 77	Ron
Wojciechowski, J.	Solobook for Bassoon, 2 vols.	Sim

Wurmser, L.	Tendres mélodies	Bil
Wurmser, L.	Solo de concours	Bil
Zonn, P.	Asanomusic	CoF

Bassoon and Piano

	Contemporary French Recital Pieces	Int
	Deep River	CF
	Morceaux de Concours et pièces d'audition	ALe
	Solo Album No. 1	B&H
Abbiate, L.	Scherzino	CF
Adams, S.	Holy City	NK
Albéniz, I.-Amaz	Mallorca. Barcarola	UME
Albéniz, I.-Amaz	Puerta da tierra	UME
Alexander, J.	Patterns	Bou
Ambrosius, H.	Sonata	FrH
Ameller, A.	Fagotin	HE
Ameller, A.	Gaspesie	ALe
Ammann, B.	Metaphories	EdT
Ancelin, P.	La Naissance de Gargantua	EdO
Antonietto -Oubradous	Adagio et vivace	ALe
Antufeyev, B.	Improvisation-Mazurka	MKE
Arne, T.-Craxton	Sonata No. 5	OxU
Aubin, T.	Concertino della Brughiera	ALe
Bach, J.C.-Wojciechowski	Concerto, Bb	HSM
Bach, J.C.-Wojciechowski	Concerto, Eb	HSM
Bach, J.S.-Lalliet	Aria, D	Dur
Bach-Gounod	Ave Maria	CF
Bach, J.S.-Krane	Bach for Bassoon	Spr
Bach, J.S.-Tervokhin	Concerto for Viola, c	MKE
Bach, J.S.-Stouffer	Minuet	Ken
Bach, J.S.-Cazden	Siciliano (BWV 1063	Spr
Bacon, E.	The Woodchuck	Ron
Baines, F.	Introduction and Hornpipe	S&C
Bakaleinikoff, V.	Ballad, Humoresque and March Eccentric	B-M
Balfe, W.-Buchtel	I Dreamt I Dwelt in Marble Halls	NK
Bariller, R.	Fantaisie	ALe
Barraine, E.	Chiens de paille	Job
Bartoš, J.	Concertino op. 34	Art
Bartsch, C.	Andante	Mau
Bartsch, C.	Fantaisie	Mau
Beach, G.	Introduction and Tarentella	HeE
Becker, A.-Gruenwald	Romance	CF
Beckler, S.	Little Wind Sonata	CoA
Beekhuis, H.	Sonatine. 1948	SD
Beethoven, L. van	Adagio (Sonata Pathetique)	CF
Beethoven, L. van -Andraud	Adagio Cantabile	SM

Beethoven, L. van	Adelaide, op. 46	CF
Beethoven, L. van	Allegro (Sonata Pathetique)	CF
Beethoven, L. van -Oubradous	Minuet	ALe
Beethoven, L. van -Trinkaus	Minuet	CF
Beethoven, L. van	Sonate, op. 17	CF
Ben-Haim, P.	3 Lieder ohne Worte	ImV
Bennett, D.	Bassoonata	SM
Benoy, A. & A. Bryce -Mather	First Pieces for Bassoon, 2 vols.	OxU
Benson, W.	Song and Dance	B&H
Bentzon, N.	Study in Variations Form	SkB
Berghmans, J.	Les Oursons savants (Scenes from a Traveling Circus)	ALe
Bergmann, W.	Prelude and Fugue	S&C
Bernaud	Concertino da camera	B-M
Bernaud	Concertino da camera, Movement I	B-M
Bernier, R.	Bassonnerie	ALe
Bertholon	2 Movements	ALe
Bertoli, G. -Kaplan	3 Sonatas, d, g, F (bsn, bc)	B&N
Bertoli, G. -Kastner	Sonata Prima (bsn, bc)	SS
Bertoni, U.	Concerto	Bon
Besozzi, J. -Waterhouse	Sonata	OxU
Best, A.	Grandfather's Waltz	B-M
Best, A.	Little Elephant	B-M
Best, A.	March of the Leprechauns	B-M
Bitsch, M.	Concertino	ALe
Bitsch, M.	Rondoletto	ALe
Blazevich, V. -Garfield	Concerto No. 5	Int
Blazevich, V. -Schuman	Etude No. 86	Spr
Blazevich, V. -Schuman	Etude No. 92	Spr
Bloch, A.	Fantaisie variée	ALe
Bloch, A.	Liten svit. 1945	CF
Blomdahl, K.	Liten svit. 1945	STI
Boerlin, R.	Soliloquy	HeE
Boismortier, J. -Sharrow	Concerto, D	Int
Boismortier, J.	Concerto, D	SEM
Boismortier, J. -Boulay	Sonata (bsn, bc)	EMT
Boismortier, J.	Sonata, e	GD
Boismortier, J. -Ruf	Sonata, e, op. 26/4 (bsn, bc)	SS
Boismortier, J. -Ruf	Sonata, g, op. 26/5 (bsn, bc)	SS
Boismortier, J.	Sonata No. 5	EdR
Boizard, G.	Fantaisie	EMT
Bonacini, G. -Cacavas	Prayer of Adoration	B-M
Bond, C. -Finzi	Concerto No. 6	B&H
Bossi, M.	Improvviso	Bon
Bourdeau, E. -Dhérin	1st Solo	ALe
Bourdeau, E.	First Solo	CF
Bourdeau, E. -Voxman	Premier Solo	Rub
Bourdeau, E.	2nd Solo	ALe

Bassoon and Piano

Bourdeau, E.	Second Solo	CF
Bozay, A.	Episodi. 1959	EMB
Bozza, E.	Burlesque	ALe
Bozza, E.	Concertino op. 49	ALe
Bozza, E.	Espièglerie	ALe
Bozza, E.	Fantasy	ALe
Bozza, E.	Nocturne-Danse	ALe
Bozza, E.	Prelude and Divertissement	ALe
Bozza, E.	Récit, sicilienne and rondo	ALe
Bozza, E.	Shiva	ALe
Braga, G. -Lalliet	Serenata	Dur
Braga, G. -Laube	Toada	CF
Brahms, J. -Cacavas	Tears	B-M
Bratton, J. -Sears	Teddy Bear's Picnic	War
Braun, R.	Spirituals	YM
Brenta, G.	Air varié pour les belles écouteuses	ALe
Briegel, G.	Basso Profundo	GFB
Brogi -Andreoni	Visione veneziana	Ric
Bruns, V.	Concerto	MCA
Bruns, V.	Concerto No. 2, op. 15	FrH
Bruns, V. -Dhérin	Concerto No. 2, op. 15	Int
Bruns, V.	Concerto No. 3, op. 41	BrH
Bruns, V.	5 Stücke, op. 40	BrH
Buchtel, F.	Argonaut	NK
Buchtel, F.	At the Ball	NK
Buchtel, F.	Chant d'amour	Vol
Buchtel, F. -arr.	Cielito Lindo	NK
Buchtel, F.	Crescent march	B-M
Buchtel, F.	Falstaff	NK
Buchtel, F. -arr.	Grandfather's Clock	NK
Buchtel, F.	Harlequin	NK
Buchtel, F.	The Huntress	NK
Buchtel, F.	Intermezzo	NK
Buchtel, F.	Janus	NK
Buchtel, F.	Jolly sailor	B-M
Buchtel, F.	Neptune	NK
Buchtel, F.	Pied Piper	NK
Buchtel, F.	Valse Romantique	Vol
Buchtel, F.	Waltz Medley	NK
Büchtger, F.	4 Kleine Stücke. 1964	B&N
Busser, H.	Cantilena and Rondo, op. 75	ALe
Busser, H.	Concertino op. 80	ALe
Busser, H.	Pièce in C, op. 45	ALe
Busser, H.	Pièce de Concours, op. 66	ALe
Busser, H.	Portuguesa, op. 106	ALe
Busser, H.	Récit et thème varié, op. 37	ALe
Busser, H.	Recitative and Theme with Variations, op. 37	CF
Buononcini, G. -Parr	Aria	HE

Bassoon and Piano

Butterworth, N.	A Mozart Album	Cha
Buttkewitz, J.	Sonata	Pet
Cacavas, J.	Preludio	B-M
Cacavas, J.	Winterscape	B-M
Caix d'Hervelois, L.-Oubradous	La Napolitaine	ALe
Caix d'Hervelois, L.-Oubradous	Plainte	ALe
Caldara, A.-Cacavas	Alma del core	B-M
Cammarota, C.	Recitative, Intermezzo e Danza	Edi
Carissimi, G.-Barnes	Heart Victorious	Spr
Cariven	Arioso	Com
Cariven	Cantabile	Com
Carre, J.	Doodling	See
Casadesus, R.	2 Pièces, op. 61	Dur
Castérède, J.	Fileuse	ALe
Cecconi, M.	Badinage	Com
Cecconi, M.	Concertino	Com
Cervetto, G.-Oubradous	Sicilienne	ALe
Challan, H.	Fantaisie	ALe
Childs, B.	Sonata	TP
Chopin, F.	Cavatina	NK
Chopin & Glazounov-Kostlan	Etude	MKE
Chopin, F.-Stouffer	Nocturne, op. 9/1	Ken
Clement, F.	Silvertone Polka	Vol
Clérisse, R.	Notturno	ALe
Clérisse, R.	Thème de Concours	ALe
Cohen, S.	Danse Grotesque	B-M
Cohen, S.	Song of the Troubadour	B-M
Cohn, A.	Declamation and Toccata	E-V
Cohn, A.	Hebraic Study	E-V
Colaço Osorio-Swaab, R.	Cavatine. 1942	SD
Corelli, A.-Parr	Adagio, a	HE
Corelli, A.-Setaccioli	Adagio	Ric
Corelli, A.-Sharrow	Sonata, d	Int
Coriolis, E. de	Petite pièce	ALe
Corrette, M.-Ruf	Sonate, d, op. 20/2 (bsn, bc)	WMS
Coulthard, J.	Lyric Sonatina	Wat
Custer, A.	Divertimento	MCA
Dagnelies, D.	Fantaisie variée	ScF
Danks, H.	Silver Threads Among the Gold	CF
Danzi, F.-Münster	Concerto, F	Leu
Darcy, R.	Sonate	Mau
Dautremer, M.	Fantasuite	ECh
Dautremer, M.	Marche noble	Com
David, F.	Concertino op. 4	Sim
David, F.	Concertino op. 12	Bil
David, F.-Laube	Concertino op. 12	CF
David, F.-Kovar	Concertino op. 12	Int
David, F.-Voxman	Concertino op. 12	Rub
Dearnley, C.-arr.	8 Easy Pieces by Classical	

Bassoon and Piano

		Composers	Che
Dearnley, C.-arr.		More Easy Pieces by	
		Classical Composers	Che
Debaar, M.		Légende et Caprice	EMb
Debussy, C.		The Little Negro	ALe
Debussy, C.-Paine		Sarabande	B-M
De Jong, M.		Concert Piece, op. 50	HeE
DeLamarter, E.		Arietta	War
Del Busto, A.		Danza Canonica	MCA
Denza, L.-Paine		Funiculi, funicula	B-M
Depelsenaire, J.		Funambules	EMT
Depelsenaire, J.		Recitative and Air	GD
Depelsenaire, J.		Sur l'Etang	GD
Desportes, Y.		Chanson d'Antan	ALe
Devienne, F.		Student Concerto, C	FrH
Dillon, R.		Lament	B&H
Dodd, P.		2 Rhythmic Interludes	B&H
Domenico, O. di		Sonatina	ALe
Donizetti, G.-Stone		Romance (Crimean Sketches)	SM
Doren, T. van		Concertstuk	EMe
Douane, J.		Fantasietta	Com
Dubois, P.		Concertino Ironico	ERR
Dubois, P.		Fanfarronade	ERR
Dubois, P.		Neuf pièces brèves	ECh
Dubois, P.		Sérénades	ALe
Dubois, P.		Tropical	ERR
Dubois, P.		Virelai	ALe
Dubrovay, L.		5 Pezzi	EMB
Duclos, R.		Fagottino	ALe
Duclos, R.		3 Nocturnos	ALe
Dunhill, T.		Intermezzo	GaM
Dunhill, T.		Lyric Suite	B&H
Duport, J.		Romance	Spr
Dutilleux, H.		Sarabande et cortège	ALe
Dvarionas, B.		Theme and Variations	MKE
Dvorak, A.		Largo (New World Symphony)	CF
Eccles, H.-Sharrow		Sonata, a	Int
Eder, H.		Concerto op. 49	LDo
Eder, H.		Sonatine, op. 34/3	LDo
Elgar, E.		Romance, op. 62	Nov
Elgar, E.-Trinkaus		Salut d'Amour, op. 12	CF
Elgar, E.-Akers		Theme from Pomp and	
		Circumstance, op. 39/1	CF
Erickson, F.-Best		Poem	B-M
Erickson, F.-Best		Serenade	B-M
Erickson, F.-Best		Song for Today	B-M
Eriksson, N.		Concerto, b	EMf
Etler, A.		Sonata	AMP
Falcinelli, R.		Berceuse	ALe
Farkas, F.		Folk song sonatina. 1955	EMB

278

Fasch, J.-Sallagar	Concerto	Hei
Fasch, J.-Klitz	Sonata, C	M&M
Fasch, J.	Sonata, C (bsn, bc)	Pet
Fauré, G.-Stoutamire	Aurora	Ken
Fauré, G.-Oubradous	Pièce	ALe
Fauré, J.-Akers	The Palms	CF
Feld, J.	Concerto. 1953	ALe
Feld, J.	Sonatine	SS
Fernström, J.	Concerto op. 80	EMf
Fibich, Z.-Andreoni	Poème	Ric
Figert, P.	Requiem for a Clown	Ken
Flament, E.	Concertpiece op. 13	CF
Flament, E.-Fields	Concertstuck op. 13	Rub
Fogg, E.-Groves	Concerto, D	Elk
Foote, W.	My Grandfather's Clock	CF
Foote, W.	My Grandfather's Clock	PrA
Forêt, F.	Pièces brèves	ALe
Forêt, F.	3 Pièces	Bil
Foster, I.	Serenade, op. 10/1	GaM
Foster, I.	Rondo, op. 10/2	GaM
Françaix, J.	Divertissement	SS
Franck, C.-Paine	Panis angelicus	B-M
Francl, J.	Dumka-Elegie-Tanz	Art
Frans, A.	De grompot (Le Grognon)	EMe
Frescobaldi, G.-Cerha	Canzoni	LDo
Frešo, T.	Composition	SHF
Fuchs, J.-Gábry	Concerto, Bb	SS
Fučik, J.	Der Alte Brumm bar	HeE
Fuleihan, A.	Concertino	B&H
Gabaye, P.	Toccatina	ALe
Gabelles, G.	Fantaisie	Bil
Gagnebin, H.	Scherzetto	ALe
Galliard, J.-Weisberg	6 Sonatas, 2 vols.	Int
Galliard, J.-Marx	6 Sonatas, 2 vols.	M&M
Galliard, J.-Marx	Sonata, a, No. 1	HE
Galliard, J.-Ruf	Sonate, F, No. 3 (bsn, bc)	WMS
Galliard, J.-Marx	Sonata, e, No. 4	HE
Galliard, J.-Marx	Sonata, d, No. 5	Pet
Galliard, J.-Marx	Sonata, C, No. 6	Pet
Galliard, J.-Ruf	Sonata, G (bsn, bc)	SS
Galliard, J.	Suite No. 1	B-M
Galliard, J.	Suite No. 2	B-M
Gallois-Montbrun, R.	Improvisation	ALe
Gallon, N.	Récit et Allegro	EdL
Garfield, B.-arr.	Concert Album	EdM
Garfield, B.	Soliloquy	EdM
Garfield, B.	2 Pieces	EdM
Gartenlaub, O.	Profiles	EMT
Gartenlaub, O.	Sonatina	EMT
Gastyne, S. de	Sonatina op. 58. 1968	Fer

Geiser, W.	Capriccio op. 33a. 1943	B&N
Geist, K.	3 Pieces on Mari Themes, op. 20	MKE
Genzmer, H.	Introduction and Allegro	Pet
Gerschefski, E.	"America" Variations for Winds, op. 44/5	CoF
Gerschefski, E.	"America" Variations for Winds, op. 45/6	CoF
Geviksman, V.	Melody-Humoresque	MKE
Gillis, D.	Brushy Creek	B&H
Glazunov, A.-Zuyevich	Concerto for Saxophone	MKE
Glazunov, A.	Serenade Espagnole, op. 20/2	CF
Glière, R.-Kovar	Humoresque, op. 35	Int
Glière, R.-Kovar	Impromptu, op. 35	Int
Glinka, M.	Romance Melody	Spr
Gluck, C.	Largo	For
Godard, B.-Trinkaus	Berceuse (Jocelyn)	CF
Godfrey, F.	Lucy Long	CF
Golz, W.	Romanza	See
Goossens, E.	Vieille chanson à boire	ALe
Gossec, F.	Gavotte	NK
Gotkovsky, I.	Variations Concertantes	EMT
Gottwald, M.	Fantasie Heroique	CF
Gounod, C.-Walters	March of a Marionette	Rub
Gounod, C.-Mullaly	Dio Possente (Faust)	CF
Grafe, F.	Grand Concerto	CF
Granados, E.-Amaz	Spanish Dance No. 2. Oriental	UME
Granados, E.-Amaz	Spanish Dance No. 5. Andaluza	UME
Graun, J.-Töttcher	Concerto, Bb	HSM
Graupner, C.-Schroeder	Concerto, C	Leu
Grétry, A.-Marteau	Ariette	Lud
Grieg, E.-Simpson	Hall of the Mountain King	B-M
Grieg, E.-Paine	Sonata	B-M
Grondahl, L.	Concerto. 1942	SPD
Groot, C. de	Bassonnerie. 1962	SD
Grovlez, G.	Sicilienne and Allegro Giocoso	ALe
Grudzinski, C.	Impressions	AP
Guide, R. de	Elégie et consolation	ALe
Guillou, G.	Ballade	GrF
Haan, S. de	Scherzo	S&C
Handel, G.-Barr	Allegro (Concerto, f)	Lud
Handel, G.-Gee	Andante and Allegro	SM
Handel, G.	Cantilena	NK
Handel, G.	Celebrated Largo	Dur
Handel, G.-Brisset	Célèbre largo	EdR
Handel, G.-Pezzi	Concerto, c	SM
Handel, G.-Kostlan	Concerto for Oboe, G, Movement II	MKE
Handel, G.-Sharrow	Concerto, g	Int

Bassoon and Piano

Handel, G.	A Handel Solo Album	OxU
Handel, G.-Barr	Sarabande	Lud
Handel, G.-Barnes	Sound an Alarm	Spr
Hanus, J.	Short Story	Gen
Hanus, J.	Short Stories No. 4	Gen
Harrison, P.	Faggot Dance	Cha
Hassler, L.-Laube	Allegro Moderato (Concerto)	CF
Hassler, L.-Laube	Andante and Rondo (Concerto)	CF
Haydn, F.	Andante (Concerto)	Spr
Haydn, F.-Paine	Minuet	B-M
Haydn, F.-Muller	Sonatine	Mau
Haydn, F.-Stouffer	Vivace	Ken
Heilmann, H.	Sonata seria	Hei
Heinichen, J.-Angerhoefer	Sonata, D (bsn, bc)	Pet
Hekster, W.	Music for Bassoon and Piano	SD
Henneberg, A.	Concertino	EMf
Hernried, R.	Little Grotesque	GFB
Hernried, R.	Serenade Burlesque	GFB
Hertel, J.-Sallagar	Concerto, a	Hei
Hertel, J.	Concerto, Bb	MR
Hess, W.	7 Recital Pieces, 2 vols.	HE
Hessenberg, K.	Divertimento	ALe
Hindemith, P.	Sonata. 1938	SS
Hlobil, E.	Divertimento, op. 29	Art
Hoebeke, J.	Complainte	GD
Hoffmann, A.	Alborada	B&H
Hogg, M.	Variations	Ens
Horak, A.	Concerto Piccolo	AMC
Horder, M.	Hornpipe and Trio	HE
Houdy, P.	Rondel	ALe
Hubert	Dans les pins	EdR
Hudadoff & Spire-arr.	11 Classic Solos	PrA
Hudadoff, I.-arr.	15 Intermediate Solo Series	PrA
Hudadoff, I.-arr.	Marches	PrA
Hughes, E.	A Low Minuet	JE
Hughes, E.	6 Low Solos	JE
Hummel, J.-Sharrow	Concerto	Int
Hummel, J.-Tyree	Grand Concerto	MR
Ibert, J.	Arabesque ("Carignane")	Int
Ibert, J.-Oubradous	The Crystal Cage	ALe
Ibert, J.-Oubradous	The Little White Donkey	ALe
Ibert, J.-Oubradous	The Old Beggar	ALe
Isaac, M.	Jolly Dutchman	CF
Ivanovici, J.	Waves of the Danube	B-M
Jacob, G.	Concerto	GaM
Jacobi, C.	Polonaise	ScF
Jaffe, G.	Centone Buffo Concertante	SM
Jancourt, E.	Reverie, op. 61	CF
Jeanjean, P.	Prelude and Scherzo	ALe
Jolivet, A.	Concerto	Heu

281

Jordahl, R.	Diptych	Ken
Junge, G.	Fantasie über "Im tiefen Keller"	WZ
Kabalevsky, D.-Fedulov	Toccatina, op. 27/12	MKE
Kanitz, E.	Concerto	TP
Kardos, I.	Bipartitum	Gen
Karlins, M.	4 Inventions & a Fugue	CoF
Karlins, M.	Variations and Outgrowths	CoF
Kazacsay, T.	Concerto. 1956	EMB
Kelkel, M.	Concerto op. 13	EMT
Keller, H.	Sonata	CoF
Kennaway, L.	Dance Arabesque	GaM
Kennaway, L.	Interrupted Serenade	HE
Kerrison, J.	Suite of dances	B-M
Kerrison, J.	Three young pieces	B-M
Kersters, W.	Humoresque	Mau
Kesnar, M.	Clown Festival	CF
Kesnar, M.	Concerto	CF
Kesnar, M.	Gavotte	CF
Khachaturian, A.-Schoebel	Sabre Dance	MCA
Kinyon, J.	Recital Pieces	War
Klughardt, A.	Romanze	CF
Klughardt, A.	Romanze	Spr
Knight-Clement	Rocked in the Cradle of the Deep	Vol
Kocsár, M.	Dialoghi	EMB
Koepke, P.	Rondo (Suite, G)	Rub
Kohs, E.	Sonatina	TP
Kořínek, M.	Sonatina. 1960	SHF
Kosa, G.	4 Easy pieces. 1967	EMB
Kostlan, I.	2 Concert Etudes	MKE
Kostlan, I.-comp.	6 Pieces by Russian Composers	MKE
Kostlan, I.-comp.	4 Pieces by Soviet Composers	MKE
Kostlan, I.-comp.	6 Pieces by Soviet Composers	MKE
Kostlan, I.-comp.-Schubert, Terekhin	5 Pieces by Western Classical Composers, 2 vols.	MKE
Kostlan, I.-comp.-Terekhin	6 Pieces by Western Classical Composers	MKE
Kostlan & Terekhin	4 Pieces by Schubert, Mendelssohn, Grieg	MKE
Kouguell, A.	Divertimento	AMC
Kouguell, A.	Scherzo	AMC
Kroepsch, F.	Down in the Deep Cellar	CF
Kunkel, M.	Concertino	CF
Kuprevich, V.	Scherzino	MKE
La Monaca, V.	Memories	HeE
Lamote de Grignon, J.-Amaz	Canço de Maria	UME
Lamote de Grignon, J.-Amaz	Rêverie (Schumanniana)	UME
Landowski, M.	Concerto	ECh

Lantier, P.	Danse bouffonne	ALe
Larsson, L.	Concertino, op. 45/4	B&H
Larsson, L.	Concertino, op. 45/11	B&H
Laszlo	5 Pieces	EMB
Lecail, G.	Fantaisie Concertante	ALe
Leclerc, M.	Concerto	Mau
Lemare, E.-Trinkaus	Andantino	CF
Lemare, E.-Long	Andantino	Vol
Lenom, C.-Findlay	Lullaby	CF
Lenz, M. von-Sargent	Cicero	CF
Levy, F.	Sonata. 1963	See
Levy, F.	Suite No. 1	Cor
Liagre, D.	Souvenir de Calais	Bil
Lincke, P.	Glow Worm	NK
Lisenko, N.-Litvinov	Album Leaf-Serenade	MKE
Lopatnikoff, N.	Arabesque	MCA
Lotti, A.	Arietta	EdM
Louel, J.	Burlesque. 1943	CBD
Lovell, K.	Summer Song	E?
Lovell, K.	The Swing	Elk
Lovell, K.	The Train	Elk
Lovell, K.	3 Summer Sketches	Elk
Lucas, L.	Orientale	Che
Luening, O.	Sonata	GaM
Luke, R.	Concerto	OxU
Lvovsky	Happy Day, op. 7	CF
Macbeth, A.	Forget Me Not	CF
MacBride, D.	Illegal Tender	See
MacDowell, E.-Best	To a Wild Rose	B-M
Mácha, O.	Sonate. 1963	Art
Maconchy, E.	Concertino	AlL
Maes, J.	Burlesque	EMe
Maes, J.	Morceau de Concert	EMb
Maganini, Q.	L'Après-Midi d'une Crocodile	EdM
Maganini, Q.	Rastus Ryan	CF
Maingueneau, L.	Suite brève	Dur
Maixandeau, M.	Lied et rondo	ALe
Makarov, E.	Scherzo	MR
Maltby, R.	Moon Over the Mesa	Ken
Marais, M.-Kestner	Minuets (Pièces de Viole)	FrH
Marcello, B.-Schroeder	Adagio (Sonata, e)	GaM
Marcello, B.-Merriman	Adagio and Allegro	SM
Marcello, B.-Oubradous	Allegretto	ALe
Marcello, B.-Merriman	Largo and Allegro	SM
Marcello, B.-Sharrow	Sonata, a	Int
Marcello, B.-Sharrow	Sonata, C	Int
Marcello, B.-Sharrow	Sonata, e	Int
Marcello, B.-Sharrow	Sonata, G	Int
Marcello, B.-Rudas	Sonata	EMB
Marescotti, A.	Giboulées	Job

Margoni, A.	Après une lecture de Dreiser	ALe
Mari, P.	Sonatine	EMT
Maros, R.	Concertino. 1951	EMB
Marpurg, F.-Marple	Rondeau	SM
Marteau, H.-Barnes	Morceau Vivant	Spr
Martelli, H.	Sonata	HMo
Martelli, H.	Theme & Variations, op. 74. 1950	EME
Martini, P.	Plaisir d'Amour	EdM
Massenet, J.-Trinkaus	Elegie	CF
Matz, A.	Sonatine	FrH
Maugüé, J.	Divertissements champêtres	Bil
Maurat, E.	Petites Inventions, op. 39/4	EME
Mazellier, J.	Prelude and Dance	ALe
McKay, F.	Buckboard Blues	Bar
McKay, F.	Dream Waltz	Bar
McKay, F.	Hernando's Holiday	Bar
McKay, F.	Jig for Jeanine	Bar
McKay, F.	The Powdered Wig	Bar
McKay, F.	Ye Traveling Troubador	Bar
McKay, G.	Arietta and Capriccio	BM
McKay, G.	Concert Solo Sonatine	BM
Mendelssohn, F.-Andreoni	Consolation	Ric
Mendelssohn, F.-Trinkaus	Nocturno	CF
Mendelssohn, F.-Trinkaus	On Wings of Song	CF
Mendelssohn, F.	On Wings of Song	NK
Merci, L.-Bergmann	Sonata, g, op. 3/4	S&C
Mercy, L.-Kaplan	Sonata No. 2	SM
Merle	Mummers	CF
Meulemans, A.	Rhapsodie. 1942	CBD
Meuser, E.	Concerto Oriental	Spr
Meyerbeer, G.-Trinkaus	Coronation March	CF
Middeleer, J. de	Recitativo e allegro. 1970	CBD
Mihalovici, M.	Novelette	ALe
Mihalovici, M.	Sonata	Heu
Milde, L.	Andante and Rondo, op. 25	CF
Milde, L.	Concerto, F, No. 2	MR
Milde, L.	Polonaise	MR
Milde, L.-Sharrow	Tarantella, op. 20	Int
Milde, L.	Tarantella, op. 20	MR
Milde, L.-Waterhouse	3 Study Pieces	MR
Millars	Adagio and Rondo	B&H
Miller	Wraggle-Taggle Gypsies	B&H
Miroshnikov, O.-Dhérin	Scherzo	Int
Miroshnikov, O.	Scherzo	MKE
Montfeuillard, R.	Lamento et final	Com
Moritz, E.	Scherzo	WZ
Morra, G.	Nocturnal Serenade	CF
Mortari, V.	Marche fériale	ALe
Moscheles, I.	Duo, op. 34	MR

Moszkowski, M.-Paine	Spanish dance No. 2	B-M
Mouquet, J.	Ballade, op. 54	CF
Mozart, W.-Harris	Adagio (Clarinet Concerto)	CF
Mozart, W.-Pezzi	Adagio Religioso	SM
Mozart, W.-Voxman	Andante and Menuetto	Rub
Mozart, W.-Sansone	Horn Concerto No. 1	SM
Mozart, W.-Best	Minuetto	B-M
Mozart, W.-Barnes	Per Questa Bella Mano	Spr
Mozart, W.-Oubradous	Presto	ALe
Mozart, W.-Kostlan	Rondo	MKE
Mozart, W.-Sansone	Concerto Rondo, op. 371	SM
Mozart, W.-Sansone	Sonata No. 6	SM
Mozart, W.-Muller	Sonatine	Mau
Mozart, W.-Weissman	Concerto K. 191	B&H
Mozart, W.	Concerto, Bb, op. 96	Bil
Mozart, W.-Kling	Concerto, Bb, KV 191	BrH
Mozart, W.	Concerto KV 191	CF
Mozart, W.-Dhérin	Concerto, Bb	EdR
Mozart, W.-Luck, Gütter	Concerto, Bb, K. 191	FrH
Mozart, W.-Weisberg	Concerto, Bb, K. 191	Int
Mozart, W.	Concerto, Bb, K. 191	MR
Mozart, W.	Concerto, Bb, No. 1	Pet
Mozart, W.-Moritz	Bassoon Concerto No. 1	Spr
Mozart, W.	Concerto op. 96, No. 1 Cadenzas by Pierné and Ibert	ALe
Mozart, W.-Ibert	2 Cadenzas for Mozart's Concerto No. 1	ALe
Mozart, W.	Concerto No. 2	CF
Mozart, W.	Concerto K. 451, No. 2	EdL
Mozart, W.	Concerto, Bb, K. Anh. 230a, No. 2	Pet
Mozart, W.	Bassoon Concerto No. 2	Spr
Mozart, W.-Moritz	Cadenzas for Mozart Bassoon Concertos	Spr
Müthel, J.-Wollheim	Concerto, C	B&B
Mulder, H.	Sonate No. 5, op. 54. 1944	SD
Neukomm, S.-Kaplan	Aria	Spr
Nielsen-Edwards	The Satyr	B-M
Niverd, L.	Chant mélancolique	Bil
Niverd, L.	Complainte	Bil
Niverd, L.	Historiette dramatique	Bil
Niverd, L.	Hymne	Bil
Niverd, L.	Légende	Bil
Niverd, L.	Romance sentimentale	Bil
Niverd, L.	Scherzetto	Bil
Niverd, L.	6 Petites pièces de style	Bil
Nussio, O.	Variazioni su un'Arietta di Pergolesi	UE
Offenbach, J.-Laube	La Musette	CF

Offenbach, J.	Waltz "La Perichole"	NK
Olcott, C.	My Wild Irish Rose	NK
Orban, M.	Sonate	Bil
Ord Hume, J.	Carnival	B&H
Organn, R.	The Brook	Reb
Organn, R.	Evening Shadows	Reb
Organn, R.	Gently Flowing Waters	Reb
Organn, R.	Romance	Reb
Organn, R.	Waltz of the Stars	Reb
Ostrander, A.	Paris Soir	EdM
Ottoson, D.	Concerto	EMf
Oubradous, F.	Récit et variations	ALe
Ozi, E.-Favre	Adagio et Rondo	ERS
Ozi, E.-Borrel	Grande Sonate	ERS
Ozi, E.	3rd Sonate	EdO
Paderewski, I.-Trinkaus	Minuet a l'Antique	CF
Paine, H.	Arabesque	B-M
Paine, H.	Bassoon soloist (Level 1)	B-M
Paine, H.	The Happy Hunter	B-M
Paine, H.	Scherzo	B-M
Paine, H.	The Troubador	B-M
Paine, H.	Valse	B-M
Parès, G.	Crépuscle	Bil
Parodi, R.	Concerto. 1961	Edi
Pauer, J.	Capricci	Art
Pauer, J.	Concerto	ES
Pergolesi, G.-Barnes	Canzona	Spr
Pergolesi, G.-Elkan	Se Tu M'Ami	HeE
Petit, P.	Guilledoux	ALe
Petrič, I.	Sonata	EdD
Petrie, H.-Walters	Asleep in the Deep	Rub
Petrie, H.-MacLean	Asleep in the Deep	War
Petrovics, E.	Passacaglia in Blues. 1964	EMB
Pfeiffer, F.-Hennige	Concerto, Bb	Leu
Phillips, B.	Concert Piece	CF
Phillips, I.-arr.	A Classical and Romantic Album	OxU
Pierné, G.-Garfield	Concertpiece, op. 35	Int
Pierné, G.	Concert Prélude, op. 53	EdS
Pierné, G.	Solo de Concert, op. 35	ALe
Pierné, G.-Voxman	Solo de Concert, op. 35	Rub
Pierné, P.	Thème et variations	Bil
Pierrette, M.	Sonatine	EMT
Pisk, P.	Bohemian Dance Rondo	B-M
Pleyel, I.-Block	Concerto, Bb	MR
Podkovirov, P.	Sonata	MKE
Poldini, E.-Simpson	Poupée Valsante	B-M
Ponce, M.-Simpson	Estrellita	B-M
Poot, M.	Ballade	ALe
Porret, J.	7e Solo de Concours	MM

Porret, J.	8e Solo de Concours	MM
Porret, J.	Concertino No. 17	EdR
Porret, J.	Concertino No. 18	EdR
Presle, J. de la -Oubradous	Oriental	ALe
Presle, J. de la	Petite Suite	ALe
Presser, W.	Sonatina	TP
Presser, W.	Suite	TP
Procaccini, T.	3 Pièces	ALe
Puget	Solo	ALe
Purcell, H.	Nymphs and Shepherds	NK
Rakov, N.	Etude	MKE
Raphael, G.	Berceuse	ALe
Ratez, A.	Barcarolle	EdR
Ratez, E.	Impromptu, op. 67	Bil
Ratez, E.	Variation	Ham
Rathaus, K.	Polichinelle	B-M
Rautavaara, E.	Sonata. 1965-68	MT
Ravel, M.-Schoenbach	Alborado del Gracioso	E-V
Ravel, M.	Pièce en forme de Habanera	ALe
Reicha, A.-Lebermann	Sonata, Bb	SS
Reiner, K.	Suite	CHF
Reuschel, M.	Syphax, op. 172	Bil
Reuter, F.	Suites	FrH
Reutter, H.	Sérénade	ALe
Revel, P.	Petite Suite	ALe
Rhoads, W.-arr.	10 Solos for Concert and Contest	SM
Rimsky-Korsakov, N.-Garfield	Concerto	Int
Rimsky-Korsakov, N.-Schubert	Concerto for Trombone	MKE
Rimsky-Korsakov, N.-Zuyevich	Concert Fantasy on Russian Themes, op. 33	MKE
Rivier, J.	Concerto	EdS
Rogers, B.	Soliloquy No. 2	E-V
Rollinson, T.	Rocked in the Cradle of the Deep	CF
Rose, J.	Capriccio, Elegy and Scherzetto	GaM
Rössler-Rosetti, F.-Stevens	Concerto, Bb	S&C
Rosetti, F.	Concerto, Bb	Sim
Rothgarber, H.	Interplay	SM
Rubinstein, A.-Best	Melody in F	B-M
Rubinstein, A.-Long	Romance	Vol
Russo, D.	Concerto	GZ
Russo, J.	Lo Schifoso	CoA
Ruthenfranz, R.	Divertimento	EMe
St. Clair, F.	Admiration	Vol
St. Clair, F.	Dream Time	Vol
St. Clair, F.	Golden Days	Vol
Saint-Saens, C.-Paine	Allegro Appassionata	B-M
Saint-Saens, C.-Whear	Amour viens aider	Lud

Saint-Saens, C.	Romance, op. 51	Dur
Saint-Saens, C.	Sonate op. 168	Dur
Saint-Saens, C.-Zimmermann	Sonata	Pet
Saint-Saens, C.-Trinkaus	The Swan	CF
Sammartini, G.-Oubradous	Canzonetta	ALe
Sári, J.	Meditation. 1967-68	EMB
Sauguet, H.	Barcarolle	ChM
Sauguet, H.	Un Soir a Saint-Emilion	ALe
Saveliev, B.	Concerto	MKE
Scarlatti, A.-Barnes	Aria (Tigraine)	Spr
Schaefer, C.	Capriccio	WZ
Schaefers, A.	Capriccio	HSM
Schaffrath, C.-Ruf	Duetto, f (bsn, hpcd)	Hei
Schechtman, S.	Serenade	BM
Schibler, A.	Concerto op. 85	Pet
Schibler, A.	Monologue	Pet
Schiff, H.	4 Duos. 1965	LDo
Schmidt, W.	Phantasy on an American Spiritual	Wes
Schmitt, F.-Oubradous	Andantino	ALe
Schmutz, A.	Melodie Lyrique	B-M
Schoeck, O.-Steidl	Bassklarinetten-Sonate op. 41	BrH
Schoemaker, M.	Concerto. 1947	CBD
Schoenbach, S.-arr.	Solos for the Bassoon Player	Sch
Schoenhals, F.	2 Pièces: Fragment; Esquisse	ScF
Schollum, R.	Sonatine, op. 55/3. 1956	LDo
Schollum, R.	Sonatine, op. 57/3. 1961	LDo
Schouwman, H.	Romance en Humoreske, op. 33/1, 2. 1944	SD
Schreck, G.	Sonate op. 9	CF
Schubert, F.-Paine	Allegro	B-M
Schubert, F.-Kostlan	Sonata for Arpeggione and Piano; Movement I	MKE
Schubert, F.-Isaac	3 Themes	CF
Schumann, R.	Rêverie, op. 15	Dur
Schumann, R.	Romance	CF
Schumann, R.-O'Neill	A Solo for Bassoon	Wat
Schumann, R.-Oubradous	Temps d'hiver	ALe
Schumann, R.	Traumerei	CF
Schumann, R.-Oubradous	Valse et l'Harmonieux Forgeron	ALe
Schwaen, K.	Sonatine	FrH
Schwantner, J.	Chronicon	Pet
Schwartz, E.	Romance	Gen
Schwartz, G.	International Folk Suite	SM
Schwartz, G.	Trireme	SM
Sedmidubsky, M.	Concertino	Art
Sehlbach, E.	Kammerkonzert, op. 97/4	MV
Seidel, J.	Concerto No. 2	Art
Selma y Salaverde, B. de		

Bassoon and Piano

-Kastner	Fantasia, D, No. 5 (bsn, bc)	SS
Selma y Salaverde, B. de		
-Kastner	Fantasia, F, No. 8 (bsn, bc)	SS
Senaillé, J. -Pezzi	Allegro Spiritoso	SM
Shishov	Grotesque Dance	EdM
Shostakovich, D.	Fantastic Dances	EdM
Sibelius, J. -Trinkaus	Valse Triste	CF
Siegmeister, E.	Contrasts	MCA
Siennicki, E.	Ballade	E-V
Siennicki, E.	Highland Heather	NK
Siennicki, E.	Valse Ballet	Bar
Siennicki, E.	Woodland Waltz	NK
Siqueira, J.	3 Etüden	Deu
Smirnov	Sonate	ChM
Smirnova, T.	Suite	MKE
Smith	Caprice	CF
Smith, L.	Sonata	CoF
Smolanoff, M.	Sonata	See
Spencer, W.	Dance of the Dragons	Hal
Spencer, W.	The Merry-Go-Round	Hal
Spisak, M.	Concerto	Ric
Spohr, L. -Wojciechowski	Adagio	Sim
Sporck, G.	Légende	Bil
Sporck -Oubradous	Légende, G	EdR
Srebotnjak, A.	6 Pieces	EdD
Stamitz, K. -Wojciechowski	Concerto, F	HSM
Starokadomsky, M. -Dhérin	4 Pieces, op. 25	Int
Starokadomsky, M.	4 Pieces, op. 25	MKE
Stearns, P.	3 Short Pieces	CoF
Stekel, E.	Mélodie	ALe
Stevens, H.	Sonata	CoF
Stevens, H.	3 Pieces	Pet
Stolte	Spielmusik	Pet
Sukhanek -Dhérin	Concertino	Int
Suppé, F. von -Long	Andante Maestoso (Poet and Peasant)	Vol
Sykora, V.	Dve dumky	Art
Takács, J.	Sonata Missoulana, op. 66	LDo
Tamba	Fantasy	ALe
Tansman, A.	Sonatina	EME
Tansman, A.	Suite	EME
Tchaikovsky, P. -Laube	Andante Cantabile, op. 11	CF
Tchaikovsky, P. -Kostlan	5 Pieces	MKE
Tchaikovsky, P. -Seay	Impromptu	Spr
Tchaikovsky, P. -Kostlan	Nocturne	MKE
Tchaikovsky, P. -Cacavas	Song of Sadness	B-M
Tchaikovsky, P. -Trinkaus	Song without Words	CF
Tchaikovsky, P.	Waltz	Cor
Tcherepnin, N.	Esquisse, op. 7	Spr
Telemann, G. -Barnes	Arie (Pimpinone)	Spr

Telemann, G.-Rudas	Sonata	EMB
Telemann, G.-Oromszegi	Sonate, e	EMB
Telemann, G.-Kovar	Sonata, f	Int
Templeton, A.	Elegie	MCA
Tenaglia, A.	Aria Antica	EdM
Tenaglia, A.	Aria	For
Terekhin & Kostlan	3 Pieces by Tchaikovsky, Rachmaninoff, Glazounov	MKE
Terekhin & Kostlan-arr.	4 Pieces by Glinka, Gretchaninoff, Kalinnikov	MKE
Teryokhin & Beliakov	11 Pieces	MKE
Teryokhin, R.	4 Pieces by Soviet Composers	MKE
Thiriet, A.	Theme and Variations	ALe
Thilman, J.	Sonatine op. 51	FrH
Toldra, E.-Amaz	Ave Maria	UME
Toldra, E.-Amaz	La Font	UME
Toldra, E.-Amaz	Oracio al Maig	UME
Toldra, E.-Amaz	Soneti de la Rosada	UME
Tomasi, H.	Chant Corse	ALe
Tomasi, H.	Concerto	ALe
Tomasi, H.	Danse guerrière (5 danses profanes et sacrées)	ALe
Trinkaus, G.	Lament	CF
Trinkaus, G.-arr.	World's Best-Known Pieces	CF
Trowbridge, L.	Album Leaf	See
Trowbridge, L.	Barcarolle	See
Trowbridge, L.	Chromatico	See
Ulrich, H.	Rondo Energico	CF
Vachey, H.	Musette et sabotière	ALe
Vachey, H.	3 Pièces faciles	GD
Vačkář, D.	Kammerkonzert. 1964	CHF
VanderCook, H.	Columbine	NK
Varescotti, A.	Giboulées	Job
Vaubourgoin, M.	Concerto	EMT
Vidal, P.	Adagio and Saltarella	ALe
Vilec, M.	Summer notes. 1959	SHF
Villa-Lobos, H.	Ciranda das Sete Notas	SMP
Villette, P.	Cantilène	ALe
Vincze, I.	Sonata. 1964	EMB
Vinter, G.	Reverie	Cra
Viola, A.-Kastner	Concerto, F	Hei
Viozzi	Sonata	Ric
Vivaldi, A.-Schoenbach	10 Bassoon Concerti, 2 vols.	Sch
Vivaldi, A.-Hara, Nagy	Konzert, a, F. VIII, No. 7	EMB
Vivaldi, A.-Sharrow	Concerto, a	Int
Vivaldi, A.	Concerto, a, F. VIII, No. 7, P. 72	Pet
Vivaldi, A.-Ephrikian	Concerto, a, F. VIII, No. 2	Ric
Vivaldi, A.-Ephrikian	Concerto, a, F. VIII, No. 7	Ric
Vivaldi, A.-Ghedini	Concerto, Bb, "La Notte"	Int

Bassoon and Piano

Vivaldi, A.-Vene	Concerto, Bb, "La Notte", F. VIII, No. 1	Ric
Vivaldi, A.-Lasocki	Concerto, Bb, P. 401	MR
Vivaldi, A.-Zanetti	Concerto, C, F. VIII, No. 9	Ric
Vivaldi, A.-Nagy, Szeszler	Concerto, d, F. VIII, No. 5	EMB
Vivaldi, A.-Weisberg	Concerto, d	Int
Vivaldi, A.-Sharrow	Concerto, e	Int
Vivaldi, A.-Sharrow	Concerto, F	Int
Vivaldi, A.	Concerto, F, P. 318	Pet
Vivaldi, A.-Lesko	Concerto, F, F. VIII, No. 8	Ric
Vivaldi, A.-Smith	Concerto, F, F. VIII, No. 20	Ric
Vivaldi, A.-Smith, Kardt	Concerto, g, F. VIII, No. 11	Ric
Vivaldi, A.-Smith	Concerto, g, F. VIII, No. 23	Ric
Vivaldi, A.-Garfield	Sonata, a, No. 3	Int
Vivaldi, A.-Sharrow	Sonata, Bb, No. 1	Int
Vivaldi, A.-Sharrow	Sonata, Bb, No. 4	Int
Vivaldi, A.-Sharrow	Sonata, Bb, No. 6	Int
Vivaldi, A.-Weisberg	Sonata, e	Int
Vivaldi, A.-Sharrow	Sonata, F, No. 2	Int
Vogel, J.-Wojciechowski	Concerto, C	HSM
Vorlová, S.	Miniaturen, op. 55	Pan
Voxman, H. (ed)	Concert and Contest Collection	Rub
Vuataz, R.	Promenade et poursuite	ALe
Wagner, J.	Introduction and Scherzo	SM
Wagner, R.-Trinkaus	Song to the Evening Star	CF
Wagner, R.-Trinkaus	Walther's Prize Song	CF
Waldenmaier, A.	Concerto, F, op. 14	LDo
Walker, R.	Valse Casuel	BM
Walter, H.	Jabberwocky	Rub
Walthew, R.	Introduction and Allegro	HE
Wanhal, J.-Schwamberger	Concerto, C	Sim
Ward-Steinman	Childs Play	GaM
Warren, D.	Danish Dance	Lud
Warren, D.	Mantis Dance	Lud
Watson, W.	Piece	Col
Webber, C.-arr.	First Solo Album	TP
Webber, L.	Northington Farm	AHC
Weber, A.	Palindrome	ALe
Weber, C.M. von-Bettoney	Adagio (Concerto, F)	CF
Weber, C.M. von-Flament	Andante and Rondo Ungarese, op. 35	ALe
Weber, C.M. von	Andante et rondo hongrois, op. 35	Bil
Weber, C.M. von	Ungarische Fantasie, op. 35	CF
Weber, C.M. von-Dhérin	Andante et rondo hongrois	EdR
Weber, C.M. von-Kovar	Andante and Rondo Ongarese, op. 35	Int
Weber, C.M. von	Hungarian Fantasy, op. 35	MKE
Weber, C.M. von	Andante e Rondo Ungarese, op. 35	MRL

Bassoon and Piano

Weber, C.M. von -Darvas	Andante e Rondo ongarese, op. 35	SS
Weber, C.M. von -Kovar	Concertino op. 26	Int
Weber, C.M. von -Plante	Concerto, F, op. 75	Bil
Weber, C.M. von -Schoenbach	Concerto op. 75	CF
Weber, C.M. von -Sharrow	Concerto, F, op. 75	Int
Weber, C.M. von	Concerto op. 75	MKE
Weber, C.M. von	Concerto, F, op. 75	MR
Weber, C.M. von	Concerto op. 75	MRL
Weber, C.M. von -Laube	Romanza Appassionata	CF
Weber, C.M. von -Voxman	Rondo (Concerto for Bassoon)	Rub
Weber, F.	Elephant Dance	B-M
Weber, F. -arr.	3 Favorites	B-M
Wehding, H.	Scherzo	PG
Weinberger, J.	Sonatine	CF
Weiner, S.	Concerto op. 21	MCA
Weinzweig, J.	Divertimento No. 3. 1960	MCA
Weismann, J.	Musik, op. 153	HG
Weiss, A.	10 Fancies	CoF
Weissenborn, E. -Voxman	Romanze, op. 227	Rub
Weissenborn, E. -Voxman	Song Without Words, op. 226	Rub
Weissenborn, J.	Adagio, op. 9/2	CF
Weissenborn, J.	Arioso and Humoreske, op. 9/1	CF
Weissenborn, J.	Capriccio, op. 14	CF
Weissenborn, J.	Capriccio, op. 14	FrH
Weissenborn, J. -Dhérin	Capriccio, op. 14	Int
Weissenborn, J.	Capriccio, op. 14	MKE
Weissenborn, J. -Dhérin	Nocturne, op. 9/4	Int
Weissenborn, J. -Kovar	Romance, op. 3	Int
Weissenborn, J.	6 Concert Pieces, op. 9, 2 vols.	For
Weissenborn, J. -Garfield	2 Pieces, op. 9	Int
Wending	Scherzo	Spr
Wiggins, A.	Song and Dance Man	Ken
Wilder, A.	Sonata	SF
Wilder, A.	Sonata No. 2	SM
Williams, E.	Concerto No. 5	CCo
Willner, A. -arr.	Classical Album	B&H
Wissmer, P.	Dialogue	EMT
Wolf-Ferrari, E. -Solazzi	Suite-Concertino, F, op. 16	Ric
Wright, W.	Episode Melancholique	CF
Wurmser, L.	Solo de Concours	Bil
Wurmser, L.	Tendres Mélodies	Bil
Yesev, S.	Burlesque	MKE
Yuste, M.	Solo de Concurso	UME
Zakharov -arr.	6 Pieces by Schumann, Schubert, Mendelssohn	MKE
Zamacois, J. -Amaz	Serenada d'Hivern	UME
Zaninelli, L.	Canto	E-V
Zaninelli, L.	Peg Leg Pete	B&H

Bassoon and Piano

Zbinden, J.	Ballade, op. 33, 1961	BrH
Zehm, Fr.	Pentameron	SS
Zeisl	Souvenir	B-M
Zimmerman, R.-arr.	Play a Song of America	TP
Zimmerman, R.-arr.	Play a Song of Christmas	TP
Zur, M.	3 Pieces	See
Zverev, V.	2 Pieces on Themes of Russian Folk Songs	MKE

Bassoon and Organ

Stout, A.	Serenity	Pet

Bassoon and Orchestra

Amram, D.	Concerto	Pet
Andriessen, J.	Concertino	SD
Bach, J.C.-Wojciechowski	Concerto, Bb	HSM
Bach, J.C.-Wojciechowski	Concerto, Eb	HSM
Bartolozzi, B.	Concertazioni	ESZ
Bartsch, C.	Fantaisie	Mau
Bereau, J.	Triptyque	ECh
Berghmans, J.	Les Oursons savants (Scenes from a Travelling Circus)	ALe
Bernier, R.	Bassonnerie	ALe
Bitsch, M.	Concertino	ALe
Boismortier, J. de	Concerto	EdL
Bond, C.-Finzi	Concerto No. 6	B&H
Bozza, E.	Concertino op. 49	ALe
Brauel, H.	Notturno	SS
Brenta, G.	Air varié pour les belles écouteuses	ALe
Bruns, V.	Konzert, op. 5/1	BrH
Busser, H.	Concertino	ALe
Busser, H.	Portuguesa	ALe
Busser, H.	Récit et thème varié, op. 37	ALe
Crusell, B.	Concertino, Bb	MT
Danzi, F.-Münster	Concerto, F	Leu
Dobrowolski, A.	Concerto. 1953	AP
Dubois, P.	Sérénades	ALe
Eder, H.	Concerto op. 49	LDo
Eriksson, N.	Concerto, b	STI
Fasch, J.-Sallagar	Concerto, C	Pet
Feld, J.	Concerto. 1953	ALe
Fernström, J.	Concerto op. 80. 1945	STI
Flosman, O.	Concertino. 1956	CHF
Fogg, E.-Groves	Concerto, D	Elk
Friemann, W.	Concerto eroico	AP
Fuchs, J.-Gábry	Concerto, Bb	SS
Gartenlaub, O.	Profils	EMT
Graun, J.-Töttcher	Concerto, Bb	HSM
Graupner, C.-Schroeder	Concerto, C	Leu

Graupner, C.-Noack	Concerto, c	B&N
Grovlez, G.	Sicilienne and Allegro Giocoso	ALe
Hallaste, U.	Tema con variazioni. 1955	Fin
Henneberg, A.	Concerto op. 45 (bsn, str)	STI
Hertel, J.-Sallagar	Concerto, a	Pet
Hertel, J.	Concerto	MR
Horký, K.	Concerto. 1967	CHF
Hummel, J.F.	Konzertstück, Bb, op. 201	BrH
Hummel, J.N.	Grand Concerto	MR
Jacob, G.	Concerto	GaM
Jolivet, A.	Concerto	Heu
Karjalainen, A.	Concert Suite. 1949	Fin
Kazacsay, T.	Concerto. 1955-56	EMB
Kelemen, M.	Concerto (bsn, str)	UE
Kelkel, M.	Concerto op. 13	EMT
Ketting, P.	Concertino. 1968	SD
Kozeluch, J.	Concerto, C	CHF
Landowski, M.	Concerto	ECh
Larsson, L.	Concertino, op. 45/4	CGM
Leclerc, M.	Concerto	Mau
Levy, F.	Concerto (bsn, str)	Cor
Lier, B. van	Concerto. 1950	SD
Lizio, F.-Ballola	Concerto, C	ESZ
Louel, J.	Burlesque, 1943	CBD
Lucas, L.	Oriental	Che
Luke, R.	Concerto	OxU
Lutyens, E.	Concerto, op. 8/3	Ric
Maconchy, E.	Concertino (bsn, str)	AlL
Maessen, A.	Divertimento. 1960	SD
Maingueneau, L.	Suite brève	Dur
Marescotti, A.	Giboulées	Job
Marttinen, T.	Concerto. 1966-68	Fin
Matz, A.	Concerto	BrH
Milde, L.	Concerto No. 2	MR
Mozart, W.	Concerto, Bb, K. 191	BrH
Mozart, W.	Bassoon Concerto, K. 191	EdK
Mozart, W.	Concerto op. 96, No. 1 (Cadenzas by Pierné and Ibert)	ALe
Mozart, W.-Seiffert	Concerto, Bb, K. 23a, No. 2	Pet
Mozart, W.	Bassoon Concerto No. 2	Spr
Mozart, W.-Moritz	Cadenzas for Mozart Bassoon Concertos	Spr
Müthel, J.-Wollheim	Concerto, C	B&B
Nordgren, E.	Concerto op. 66. 1966	STI
Nussio, O.	Variazioni su un'Arietta di Pergolesi (bsn, str)	UE
Ottoson, D.	Concerto	STI
Pauer, J.	Concerto	Art
Paulson, G.	Concerto op. 104. 1959	STI

Bassoon and Orchestra

Paulson, G.	Concerto op. 130. 1965	STI
Petric, I.	Concertant suite	EdD
Pfeiffer, F.-Hennige	Concerto, Bb	Leu
Phillips, B.	Concert Piece (bsn, str)	CF
Pleyel, I.	Concerto, Bb	MR
Ponse, L.	Concerto da camera, op. 34. 1962	SD
Ramovš, P.	Concerto piccolo	EdD
Rivier, J.	Concerto	EdS
Rosetti, F.	Concerto	RS
Schenker, F.	Concerto (bsn, str)	Deu
Schibler, A.	Concerto op. 85	Pet
Schwartz, E.	Concerto	Gen
Sehlbach, E.	Kammerkonzert, op. 97/4 (bsn, str)	MV
Senaillé, J.	Largo and Allegro spiritoso	WH
Siennicki, E.	Ballade	E-V
Sikorski, K.	Polyphonic Concerto. 1965	AP
Škerjanc, L.	Concerto	EdD
Spohr, L.-Hofmann	Adagio, op. 110 (bsn, str)	Pet
Stamitz, K.-Wojciechowski	Concerto, F	HSM
Stamitz, K.	Concerto, F	SS
Steinke, G.	Music	See
Stout, A.	Serenity, op. 11a	Pet
Takács, J.	Meditation, op. 66a	LDo
Tomasi, H.	Concerto	ALe
Tomasi, H.	Danse guerrière (5 danses profanes et sacrées)	ALe
Vačkář, D.	Concerto da camera (bsn, str)	Art
Villa-Lobos, H.	Ciranda das Sete Notas (bsn, str)	SMP
Viola, A.-Kastner	Concerto, F	Hei
Viola, A.-Schoenbach	Concerto	TP
Vivaldi, A.-Hara	Concerto, a, F. VII/7	EMB
Vivaldi, A.-Hara	Concerto, a, P. 72 (bsn, str)	Eul
Vivaldi, A.-Ephrikian	Concerto, a, F. VIII, No. 2	Ric
Vivaldi, A.-Ephrikian	Concerto, a, F. VIII, No. 7	Ric
Vivaldi, A.	Concerto, Bb, P. 401, "La Notte"	MR
Vivaldi, A.-Vene	Concerto, Bb, F. VIII No. 1, "La Notte"	Ric
Vivaldi, A.	Concerto, C (bsn, str)	B-M
Vivaldi, A.	Concerto, d	Int
Vivaldi, A.-Schroeder	Concerto, Bb, op. 45/8, "La Notte"	Eul
Vivaldi, A.	Concerto "La Notte"	Int
Vivaldi, A.	Concerto, C, F. VIII, No. 4	Ric
Vivaldi, A.-Kolneder	Concerto, F, P. 318	Pet
Vivaldi, A.-Smith	Concerto, F, F. VIII, No. 20	Ric
Vivaldi, A.-Smith, Kardt	Concerto, g, F. VIII, No. 11	Ric

Vivaldi, A.-Smith	Concerto, g, F. VIII, No. 23	Ric
Vivaldi, A.	Sonata, a	Int
Vivaldi, A.	Sonata, e	Int
Vogel, J.-Wojciechowski	Concerto, C	HSM
Vuataz, R.	Promenade et poursuite	ALe
Wagner, J.	Introduction and Scherzo	
	(bsn, str)	SM
Waldenmaier, A.	Concerto op. 14	LDo
Wanhal, J.	Concerto	CHF
Wanhal, J.-Schwamberger	Concerto, C	RS
Weber, C.M. von	Konzert op. 75	BrH
Weber, C.M. von	Concerto op. 75	CF
Weber, C.M. von	Bassoon Concerto op. 75	EdK
Weiner, S.	Concerto	MCA
Weinzweig, J.	Divertimento No. 3 (bsn, str)	MCA
Zbinden, J.	Ballade, op. 33	BrH

Bassoon and Band

Briegel, G.	Basso Profundo	GFB
Godfrey, F.	Lucy Long	B&H
Hartzell, D.	Egotistical Elephant	Sha
Maltby, R.	Moon Over the Mesa	Ken
Mozart, W.-Intravaia	Concerto K. 191	CF
Phillips, B.	Concert Piece	CF
Walters, H.	Jabberwocky	Rub
Wiggins, A.	Song and Dance Man	Ken

Contrabassoon and Piano

Migot, G.	Prélude	ALe

Methods and Studies

-Seith	Orchestral Studies from Operas and Concertos	BrH
-Heckel	Heckel System Fingering Chart	CF
	Trill Table for German Bassoon	CF
	Rubank Instrumental Chart (22 Key)	Rub
Allard, M.	Tablature, Trills, Diatonic and Chromatic Scales	Bil
Angerhofer, G.-ed.	Russian Orchestral Studies	FrH
Anzalone, V.	Breeze-Easy Method, 2 vols.	War
Bach, J.S.-Siebach	Bach Studies	FrH
Bach, J.S.-Siebach	Studies from the Cantatas,	

	2 vols.	FrH
Beauregard, J.	30 Etudes élémentaires	EMT
Beethoven, L. van -Junge	Orchestral Studies	FrH
Berninger, H.	Scale Exercises and Daily Studies	FrH
Bertoni, U.	12 Studies	Bon
Bertoni, U. -Sharrow	12 Studies	Int
Bitsch, M.	20 Studies	ALe
Blume, O. -arr.	36 Studies, 3 vols.	CF
Bona, P.	Rhythmical Articulation Studies	CF
Bourdeau, E.	Complete Method	ALe
Bourdeau, E.	Recueil de gammes et arpèges	ALe
Bourdeau, E. -Dhérin	30 Studies	ALe
Boutry, R.	12 Atonal Studies	ALe
Bozza, E.	11 Studies in Karnatic modes	ALe
Bozza, E.	12 Caprices	ALe
Bozza, E.	15 Daily Studies, op. 64	ALe
Bruns, V.	Fagottstudien für Fort- geschrittene, op. 32	FrH
Davies, J.	Scales and Arpeggios	B&H
Dhérin, G. -Pierné	Nouvelle technique de basson, 2 vols.	HLe
Dhérin, G. -ed.	Difficult Passages, 3 vols.	ALe
Dubois, P. -Allard	12 Studies	ALe
Eisenhauer, W.	Learn to Play Bassoon, 2 vols.	Alf
Ferling, J. -Thornton	48 Famous Studies	SM
Fields, D.	Bassoon Method	Col
Flamant, E.	Technical Exercises, op. 50, 7 vols.	ALe
Froseth, J.	The Individualized Instructor, 2 vols.	GIA
Gambaro, J. -Dhérin	18 Etudes	HLe
Gambaro, J. -Kovar	18 Studies	Int
Gatti, N.	22 Grand Exercises	Ric
Gaviniès, P. -Del Negro	18 Studies	HeE
Gekeler, K. -Hovey	Belwin Bassoon Method, 3 vols.	B-M
Giampieri, A.	Progressive Method	Ric
Giampieri, A.	16 Daily Studies for Perfection	Ric
Gumbert-Wiegand	Orchestral Studies, 3 vols.	FrH
Handel, G. -Siebach	Studies from the Operas, 2 vols.	FrH
Handel, G. -Siebach	Studies for bass instruments	FrH
Hara, L.	Bassoon Tutor, 2 vols.	EMB
Haultier, J.	Le Débutant bassoniste	ALe
Hause, W.	30 Etüden	FrH
Hendrickson, C.	Handy Manual of Fingering Charts	CF
Herfurth & Stuart	Sounds of the Winds, 2 vols.	CF

Herfurth, P.	A Tune A Day	BM
Hofmann, F.	Melodische Übungs- und Vortragsstücke, op. 36	FrH
Jacobi, C.	6 Caprices	CF
Jacobi, C.-Rudas	6 Bassoon Exercises	EMB
Jacobi, C.-Schaefer	6 Etüden, op. 15	For
Jacobi, C.-Garfield	6 Caprices	Int
Jancourt, E.	Chromatic Scale for French Bassoon	CF
Jancourt, E.	Method, Pt. II	Bil
Jancourt, E.-Kovar	26 Melodic Studies, op. 15	Int
Junge, G.-ed.	Orchestral Studies, 3 vols.	FrH
Kopprasch, C.	60 Studies, 2 vols.	CF
Kopprasch, C.-Seyffarth	60 Ausgewählte Etüden, 2 vols.	FrH
Kopprasch, C.-Kovar	60 Studies, 2 vols.	Int
Kovar, S.	24 Daily Exercises	Kov
Krakamp, E.-Muccetti	Method	Ric
Kreutzer, R.-Del Negro	20 Studies	HeE
Langey & Fischer	Tutor	CF
Leichtling, A.	Serenade-Etude, op. 37	See
Lentz, D.	Method, Vol. I	B-M
Louchez, J.	20 Etudes after Samie	ALe
Lowman, K.	10 Etudes	Wes
Martelli, H.	15 Etudes	HLe
McDowell, P.-Hovey	Daily Exercises	B-M
McDowell, P.-Hovey	Practical Studies for Bassoon, 2 vols.	B-M
Mederacke, K.	Orchestral Studies, 6 vols.	FrH
Milde, L.-Allard	25 Studies on Scales and Arpeggios (75 Studies, op. 24)	Bil
Milde, L.	25 Studies, op. 24	CF
Milde, L.	Studien über Tonleiter- und Akkordzerlegungen, op. 24	FrH
Milde, L.	25 Studies, op. 24	Int
Milde, L.	25 Etudes, op. 24	MKE
Milde, L.	Concert Studies, op. 26, 2 vols.	CF
Milde, L.	50 Konzertstudien, op. 26, 2 vols.	FrH
Milde, L.-Kovar	30 Concert Studies, op. 26, 2 vols.	Int
Milde, L.	25 Concert Etudes, op. 26	MKE
Moortel, L. van de	7 Etudes	Mau
Mueller, F. & L. Smith	A Method for Bassoon	Uni
Neukirchner, V.-Rudas	23 Bassoon Exercises	EMB
Orefici, A.-Weisberg	Bravoura Studies	Int
Orefici, A.	Bravura Studies	Ric
Orefici, A.-Sharrow	Melodic Studies	Int

Orefici, A.	Studi Melodici	ALe
Organn, R.	Overtone Series Method	Reb
Oromszegi, O.	10 Modern Etudes	EMB
Oubradous, F.	Complete Instructor, 3 vols.	ALe
Oubradous, F.	Fingering Chart	ALe
Oubradous, F.	Prelude-Studies after Cokken	ALe
Ozi, E.-Torriani	Popular Method	Ric
Ozi, E.	30 Exercises	EdH
Ozi, E.	42 Caprices	EdH
Ozi, E.	42 Caprices	FrH
Paine, H.	Bassoon Soloist (Level 1)	B-M
Paine, H. & Weber, F.	Bassoon Student (Level 1)	B-M
Paine, H.	Bassoon Student (Level 2)	B-M
Paine, H. & Ployhar, J.	Bassoon Student (Level 3)	B-M
Paine, H.	Studies and Melodious Etudes (Level 1)	B-M
Paine, H.	Studies and Melodious Etudes (Level 2)	B-M
Paine, H. & Ployhar, J.	Studies and Melodious Etudes (Level 3)	B-M
Paine, H.	Tunes for bassoon technic (Level 1)	B-M
Paine, H.	Tunes for bassoon technic (Level 2)	B-M
Paine, H. & Ployhar, J.	Tunes for bassoon technic (Level 3)	B-M
Pannier, O.	Melodische Studien	PG
Pannier, O.	Spezialstudien	PG
Parès, G.	Daily Exercises and Scales	CF
Parès, G.-Whistler	Modern Parès Foundation Studies	Rub
Penazzi, S. & B. Bartolozzi	Metodo	ESZ
Petrov, I.-Dhérin	Scale Studies	Int
Pezzi, V.	Orchestra Studies from the Works of Tschaikovsky	E-V
Piard, M.	Enseignement du contre-basson (cbsn)	ALe
Piard, M.	16 Characteristic Studies	Int
Piard, M.	90 Études, 3 vols.	Bil
Pivoňka, K.	Characteristic Studies	ALe
Pivoňka, K.	Rhythmische Etüden	Art
Pivoňka, K.	Schule	ES
Pivoňka, K.	Stupnice a rozlozene akordy	Art
Porret, J.	24 Déchiffrages manuscrits	EdR
Porret, J.	25 Déchiffrages manuscrits	EdR
Prescott, G.	Outlines of Technic	CF
Rieunier, F.	22 Déchiffrages rythmiques instrumentaux	ALe
Rode, P.-Sharrow	15 Caprices	Int
Romero	Método	UME

Ruggiero, G.	8 Etudes atonales	ALe
Rusch, H. & A. Barto	Breath Control and Tuning and Intonation Studies	CF
Satzenhofer, J.-Kovar	24 Studies	Int
Saveliev, P.-comp.	Orchestral Difficulties from Ballets by Soviet Composers	MKE
Schoenbach, S.	20th Century Orchestra Studies	Sch
Seith, H.	Orchesterstudien (cbsn)	BrH
Siennicki, E.	Technical Growth for the Bassoonist	S-B
Siqueira, J.	Etüden (bsn & pf)	Deu
Skornicka, J.	Elementary Method	Rub
Slama, A.	66 Etüden	ECM
Slama, A.	66 Etudes	FrH
Slama, A.	66 Studies	Int
Stadio, C.	Orchestra Studies	Ric
Strauss, R.-Böhm	Sinfonische Werke	FrH
Strauss, R.	Orchestral Studies	Int
Strauss, R.-Boehm	Orchestra Studies	Pet
Taylor	20 Melodic Studies	CF
Uhl, A.	15 Etudes	SS
Vauiet, A.-Voxman	20 Studies	Rub
Vobaron, E.	4 Lessons and 17 Studies, op. 1	CF
Vobaron, E.	32 Celebrated Melodies for Trombone	CF
Vobaron, E.	34 Etudes	CF
Voxman, H.	Intermediate Method	Rub
Voxman, H. & W. Gower	Advanced Method	Rub
Wagner, R.-Mages	Orchestral Studies, 3 vols.	FrH
Wagner, R.	Orchestral Studies	Int
Weissenborn, J.-Ambrosio	Method for Bassoon	CF
Weissenborn, J.-Bettoney	Method for Bassoon	CF
Weissenborn, J.-Schaefer	Practical School for Bassoon	For
Weissenborn, J.-Schaefer	Fagottschule	FrH
Weissenborn, J.	Studies, op. 8, 2 vols.	CF
Weissenborn, J.	Studies, op. 8, 2 vols.	Int
Weissenborn, J.-Terekhin	50 Etudes, 2 vols.	MKE
Weissenborn, J.	Bassoon Studies, op. 8, 2 vols.	Pet
Wunderlich, F.	Arpeggios (Chords)	CF
Zakharov, F.-comp.	Orchestral Difficulties from Symphonic Works of Russian Composers, 2 vols.	MKE

Saxophone

Unaccompanied Solos

	Album Salabert, 2 vols.	EdS
	Favorites through the Years	SF
	Recueil de Six Morceaux	EdS
Adler, S.	Canto IV	Dor
Anderson, L.	Music of LeRoy Anderson	B-M
Arma, P.	Soliloque	Bil
Ayscue, B.	3 Pièces	ArM
Bach, J.S.-Kasprzyk	Suite, C, No. 1 (bar sax)	SM
Bach, J.S.-Londeix	Suite No. 3	HLe
Bach, J.S.-Kasprzyk	Suite, A, No. 3 (bar sax)	SM
Bach, J.S.-Kasprzyk	Suite No. 4 (bar sax)	SM
Bellisario, A.	Improvviso	EBe
Blank, A.	3 Novelties	Dor
Bonneau, P.	Caprice en forme de valse	ALe
Bozza, E.	Improvisation and Caprice	ALe
Bozza, E.	Pièce brève	ALe
Buel, C.	Reflections on Raga Todi	Dor
Caravan, R.	Sketch	See
Childs, B.	Sonatina	TP
Cohn, J.	Baroque Suite	EdM
Couf, H.	Introduction, Dance, and Furioso	B-M
Cunningham, M.	Rara Avis, op. 19	EQM
Damais, E.	5 Divertissements	Bil
Daneels, F.	Suite	ScF
Debussy, C.-Londeix	Syrinx	Job
Dubois, P.	Sonata d'étude	ALe
Dubois, P.	Suite Française	ALe
Eisma, W.	Non-lecture II	SD
Franco, J.	Sonata	CoF
Hartley, W.	Petite Suite	Cre
Heussenstamm, G.	Saxoclone	See
Hudadoff, I.-arr.	50 Standard Solo Series	PrA
Joachim, O.	Expansion	Ber
Kanitz, E.	Little Concerto	ArM
Karkoff, M.	Nio solominatyrer, op. 8b. 1953	STI
Klein, L.	6 Exchanges	Ten
Kupferman, M.	7 Inversions	Gen
Kynaston	Dance Suite	Wes
Lazarus, D.	Sonate	Dur
Lemeland, A.-Pierlot	Scansions	Bil
Massias, G.	Suite monodique	Bil
Noda, R.	Improvisation I	ALe
Ott, J.	Quartet for Solo Saxophone	Dor
Pero, H.	Bunte Träume	RuE
Persichetti, V.	Parable XI	E-V

Rancati, A.	Idealsax	GZ
Rueff, J.	Sonata	ALe
Schmidt, W.	Music	Wes
Schwartz, E.	Music for Soloist and Audience	CoA
Sclater, J.	Suite	TP
Silverman, F.	3 Movements (sop sax)	See
Smith, S.	Mute	See
Smolanoff, M.	Parables	See
Snyder, R.	Variations	ArM
Stein, L.	Phantasy	Dor
Stockhausen, K.	Spiral	UE
Tautenhahn, G.	Dorn Dance for Tenor Sax	Wes
Tomasi, H.	Evocations	ALe
Wagner, J.	Monologue	Dor

Soprano Saxophone

Soprano Saxophone and Piano

Ackermans, H.	Paysage Nordique	EMb
Baeyens, H.	Canzonetta	EMb
Dindale, E.	Bucolique	EMb
Dindale, E.	Canzonetta	EMb
Dindale, E.	Danse Paysanne	EMb
Dyck, V.-Mule	2nd Légende hébraïque	Bil
Fuerstner, C.	Conjurations, op. 45	EQM
Goeyens, A.	Mélodie Anglaise	EMb
Haydn, F.-Strauwen	La 7e parole du Christ	ScF
Leclercq, E.	Intimité	EMb
Leclercq, E.	Moment heureux	EMb
Moortel, L. van de	Capriccio	Mau
Myers, R.	Movements	ArM
Painparé, H.	Fantaisies de salon sur des opéras célèbres	ScF
Platti, G.-Rousseau	Sonata, G	EQM
Rougnon, P.	Valse Lente	GrF
Schumann, R.-Nihill	3 Romances (published separately)	Dor
Strauwen, J.	Conte pastoral	ScF
Villa-Lobos, H.	Fantasia, op. 630. 1948	SMP
Zuckert, L.	Indian Lullaby. 1970	Can

Soprano Saxophone and Orchestra

Borris, S.	Concerto op. 120	S-V
Glaser, W.	Canto. 1970 (sop sax, str)	STI
Lukáš, Z.	Concerto. 1963	CHF
Myers, R.	Movements	ArM
Villa-Lobos, H.	Fantasia, op. 630. 1948	SMP

Soprano Saxophone and Band

Andrieu, F.	Impressions Napolitaines	EdR
Escudié, L.	Fantaisie No. 4	EdR
Moussart	Oboe-Mazurka	EdR

Alto Saxophone

Alto Saxophone and Piano

	Broadway Showcase	War
	Deluxe Songs Solo Album	Wat
	Easy to Play Pieces	Ash
	Easy Saxophone Solos	MS
	More Easy Saxophone Solos	MS
	Elementary Alto Saxophone Solos	MS
	40 Hits of Our Times	MCA
	40 More Hits of Our Times	MCA
	53 Masterpieces	B-M
	Great Themes Made Easy	War
	Indispensable Folio	Rub
	Intermediate Pieces	Ash
	Morceaux de Concours et pièces d'audition	ALe
	Radio Collection of National Songs & Hymns	Rub
	Sacred Solos	Rub
	Saxophone Hour	Rub
	Soloist Folio	Rub
	Black Eyes	GFB
	Caissons Go Rolling Along	NK
	Contemporary French Recital Pieces, 2 vols.	Int
	Deep River	CF
	Deep River	GFB
	In Old Vienna	McK
	Londonderry Air	GFB
	Londonderry Air	MM
	Sometimes I Feel	MM
	Song of the Volga Boatmen	GFB
	Turkey in the Straw	McK
Abato & Caiazza	Crazy Mixed-Up Mice	CCo
Absil, J.	Fantaisie-Caprice	HLe
Absil, J.	5 Easy Pieces, op. 138	HLe
Absil, J.	Sonata op. 115	HLe
Achron, J.-Gurewich	Impressions, op. 32/1	UE
Ackermans, H.	Doux poème	ALe

Ackermans, H.	Mélodie Valse	ALe
Ackermans, H.	Paysage Nordique	EMb
Ackermans, H.	Petite fantaisie Italienne	ALe
Adam, A.	O Holy Night	Rub
Adams, S.-Glenn	Holy City	B&H
Adams, S.-DeLamater	The Holy City	Rub
Akimenko, T.	Eclogue	SM
Albéniz, I.	Chant d'amour	ALe
Albéniz, I.-Amaz	Mallorca. Barcarola	UME
Albéniz, I.-Amaz	Puerta de tierra	UME
Albéniz, I.	Tango, op. 165/2	CF
Albéniz, I.	Tango, op. 165/2	SS
Albinoni, T.	Adagio	Com
Aldrich, F.	Love and Flowers	Cen
Aletter, W.	Rendezvous	Bos
Allgen, C.	Preludium och Carmen	
	perlotense	STI
Ameller, A.	Baie Comeau	ALe
Ameller, A.	Concertino op. 125	Com
Ameller, A.	Jeux de table	HLe
Ameller, A.	Lirico	Com
Ameller, A.	Pointe-au-pic	ALe
Ameller, A.	La Sauge	HLe
Ameller, A.	Suite after Jean Philippe	
	Rameau	EMT
Amiot, J.	Sérénade	EdR
Anderson, G.	Sonata	SM
Anderson, L.	Belle of the ball	B-M
Antonini, F.	Divertissement tzigane	Bil
Arban, J.	Oberto. Air Varie	MM
Archer, V.	Sonata	Ber
Arditi, L.	Il Bacio (The Kiss)	Cen
Ariosti, A.-Mule	Gigue	ALe
Arndt, F.	Nola	SF
Auber, D.-Hekker	Angela Aria	T-M
Aubert, J.	Gigue	EdM
Auclert, P.	Comme un vieux nöel	Bil
Avignon, J.	Spirituel et danse exotique	Bil
Avon, E.-Klump	Danse Joyeuse	CF
Bach, C.-Gallo	Spring's Awakening	CF
Bach, J.C.-Trillat	Allegro Siciliano	GD
Bach, J.C.-Marteau	Andante Cantabile	Lud
Bach, J.S.-Mule	Adagio	ALe
Bach, J.S.-Mule	Adagio (Organ Pieces)	ALe
Bach, J.S.-Mule	Adagio and Andante	ALe
Bach, J.S.-Mule	Air (Suite, D)	ALe
Bach, J.S.-Mule	Allegro	ALe
Bach, J.S.-Mule	Andante	ALe
Bach, J.S.-Mule	Andante and Allegro	ALe
Bach, J.S.-Mule	Aria (Suite, D)	ALe

Alto Saxophone and Piano

Bach, J.S.-Kent	Arioso (Cantata No. 156)	CF
Bach, J.S.-Gounod	Ave Maria	Cen
Bach, J.S.-Mule	Badinérie (Suite, b)	ALe
Bach, J.S.-Mule	Bourrée (Suite, C)	ALe
Bach, J.S.-Mule	Fughetta	ALe
Bach, J.S.-Mule	Gavotte & Musette (Suite No. 6)	ALe
Bach, J.S.-Mule	Gavottes	ALe
Bach, J.S.-Sibbing	Largo and Allegro (Violin Sonata, f)	Dor
Bach, J.S.-Mule	Louré (Suite, C)	ALe
Bach, J.S.-Chauvet	Louré	Com
Bach, J.S.-Rascher	Minuet	B-M
Bach, J.S.-Londeix	Scherzetto	ALe
Bach, J.S.-Mule	Sicilienne	ALe
Bach, J.S.-Gateau	Sonate No. 2	Bil
Bach, J.S.-Mule	Sonata No. 4 (flute)	ALe
Bach, J.S.-Mule	Sonata No. 6 (flute)	ALe
Bach, J.S.-Rascher	2 Preludes	Cha
Bach, J.S.-Mule	Vivace	ALe
Bachmann, G.-Lefèbre	Danse Bretonne	CF
Badings, H.	Cavatina. 1952	SD
Badings, H.	Concerto	SD
Badings, H.	La Malinconia. 1949	SD
Bäck, S.	Elegy	WH
Baeyens, H.	Adagio et Animato	EMb
Baeyens, H.	Canzonetta	EMb
Balay, G.	Pièce de Concours	ALe
Balfe, W.	Bohemian Girl Airs	Vol
Barat, J.-Voxman	Elegie	Rub
Barat, J.	Fantaisie	ALe
Barat, J.	Nostalgie	ALe
Barbier, R.	Pièce concertante, op. 95. 1959	CBD
Bariller, R.	Fan'jazz	ALe
Bariller, R.	Rapsodie Bretonne	ALe
Barnard, D.	Plains of Peace	Bos
Barnard, G.	Punch & Judy	Bar
Barnes	Arioso and Caprice	Big
Barnes	Valse Impromptu	Big
Barnes, C.	Young Artist	B&H
Barnes, C.	Young Genius	B&H
Barnes, C.	Young Maestro	B&H
Barnes, C.	Young Virtuoso	B&H
Barnhouse, C.	God Be With You	Bar
Barnhouse, C.	Let the Lower Lights Be Burning	Bar
Barnhouse, C.-arr.	Meditation Religioso (Last Hope)	Bar
Barnhouse, C.	Refuge	Bar
Barnhouse, C.	Silver Lining	Bar

305

Barnhouse, C.	Sweet By and By	Bar
Barraine, E.	Improvisation	Bil
Bartlett, J.-Hummel	A Dream	Rub
Bartók, B.-Harris	Evening in the Country	Lud
Bassett, L.	Music	Pet
Bataille, P.	Badine-badine	Bil
Bauman, P.-Rascher	Concert in the Forest	B-M
Bean	Bubble Dance	CF
Beaucamp, A.	Chant Elégiaque	ALe
Beaucamp, A.	Tarantella	ALe
Beaumont, P.	Con Amore	Cen
Beck, C.	Nocturne	HLe
Becker, J.	Romance	CF
Beeckman, N.	Concertino militaire	Bil
Beeckman, N.	Elégie, op. 14/1	Bil
Beeckman, N.	Meditation No. 1	T-M
Beeckman, N.	Meditation No. 2	T-M
Beeckman, N.	Rhapsodie flamande, op. 28	ScF
Beeckman, N.	2nd Morceau de concert	Bil
Beeler, W.-arr.	Christmas Favorites	Sch
Beethoven, L. van-Bettoney	Adagio (Sonata Pathetique)	CF
Beethoven, L. van-Buchtel	Adagio (Sonata Pathetique)	NK
Beethoven, L. van	Adelaide, op. 46	CF
Beethoven, L. van-Mule	Little Waltz	ALe
Beethoven, L. van	Minuet, G	Cen
Beethoven, L. van	Minuet, G	McK
Beethoven, L. van-Trinkaus	Minuet	CF
Beethoven, L. van	Minuetto	MM
Beethoven, L. van	Moonlight Sonata (Adagio)	Cen
Beethoven, L. van-Lefèvre	Romance	CF
Beethoven, L. van-Anzalone	Romance	Ken
Beethoven, L. van	Rondo, op. 17	EdM
Bellisario, A.	Improvviso	EBe
Ben-Haim, P.	3 Songs without Words	Isr
Bennett, D.	Moderne	CF
Bennett, D.	Saxophone Royale	SM
Benson, W.	Aeolian Song	MCA
Benson, W.	Cantilena	B&H
Benson, W.	Concertino	MCA
Benson, W.	Farewell	MCA
Bergson, M.	Scene and Air (Luisa di Montfort)	CF
Bergson, M.	Scéne et Air	MM
Berlioz, G.	Air à danser	Bil
Berlioz, H.	3 Songs (Damnation of Faust)	EdM
Bernard, G.	Punch & Judy	Bar
Bernier, R.	Homage to Sax	ALe
Berthelot, R.	Adage & Arabesque	ALe
Berthomieu, M.	Suite brève	HLe
Bettoney, H.-arr.	Dark Eyes	CF

Bettoney, H.-arr.	Song of the Volga Boatmen	CF
Beydts, L.	Romanesque	ALe
Bialosky, M.	Fantasy Scherzo	Wes
Bigot, E.	Prélude et Danse	ALe
Billault	Grand solo de concert	EdR
Bilotti, A.	Sonata	TP
Binge, R.	Concerto	IA
Bitsch, M.	Villageoise	ALe
Bizet, G.	Agnus Dei (L'Arlésienne)	EdM
Bizet, G.	Agnus Dei	HeE
Bizet, G.-Chardon	L'Arlésienne	ECh
Bizet, G.-Gee	Intermezzo	CF
Bizet, G.-O'Neill	Intermezzo (L'Arlésienne No. 2)	Wat
Bizet, G.	Menuet de L'Arlésienne	MM
Bizet, G.	Minuet (L'Arlésienne)	NK
Bizet, G.-Chardon	Soli de L'Arlésienne	ECh
Bizet, G.-Hummel	Solo de L'Arlésienne	Rub
Blaauw, L.	Ballade	T-M
Blaauw, L.	Nocturne en Humoresque	T-M
Blaauw, L.	2 Karakterstukken	T-M
Blaauw, L.	2 Romances	T-M
Blake-Haring	Memories of You	ShB
Blanc, J.	Aubade et impromptu	Bil
Blémant, L.	Sous les sapins	ALe
Blin, L.	Gentiment	Com
Bliss-Barnhouse	Let the Lower Lights Be Burning	Bar
Bloch, A.	Les Maisons de l'Eternité	GrF
Boccherini, L.-Mule	Adagio	ALe
Boccherini, L.	Menuet	CF
Bond, C.	Perfect Day	BM
Bonneau, P.	Concerto	ALe
Bonneau, P.	Pièce concertante dans l'esprit "Jazz"	ALe
Bonneau, P.	Suite	ALe
Borodin, A.-Buchtel	Polovetsian Dances	NK
Borodin, A.-Walters	Polovtsian Dance (Prince Igor)	Rub
Bottje, W.	Concertino	Col
Boucard, M.	Sonatine No. 1	EdR
Bouillon, P.	Papillon	MM
Bournonville, A.-Gee	Danse pour Katia	SM
Bourrel, Y.	Sonate	Bil
Boutry, R.	Divertimento	ALe
Boutry, R.	Sérénade	EdS
Bowman-Haring	12th Street Rag	ShB
Bozza, E.	Aria	ALe
Bozza, E.	Le Campanile	ALe
Bozza, E.	Chanson à bercer	ALe
Bozza, E.	Concertino	ALe

Alto Saxophone and Piano

Bozza, E.	Diptyque	ALe
Bozza, E.-Hite	Divertissement	SM
Bozza, E.-Mule	Fantaisie Italienne	ALe
Bozza, E.	Gavotte des damoiselles	ALe
Bozza, E.	Impromptu and Dance	ALe
Bozza, E.	Menuet des pages	ALe
Bozza, E.	Nocturne Danse	ALe
Bozza, E.	Parade des petits soldats	ALe
Bozza, E.	Petite Gavotte	ALe
Bozza, E.	Prélude et divertissement	ALe
Bozza, E.	Pulcinella, op. 53/1	ALe
Bozza, E.	Rêves d'enfants	ALe
Bozza, E.	Scaramouche, op. 53/2	ALe
Bozza, E.	Tarantelle	ALe
Braga, G.	Angel's Serenade	Cen
Braga, G.-Clarke	The Angel's Serenade	CF
Braga, G.-Vereecken	The Angel's Serenade	CF
Braga, G.	Serenata	Dur
Brahe, M.-Glenn	Bless This House	B&H
Brahe, M.-Glenn	I Passed By Your Window	B&H
Brahms, J.	Chant Populair	MM
Brahms, J.	Hungarian Dance No. 5	CF
Brahms, J.-Davis	Hungarian Dance No. 5	Rub
Brahms, J.	Lullaby	CF
Brahms, J.-Andreoni	Lullaby, op. 49/4	Ric
Brahms, J.-Baudrier	Popular Song	MM
Brahms, J.-Andreoni	Valzer, op. 39/15	Ric
Brandon, S.	Introduction and Dance. 1969	Man
Braun, R.	Spirituals	YM
Bréard, R.	1st Suite	ALe
Bréard, R.	Prélude cadence	ALe
Brenta, G.	Saxiana	ALe
Briegel, G.	Cathedral Echoes	GFB
Briegel, G.	Soloette	GFB
Briegel-Tucker	Triplets	GFB
Briegel, G.-arr.	2 Stephen Foster Melodies	GFB
Brindel, B.	Autumnal Meditation	MCA
Brindel, B.	Suite	TP
Brown, C.	Arlequinade	ALe
Brown, C.	Au fil du vent	Com
Brown, C.	En promenade	HLe
Brown, N.	Sonata	CoA
Bruniau, A.	Fantaisie tyrolienne	Bil
Bruniau, A.	Fantaisie variée	Bil
Bruniau, A.	Grande introduction et polonaise	Bil
Bruniau, A.	Sur la montagne	Bil
Buchtel, F.	At the Ball	NK
Buchtel, F.	Beau Brummel	NK
Buchtel, F.	Chant d'amour	Vol
Buchtel, F.-arr.	Cielito Lindo	NK

Buchtel, F.	Cynthia	NK
Buchtel, F.	Fandango	NK
Buchtel, F.	First Book of Solos	Col
Buchtel, F.	The Flatterer	B-M
Buchtel, F.	Golden glow waltz	B-M
Buchtel, F.	Harlequin	NK
Buchtel, F.	High stepper's march	B-M
Buchtel, F.	Intermezzo	NK
Buchtel, F.	Jovial Mood	NK
Buchtel, F.	Jupiter	NK
Buchtel, F.-arr.	Marines Hymn	NK
Buchtel, F.	Minstrel Boy	NK
Buchtel, F.	My Buddy Waltz	NK
Buchtel, F.	Pied Piper	NK
Buchtel, F.	Serenade	NK
Buchtel, F.	Spanish Gypsy	NK
Buchtel, F.	Tango	NK
Buchtel, F.	Valse Romantique	Vol
Bullard, R.	Judy	Ken
Bumcke, G.	Concert Waltz, op. 48	Sim
Burgstahler, E.	The Caballero	PrA
Burgstahler, E.	Saucy Sax	PrA
Burgstahler, E.	Sax Ripple	PrA
Busser, H.-Mule	Aragon	ALe
Busser, H.-Mule	Asturia	ALe
Busser, H.	Au pays de Léon et de Salamanque, op. 116	ALe
Busser, H.-Paquot	12 Melodic Studies	ALe
Butterfield, J.	When You and I Were Young	Cen
Calmel, R.	Nocturne	Com
Calmel, R.	Suite	Mau
Camilleri, C.	Suite	Wat
Campra, A.-Mule	Gavotte (Achille et Déidamie)	ALe
Campra, A.-Mule	Sérénade et Bourrée (Les Fêtes Vénitiennes)	ALe
Canivez, L.	Fantaisie de Concert, op. 127	T-M
Cappelo, J.	Alla Kreisler, Valse	EMb
Capua, E. di	O Sole Mio	CF
Carion, F.	Elégie	EMb
Carissimi, G.-Barnes	Heart Victorious	Spr
Carle, R.-Wheeler	Idylwild	Vol
Carles, M.	Cantilène	ALe
Carlid, G.	Triad. 1950	STI
Carter, B.	Summer Night	KPM
Carter, T.-Bettoney	Onward Christian Soldiers	CF
Caruso, E.	Flora Belle	GFB
Casadesus, F.	Romance provençale et danse	HLe
Castérède, J.	Scherzo	ALe
Cecconi, M.	Ariette	Com
Chailleux, A.	Andante et allegro	ALe

Alto Saxophone and Piano

Chailleux, A.-Voxman	Andante and Allegro	Rub
Challan, R.	Concerto	ALe
Chaminade, C.	Pastorale Enfantine, op. 12	CF
Chapelle	Une Sérénade	CF
Charpentier, J.	Gavambodi 2	ALe
Chèdeville, N.	Scherzo	EdM
Chenette, E.	Sax King	CF
Chenette, E.	The Sax Prince	CF
Chenette, E.	The Sax Princess	CF
Chenette, E.-Alford	Sax Simplicity	CF
Chenette, E.	Sax Sweetness	CF
Chenette, E.	Valse Joliet	CF
Cho, G.	Sonata	SM
Chopin, F.-Mule	Etude No. 3	ALe
Chopin, F.-Rousseau	Largo	EQM
Chopin, F.	Minute Waltz, op. 64/1	GFB
Chopin, F.-Delcampe	Nocturne, op. 9/2	EMb
Chopin, F.-Stouffer	Nocturne, op. 55/1	Ken
Chopin, F.-York	Nocturne	BM
Chopin, F.-Mule	2nd Nocturne	ALe
Chopin, F.-Chauvet	Nocturne No. 2	Com
Chopin, F.-Chauvet	Nocturne No. 5	Com
Chopin, F.-Edwards	Polonaise	B-M
Chopin, F.-Mule	Prélude No. 15	ALe
Chopin, F.-Mule	Tristesse, op. 10/3	ALe
Chopin, F.-Chauvet	La Tristezza	Com
Chopin, F.-Martin	Tristesse	EdR
Chopin, F.-Delcampe	Valse de Chopin, op. 64/1	EMb
Chopin, F.-Chauvet	Valse	Com
Chopin, F.-Mule	Waltz No. 6	ALe
Chopin, F.-Mule	Waltz No. 7	ALe
Christol	Le Coeur de ma mie	MM
Christophe	Les Petits Oiseaux	T-M
Cirri, G.	Arioso	EdM
Ciry, M.	Capriccio, op. 52	S&C
Clarke, H.	Apollo Polka	CF
Clarke, H.	Artemis Polka	CF
Clarke, H.	Fontana	CF
Clarke, H.	Hebe Lullaby	CF
Clarke, H.	Trixie Valse	CF
Clarke, H.	Venus Waltz	CF
Classens, H.	1er Concertino	Com
Classens, H.	2e Concertino	Com
Classens, H.	Introduction and Scherzo	Com
Classens, H.	Jerusalem	Com
Classens, H.	Venise	Com
Clement, F.	Evening Zephyr	Bar
Clement, F.	Silvertone Polka	Vol
Clérisse, R.	Bergerette	Bil
Clérisse, R.	Caprice	Com

Clérisse, R.	Chanson à bercer	ALe
Clérisse, R.	A l'ombre du clocher	ALe
Clérisse, R.	Rêverie	ALe
Clérisse, R.	Sérénade téssinoise	Com
Clérisse, R.	Sérénade variée	ALe
Coates, E.	Saxo Rhapsody	Cha
Cofield, F.	Chartreuse	Rub
Coggins, W. & F. Weber	Alto saxophone soloist (Level 1)	B-M
Coggins, W.	Aria	B-M
Cohen, S.	Dreamy River	B-M
Colin, C.-Cailliet	Eighth Solo	SM
Combelle, F.-Voxman	Fantaisie Mauresque	Rub
Combelle, F.	1st Solo de concert	Bil
Combelle, F.	Malbrough (thème et variation)	Bil
Conklin	Handy Andy	CF
Constant, F.	Concerto. 1963	EMe
Constant, F.	Fantasia, op. 41	Bil
Constant, M.	Concert Music. 1954	ALe
Corelli, A.-Mule	Adagio	ALe
Corelli, A.	Air and Dance	EdM
Corelli, A.-Chauvet	Gavotte--courante	Com
Corelli, A.-Coggins	Gigue	B-M
Corelli, A.	Gigue	EdM
Corelli, A.-Chauvet	Prelude--gigue	Com
Corelli, A.-Chauvet	Sarabande--gavotte	Com
Corelli, A.-Chauvet	Sarabande--gigue	Com
Corelli, A.	Sonata, F	EdM
Corelli, A.-Rascher	Variations on a Gavotte	Cha
Coriolis, de	Pavane	ALe
Corniot, R.	Eglogue and Pastoral Dance	ALe
Couleuvrier, A.	Andante religieux No. 2	EdR
Couperin, F.-Mule	Berceuse en rondeau	ALe
Couperin, F.-Mule	Les Jeunes Seigneurs	ALe
Couperin, F.-Mule	Musette of Taverny	ALe
Couperin, F.-Mule	Rondo (Les Moissonneurs)	ALe
Cowan, D.	Impressions	B&H
Cowan, D.	Morceau de Genre	B&H
Cowan, D.	Reflections	B&H
Cowell, H.	Air and Scherzo. 1961	AMP
Cragun, J.	Concerto No. 1	Rub
Crawford-Kent	The Army Air Corps	CF
Creston, P.	Concerto, op. 26	Sch
Creston, P.	Sonata op. 19	Sha
Creston, P.	Suite	Sha
Cui, C.	Cantabile, op. 36/2	CF
Cui, C.	Orientale, op. 50/9	CF
Cui, C.-Mule	En partant	ALe
Cunningham, M.	The Nightingale	CoA

311

Cunningham, M.	Sonata	See
Dahm, P.-arr.	Concert Album	EdM
Dahm, P.-arr.	Paris Soir	EdM
Damase, J.	Concertstück, op. 16	ALe
d'Ambrosio, A.-Hummel	Canzonetta	Rub
Damm, A.-Thornton	Columbus--American Fantasia	CF
Dancla, C.	Rêverie et Polka	MM
Dandelot, G.	Sonatina. 1966	EME
Daneau, N.	Piasaxo	T-M
Danks, H.	Silver Threads Among the Gold	Cen
Danks, H.	Silver Threads Among the Gold	CF
Dautremer, M.	Concerto op. 61	HLe
Dautremer, M.	Emotion	HLe
Dautremer, M.	Rêverie interrompue	ALe
Dautremer, M.	Tango and Tarantella	ALe
Debaar, M.	Prélude et Humoresque	EMb
DeBueris, J.	Miami Moon	CF
DeBueris, J.	Miami Shore	CF
Debussy, C.	Air de Lia	EdM
Debussy, C.-Mule	Clair de Lune	Job
Debussy, C.-Koepke	Clair de Lune	Rub
Debussy, C.-Cazden	Clair de Lune	Spr
Debussy, C.-Branga	En Bateau (Petite Suite)	Dur
Debussy, C.-Viard	La Fille aux cheveux de lin	Dur
Debussy, C.-Branga	Golliwogg's Cake Walk	Dur
Debussy, C.-Branga	Jimbo's Lullaby, Berceuse des Elephants	Dur
Debussy, C.	The Little Negro	ALe
Debussy, C.	Mandoline	EdM
Debussy, C.-Branga	Minstrels	Dur
Debussy, C.-Viard	La Plus que lente	Dur
Debussy, C.	Rapsodie	Dur
Debussy, C.-Mule	Rêverie	Dor
Debussy, C.-Mule	Rêverie	Job
Decruck, F.	Sonate, c#	Bil
Decruck, M.	3rd Chant lyrique	ALe
Decruck, M.	5th Chant lyrique	ALe
Dedrick, A.	A Tune for Christopher	Ken
DeLamater, E.-arr.	Adeste Fidelis	Rub
DeLamater, E.	Christmas Festival	Rub
Delannoy, J.	Grande fantaisie sur la dernière pensée de Weber	ScF
Delannoy, J.	Maitre Corbeau	ScF
Delaunay, R.	Au fil de l'eau	Bil
Delden, L. van	Sonatina op. 36. 1952	SD
Delibes, L.-Davis	Coppelia	Rub
Delmas, M.	Conte rose	Bil

Alto Saxophone and Piano

Delmas, M.	Soir d'été	Bil
Delmas, M.	Variation tendre	Bil
DeLuca, J.	Beautiful Colorado	CF
DeLuca, J.	Bravo Polka	Vol
DeLuca, J.	Minuet Scherzo	Bar
DeLuca, J.	Sentimentale	CF
DeLuca, J.	Thoughts of Gold	CF
Delvincourt, C.	Grenadine	ALe
Delvincourt, C.	Linzer tart	ALe
Delvincourt, C.	Nègre en chemise	ALe
Delvincourt, C.	Plum-pudding	ALe
Delvincourt, C.	Puits d'amour	ALe
Delvincourt, C.	Rahat loukhoum	ALe
Demany, J.	Aurore, Valse	EMb
Demersseman, J.-Voxman	Allegretto Brillante	Rub
Demersseman, J.	Fantaisie originale	Bil
Denisov, E.	Sonata	ALe
Depelsenaire, J.	Baroque	GD
Depelsenaire, J.	Concertino da camera	EMT
Depelsenaire, J.	Concertino No. 6 (Les Confidences)	HLe
Depelsenaire, J.	Funambules	EMT
Depelsenaire, J.	Prélude et divertissement	ECh
Depelsenaire, J.	Prélude et Scherzetto	ECh
Depelsenaire, J.	Recitative and Air	GD
Depelsenaire, J.	Sonatine, f	Com
Depelsenaire, J.	Spirals (Volutes)	GD
Depelsenaire, J.	Suite Concertante	EMT
Derksen, B.	Kapriolen, op. 28	B&B
Dervaux, A. & Moutet	Nocturne en Saxe	Com
Dervaux, A.	Petite suite en saxe	Bil
Deschamps, J.-Grant	Danse arabe	Bil
Desenclos, A.	Prélude, Cadence and Finale	ALe
Despalj, P.	Concerto	SM
Desprez, F.	Esquisse poétique	Mau
Desprez, F.	Loryette	Mau
Destouches, A.-Mule	Pastorale and Passepied (Issé)	ALe
Di Capua, E.	O Sole Mio	Cen
Di Domenica, R.	Sonata	MJQ
Diemente, E.	Response	See
Diercks, J.	Suite	Ten
Dijk, J. van	Sonata. 1953	SD
Dillon, H.	Sonate. 1949	EdS
Dindale, E.	Bucolique	EMb
Dindale, E.	Canzonetta	EMb
Dindale, E.	Danse Paysanne	EMb
Dindale, E.	Lied	EMb
Dinicu & Heifetz	Hora Staccato	CF
Donizetti, G.	Lucia di Lammermoor	Cen
Donizetti, G.-Vereecken	Sextet (Lucia di Lammermoor)	CF

Donizetti, G.	Sextette (Lucia)	Vol
Donjon, J.	Invocation	CF
Dorado -Wheeler	Dos Amigos	Vol
Doran, M.	Lento and Allegro	Wes
Dorsselaer, W. van	Conte de Versailles	Bil
Dorsselaer, W. van	Feux Follets	MM
Dorsselaer, W. van	Musicolor	Bil
Douane, J.	Capriccio	HLe
Douse, K.	Cynthia	CF
Drdla, F.-Damm	Souvenir	CF
Drdla, F.	Souvenir	JoW
Drdla, F.-Cragun	Souvenir	Rub
Dressel, E.	Bagatelles	R&E
Dressel, E.	Konzert op. 27	R&E
Dressel, E.	Partita	R&E
Drigo, R.	Canzone Barcarola	B-M
Drigo, R.	Harlequin Serenade	Cen
Drigo, R.	Serenade	Cen
Drigo, R.-Damm	Serenade (Les Millions d'Arlequin)	CF
Drigo, R.-Saenger	Valse Bluette	CF
Drigo, R.	Valse Melodie	· B-M
Drusiani, C.	Old sax--slow fox	GZ
Dubois, P.	Concerto	ALe
Dubois, P.	Concertstück	ALe
Dubois, P.	Divertissement	ALe
Dubois, P.	Les Ecureuils	ERR
Dubois, P.	In French Style	ALe
Dubois, P.	Grave et Scherzo mécanique	ERR
Dubois, P.	In Hungarian Style	ALe
Dubois, P.	Le Lièvre et la tortue	ALe
Dubois, P.	Mazurka (Hommage à Chopin)	ALe
Dubois, P.	In Parisian Style	ALe
Dubois, P.	In Russian Style	ALe
Dubois, P.	Sonata	ALe
Dubois, P.	Sonatina	ALe
Dubois, P.	2nd Sonatine	ALe
Dubois, P.	In Spanish Style	ALe
Dubois, P.	10 Figures a danser	ALe
Ducat, A.	Esquisse	Mau
Duclos, R.	Pièce brève	ALe
Dukas, P.-Mule	Alla Gitana	ALe
Dupont, P.	Romance, Bb	ALe
Duport, J.	Romance	Spr
Durand, A.	First Valse, op. 83	CF
Durand, A.-Iasilli	Valse, Eb, op. 83	CF
Duyck, G.	Introductie et dans	Mau
Duysburg, F.	Prélude et Danse	EMb
Dvořák, A.-Johnson	Air Gracile, op. 54/1	Rub

Alto Saxophone and Piano

Dvořak, A.	Humoreske	Cen
Dvořak, A.	Humoreske	McK
Dvořak, A.-Bumcke	Humoresque, op. 101/7	Sim
Dvořak, A.	Largo (New World Symphony)	CF
Dvořak, A.-Briegel	Songs My Mother Taught Me	GFB
Dyck, V.-Mule	1st Légende hébraïque	Bil
Eccles, H.-Rascher	Sonata	E-V
Eccles, H.-Bowder	Sonata, g	Roc
Eckard, W.	Highlights of Familiar Music	TP
Edelson, E.	Night Song	EdM
Effinger, C.	Solitude	Dor
Eisenmann, W.	Duo Concertante	CF
Eisenmann, W.	Nevermore	Ken
Elgar, E.	Salut d'Amour	Cen
Elgar, E.-Trinkaus	Love's Greeting	CF
Elgar, E.	Salut d'Amour, op. 12	SS
Elgar, E.-Glenn	Pomp and Circumstance No. 1	B&H
Elgar, E.-Akers	Theme from Pomp and Circumstance	CF
Emmerechts, R.	Soir	GrF
Emmett, D.	Dixie's Land	McK
Engelmann, H.	Integrale, op. 14a. 1954	A&S
Engelmann, H.	Melody of Love	TP
Erdna	6 Swing Pieces	dS
Erickson, F.	Concerto	Bou
Eriksson, N.	Concerto	EMf
Erwin-Sears	I Kiss Your Hand, Madame	War
Escudié, H.-Prendiville	Third Fantasia, op. 46	CF
Escudié, H.	3e Fantasie	MM
Escudié, H.	4e Fantasie	MM
Escudié, L.	Fantaisie originale	EdR
Escudié, L.	Fantaisie sur le carnaval de Vénise	EdR
Escudié, L.	6 Andantes	EdR
Espejo, C.-Mule	Complainte Andalouse, op. 19	HLe
Ettore, E.	L.T. the Kid	CoA
Evans, E.	Sweet and Dainty	CF
Evans, T.	Lady of Spain	SF
Evartt, R.	Eleonora	EMe
Eychenne, M.	Sonate	Bil
Fabre, C.-Harris	Second Reverie	CF
Fasch, J.-Rascher	Sonata, C	M&M
Fauconier, B.	Cantabile, op. 143	ScF
Faulx, J.	Bagatelle	HeE
Faulx, J.	Comme Alors, Valse	EMb
Faulx, J.	Pièce de Concert	EMb
Faulx, J.	Romance	EMb
Fauré, G.	Pièce	ALe
Fauré, J.	Les Rameaux (Palms)	Cen
Fauré, J.	The Palms	CF

Felix -arr.	3 Canzonettas of the 17th Century	EdM
Fernandez, C.	Cielito Lindo	GFB
Ferstl, E.	Crying Sonata	EMo
Fesch, W. de -Kaplan	Canzonetta	Spr
Fesch, W. de -Jones	Sonata, F	EQM
Field	Ten dancing fingers	B-M
Fievet, P.	Chant Lyrique	GD
Fillmore, H.	An Earl	CF
Fiocco, J. -Rascher	Allegro	Bou
Fischer, C.	Nellie Gray	CF
Flament, E. -Mule	Romance	ALe
Flégier, A.	Villanelle du Midi	EdM
Flothuis, M.	Kleine Suite, op. 47. 1952	SD
Flotow, F. von -De Rooij	Martha	MM
Fontyn, J.	Dialogues	ECh
Forestier, J.	Solo	MM
Forêt, F.	2 Pièces	Dur
Foster, S.	Jeanie With the Light Brown Hair	GFB
Foster, S. -Smith, Holmes	Old Black Joe	CF
Foster, S. -Fisher	My Old Kentucky Home	CF
Fox, J. -Rascher	Minuet	B-M
Frackenpohl, A.	Variations	Sha
Françaix, J.	5 Danses Exotiques	SS
Franck, C. -Leonard	Panis Angelicus	B-M
Franck, C.	Panis Angelicus	GFB
Franck, C. -Mule	Pièce II	ALe
Frangkiser, C.	Melody Perchance	B-M
Frangkiser, C.	Moraine Reverie	B-M
Frangkiser, C.	Spring Blossoms	B-M
Frangkiser, C.	Spring Waltz	B-M
Frank, M. -McCathren	Cathedral Song	EBM
Frank, M.	Evening Reverie	Ken
Frank, M. -McCathren	Legend for Sax	EBM
Fredrickson -Coggins	Cantilena	B-M
Frey, H. -arr.	Anchors Aweigh	Big
Fricker, P.	Aubade	S&C
Fučik, J.	Der Alte Brumm bar	HeE
Fučik, J.	Entrée des Gladiateurs	EdS
Fusco, G.	Flirting (La bella viennese)	GZ
Gabaye, P.	Printemps	ALe
Gabelles, G.	Andante appassionato	Bil
Gabelles, G.	Fantaisie-Caprice	GrF
Gaillard, M.	Noite sobre o tejo (nuit sur le tage)	Bil
Gal, H.	Suite op. 102b	Sim
Gallaher, S.	Impressions of Summer	SM
Gallet, J.	Andante et jeu	Bil
Gallet, J.	Berceuse et promenade	Bil

Alto Saxophone and Piano

Gallois-Montbrun, R.	Intermezzo	ALe
Gallois-Montbrun, R.	6 Musical Study Pieces	ALe
Garland-Haring	In the Mood	ShB
Garlick, A.	5 Study Patterns	See
Garlick, A.	Rhapsody	See
Gaubert, P.-Mule	Intermède champêtre	ALe
Gautier, L.—Vereecken	The Secret	CF
Gautier, L.-Davis	Le Secret (Intermezzo)	Rub
Gaylord-arr.	Let Us Have Music for Saxophone	CF
Gee, H.	Ballade	PrA
Geiger-Polla	Just for Tonight	EBM
Geist, C.	Andante Pastorale, op. 13	CF
Genin, P.-Mule	Carnival de Vénise, op. 14	Bil
Genin, P.-Mule	Solo de concours, op. 13	Bil
Gerschefski, E.	Workout, op. 18/4	CoF
Gerschefski, E.	"America" Variations for Winds, op. 44/8, 9	CoF
Gershwin, G.	Andante and Finale (Rhapsody in Blue)	War
Gershwin, G.-Rascher	Second Prelude	War
Giazotto & Albinoni-Orsomando	Adagio, g	Ric
Gilmore, C.	Martinello	Rub
Giordani, G.	An 18th Century Air	EdM
Giordano, T.	Fantasy	SM
Girlamo-Coggins	Matador	B-M
Girnatis, W.	Sonatina, f	HSM
Glaser, W.-Rascher	Carnival of Venice	Cha
Glazounov, A.	Concerto	ALe
Glière, R.	Valse Triste, op. 35/7	CF
Glinka, M.-Gurewich	The Lark	CF
Glover, S.	Rose of Tralee	MM
Gluck, C.	Ach Ich habe Sie verloren	MM
Gluck, C.-Mule	Andante and Musette (Armide)	ALe
Gluck, C.-Mule	Chaconne (Armide)	ALe
Gluck, C.-Mule	Elysian Fields (Orpheus)	ALe
Gluck, C.-Mule	Gavotte	ALe
Gluck, C.-Coggins	Gavotte	B-M
Gluck, C.-Rascher	Tambourin	B-M
Gluck, C.	2 Classic Airs	EdM
Gocht, J.	Impressions 65	FrH
Godard, B.	Lullaby (Jocelyn)	Cen
Godard, B.-Trinkaus	Berceuse	CF
Godard, B.	Berceuse de Jocelyn	MM
Godard, B.-Conklin	Canzonette, op. 35	CF
Godfrey, F.	Lucy Long	CF
Goeyens, A.-Buchtel	All 'Antica	NK
Goeyens, A.	Berceuse	EMb
Goeyens, A.	Mélodie Anglaise	EMb
Goeyens, A.	Prélude, Sarabande et Finale	EMb

Alto Saxophone and Piano

Golterman, C.-Webb	Cantilena (A Minor Concerto, op. 14)	B-M
Gonez, P.-Freed	Hora Legato	Bou
Gossec, F.-Mule	Rondo and Tarantella (La Fête du village)	ALe
Gotkovsky, I.	Concerto	EMT
Gottwald	Friendship	SM
Gounod, C.	Ave Maria	CF
Gounod, C.	The Calf of Gold (Faust)	EdM
Gounod, C.	Célèbre sérénade	ALe
Gounod, C.-Mullaly	Dio Possente	CF
Granados, E.	Andaluza	MM
Granados, E.-Amaz	Spanish Dance No. 2. Oriental	UME
Granados, E.-Amaz	Spanish Dance No. 5. Andaluza	UME
Granados, E.-Amaz	Spanish Dance No. 6 Rondalla Aragonesa	UME
Green, H.	Berceuse	PMP
Green, P.	Silhouette	Bos
Gretchaninov, A.-Voxman	At the Hearth (Au Foyer)	Rub
Gretchaninov, A.-Voxman	Evening Waltz (Valse dans le Soir)	Rub
Gretchaninoff, A.	Memory of a Distant Friend	ALe
Gretchaninoff, A.	Phantasm	ALe
Grétry, A.-Paque	Air de Richard Coeur de Lion	T-M
Grétry, A.-Londeix	Panurge, Ariette	ALe
Grieg, E.	Berceuse	CF
Grieg, E.	I Love You	Cen
Grieg, E.-Strauwen	Soir dans les montagnes	ScF
Grieg, E.	To Spring	Cen
Grillaert, O.	Fantaisie Varié	EMe
Grofé, F.	Valsanne	Big
Grofé, F.	Valse Annette	Big
Grooms, C.	Famous Scotch Airs, Var.	Cen
Grooms, C.	Home Favorites, Var.	Cen
Grooms, C.	Neapolitan Favorites, Var.	Cen
Grooms, C.	Ocean Echos	Cen
Grooms, C.	Plantation Echoes, Var.	Cen
Grooms, C.-arr.	Two Guitars (Russian Song)	Cen
Grovlez, G.	Sarabande and Allegro	ALe
Gruber-Kent	The Caissons Go Rolling Along	CF
Grundman, C.	Concertante	B&H
Guilhaud, G.-Mule	Premier Concertino	Bil
Guilhaud, G.-Voxman	First Concertino	Rub
Guillaume, E.	Andante et Scherzo	EMb
Guillou, G.	Ballade	GrF
Guillou, R.	Sonatina	ALe
Gurewich, J.	Ballet Fantastique	Sch
Gurewich, J.	Capriccio, op. 120	Sch
Gurewich, J.	Concertino, e, op. 102	Rub
Gurewich, J. `	Concerto, e	Rub

Gurewich, J.	Fantasy, f	Ric
Gurewich, J.	Jota (Danse espagnole)	Sch
Gurrieri, A.	Topolino	GZ
Haass, H.	Mixtura	HG
Haenecour-Rio	Volupte, Valse	EMb
Haeyer, F. d'	Introduction et Allegro	EMe
Hagen, E.-Haring	Harlem Nocturne	ShB
Halévy, J.	The Cardinal's Air (La Juive)	EdM
Handel, G.-Gee	Adagio and Allegro	SM
Handel, G.-Rousseau	Adagio and Allegro	W-J
Handel, G.-Mule	Adagio, Larghetto and Finale	ALe
Handel, G.-Rascher	Air Varie	Bou
Handel, G.-Mule	Allegro	ALe
Handel, G.-Barr	Allegro (Concerto, f)	Lud
Handel, G.-Mule	Allegro, Largo and Finale	ALe
Handel, G.-Mule	Bourrée	ALe
Handel, G.-Chauvet	Bourrée	Com
Handel, G.	Cantilena	NK
Handel, G.-Mule	Gavottes	ALe
Handel, G.-Mule	The Harmonious Blacksmith	ALe
Handel, G.-Mule	Largo	ALe
Handel, G.-Brisset	Célèbre largo (air de Xerxes)	Bil
Handel, G.	Largo	CF
Handel, G.-Viard	Largo	EdS
Handel, G.	Largo	MM
Handel, G.	Minuet (Berenice)	Wat
Handel, G.-Mule	Pastorale	ALe
Handel, G.-Barr	Sarabande (Concerto, f)	Lud
Handel, G.	Sarabande	MM
Handel, G.-Mule	Sicilienne and Gigue	ALe
Handel, G.-Londeix	Sonata No. 1	ALe
Handel, G.-Mule	Sonata No. 1 (flute)	ALe
Handel, G.-Mule	Sonata No. 2 (violin)	ALe
Handel, G.-Rascher	Sonata No. 3	Cha
Handel, G.-Mule	Sonata No. 4 (flute)	ALe
Handel, G.-Mule	Sonata No. 6 (violin)	ALe
Handel, G.-Rascher	Sonata No. 13	E-V
Handel, G.-Londeix	Sonata, g	ALe
Handel, G.-Barnes	Sound an Alarm	Spr
Handel, G.	3 Dances and an Air	EdM
Harlan, C.	Fantasy	Byr
Harris, A.-arr.	Farewell to Cucullain (Kerry Tune)	CF
Harris, F.	Ballroom Echoes	Lud
Harris, F.	Charming Ballerina	Bar
Harris, F.	Fairy Princess	Lud
Harris, F.	Marilee	Bar
Harris, F.	Ocean Beach Valse	Lud
Harris, F.	A Rendezvous in the Forest	Bar
Harris, F.	Sax Caprice	Lud

Hartley, W.	Concerto	Tri
Hartley, W.	Duo	TP
Hartley, W.	Song	Ten
Hartmann, J.	Fatherland	MM
Hartmann, J.-Laurendeau	Longing For Home	CF
Hartmann, J.	Mia	MM
Hartmann, J.	The Return	MM
Hartzell	Two Rogues	Tem
Hasquenoph, P.	Concertino	Heu
Hawthorne, A.	Whispering Hope	GFB
Haydn, F.-Mule	Canzonetta (The Seasons)	ALe
Haydn, F.-Speets	Gratias	T-M
Haydn, F.-Rascher	Minuet	B-M
Haydn, F.	Serenade	CF
Haydn, F.	Serenade	MM
Hayes, H.	Keep Going, Don't Stop	Bos
Heck, A.	Concertino op. 41	Com
Heiden, B.	Solo. 1969	AMP
Heiden, B.	Sonata	S&C
Heider, W.	Sonata in Jazz	A&S
Heldenberg, A.	Improvisatie	Mau
Heltman	Mary Jane Waltz	Vol
Henderson-Sears	The Birth of the Blues	War
Hennessy, S.-Laurent	Sonatine Celtique, op. 62	EME
Henning, R.	Equipose	Dor
Herbert, V.-Harris	Gypsy Love Song	Lud
Herbert, V.	Gypsy Love Song	NK
Hermann, L.	Air varie	ScF
Herrmann, T.	Grande fantaisie	ScF
Heuberger, R.-Kreisler, Leeson	Midnight Bells	CFo
Heuberger, R.-Kreisler, Leidzen	Midnight Bells	CFo
Heumann, H.-Voxman	Slavonic Fantasy	Rub
Hindemith, P.	Sonata. 1943	SS
Hoffman, E.	In Modo di Trentotto	SM
Hoffmann, A.	Alborada	B&H
Hoffmann, A.	Jota Aragonesa	B&H
Hoffmann, A.	Serenade Basque	B-M
Holbrook-Barnhouse	Refuge	Bar
Holmes, G.-arr.	Auld Lang Syne	CF
Holmes, G.	Cosette	Bar
Holmes, G.	Zayda	Bar
Houdy, P.	Romanesca	ALe
Hubert, R.	Un Soir	EdR
Hudadoff & Spire	11 Classic Solos	PrA
Hudadoff, I.-arr.	15 Intermediate Solo Series	PrA
Hudadoff, I.-arr.	Marches	PrA
Hughes-Pelz	Moods and Contrasts	SF
Hunter, L.	Saxene	B-M

Hupperman, W.	Valse Tyrolienne	EMb
Hurrell, C.	Bingo	GFB
Hurrell, C.	Dark Distance	CF
Hurrell, C.	Gypsy Dreams	GFB
Hurrell, C. -arr.	Meadowland	Rub
Hurrell, C.	Silver Shadows	GFB
Hurrell, C.	Summer Night	GFB
Hurrell, C.	Tango Gitano	CF
Husa, K.	Concerto	AMP
Husa, K.	Elégie en rondeau	ALe
Iannaccone, A.	Remembrance	Ten
Iasilli, G.	Goldie	CF
Ibert, J.	The Abandoned Palace (Histoires)	ALe
Ibert, J.	Aria	ALe
Ibert, J.	Bajo la mesa (Histoires)	ALe
Ibert, J.	Concertino da camera	ALe
Ibert, J.	The Crystal Cage (Histoires)	ALe
Ibert, J.	Dans la maison triste (Histoires)	ALe
Ibert, J.	The Golden Age (Le Chevalier Errant)	ALe
Ibert, J. -Mule	Histoires	ALe
Ibert, J.	The Little White Donkey (Histoires)	ALe
Ibert, J.	La Marchande d'eau fraiche (Histoires)	ALe
Ibert, J.	La Meneuse de tortues d'or (Histoires)	ALe
Ibert, J.	The Old Beggar (Histoires)	ALe
Ilyinsky, A. -Coggins	Berceuse	B-M
Indy, V. d'	Choral varié, op. 55	Dur
Irons, E.	Echoes from the Painted Desert	CF
Isaac & Lillya -arr.	Sacred Music	CF
Isaac & Lillya -arr.	Album of Favorite Saxophone Solos	Col
Jacob, G.	Rhapsody	GaM
Jacob, G.	Variations on a Dorian Theme	JE
Jacobi, W.	Sonata	Bou
Jarnefelt, A. -Leonard	Berceuse	B-M
Jahrl	Frolic of the Keys	GFB
Jakma, F.	Novelette	T-M
Jakma, F.	Sancta Lucia	MM
Jakma, F.	Valse Caprice	T-M
Jeanjean, P.	Heureux temps	Bil
Jeanjean, P.	Rêverie de printemps	Bil
Jessel, L. -Polla	Parade of the Wooden Soldiers	EBM
Jettl, R.	Schmetterling	JKM
Jettl, R.	Serenata	JKM

Jettl, R.	Spanisches Ständchen	JKM
Johanson, S.	Fem expressioner	EMf
Johanson, S.	Sonat. 1949	EMf
Johnson, C.-arr.	Sacred Solos	Rub
Johnson, W.	Encantada	PrA
Jolivet, A.	Fantasy-Impromptu	ALe
Joly, D.	Cantilena and Dance	ALe
Kanitz, E.	Sonata Californiana	CF
Karkoff, M.	Concertino op. 15	EMf
Karkoff, M.	4 Stycken	EMf
Karkoff, M.	Nio solominiatyrer	EMf
Karkoff, M.	Rapsodisk fantasi, op. 8a. 1953	STI
Kaspar, E.	Within and Beyond	See
Kay, F.	La Quataine	PrA
Keithley	I'll Never Find a Pal Like You	McK
Keithley	When Shadows Fall	McK
Kelkel, M.	Rhapsodie, op. 12	Ric
Kennedy, A.-Hummel	Star of the East	Rub
Kennedy, H.	Star of Hope (Reverie)	Cen
Kerma	Lovely, Valse	EMb
Kerma	Rudy's Fingers	EMb
Kerma	Seduction, Valse	EMb
Kesnar, M.	Pastorale	CF
Ketèlbey, A.	In a Persian Market	Bos
Ketèlbey, A.	Sanctuary of the Heart	Bos
Khachaturian, A.-Schoebel	Sabre Dance	MCA
Kiefer, W.-Holmes	Elena Polka	Bar
King-Garrison	Song of the Islands	EBM
King, K.	Night in June	Bar
King, K.	Night in June	Wat
Kinyon, J.	Program Pieces	War
Kinyon, J.	Recital Pieces	War
Klauss, N.-McCathren	Holiday Waltz	CF
Kleinsinger, G.	Street Corner Concerto	Cha
Klickmann, F.	Sweet Hawaiian Moonlight	McK
Klickmann, F.	Trail to Long Ago	McK
Klickmann, F.	Weeping Willow Lane	McK
Klosé, H.-Corroyez	Solo	ALe
Klughardt, A.	Romanze	Spr
Knight-Clement	Rocked in the Cradle of the Deep	Vol
Koch, E. von	Concerto	EMf
Koch, E. von	Vision	EMf
Koechlin, C.-Londeix	Etudes	EFM
Köhler, E.-Conklin	The Butterfly (Papillon)	CF
Krantz, A.-Gurewich	Tourbillon	CF
Krein, M.	Serenade	B&H
Kreisler, F.-Gurewich	Caprice Viennois	CFo
Kreisler, F.-Brandl	Caprice Viennois--Alter	

	Refrain	SS
Kreisler, F.-Gurewich	Liebesfreud	CFo
Kreisler, F.-Gurewich	Liebesleid	CFo
Kreisler, F.	Liebesfreud, Liebesleid,	
	Schön Rosmarin	SS
Kreisler, F.-Leidzen	Miniature Viennese March	CFo
Kreisler, F.-Gurewich	The Old Refrain	CFo
Kreisler, F.-Leeson	Rondino on a theme of	
	Beethoven	CFo
Kreisler, F.-Gurewich	Schön Rosmarin	CFo
Krol, B.	Aria e Tarantella, op. 37	Sim
Krol, B.	Sonata op. 17	FrH
Krumlovsky, C.	Concertino	ALe
Kugerl, H.	Rhapsodie	LK
Kuehn, C.-Lefèbre	Adagio (Military Concerto)	CF
Kuhlau, F.	Menuett	NK
Kupferman, M.	In Two Bits	Gen
Kupferman, M.	3 Pieces in Slow Motion	Gen
Labate, B.	Intermezzo Polka	CF
Lack, T.	Idilio	Cen
Lacome, P.-Andraud	Rigaudon	SM
Lacour, G.	Hommage à Jacques Ibert	Bil
Lajtha, L.	Intermezzo	ALe
Lake, M.-arr.	Annie Laurie	CF
Lake, M.	Naida	Lud
Lalo, E.-Mule	Lento (Chants russes)	ALe
Lalo, E.	Le Roi d'Ys	MM
Lamote de Grignon, J.-Amaz	Canço de Maria	UME
Lamote de Grignon, J.-Amaz	Rêverie (Schumanniana)	UME
Lamy, W.	Saxo-Trick	EMb
Lamy, W.	Turlight, Valse	EMb
Lancen, S.	Légende heureuse	Bil
Lancen, S.	Saxophonie	Bil
Lane, R.	Suite	B&H
Lange, G.	Blumenlied (Flower Song)	Cen
Lange, G.	Blumenlied (Flower Song)	CF
Lansing, A.	Darkey's Dream	McK
Lantier, P.	Allegro Arioso et Final	HLe
Lantier, P.	Euskaldunak	Bil
Lantier, P.	Sicilienne	ALe
Laparra, R.	Prelude valse and Irish reel	ALe
Larmanjat, J.	4 Pièces de concert	Dur
Larsen, E.	Concerto	WH
Larsson, L.	Concerto op. 14	CGM
Lassen, E.	At Devotions	EdM
Latham, W.	Sisyphus. 1971	Bil
Laurendeau, L.-arr.	Flow Gently Sweet Afton	CF
Lavaine-Goudefroy	Souvenirs et regrets	GrF
Law, A.	Tawny Port	ATL
Lax, F.	Bonnie Scotland, op. 101	CF
Lebrun, G.	Chant du Berger	EMb

Lecail, G.-Voxman	Fantaisie Concertante	Rub
Leclair, J.-Mule	Adagio	ALe
Leclair, J.-Mule	Adagio, Allemande and Gigue	ALe
Leclair, J.-Mule	Adagio and Aria	ALe
Leclair, J.-Mule	Andante	ALe
Leclair, J.-Mule	Aria	ALe
Leclair, J.	Danse Provençale	EdM
Leclair, J.-Mule	Gavotte and Vivace	ALe
Leclair, J.-Mule	Gigue	ALe
Leclair, J.-Mule	Largo and Vivace	ALe
Leclair, J.-Mule	Musette	ALe
Leclair, J.-Gorner	Sonata, g	SM
Leclercq, E.	Charmeuse	EMb
Leclercq, E.	Concertino	Bil
Leclercq, E.	Intimité	EMb
Leclercq, E.	Moment heureux	EMb
Leclercq, E.	Tendresse	EMb
Lecuona, E.-Simon	Andalucia	EBM
Lecuona, E.-Simon	Malaguena	EBM
Leeson, C.	Concertino	SM
Lefèbvre, C.-Cailliet	Andante and Allegro	SM
Lehar, F.-Klickmann	Frasquita Serenade	EBM
Lehar, F.-Weber	Vilia	B-M
Leinert, F.	Sonate. 1952	BrH
Leleu, J.	Danse Nostalgique	HLe
Lemaire, J.	Deuxième Ballade	ALe
Lemaire, J.	Musique légère	ALe
Lemare, E.	Andantino	CF
Lemare, E.-Long	Andantino	Vol
Lemare, E.	Cathedral Meditation	Cen
Lenom, C.-Findlay	Lullaby	CF
Leonard, B.	Culligan Man	B-M
Leonard, B.	Feather River	B-M
Leonard, C.	Recitative and Abracadabra	Bou
Leoncavallo, R.	Arioso (Pagliacci)	Cen
Leoncavallo, R.-Barnes	Mattinata	Lud
Leroux, X.-Mule	Romance, a, No. 1	ALe
Leroux, X.-Mule	Romance, A, No. 2	ALe
Lesier, E.	Prélude et rondo	Bil
Lessage-Lacroix	La Sérénade en 3 Temps	EMb
Letellier & Lecomte	Ballade	EdR
Letorey, P.	Papotages	Bil
Leybach, I.	Fifth Nocturne, G	Cen
Liddle, S.-Glenn	How Lovely Are Thy Dwellings	B&H
Liliuokalani, Queen	Aloha Oe	CF
Liliuokalani, Queen	Aloha Oe	McK
Lincke, P.-Polla	Glow-Worm	EBM
Lincke, P.	Glow Worm	NK
Lincke, P.-Walters	The Glowworm	Rub
Lincke, P.-Polla	March of the Siamese	EBM

Lincke, P.-Polla	Spring Beautiful Spring	EBM
Liszt, F.-Smith	Liebestraum	Bar
Liszt, F.	Love Dreams (Liebestraum)	Cen
Liszt, F.-Bettoney	Liebestraume	CF
Liszt, F.-Chauvet	Rêve d'amour	Com
Llewellyn, E.	My Regards	War
Loeillet, J.-Merriman	Sonata	SM
Lomani, B.	3 Miniatures	PWM
Londeix, J.-arr.	A la découverte de la musique des XVIIe et XVIIIe siècles, 3 vols.	HLe
Londeix, J.	Tableaux Aquitains No. 1: Bachelette	ALe
Londeix, J.	Tableaux Aquitains No. 2: La Gardeuse de Porcs	ALe
Londeix, J.	Tableaux Aquitains No. 3: Le Traverseur de Landes	ALe
Londeix, J.	Tableaux Aquitains No. 4: Le Raconteur d'Histoire	ALe
Lonque, A.	Morceau de Concours	EMb
Lonque, G.	Images d'Orient	ALe
Lotter, A.	Rouge et Noir	B&H
Lotti, A.	Arietta	EdM
Lotzenhiser, G.	Accelerando	B-M
Lotzenhiser, G.	Poco Waltz	B-M
Luigini, A.-Conklin	Ballet Egyptien, No. 3	CF
Lully, J.-Mule	Air Tendre and Courante	ALe
Lully, J.	Dances for the King	EdM
Lully, J.-Mule	Gavotte	ALe
Lully, J.-Mule	Minuet (Le Bourgeois Gentilhomme)	ALe
Lully, J.-Mule	Passacaglia and Passepied (Phaéton)	ALe
Lully, J.-Londeix	Sarabande et Gavotte	ALe
Lunde, L.	Sonata	SM
Macbeth, A.	Intermezzo "Forget Me Not"	CF
MacDowell, E.-Coggins	To a Wild Rose	B-M
MacDowell, E.-Isaac	To a Wild Rose	CF
MacDowell, E.	To a Wild Rose	MM
Macker, R.	Saxo-Rag	EMb
Maertens, J.	Moments Tristes	Mau
Maganini, Q.	La Romanesca	EdM
Maganini, Q.	Song of a Chinese Fisherman	EdM
Mahy, A.	Aubade	MM
Maillot, J.	Prélude et Divertissement	EMT
Malézieux, G.	Mélodie Religieuse	EdS
Malézieux, G.	Romance sans paroles	EdS
Malézieux, G.	Sur le Lac	EdS
Malipiero, G.-Mule	Canto nell' infinito	ALe
Malotte, A.-Lake	The Lord's Prayer	Sch

Mana-Zucca	Walla-Kye, op. 115	CMP
Marc, E.	Pierrot et Columbine	Bil
Marchetti, F.-Hurrell	Fascination	Rub
Mareczek, F.	Summer Evening on the Mountain	WZ
Marie, G.-Chauvet, Dias, Wiedoeft	La Cinquantaine	Bil
Marie, G.	La Cinquantaine	CF
Marie, G.-Dias	Pasquinade	Bil
Marie, G.-Chauvet, Wiedoeft	Sérénade badine	Bil
Marie, G.	Serenade "Badine"	CF
Marie, G.-Davis	Badine	Rub
Markovitch, I.	Complainte et danse	ALe
Marshall, C.-Glenn	I Hear You Calling Me	B&H
Marteau, H.-Barnes	Morceau Vivant	Spr
Martelli, H.	3 Esquisses, op. 55	EME
Martelli, H.	Kadenz, Interludium und Rondo, op. 78	EME
Martin, R.	Sérénade à Corinne	EdR
Martini, J.	Celebrated Romance	ALe
Martini, P.	Canzona	MM
Martini, P.-Mule	Gavotte (Les Moutons)	ALe
Martini, P.-Rascher	Gavotte	Cha
Martini, P.-Mule	Grave	ALe
Martini, J.P.-Mule	Plaisir d'Amour	ALe
Martini, J.P.	Plaisir d'Amour	EdM
Martini, J.P.	Plaisir d'Amour	MM
Martini, J.P.-Overveld	Plaisir d'Amour	T-M
Mascagni, P.-Wagner	Intermezzo Sinfonico (Cavalleria Rusticana)	CF
Mascagni, P.	Intermezzo (Cavalleria Rusticana)	CF
Mascagni, P.	Intermezzo	McK
Mascagni, P.-Schaefer	Siciliana	War
Mason, T.	Canzone da Sonar	SM
Massenet, J.	Andante	CF
Massenet, J.-Trinkaus	Elegy	CF
Massenet, J.-Mule	Mélodie-Elégie des Erinnyes	Job
Massenet, J.	Herod's Air (Herodiade)	EdM
Massenet, J.	2 Operatic Scenes	EdM
Massenet, J.	Valse des Esprits (Griselidis)	EdM
Massenet, J.	The Virgin's Last Slumber	CF
Masten, I.-Hanson	Believe Me If All Those Endearing Young Charms	Lud
Masten, I.	Bonnie Eloise	Lud
Mather, B.	Elegy	Wat
Maurat, E.	Petites Inventions, op. 21, No. 1	EME
Maurice, P.	Tableaux de Provence	HLe
Mayeur, L.-arr.	Carnival of Venice	HLe

Mazellier, J.	Fantaisie-ballet	ALe
Mazellier, J.	Quick	HLe
Mazellier, J.	Spleen	HLe
Mazellier, J.	Thème varié languedocien	EdS
McBride, R.	Boogie	CoF
McBride, R.	Parking on the Parkway	CoF
McBride, R.	The World Is Ours	CoF
McCathren, D.	Latin Holiday	Hal
McCoy -Stuart	Trio (Lights Out March)	CF
McKay, F.	Buckboard Blues	Bar
McKay, F.	Dream Waltz	Bar
McKay, F.	Hallowe'en Time	Bar
McKay, F.	Hernando's Holiday	Bar
McKay, F.	Jig for Jeanine	Bar
McKay, F.	The Powdered Wig	Bar
McKay, F.	A Rendezvous in the Forest	Bar
McKay, F.	Ye Traveling Troubador	Bar
McKay, G.	Arietta and Capriccio	BM
McKay, G.	Concert Solo Sonatine	BM
Meacham, F.	American Patrol	Cen
Meacham, F. -Kent	American Patrol	CF
Meacham, F. -Hummel	American Patrol	Rub
Méhul, E. -Mule	Rondeau basque	ALe
Mellish -arr.	Drink To Me Only With Thine Eyes	GFB
Mendelssohn, F. -Mule	Andante	ALe
Mendelssohn, F. -Chauvet	Andante du concerto	Com
Mendelssohn, F.	Frühlingslied (Spring Song)	MM
Mendelssohn, F. -Trinkaus	Nocturno	CF
Mendelssohn, F. -Trinkaus	On Wings of Song	CF
Mendelssohn, F. -Andreoni	On Wings of Song	Ric
Mendelssohn, F. -Mayeur	Romance sans Paroles, op. 30/1	CF
Mendelssohn, F.	Soldier's March	NK
Mendelssohn, F. -Mule	Song without Words, No. 1	ALe
Mendelssohn, F. -Mule	Song without Words op. 38, No. 3	ALe
Mendelssohn, F. -Mule	Songs without Words, No. 20	ALe
Mendelssohn, F. -Mule	Spring Song	ALe
Mendelssohn, F.	Spring Song	Cen
Mendelssohn, F.	Spring Song	CF
Menéndez, J.	Lamento and Tarentella. 1953	UME
Merck, L.	Fantaisie Varié	T-M
Meriot & Classens	Le Nouveau Saxophone Classique, 4 vols.	Com
Meyer, J.	Genêts et bruyères	ALe
Meyer, J.	Novelette	SS
Meyerbeer, G. -Trinkaus	Coronation March	CF
Meylink, C.	Valse élégante	EdH
Middeleer, J. de	Recitativo e allegro. 1970	CBD

327

Mignion, R.	Pastorale	Bil
Mignion, R.	Invocation et Marche	Bil
Milhaud, D.	Dance	Int
Milhaud, D.	Scaramouche	EdS
Milli-Faulx	Flirt in the Dancing	EMb
Mirante, T.	Prelude and March	PrA
Molloy, J.	Love's Old Sweet Song	McK
Mondonville, C.-Mule	Tambourin	ALe
Mondonville, J.-Hemke	Sonata No. 6	SM
Monfeuillard, R.	Dialogue joyeux	ALe
Monfeuillard, R.	Nocturno	ALe
Monsigny, P.-Mule	Gavotte (La Reine de Golconde)	ALe
Monsigny, P.-Mule	Scherzo (Les Aveux indiscrets)	ALe
Monti, V.	Csardas	CF
Monti, V.-Ayala, Bernadaus	Czardas No. 1	Ric
Moortel, L. van de	Capriccio	Mau
Moreau, L.-Mule	Evocations rythmiques	ALe
Moreau, L.	Pastorale	ALe
Morée, L. de	Sérénade	T-M
Morel	Norwegian Cradle Song	Cen
Moritz, E.-Leeson	Intermezzo	SM
Moritz, E.	Sonata No. 1	SM
Moritz, E.	Sonata No. 2	SM
Morra, G.	Nocturnal Serenade	CF
Morra, G.	Romantique	CF
Morris-arr.	Drink To Me Only With Thine Eyes	Vol
Morrison, J.	Past the Solstice	CoF
Morrissey, J.	Nightfall	EBM
Mortari, V.	Melodia	ALe
Moszkowski, M.	Serenade, op. 15/1	CF
Moulaert, R.	Tango-Caprice	EMb
Moussorgsky, M.-Gee, McCathren	The Old Castle	EBM
Mozart, W.-Mule	Adagio (Clarinet Concerto)	ALe
Mozart, W.	Adagio (Clarinet Concerto, op. 107)	CF
Mozart, W.-Buchtel	Mozart Adagio	NK
Mozart, W.-Chauvet	Air de Chérubin	Com
Mozart, W.-Rascher	Ave Verum Corpus	B-M
Mozart, W.	Concerto K. 191	EdM
Mozart, W.-Sansone	Concert Rondo, op. 371	SM
Mozart, W.-Mule	Gavotte sentimentale (Les Petits Riens)	ALe
Mozart, W.-Londeix	Menuet (Divertissement, D)	ALe
Mozart, W.-Chauvet	Menuet	Com
Mozart, W.-Voxman	Minuet (Haffner Music, K. 250)	Rub
Mozart, W.-Lemarc	Papageno Aria	T-M
Mozart, W.-Evertse	Priester Aria	T-M
Mozart, W.-Willaman	Solo (String Quartet, K. 465)	Spr

Msarurgwa -Haring	Skokiaan	ShB
Muczynski, R.	Sonata op. 29	Sch
Mueller	Praeludium, Chorale,	
	Variations & Fugue	EdM
Muldermans, J.	Fantaisie brillante	EdR
Muldermans, J.	Fantaisie Variée	Lud
Murgier, J.	Concerto	EMT
Murgier, J.	2 Pièces brèves	HLe
Myddleton, W. -Polla	Down South	EBM
Myers, R.	3 Short Pieces	ArM
Myers, T.	Sonatine	CoA
Naissoo, U.	Improvisation	MKE
Nelhybel, V.	Allegro	BM
Nessler, V. -Lureman	De Rattenvanger van Hameln	T-M
Neukomm, S. -Kaplan	Aria	Spr
Nevin, E. -Hummel	Mighty Lak' A Rose	Rub
Nevin, E.	Narcissus	BM
Nevin, E. -Edwards	Narcissus	B-M
Nevin, E. -Hummel	Narcissus	Rub
Nevin, E.	Le Rosaire	Bil
Nevin, E.	Rosary	BM
Niehaus, L.	Of Days Remembered	Wes
Niehaus, L.	Palo Alto	Wes
Niehaus, L.	Waltzin' the Blues Away	Wes
Nivelet, V.	Brillantes variations	ALe
Nivelet, V. -Médinger	Ma bergère	ALe
Niverd, L.	Autumn Twilight	GD
Niverd, L.	Insouciance	EdR
Niverd, L.	Recueillement	EdR
Niverd, L.	6 Petites pièces de style	
	(Published separately)	Bil
Niverd, L.	6 Pièces brèves	Com
Norden, H.	Carousel	Hal
Nott	Rhapsodic Song	Sha
Nyquist, M.	Echo Lake	B-M
Offenbach, J.	Barcarolle (Tales of Hoffman)	Cen
Offenbach, J.	Barcarolle	CF
Offenbach, J.	Barcarolle	McK
Offenbach, J. -Scull	Barcarolle	Vol
Offenbach, J.	La Musette	CF
Offenbach, J.	Waltz La Perichole	NK
O'Hagan	Nocturne	Tem
Olcott, C. -Hummel	My Wild Irish Rose	Rub
Olesen, W.	6 Saxophone Pieces, vol. 2	WH
O'Neill, C.	Clover Leaf	Wat
O'Neill, C.	Introduction and Valse de	
	Salon	Wat
Organn, R.	The Brook	Reb
Organn, R.	Falling Leaves	Reb
Organn, R.	Nocturne	Reb

Organn, R.	Star of the North	Reb
Organn, R.	Waltz of the Stars	Reb
Orrego-Salas, J.	4 Liriche Brevi	SMP
Ortolani, O.	More (Mondo Cane)	EBM
Ostrander, A.	Concert Piece in Fugal Style	EBM
Ostransky, L.	Suite	Rub
Oubradous, F.	Récit & Variations	ALe
Paderewski, I.-Trinkaus	Minuet a l'Antique	CF
Paderewski, I.	Romance (Song of the Voyager)	CF
Paganini, N.-Parola	Carnival of Venice	Ric
Painparé, H.	Variations de concert	ScF
Pala, J.	Fantaisie	T-M
Paladilhe, E.-Voxman	Concertante	Rub
Panella	Jack and Jill	Vol
Panella	Jolly Two	Vol
Panella	Tom and Jerry	Vol
Panella	Two Bachelors	Vol
Panella	Two Gnomes	Vol
Panella	Two Lovers	Vol
Paris Kerjullou, C.	Divertissement	EdR
Parish & Signorelli	Blues serenade	B-M
Parnell	Espanola Jazz	CF
Pascal, C.	Impromptu	Dur
Pascal, C.	Sonatine	Dur
Paul, G.	Estilian Caprice	Rub
Paulson, G.	Concerto	EMf
Payne, F.	Toccata	Sha
Pellegrin, A.	Première fantaisie	GrF
Pelz, W.	Sundown	B-M
Pelz, W.	Valse Lyrique	B-M
Perfect, A.	Two Little Chums	CF
Pergolesi, G.-Barnes	Canzona	Spr
Pergolesi, G.-Ephross	Nina	SM
Pergolesi, G.-Elkan	Se Tu M'Ami	HeE
Perrin, M.	Agilité, Chromatic Study	GD
Perrin, M.	Arlequins	ALe
Perrin, M.	Bagatelle	Com
Perrin, M.	Berceuse	ALe
Perrin, M.	Complainte	Com
Perrin, M.	Elégie	GD
Perrin, M.	Gypsy Fantasy	GD
Perrin, M.	Melody	GD
Perrin, M.	Mirage	ALe
Perrin, M.	Nocturne	GD
Perrin, M.	Poème	ALe
Perrin, M.	Rêves	ALe
Perrin, M.	Whirlwind	GD
Pessard, E.	Andalouse	NK
Pestalozza, A.	Ciribiribin	CF
Pestalozza, A.	Ciribiribin	NK

Petit, A.	1st Etude de concours	Bil
Petit, A.-Findlay	Premier Etude De Concours	CF
Petit, P.	Andante et fileuse	ALe
Petit, P.	Saxopéra	ALe
Philiba, N.	Concerto	Bil
Philiba, N.	Sonate	Bil
Philidor, F.-Mule	Ego dis amicum (Chant d'Eglise)	ALe
Philidor, F.-Mule	Rigaudon (Ernelinde)	ALe
Phillips, I.	A Classical and Romantic Album	OxU
Pierné, G.-Mule	Canzonetta, Bb	ALe
Pierné, G.-Petiot	Canzonetta, Bb	ALe
Pierné, G.-Gee	Canzonetta	SM
Pierné, G.-Bettoney	March of the Little Tin Soldiers, op. 14/6	CF
Pierné, G.	March of the Tin Soldiers	NK
Pierné, G.-Gee	Serenade	SM
Pierné, G.	Sérénade, op. 7	ALe
Pierné, P.	Prélude et scherzo	Bil
Pierné, P.	Scherzo	Bil
Pierné, P.	Le Vol de la mouche	Bil
Pinard, A.	Darling	CF
Pinard, A.	Just A Little Song of Love	CF
Pinard, A.	Yearning	CF
Planel, R.	Christmas Tale	ALe
Planel, R.	Conte de Noël	ALe
Planel, R.	Danseuses	ALe
Planel, R.	Girls Dancing	ALe
Planel, R.	Italian Serenade	ALe
Planel, R.	Muleteer's Song	ALe
Planel, R.	Prélude et saltarelle	ALe
Planel, R.	Sad Song	ALe
Planel, R.	Sentimental Waltz	ALe
Planel, R.	Suite Romantique, 6 Pieces	ALe
Platti, G.-Hervig	Sonata op. 3, No. 5	Rub
Polleri, A.-tr.	Saxino, Easy Transcriptions, 9 vols.	GD
Ponce, M.	Estrellita	CF
Porret, J.	Concertino No. 9	EdR
Porret, J.	Concertino No. 10	EdR
Porret, J.	Dialogue	EdR
Porret, J.	Papillons	EdR
Porret, J.	17e Solo de Concours	MM
Porret, J.	18e Solo de Concours	MM
Porret, J.	19th Solo de concours	EdR
Porret, J.	20th Solo de concours	EdR
Porret, J.	Villanelle fleurie	EdR
Porter, C.-Gossette	Begin the Beguine	War
Poulain, S.	Mélodie	EMb

331

Praetorius, M.-Rascher	From heaven high	B-M
Presle, J. de la	Orientale	ALe
Presser, W.	Prelude and Rondo	Ten
Prokofiev, S.	Kije's Wedding (Lt. Kije)	EdM
Puccini, G.-Andreoni	Mi chiamano Mimì (La Bohème)	Ric
Puccini, G.-Andreoni	Quando men vo' (La Bohème)	Ric
Puccini, G.-Andreoni	Vissi d'arte (Tosca)	Ric
Purcell, H.	Dance Suite	EdM
Purcell, H.	Nymphs and Shepherds	NK
Purcell, H.-Kaplan	Saraband	Spr
Purcell, H.	Sonata, g	EdM
Purcell, H.	Suite, F	EdM
Purcell, H.-Rascher	2 Bourrees	Bou
Quilling, H.	Suite	ArM
Raaff, A. de	Papillon	EdH
Rabaud, H.	Solo de Concours	EdM
Rabaud, H.-Gee	Solo de Concours	SM
Rachmaninoff, S.	Vocalise	EdM
Raff, J.	Cavatina	CF
Rameau, J.-Mule	Gavotte (Le Temple de la gloire)	ALe
Rameau, J.-Mule	Gavotte and Minuet (Hippolyte et Aricie)	ALe
Rameau, J.-Mule	Minuet (Castor et Pollux)	ALe
Rameau, J.-Mule	Passepied (Castor et Pollux)	ALe
Rameau, J.-Mule	Rigaudon (Dardanus)	ALe
Rameau, J.-Rascher	Rigaudon	Cha
Rameau, J.	Rigadon de Dardanus	EdM
Rameau, J.-Mule	Rondo (L'Indiscrète)	ALe
Rameau, J.-Mule	Saraband and Rigaudon (Les Fêtes de l'Hymen)	ALe
Rameau, J.-Mule	Tambourin	ALe
Rameau, J.-Scarmolin	La Villageoise	Lud
Rancati, A.	Lovely	GZ
Ranger, A.-arr.	Country Gardens	CF
Ranger, A.	The Old Refrain	CF
Ranger, A.-arr.	A Wreath of Holly	CF
Raphael, G.	Concertino op. 71. 1951	BrH
Raphael, G.	Rècitatif	ALe
Raphling, S.	Sonata No. 2	Gen
Rarig, J.	Dance Episode	Wes
Rasbach, O.	Trees	BM
Rascher, S.-arr.	American folk tune	B-M
Rascher, S.-arr.	Blue Tail Fly	B-M
Rascher, S.-arr.	Drink to me only	B-M
Rascher, S.-arr.	Flowers lullaby	B-M
Rascher, S.-arr.	Fox You Stole the Goose	B-M
Rascher, S.-arr.	Hunters Chorus	B-M
Rascher, S.-arr.	Joys of Life	B-M
Rascher, S.-arr.	Quempas tune	B-M

Rascher, S.-arr.	Two melodies from Bavaria	B-M
Ratez, A.	Pièce romantique	GrF
Ravel, M.-Viard	Five o'clock (l'Enfant et les sortilèges)	Dur
Ravel, M.-Branga	Pavane de la Belle au Bois dormant	Dur
Ravel, M.-Bettoney	Pavane Pour Une Infante Défunte	CF
Ravel, M.	Pavane	EdM
Ravel, M.-Walters	Pavane	Rub
Ravel, M.	Pièce en forme de habanera	ALe
Raymond, L.	Design	Wes
Redouté, J.	Mélodie	EMb
Reed, A.	Ballade	SM
Regt, H. de	Musica	SD
Rehfeldt, P.	Wisconsin River Waltz	SHM
Rehl, R.	The Duchess	Rub
Rehl, R.	Nimble Fingers	Rub
Rehl, R.	Solo De Luxe	Rub
Reiner, K.	2 Kompositionen	CHF
Reinl	Indiscretion	JKM
Reinl	Melodie	JKM
Rema	Gentille Sérénade	Mau
Rema	Impromptu et Allegro	Mau
Reuschel, M.	Syphax, op. 172	Bil
Reutter, H.	Elégie	ALe
Reutter, H.	Pièce concertante. 1968	SS
Rex, H.	Preludio and movendo	B-M
Richard, C.	L'Alliance	EdS
Richard, C.	Le Tour de France	EdS
Richards, J.	Falcaro	Bar
Richards, J.	Sunbeams	Bar
Richards, J.	Villetta	Bar
Rieunier, J.	Linéal	ALe
Rimmer, W.	Saxonia	HeE
Rimsky-Korsakov, N.-Bettoney	Flight of the Bumble Bee	CF
Rimsky-Korsakov, N.-Davis	Flight of the Bumblebee	Rub
Rimsky-Korsakov, N.-Bettoney	Hymn to the Sun	CF
Rimsky-Korsakov, N.-Colby	Hymn to the Sun	Rub
Rimsky-Korsakov, N.	Song of India	Cen
Rimsky-Korsakov, N.-Gurewich	Song of India (Sadko)	CF
Rimsky-Korsakov, N.	Chanson Indoue	Com
Rimsky-Korsakov, N.-Letellier	Chanson Indoue	EdR
Rimsky-Korsakov, N.	Song of India	NK
Rimsky-Korsakov, N.-Hummel	Song of India	Rub
Rivier, J.-Mule	Concertino	EdS
Robel	Kitty's Waltz	Vol
Rocereto-Morgan	Meditation	Vol
Roelens, A.-Mule	Menuet Vif	Job
Rogers	Modern air	B-M

Alto Saxophone and Piano

Rogister, F.	Concertino	Bos
Rollé, E.	Air Varié	EdS
Rollinson, T.	Rocked in the Cradle of the Deep	CF
Rossini, G.-Hekker	Basilio Aria	T-M
Rossini, G.-Lemarc	Cavatine (Semiramis)	T-M
Rossini, G.-Paque	Cavatine de Tancrede	T-M
Rossini, G.	Inflammatus	CF
Rossini, G.-Hekker	Rosine's Aria	T-M
Rossini, G.-Lureman	De Italianen in Algiers	T-M
Rossini, G.-Andreoni	Una Voce poco fa (Barber of Seville)	Ric
Rossini, G.-Rascher	Village Dance	B-M
Roubanis-Edwards	Misirlou	B-M
Rougnon, P.	Cantabile	GrF
Rougnon, P.	Solo de Concert	GrF
Rougnon, P.	2nd Solo de Concert	GrF
Round, H.	The Ash Grove	MM
Round, H.	Jenny Jones	MM
Round, H.	Kelvin Grove	MM
Round, H.	The Rosy Morn air varie	MM
Round, H.	Zenobia	MM
Royal, D.-arr.	Marines Hymn	Cen
Rubinstein, A.	Melodie in F	CF
Rubinstein, A.	Melodie	MM
Rubinstein, A.	Melody in F	NK
Rubinstein, A.	Romance	SF
Rubinstein, A.-Long	Romance	Vol
Rueff, J.	Chanson et passepied	ALe
Rueff, J.	Concertino op. 17	ALe
Rulst-Rema	Allegro rondo	Mau
Rulst-Rema	Carazzevole	Mau
Rulst-Rema	Con gentillezza	Mau
Rulst-Rema	Gavotte et Musette	Mau
Rulst-Rema	Grazioso	Mau
Rulst-Rema	Minuetto	Mau
Rungis, R. & F. Meurice	Caprice	HLe
Rungis, R. & F. Meurice	Oriental	HLe
Rungis, R. & F. Meurice	Scherzo	HLe
Rungis, R. & F. Meurice	Sérénade	HLe
Russell, A.	Particles	Bou
Saeys, E.	Romance	Mau
Saint-Saens, C.	Andantino du Prélude du Déluge	Dur
Saint-Saens, C.	Le Cygne (The Swan)	Cen
Saint-Saens, C.-Trinkaus	The Swan	CF
Saint-Saens, C.	Le Cygne	Dur
Saint-Saens, C.	My Heart At Thy Sweet Voice	Cen
Saint-Saens, C.-Brooke	My Heart At Thy Sweet Voice	CF
Saint-Saens, C.-Tobani	My Heart At Thy Sweet Voice	CF

Alto Saxophone and Piano

Saint-Saens, C.-Branga	Rêverie du Soir (Suite Algérienne)	Dur
Saint-Saens, C.	Romance	EdM
Saint-Saens, C.	2 Pavanes	EdM
Salmon, R.	Nonchalance	Com
Sammartini, G.-Preisler	Allegro	HeE
Sammartini, G.	Canto Amoroso	MM
Sannella	Intervals	B-M
Sannella	June Bells	B-M
Sannella	Memories	B-M
Sannella	Ripples	B-M
Sannella	Saxo-Reel	B-M
Sanner, L.	Sonatin	STI
Sasamori, T.	Variations on Taki's "Kojo No Tsuki"	SMP
Sauguet, H.	Sonatine bucolique	ALe
Savard, A.	Morceau de Concours	ALe
Scarlatti, A.-Barnes	Aria (Tigraine)	Spr
Scarmolin, L.	Bolero	PrA
Scarmolin, L.	Polka Fantasia	B-M
Schaefer, A.	The Soloist	CF
Schaefer	David's Dream	CF
Schaeffer, A.	The Beau Brummel	CF
Schaeffer, A.	The Show-Man	CF
Schaeffer, D.	The Boy Scout	CF
Schaeffer, D.	Ladder of Fame	CF
Schaeffer, D.	Licorice and Lillipops	PrA
Schaeffer, D.	The Neophite	CF
Schaeffer, D.	The Noble Duke	CF
Schinelli, E.	Never	GZ
Schmidt, A.	2 Pièces	Mau
Schmidt, W.	A Little Midnight Music	Wes
Schmitt, F.	Légende, op. 66	Dur
Schmutz, A.	Divertimento	Lud
Schmutz, A.	Sonata	SMP
Schubert, F.-Traxler	Ave Maria	B-M
Schubert, F.	Ave Maria	CF
Schubert, F.-Baudrier	Berceuse	MM
Schubert, F.-Overveld	Du bist die Ruh'	T-M
Schubert, F.-Londeix	Impromptu	ALe
Schubert, F.	Moment Musical	CF
Schubert, F.-Cochrane	The Post	CF
Schubert, F.-Mule	Sérénade	ALe
Schubert, F.-Damm	Serenade	CF
Schubert, F.	Serenade	Cen
Schubert, F.-Overveld	Ständchen	T-M
Schubert, F.-Londeix	Suite de Valses, op. 3	ALe
Schumann, R.-Chauvet	Chant du soir	Com
Schumann, R.	Einsame Blumen	Spr
Schumann, R.-Andreoni	The Happy Farmer	Ric

Schumann, R.-Mule	Scènes d'enfants, Rêverie	ALe
Schumann, R.-Viard	Rêverie	EdS
Schumann, R.-Coggins	Romance No. 1	B-M
Schumann, R.-Mule	St. Nicholas (Album for the Young)	ALe
Schumann, R.-Hemke	3 Romances	SM
Schumann, R.-Rascher	Traumerei	B-M
Schwarenka, X.	Polish Dance	CF
Sclater, J.	Suite for Saxophone	Dor
Scriabin, A.-Diercks	Prelude, op. 9/1; Etude, op. 8/2	Wes
Scull, J.	Beneath Thy Window	Vol
Seellenne, T.	Berceuse	EMb
Seleski, L.	Interlude Romantique	Ken
Semler-Collery, A.	Lied	Bil
Semler-Collery, J.	Barcarolle & Dance	EME
Semler-Collery, J.	Etudes Concertante	EME
Semler-Collery, J.	Fantaisie-Caprice. 1965	EME
Semler-Collery, J.	Mélodie Expressive	EME
Semler-Collery, J.	Récit and Scherzando	ALe
Senaillé, J.-Gee	Allegro Spiritoso	SM
Shishov, I.	Grotesque Dance (The Master Barber)	EdM
Shostakovich, D.	Danses Fantastiques	EdM
Shostakovich, D.	Satirical Dance (The Bolt)	EdM
Sibelius, J.-Johnson	Swan of Tuonela	B-M
Sibelius, J.	Valse Triste	Cen
Sibelius, J.-Trinkaus	Valse Triste	CF
Siegel, A.	Pasquinade	See
Siegmeister, E.	Down River	MCA
Simpson	Andante con moto	Wat
Simpson	Reverie	Wat
Singelée, J.	Fantaisie Pastorale	MM
Skolnik, W.	Meditation	TP
Skolnik, W.	Sonatina	TP
Slechta, T.	Father of Waters	CF
Smith, C.	Among the Sycamores	Bar
Smith, C.	From Day to Day	CF
Smith, C.	Helen	CF
Smith, C.	Italiana	Bar
Smith, C.	Life's Lighter Hours	Bar
Smith, C.	Milady's Pleasure	Bar
Smith, C.	On Pleasure Bent	CF
Smith, C.	My Song of Songs	CF
Smith, C.	Rainbow Hues	Bar
Smith, C.	Smithsonian	Bar
Smith, C.	The Spirit of Joy	CF
Smith & Holmes	Believe Me If All Those Endearing Young Charms	CF
Smith & Holmes	Call of the Sea	Bar

Smith & Holmes	The Caribbean	CF
Smith & Holmes	Drink To Me Only With Thine Eyes	CF
Smith & Holmes	Massa's in the Cold, Cold Ground	Bar
Smith & Holmes	Silver Threads among the Gold	Bar
Smith & Holmes	Through Shadowed Vales	Bar
Smith & Holmes	Wayfarer	Bar
Smolanoff, M.	Concertino	E-V
Snyder, R.	7 Epigrams	SM
Snyder, R.	Sonata	TP
Sontag, C.	An Evening Serenade	CF
Souffriau, A.	Concertino	EMb
Soule, E.	Serenade	Sha
Sousa, J.	Stars and Stripes Forever	NK
Sousa, J.-Walters	Stars and Stripes Forever	Rub
Spencer, W.	Silvatones	CF
Sporck, G.	Méditation	Bil
Sporck, G.	Novelette	Bil
Stache, H.	Crépuscule	Mau
Stache & Rema	Romance	EMb
Staigers, D.	Carnival of Venice	CF
Staigers, D.	Hazel	CF
St. Clair, F.	Admiration	Vol
St. Clair, F.	Dream Time	Vol
St. Clair, F.	Golden Days	Vol
Steiner, G.	Concerto	CCo
Steiner-Schoenfeld	Tara Theme	War
Stevens, H.	Dittico	JB
Still, W.	Romance	Bou
Stradella, A.	Air d'église	Com
Strandsjö, G.	Liten svit	EMf
Strauss, J.-Bettoney	Blue Danube Waltz	CF
Strauss, J.-Jolliff	Tritsch-Tratsch Polka	Rub
Strauss, O.-Harris	A Waltz Dream	Lud
Strauss, R.-Walters	Allerseelen	Rub
Strauss, R.	Zueignung	EdM
Strauwen, J.	Andante Varié	EMb
Stravinsky, I.	Dance of the Princesses (The Firebird)	EdM
Strimer, J.	Orientale	ALe
Strimer, J.	Pastorale Caucasienne	Dur
Strimer, J.	Sérénade	ALe
Stuart, H.-arr.	BMCO Famous Saxophone Favorites	BM
Stults, R.-Hummel	The Sweetest Story Ever Told	Rub
Sullivan, A.	The Lost Chord	Cen
Sullivan, A.	Lost Chord	CF
Sullivan, A.	The Lost Chord	MM

Alto Saxophone and Piano

Suppé, F. von -Long	Andante Maestoso (Poet and Peasant)	Vol
Takács, J.	2 Fantastics, op. 88	LDo
Tartini, G. -Mule	Grave	ALe
Tartini, G.	Introduction and Allegro Assai	EdM
Tate, P.	Concerto	OxU
Tautenhahn, G.	Elegy	See
Tchaikovsky, P.	Andante Cantabile, op. 11	CF
Tchaikovsky, P.	Autumn Song	HeE
Tchaikovsky, P. -Cailliet	Canzonetta (Violin Concerto)	Leb
Tchaikovsky, P.	Chanson Triste	CF
Tchaikovsky, P.	Chant sans Paroles	CF
Tchaikovsky, P. -Hurrell	Danse Arabe (The Nutcracker Suite)	Rub
Tchaikovsky, P. -Lemarc	Herfstlied, op. 37	T-M
Tchaikovsky, P. -Seay	Impromptu	Spr
Tchaikovsky, P. -Bettoney	The Sleeping Beauty	CF
Tchaikovsky, P.	3 Pieces (Album for Children)	EdM
Tchaikovsky, P. -Harris	Waltz	Lud
Tcherepnine, A.	Sonatine sportive	ALe
Teal, L. -arr.	Program Solos	TP
Teal, L. -arr.	Solos for the Alto Saxophone Player	Sch
Telemann, G. -Londeix	Sonata, a	ALe
Telemann, G. -Londeix	Sonata, Eb	ALe
Tenaglia, A.	Aria Antica	EdM
Thiriet, M.	Adagio	ALe
Thomas, A.	Romance (Raymond)	Cen
Thomas	Waltz Pastel	SHM
Thomé, F.	Fantaisie	ALe
Thomé, F. -Leonard	Simple Aveu	B-M
Thomé, F.	Simple Aveu (Confession)	Cen
Thomé, F.	Simple Aveu	Dur
Thompson	Bubble and Squeak	Vol
Thompson	Carolyn Melodie	Vol
Thompson	Remembrance	Vol
Thompson	Song of Spring	Vol
Thompson	Suite d'amour	Vol
Thompson	Valse Caprice	Vol
Thompson	Valse Minah	Vol
Thornton, E.	Une Pensée Lointaine	CF
Titl, A.	Serenade	CF
Toldra, E. -Amaz	Ave Maria	UME
Toldra, E. -Amaz	Dels Quatre Vents	UME
Toldra, E. -Amaz	La Font	UME
Toldra, E. -Amaz	Oracio al Maig	UME
Toldra, E. -Amaz	Soneti de la Rosada	UME
Toll, R.	Legerete	CF
Toll, R.	Lullaby	CF
Tomasi, H.	Ballade	ALe

Tomasi, H.	Chant Corse	ALe
Tomasi, H.	Concerto	ALe
Tomasi, H.	Introduction and Dance	ALe
Tomer-Barnhouse	God Be With You	Bar
Toselli, E.-Leonard	Serenade	B-M
Toselli, E.	Serenade	BM
Tosti, F.	Good-Bye	Cen
Totzauer	Legende	JKM
Tourneur, G.	Part One of Concerto after Mozart	ALe
Tournier, F.	Prélude et Scherzo	HLe
Tournier, F.	Variations on a Theme of Claude Lejeune	ALe
Trinkaus, G.	Lament	CF
Trinkaus, G.-arr.	World's Best-Known Pieces	CF
Trowbridge, L.	Album Leaf	See
Trowbridge, L.	In Retrospect	See
Trowbridge, L.	Organum Metamorphoses	See
Tubin, E.	Sonat. 1951	STI
Turkin, M.	Sonata	TP
Tuthill, B.-Leeson	Sonata	SM
Vallier, J.	Suite	Com
Vandelle, R.	Prélude	ALe
Vandelle, R.	Prelude and Gigue	ALe
VanderCook, H.	Daisies	NK
VanderCook, H.	Ivy	NK
VanderCook, H.	Marigold	NK
VanderCook, H.	Tulip	NK
Van Dijk, R.	Sonata Movement. 1960	Can
Van Moer, J.	Solo No. 1	EMb
Vaute, M.	Cantilene variee	Mau
Veach, D.	Blue Lagoon	PrA
Veach, D.	Wind Currents	CF
Vellones, P.	Concerto	HLe
Vellones, P.-Mule	Rapsodie, op. 92	HLe
Verdi, G.	Ah, forse e lui (La Traviata)	Ric
Verdi, G.-Andreoni	Caro nome (Rigoletto)	Ric
Verdi, G.	Celeste Aida (Aida)	Cen
Verdi, G.	La Donna e Mobile	Cen
Verdi, G.	Grand Air (The Masked Ball)	EdM
Verdi, G.	Miserere, Il Trovatore	Cen
Verdi, G.-Bassi, Bettoney	Rigoletto	CF
Verdi, G.-Andreoni	Tacea la notte placida (Il Trovatore)	Ric
Vereecken, B.	Cheerfulness	Bar
Vereecken, B.	Don Gonzales	CF
Vereecken, B.	Shepherd's Dream	Bar
Vereecken, B.	Waternymphs	Bar
Viard, J.	Capriccio	EdS
Vidal, P.	Melody	ALe

Alto Saxophone and Piano

Villa-Lobos, H.-Goehr	Song of the Black Swan	EBM
Vivaldi, A.	Concerto, a	EdM
Vivaldi, A.	Rain (The Seasons)	EdM
Vivaldi, A.-Hunt	Sonata, op. 1/7	CF
Vivaldi, A.	Sonata, g	M&M
Vivaldi, A.	Suite, c	EdM
Vivier, F.	Enchantress	CF
Vogt	Boat Song	Cen
Vogt	Dream Waltz	Cen
Vogt	Remembrance	Cen
Vogt	Sax-o-moan	Cen
Vogt	Saxonade	Cen
Vogt	Saxonola	Cen
Volleman, A.	Improvisatie en Allegro	Mau
Von Kreisler, A.	2 Impressions	SM
Votquenne, V.	Barcarolle	EMb
Votquenne, V.	Fioriture	EMb
Voxman, H. (ed)	Concert and Contest Collection	Rub
Wadsworth	Co-Ed Capers	GFB
Wagner, R.	Bridal Chorus	McK
Wagner, R.	Dreams	CF
Wagner, R.-Lefèbre	Pilgrim's Chorus	CF
Wagner, R.-Trinkaus	Pilgrim's Chorus	CF
Wagner, R.	Romance (Tannhauser)	Cen
Wagner, R.-Roberts	Song to the Evening Star	CF
Wagner, R.-Trinkaus	Song to the Evening Star	CF
Wagner, R.	Evening Star	McK
Wagner, R.-Trinkaus	Walther's Prize Song	CF
Walker, R.	Ballade	Ken
Walker, R.	Reminiscence	PrA
Walker, R.	Valse Casuel	BM
Walker	Elaine	CF
Walker	Evelyn	CF
Wallace-Round-Henton	Scenes That Are Brightest (Maritana)	CF
Walters	Episode	SM
Walters, H.-arr.	Amazing Grace	Rub
Walters, H.-arr.	Fat Boy Polka	Rub
Walters, H.-arr.	Sakura, Sakura (Cherry Blossoms)	Rub
Walters, H.	Shindig (Folk song Fantasy)	Rub
Walters, H.-arr.	When the Saints Go Marching In	Rub
Wangermée, F.	Ambassador, Valse	EMb
Ward, D.	An Abstract	SM
Warren, D.	Chorale Fantasy	Lud
Warren, D.	Cumberland	Lud
Warren, D.	Danish Dance	Lud
Watters, C.	Valse Coquette	B&H
Webber, C.-arr.	First Solo Album	TP
Weber, A.	Mélopée	ALe

Weber, A.	Saxetto	ALe
Weber, C. M. von -Delcampe	Andante et Rondo	EMb
Weber, C. M. von -Davis	Concertino	Rub
Weber, C. M. von -Grignon	Concerto op. 73, No. 1	UME
Weber, C. M. von -Mule	Little Waltz and Tyrolienne	ALe
Weber, C. M. von -Mule	Waltz (Der Freischütz)	ALe
Weber, F.	Evening Shadows	B-M
Weber, F.	Sentimental Lady	B-M
Weber -Mule	Carnaval de Vénise	ALe
Weber	Mélodie	ALe
Webster -Barnhouse	Sweet By and By	Bar
Weinberger, J.	Concerto	SM
Welander, W.	Arietta	CF
Westendorf, T.	I'll Take You Home Again Kathleen	GFB
Whitney, M.	Introduction and Samba	Bou
Whitney, M.	Melancholy	Spr
Whitney, M.	Rumba	Bou
Wiedoeft, R. -arr.	Anchors Aweigh	Big
Wiedoeft, R.	Danse Hongroise	Big
Wiedoeft, R. -arr.	Manhattan Serenade	Big
Wiedoeft, R. -arr.	On the Trail	Big
Wiedoeft, R.	Rubenola	Big
Wiedoeft, R.	Saxarella .	Big
Wiedoeft, R.	Sax-O-Doodle	Big
Wiedoeft, R.	Sax-O-Minute Waltz	Big
Wiedoeft, R.	Saxophobia	Big
Wiedoeft, R.	Sax-O-Trix	Big
Wiedoeft, R.	Valse Erica	Big
Wiedoeft, R.	Valse Marilyn	Big
Wiedoeft, R.	Valse Mazanetta	Big
Wiedoeft, R.	Valse Vanite	Big
Wiedoeft, R.	Velma	Big
Wiedoeft, R.	Waltz Llewellyn	Big
Wiedoeft, R.	Wiedoeft's Rubato	Big
Wieniawski, H.	Romance (2nd Concerto)	CF
Wiggins, A.	Conversation	Ken
Wilber, R.	Serenade	B-M
Wilber, R.	Valse Clintine	B-M
Wilder, A.	Sonata No. 1	SF
Wilsam, J.	Floralie	EMb
Wilson, G.	Moonlight on the Hudson, op. 60	Cen
Wilson, G.	The Wayside Chapel	Cen
Wirth, C.	Beyond These Hills	SP
Wirth, C.	Dark Flows the River	SP
Wood, S.	Alamada	MM
Wood, W.	Let 'Er Go	Cen
Wurmser, L.	Bagatelles	Bil

Wurmser, L.	Barcarolle	Bil
Wurmser, L.	Esquisses	Bil
Wurmser, L.	Fantasia	EMT
Wurmser, L.	Frivole	Bil
Wurmser, L.	Pochade	Bil
Wurmser, L.	Tristesse	Com
Young, G.	Contempora Suite	B-M
Yradier, E.	The Dove (La Paloma)	Cen
Yradier, E.-Lefèbre	La Paloma	CF
Yradier, E.-Whiting	La Paloma	CF
Yradier, E.	La Paloma	MM
Zamacois, J.-Amaz	Serenada d'Hivern	UME
Zambarano, A.	Neapolitan Tarantella	Sha
Zeller, K.	Schenkt Man Sich Rosen in Tirol	MM
Zimmerman, R.-arr.	Play A Song of America	TP
Zimmerman, R.-arr.	Play a Song of Christmas	TP

Alto Saxophone and Organ

Schmidt, W.	Variegations	Wes
Smith, S.	One for Two	See

Alto Saxophone and Orchestra

Badings, H.	Concerto	EMo
Bariller, R.	Rapsodie Bretonne	ALe
Bernier, R.	Hommage to Sax	ALe
Binge, R.	Concerto	EBM
Bonneau, P.	Concerto	ALe
Bonneau, P.	Pièce concertante dans l'esprit "Jazz"	ALe
Bonneau, P.	Suite	ALe
Boutry, R.	Divertimento	ALe
Boutry, R.	Sérénade	EdS
Božič, D.	Concerto	EdD
Bozza, E.	Concertino	ALe
Brenta, G.	Saxiana	ALe
Briegel, G.	Soloette	GFB
Briegel & Tucker	Triplets	GFB
Busser, H.	Au pays de Léon et de Salamanque, op. 116	ALe
Camarata, S.	Rhapsody	B-M
Camilleri, C.	Suite	Che
Challan, R.	Concerto	ALe
Chopin, F.	Minute Waltz	GFB

342

Clérisse, R.	Chanson à Bercer	ALe
Constant, M.	Concert Music	ALe
Corniot, R.	Eglogue and Pastoral Dance	ALe
Cowell, H.	Air & Scherzo	AMP
Creston, P.	Concerto	Sch
Damase, J.	Concertstück	ALe
Debussy, C.	Rhapsody	CF
Debussy, C.	Rapsodie	Dur
Dijk, J. van	Concertino. 1956	SD
Dressel, E.	Konzert op. 27	R&E
Dubois, P.	Concerto	ALe
Dubois, P.	Divertissement	ALe
Dubois, P.	Le Lièvre et la tortue	ALe
Dubois, P.	Sonatina	ALe
Ducat, A.	Esquisse	Mau
Eisenmann, W.	Concerto da camera (asax, str)	UE
Eriksson, N.	Concerto	STI
Farberman, H.	Concerto	Gen
Foster, S.-Briegel	2 Stephen Foster Melodies	GFB
Glazounov, A.	Concerto	ALe
Gotkovsky, I.	Concerto	EMT
Gunaropulos, Y.	Concerto, Bb, No. 2. 1946	Fin
Hasquenoph, P.	Concertino (sax, str)	Heu
Heider, W.	Typen	A&S
Husa, K.	Elégie en rondeau	ALe
Ibert, J.	Concertino da camera	ALe
Indy, V. d'	Choral Varié, op. 55	CF
Indy, V. d'	Choral Varié, op. 55	Dur
Jacob, G.	Rhapsody	GaM
Jahrl	Frolic of the Keys	GFB
Karkoff, M.	Concertino op. 15. 1955	STI
Kelkel, M.	Rhapsodie	Ric
Keuris, T.	Concerto	SD
Koch, E. von	Concerto. 1958	STI
Koch, F.	Concertino	See
Korn, P.	Concerto	B-M
Krumlovsky, C.	Concertino	ALe
Kügerl, H.	Rhapsodie	LK
Lacour, G.	Hommage à Jacques Ibert, Concertino	Bil
Larsen, E.	Concerto	WH
Larsson, L.	Saxophone Concerto, op. 14	CGM
Lonque, G.	Images d'Orient	ALe
Malipiero, G.	Serenissima	UE
Martin, F.	Ballade	UE
Milhaud, D.	Scaramouche	EdS
Moller, K.	Rhapsodi	WH
Murgier, J.	Concerto	EMT
Pálenícek, J.	Concerto. 1955	CHF
Paulson, G.	Concerto op. 105. 1959	STI

Perrin, M.	Mirage	ALe
Philiba, N.	Concerto	Bil
Porcelijn, D.	Pulverization II. 1973	SD
Ramans, G.	Concerto	MKE
Raphael, G.	Concertino op. 71. 1951	BrH
Rarig, J.	Night Song (asax, str)	Wes
Ravel, M.	Pièce en forme de habanera	ALe
Rivier, J.	Concertino	EdS
Rueff, J.	Concertino op. 17	ALe
Schäffer, B.	S·alto. 1963	AP
Schmitt, F.	Légende, op. 66	Dur
Semler-Collery, J.	Fantaisie-Caprice. 1965	EME
Tate, P.	Concerto (asax, str)	OxU
Tomasi, H.	Ballade	ALe
Tomasi, H.	Concerto	ALe
Tomasi, H.	Introduction and Dance	ALe
Voormolen, A.	La Sirène. 1949	SD
Welander, W.	Arietta	STI
Welander, W.	Concertino. 1963 (asax, str)	STI
Yoshioka, E.	Arioso	ArM
Zender, H.	Concertino op. 5. 1952	BrH

Alto Saxophone and Band

	Londonderry Air	GFB
Andrieu, F.	L'Angelus du soir	EdR
Andrieu, F.	Divertissement	EdR
Andrieu, F.	A une étoile	EdR
Badings, H.	Concerto	SD
Becker, E.	Ernestonia	Vol
Bennett, D.	Saxophone Royale	SM
Benson, W.	Concertino	MCA
Bergson, M.-Veenendaal	Louise de Montfoort	MM
Bilik, J.	Concerto	CFC
Binge, R.	Romance	EBM
Bléger, A.	Les Echos de Barcelone	EdR
Briegel, G.	Soloette	GFB
Briegel & Tucker	Triplets	GFB
Bruniau, A.	Fantaisie Tyrolienne	EdR
Bruniau, A.	Fantaisie variée	EdR
Bruniau, A.	Grande Introduction et Polonaise	EdR
Bruniau, A.	Sur la Montagne	EdR
Bunton, E.	Alto Mood	Ken
Cacavas, J.	Midnight Soliloquy	Vol
Chopin, F.	Minute Waltz	GFB
Chopin, F.-Martin	Tristesse	EdR
Coates, E.	Saxo Rhapsody	Cha
Cofield, F.	Chartreuse	Rub
Dahl, I.	Concerto	AMC
Davis, A.	Solo Silhouette	Ken

DeLuca, J.-Roberts	Beautiful Colorado	CF
DeVille, P.-Brockton	Blue Bells of Scotland	CF
Dittrich, F.	Concertino	BrH
Eccles, H.-Bowder	Sonata	Roc
Elgar, E.-Luckhardt	Land of Hope and Glory	B&H
Erickson, F.	Concerto	Bou
Everaarts, M.	Solo	T-M
Filas, T.	Concerto for Doubles (asax/ cl/bcl, B)	BM
Foster, S.	Beautiful Dreamer; Jeanie with the Light Brown Hair	GFB
Godard, B.-Fernand	Berceuse de Jocelyn	EdR
Grundman, C.	Concertante	B&H
Hagen, E.-Reed	Harlem Nocturne	CFC
Handel, G.-De Noslin	Célèbre largo	EdR
Hartley, W.	Concerto	Tri
Husa, K.	Concerto. 1967	AMP
Jahrl	Frolic of the Keys	GFB
Koch, F.	Concertino	See
Lake, M.	Naida	Lud
Lawrence & Newsom	Contentment	Ken
Leoncavallo, R.-Barnes	Mattinata	Lud
Lieb, D.	Short Ballet	Ken
Lieurance, T.-Lake	By the Waters of Minnetonka	CF
Logan, R.	Presto Chango	TP
Logan, R.	Sugar and Spice	Bar
Losey, F.	Ambassador Polka	Vol
Masten, I.	Bonnie Eloise	Lud
Mellish-arr.	Drink To Me Only With Thine Eyes	GFB
Miller, E.	Fantasy-Concerto	ACA
Moffitt	Talent Scout	CF
Morrissey, J.	Nightfall	EBM
Mozart, W.	Larghetto (Quintet, op. 108)	EdR
Muldermans, J.	Fantaisie brillante	EdR
Nestico, S.	Persuasion	SP
Niehaus, L.	Palo Alto	Wes
Quilling, H.	Suite	ArM
Rarig, J.	Dance Episode	Wes
Reed, A.	Ballade	SM
Rex, H.	Preludio and Movendo	B-M
Rimsky-Korsakov, N.-Christol	Chanson Hindoue (Sadko)	EdR
Schaefer, A.	Troubadours	CF
Schumann, R.-Martin	Célèbre Rêverie	EdR
Seleski, L.	Interlude Romantique	Ken
Staigers, D.	Carnival of Venice	CF
Wallace & Round-Henton	Maritana	CF
Watters, C.	Valse Coquette	B&H
Whitney, M.	Introduction and Samba	Bou
Whitney, M.	Rumba	Bou

Wiggins, A.   Conversation   Ken

C Melody Saxophone

C Melody Saxophone and Piano

	In Old Vienna	McK
	Turkey in the Straw	McK
Balfe, W.	Bohemian Girl Airs	Vol
Beethoven, L. van	Minuet, G	CF
Beethoven, L. van	Minuet, G	McK
Buchtel, F.	Chant d'amour	Vol
Buchtel, F.	Valse Romantique	Vol
Clement, F.	Silvertone Polka	Vol
Donizetti, G.	Sextette (Lucia)	Vol
Drigo, R. -Damm	Serenade	CF
Drigo, R. -Saenger	Valse Bluette	CF
Durand, A.	First Valse	CF
Dvořak, A.	Humoreske	McK
Elgar, E.	Salut d'Amour	CF
Emmett, D.	Dixie's Land	McK
Geiger -Polla	Just for Tonight	EBM
Glinka, M. --Gurewich	The Lark	CF
Heltman	Mary Jane Waltz	Vol
Holmes, G. -arr.	Auld Lang Syne	CF
Jessel, L. -Polla	Parade of the Wooden Soldiers	EBM
Keithley	I'll Never Find a Pal Like You	McK
Keithley	When Shadows Fall	McK
King -Garrison	Song of the Islands	EBM
Klickmann, F.	Sweet Hawaiian Moonlight	McK
Klickmann, F.	Trail to Long Ago	McK
Klickmann, F.	Weeping Willow Lane	McK
Knight -Clement	Rocked in the Cradle of the Deep	Vol
Lansing, A.	Darkey's Dream	McK
Liliuokalani, Queen	Aloha Oe	McK
Lincke, P. -Polla	Fireflies	EBM
Lincke, P. -Polla	Glow-Worm	EBM
Lincke, P. -Polla	March of the Siamese	EBM
Lincke, P. -Polla	Spring Beautiful Spring	EBM
Mascagni, P.	Intermezzo	McK
Molloy, J.	Love's Old Sweet Song	McK
Morris -arr.	Drink to Me Only With Thine Eyes	Vol
Myddleton, W. -Polla	Down South	EBM
Offenbach, J.	Barcarolle	McK
Offenbach, J. -Scull	Barcarolle	Vol

Ortolani, O.	More (Mondo Cane)	EBM
Panella	Jack and Jill	Vol
Panella	Jolly Two	Vol
Panella	Tom and Jerry	Vol
Panella	Two Bachelors	Vol
Panella	Two Gnomes	Vol
Panella	Two Lovers	Vol
Pinard, A.	Darling	CF
Pinard, A.	Just a Little Song of Love	CF
Pinard, A.	Yearning	CF
Rimsky-Korsakov, N.	Song of India	CF
Robel	Kitty's Waltz	Vol
Rubinstein, A.-Long	Romance	Vol
Scull, J.	Beneath Thy Window	Vol
Smith, C.	From Day To Day	CF
Smith, C.	On Pleasure Bent	CF
Smith, C.	The Spirit of Joy	CF
Smith & Holmes	Drink To Me Only With Thine Eyes	CF
Smith & Holmes	Old Black Joe	CF
Sontag, C.	An Evening Serenade	CF
St. Clair, F.	Admiration	Vol
St. Clair, F.	Dream Time	Vol
St. Clair, F.	Golden Days	Vol
Suppé, F. von-Long	Andante Maestoso (Poet and Peasant)	Vol
Thompson	Carolyn Melodie	Vol
Thompson	Remembrance	Vol
Thompson	Suite d'amour	Vol
Thompson	Valse Caprice	Vol
Thompson	Valse Minah	Vol
Wagner, R.	Bridal Chorus	McK
Wagner, R.	Evening Star	McK
Webber, C.-arr.	First Solo Album	TP
Zimmerman, R.-arr.	Play A Song of Christmas	TP

Tenor Saxophone

Tenor Saxophone and Piano

Black Eyes	GFB
Easy Does It, 3 vols.	War
Broadway Showcase	War
55 Masterpieces	B-M
40 Hits of Our Times	MCA
40 More Hits of Our Times	MCA
Indispensable Folio	Rub
In Old Vienna	McK
Londonderry Air	GFB

	Londonderry Air	MM
	Song of the Volga Boatmen	GFB
	Turkey in the Straw	McK
Ackermans, H.	Paysage Nordique	EMb
Aerts, F.	Fantaisie Varié	T-M
Albéniz, I.-Amaz	Mallorca. Barcarola	UME
Albéniz, I.-Amaz	Puerta de tierra	UME
Albinoni, T.-Joosen	Concerto, Bb	MM
Albinoni, T.	Concerto, op. 9/2	MM
Aldrich, F.	Love and Flowers	Cen
Aletter, W.	Rendezvous	Bos
Alschausky, J.	Waltzer--Arie No. 2	CF
Ameller, A.	Baie Comeau	ALe
Ameller, A.	Kryptos	HE
Ameller, A.	Pointe-au-pic	ALe
Anderson, G.	Sonata	SM
Andrieu, F.	Concertino No. 3	EdM
Andrieu, F.	Rondo Caprice	EdM
Andrieu, F.	Rossignol d'amour	Bil
Arban, J.	Oberto. Air Varie	MM
Arban, J.-Vanasek	Perpetual Motion	MCA
Arlen, H.-Sears	Blues in the Night	War
Arndt, F.	Nola	SF
Arne, T.	Drink to Me Only	MM
Auber, D.-Hekker	Angela Aria	T-M
Aubert, J.	Gigue	EdM
Avon, E.	Danse Joyeuse	CF
Bach, C.-Gallo	Spring's Awakening	CF
Bach, J.S.-Davis	Allegro (Suite No. 3, viola da gamba)	Wes
Bach, J.S.	Andante (Sinfonia)	MM
Bach, J.S.-Schmidt	Adagio (Sonata No. 3, viola	
Bach, J.S.-Kent	Arioso (Cantata No. 156)	CF
Bach, J.S.-Gounod	Ave Maria	Cen
Bach, J.S.-Gounod	Ave Maria	MM
Bach, J.S.-Mule	Bourrée (Suite, C)	ALe
Bach, J.S.-Rascher	Gavotte and Bourree	B-M
Bach, J.S.-Coggins	Minuet, d	B-M
Bach, J.S.-Rascher	Musette	B-M
Bach, J.S.-Londeix	Scherzetto	ALe
Bach, J.S.-Gee	Sonata No. 4	SM
Baeyens, H.	Canzonetta	EMb
Baimgartner	Noch sind die Tagen der Rosen	MM
Balfe, W.	Bohemian Girl Airs	Vol
Barat, J.-Voxman	Berceuse	Rub
Bariller, R.	Fan'jazz	ALe
Barnard, D.	Plains of Peace	Bos
Barris-Ventura	Wrap Your Troubles in Dreams	ShB

Bartók, B.-Harris	Evening in the Country	Lud
Beeler, W.-arr.	Christmas Favorites	Sch
Beethoven, L. van	Adelaide	CF
Beethoven, L. van -Andreoni	Minuet, G	Ric
Beethoven, L. van	Minuet, G	CF
Beethoven, L. van -Trinkaus	Minuet	CF
Beethoven, L. van	Minuet, G	McK
Beethoven, L. van	Minuetto	MM
Beethoven, L. van	Rondo (op. 17)	EdM
Bellini, V.-Joosen	Concerto	MM
Benda, F.	Introduction and Dance	EdM
Benda, F.	Sonata, F	EdM
Bennett, D.	Concerto, g, Movement I	CF
Benson, W.	Farewell	MCA
Bergson, M.	Scene and Air (Luisa di Montfort)	CF
Bergson, M.	Louise de Montfoort--Scene et Air	MM
Berlioz, H.	3 Songs (The Damnation of Faust)	EdM
Bisselink, P.	Izegrim	MM
Bizet, G.	Adagio (Symphony, C)	EdM
Bizet, G.	Agnus Dei (L'Arlésienne)	EdM
Bizet, G.	Agnus Dei	MM
Bizet, G.	Menuet de L'Arlésienne	MM
Blaauw, L.	Ballet Scene	T-M
Blaauw, L.	2 Eenvoudige voordrachts-stukken	T-M
Blaauw, L.	2 Karakterstukken	T-M
Blake -Ventura	Memories of You	ShB
Blavet, M. -Joosen	Sonatine	MM
Bléger, A.	Souvenir de Valence	MM
Blémant, L.	Sous les sapins	ALe
Boccherini, L.-Mule	Adagio	ALe
Boccherini, L.	Menuet	CF
Boccherini, L.	Menuet	MM
Boni, P.-Voxman	Largo and Allegro	Rub
Borodin, A.-Buchtel	Polovetsian Dances	NK
Borodin, A.-Walters	Polovtsian Dance (Prince Igor)	Rub
Borowski, F.-Harris	Valsette	Lud
Bouillon, P.	La Pluie d'Or	MM
Bowman -Haring	12th Street Rag	ShB
Boyce, W.-Brink	Moderato en Larghetto	T-M
Bozza, E.	Impromptu and Dance	ALe
Braga, G.	Angel's Serenade	Cen
Braga, G.	Angel's Serenade	CF
Brahms, J.-Rascher	Sapphic Ode	B-M
Brandt	Air Varie	T-M
Briegel, G.	Cathedral Echoes	GFB
Briegel, G.	Little Shepherd	GFB

Briegel, G.	Soloette	GFB
Briegel, G.-arr.	2 Stephen Foster Melodies	GFB
Buchtel, F.	Beau Brummel	NK
Buchtel, F.-arr.	Blue Bells of Scotland with variations	B-M
Buchtel, F.	Bolero	NK
Buchtel, F.	Chant d'amour	Vol
Buchtel, F.	Crown Prince	NK
Buchtel, F.-arr.	Holy City	NK
Buchtel, F.	Janus	NK
Buchtel, F.	Jupiter	NK
Buchtel, F.	King's Jester	NK
Buchtel, F.	Meditation (Sonatina in F)	NK
Buchtel, F.	Merrymakers Gavotte	NK
Buchtel, F.	My Buddy	NK
Buchtel, F.	Novelette	NK
Buchtel, F.	Romantica	NK
Buchtel, F.	Valse Romantique	Vol
Burger, J.	Dans van de Sultan	MM
Burger, J.	Herdersdans	MM
Burger, J.	Illusie	MM
Butterfield, J.	When You and I Were Young	Cen
Buzzi-Peccia	Lolita	Ric
Camidge, M.-Joosen	Sonatine, Bb	MM
Canivez, L.	Air Varie, op. 31	T-M
Cardillo	Core'ngrato	Ric
Chaminade, C.	Pastorale Enfantine	CF
Chapelle	Une Serenade	CF
Chenette, E.	Sax King	CF
Chenette, E.	The Sax Prince	CF
Chenette, E.	The Sax Princess	CF
Chenette, E.	Valse Joliet	CF
Chopin, F.-Mule	Prelude No. 15	ALe
Chopin, F.-Andreoni	Tristezza, op. 10/3	Ric
Cimarosa, D.-Joosen	Sonata, Bb	MM
Cirri, G.	Arioso	EdM
Clarke, H.	Bride of the Waves	War
Clarke, H.	Southern Cross	War
Clarke, I.	Trixie Waltz	CF
Clarke, I.	25 Christmas Carols	BM
Clarke, I.	25 Hymns	BM
Clement, F.	Evening Zephyr	Bar
Clement, F.	Silvertone Polka	Vol
Clérisse, R.	A l'hombre du clocher	ALe
Clérisse, R.	Prélude et divertissement	Bil
Clérisse, R.	Sérénade variée	ALe
Coggins, W. & F. Weber	Tenor saxophone soloist (Level 1)	B-M
Cohen, S.	Introduction and Czardas	War
Confrey, Z.	Dizzy fingers	B-M

Confrey, Z.	Kitten on the keys	B-M
Corelli, A.	Air and Dance	EdM
Corelli, A.	Gavotte	B-M
Corelli, A.	Gigue	EdM
Corelli, A.	Sonata, F	EdM
Corelli, A.	Suite, Bb	EdM
Couperin, F.	Air de Diable	EdM
Couperin, F.-Mule	Berceuse en rondeau	ALe
Crawford-Kent	The Army Air Corps	CF
Cui, C.	Cantabile	CF
Cunningham, M.	Trigon, op. 31	EQM
Dabney-Ventura	Make the Whole World Shine	ShB
Dagnelies, D.	Fantaisie variée	ScF
Dahm, P.-arr.	Concert Album	EdM
Dahm, P.-arr.	Paris Soir	EdM
Dailey, D.-arr.	Concert Pieces	Wah
Dalen, H. van	Romance	HeE
Dancla, C.	Air Varié sur un Thème de Donizetti	MM
Dancla, C.	Andante et Mazurka	MM
Dancla, C.	Ballade et Air de Ballet	MM
Dancla, C.	Petite Etude et Polonaise	MM
Dancla, C.	Romance et Valse	MM
Danks, H.	Silver Threads Among the Gold	Cen
Danks, H.-De Rooij	Silver Threads Among the Gold	HeE
Debussy, C.	Air de Lia	EdM
Debussy, C.	Mandoline	EdM
Dedrick, A.	Shadows	Ken
Dedrick, A.-arr.	Viennese Refrain	Ken
DeLamater, E.	Christmas Festival	Rub
DeLaney-Coggins	Contest Piece	B-M
Delbecq, L.	Enfantillage	MM
Delbecq, L.	Flanerie	MM
Delbecq, L.	Gemini	MM
Delbecq, L.	Juliana	MM
Delbecq, L.	Melodia	EdR
De Leva-Andreoni	'E spingole frangese	Ric
Delhaye, A.	Silver Threads, air varie	MM
DeLuca, J.	Beautiful Colorado	CF
DeLuca, J.	Bravo Polka	Vol
DeLuca, J.	Minuet Scherzo	Bar
DeLuca, J.	Sentimentale	CF
DeLuca, J.	Thoughts of Gold	CF
Demersseman, J.	Fantaisie pastorale	Bil
Demersseman, J.	In Arcadie	MM
Denza, L.-Andreoni	Funiculì-funiculà	Ric
Di Capua, E.	O Sole Mio	Cen
Di Capua, E.	O Sole Mio	CF

Tenor Saxophone and Piano

Dindale, E.	Bucolique	EMb
Dindale, E.	Canzonetta	EMb
Dindale, E.	Danse Paysanne	EMb
Dinicu-Heifetz	Hora Staccato	CF
Donizetti, G.-Paque	Cavatine d'Anna Bolena	T-M
Donizetti, G.	Lucia di Lammermoor	Cen
Donizetti, G.-Andreoni	Una Furtiva lagrima (L'Elisir d'amore)	Ric
Donizetti, G.	Sextette (Lucia)	Vol
Donjon, J.-Whiting	Invocation	CF
Dorsselaer, W. van	Feux Follets	MM
Dorsselaer, W. van	Solo de concours	Bil
Drake-arr.	Let Us Have Music for Tenor Saxophone	CF
Drdla, F.-Damm	Souvenir	CF
Drigo, R.	Canzone Barcarola	B-M
Drigo, R.	Demande d'Amour	B-M
Drigo, R.	Harlequin Serenade	Cen
Drigo, R.	Serenade	Cen
Drigo, R.-Damm	Serenade	CF
Drigo, R.	Smile of Columbine	B-M
Drigo, R.	Valse Melodie	B-M
Dubois, P.	Fantaisie	ECh
Duport, J.	Romance	Spr
Durand, A.	First Valse, op. 83	CF
Durand, E.	Le Biniou	EdS
Duysburg, F.	Prelude and Dance	HeE
Dvořak, A.	Humoreske	Cen
Dvořak, A.	Humoreske	McK
Dvořak, A.	Humoresque	MM
Dvořak, A.-Leonard	Slavonic Dance	B-M
Dvořak, A.	Songs My Mother Taught Me	GFB
Elgar, E.	Salut d'Amour	Cen
Elgar, E.-Trinkaus	Love's Greeting	CF
Elgar, E.-Akers	Theme from Pomp and Circumstance	CF
Emmett, D.	Dixie's Land	McK
Engelmann, H.	Melody of Love	TP
Erdna	6 Swing Pieces	EdS
Escudié, H.	3e Fantasie	MM
Escudié, H.	4e Fantasie	MM
Evans, E.	Spanish Eyes	CF
Evans, E.	Sweet and Dainty	CF
Evans, T.	Lady of Spain	SF
Faulx, J.	Bagatelle	HeE
Faulx, J.	Petite Pièce	EMb
Fauré, G.-Stoutamire	Aurora	Ken
Fauré, J.	Les Rameaux	Cen
Felix-arr.	3 Canzonettas of the 17th Century	EdM

Fernandez, C.	Beautiful Heaven (Cielito Lindo)	GFB
Field, J.	Notturno	MM
Fillmore, H.	An Earl	CF
Fiocco, J.-Balbo	Allegro (Premiere Suite)	SF
Fiocco, J.-Londeix	Concerto (Cello)	ScF
Flégier, A.	Villanelle du Midi	EdM
Flotow, F. Von-De Rooij	Tenor Aria (Martha)	HeE
Fontaine, E.	El Vestas	PrA
Foster, S.	Beautiful Dreamer	MM
Foster, S.	Jeanie With the Light Brown Hair	
Foster, S.	Jeanie With the Light Brown Hair	GFB
	Jeanie with the Light Brown Hair	MM
Foster, S.-Fisher	My Old Kentucky Home	CF
Foster, S.	Sweetly She Sleeps	HeE
Franck, C.	Panis Angelicus	GFB
Frangkiser, C.	Theme from Alaskan Night	B-M
Friml, R.	Donkey Serenade	BM
Gade-Sears	Jalousie	War
Galliard, J.-Rascher	Sonata IV	M&M
Garland-Haring	In the Mood	ShB
Gatti-Morra	Concertino, Bb	CF
Gaudron, R.	Andante et allegretto	Bil
Gee, H.	Ballade	PrA
Geiger-Polla	Just for Tonight	EBM
German, E.-Voxman	Pastorale and Bourree	Rub
Gershwin, G.	Andante and Finale (Rhapsody in Blue)	War
Gershwin, G.-Sears	Blues (An American in Paris)	War
Gilmore, C.	Martinello	Rub
Giordani, G.	An 18th Century Air	EdM
Girlamo-Coggins	Matador	B-M
Glinka, M.-Gurewich	The Lark	CF
Glinka, M.	Romance Melody	Spr
Glover, S.	Rose of Tralee	MM
Gluck, C.-Mule	Gavotte	ALe
Gluck, C.	2 Classic Airs	EdM
Godard, B.	Lullaby (Jocelyn)	Cen
Godard, B.-Bettoney	Berceuse	CF
Godard, B.-Roberts	Berceuse (Jocelyn)	CF
Godard, B.-Trinkaus	Berceuse	CF
Godard, B.	Berceuse (Jocelyn)	MM
Godfroid	Valsette	T-M
Goeyens, A.-Buchtel	All 'Antica	NK
Goeyens, A.	Mélodie Anglaise	EMb
Goldman, E.	American Caprice	CF
Goldman, E.	On the Mall in the Twilight	CF
Gossec, F.	Sonata	MM
Gounod, C.-Mullaly	Dio Possente (Cavatina)	CF
Gounod, C.-Walters	March of a Marionette	Rub

Tenor Saxophone and Piano

Gounod, C.-Lureman	Recitatief, Cavatine en Allegretto	T-M
Granados, E.-Amaz	Spanish Dance No. 2. Oriental	UME
Granados, E.-Amaz	Spanish Dance No. 5. Andaluza	UME
Granados, E.-Amaz	Spanish Dance No. 6. Rondalla Aragonesa	UME
Grétry, A.-Paque	Air de Richard Coeur de Lion	T-M
Grétry, A.-Londeix	Panurge	ALe
Grieg, E.	Berceuse	CF
Grieg, E.	I Love You	Cen
Grieg, E.	Ich Liebe Dich	MM
Grieg, E.	Letzter Frühling	MM
Grieg, E.	Poème Erotique	MM
Grieg, E.	Solvejgs Lied	MM
Grooms, C.	Famous Scotch Airs, Var.	Cen
Grooms, C.	Home Favorites, Var.	Cen
Grooms, C.	Neapolitan Favorites, Var.	Cen
Grooms, C.	Ocean Echoes, Var.	Cen
Grooms, C.	Plantation Echoes, Var.	Cen
Gruber -Kent	The Caissons Go Rolling Along	CF
Guilhaud, G.-Voxman	First Concertino	Rub
Hagen, E.-Haring	Harlem Nocturne	ShB
Halévy, J.-Balogh	Serenata	Lud
Handel, G.-Barr	Allegro (Concerto, f)	Lud
Handel, G.-Gee	Andante and Allegro	SM
Handel, G.-Voxman	Concerto, g	Rub
Handel, G.-Rascher	Largo	B-M
Handel, G.	Largo	MM
Handel, G.-Barr	Sarabande (Concerto, F)	Lud
Handel, G.-Coggins	Sicilienne and Gigue	B-M
Handel, G.	Sonata, F	EdM
Handel, G.-Londeix	Sonata, g	ALe
Handel, G.-Londeix	Sonata No. 1	ALe
Handel, G.	3e Sonata	MM
Handel, G.-Kaplan	Sonata	Spr
Handel, G.	3 Dances and an Air	EdM
Harris -arr.	Farewell To Cucullain (Kerry Tune)	CF
Harris, F.	Ballroom Echoes	Lud
Harris, F.	Charming Ballerina	Bar
Harris, F.	Marilee	Bar
Harris, F.	Ocean Beach Valse	Lud
Harris, F.	Sax Caprice	Lud
Harris, F.	Sherilee Waltzes Nos. 1 & 2	Lud
Harris, F.	2 Marionettes	Lud
Hartley, W.	Poem. 1967	TP
Hartmann, J.	The Return	MM
Hasse, J.-Joosen	Concerto, g	MM
Hawkins, C.	Devotion	KPM
Hawkins, C.	What Is the Name?	KPM

Tenor Saxophone and Piano

Hawthorne, A.	Whispering Hope	GFB
Haydn, F.	Andante (Concerto)	Spr
Haydn, F.	Concerto	MM
Haydn, F.-Speets	Gratias	T-M
Haydn, F.	Serenade	MM
Haydn, F.-Rascher	A Theme by Joseph Haydn	B-M
Haydn, F.	Thema con Variazione	MM
Hayes, H.	Keep Going, Don't Stop	Bos
Heldenberg, A.	Improvisatie	Mau
Heltman	Mary Jane Waltz	Vol
Herbert, V.-Harris	Gypsy Love Song	Lud
Hofmann-Lureman	Cavatine en Polacca	T-M
Holmes, G.	Auld Lang Syne	CF
Holmes, G.	Cosette	Bar
Holmes, G.	Zayda	Bar
Hook, J.-Joosen	Engelse Sonate	MM
Houlik, J.	2 Lyric Pieces	SM
Hubert, R.	Un Soir	EdR
Hudadoff & Spire	11 Classic Solos	PrA
Hudadoff, I.-arr.	15 Intermediate Solo Series	PrA
Hudadoff, I.-arr.	Marches	PrA
Hummel, H.-arr.	The Foggy Dew	Rub
Hurrell, C.	Dark Distance	CF
Hurrell, C.	Gypsy Dreams	GFB
Hurrell, C.-arr.	Meadowland	Rub
Hurrell, C.	Silver Shadows	GFB
Hurrell, C.	Summer Night	GFB
Hurrell, C.	Summer Serenade	Rub
Hurrell, C.	Tango Gitano	CF
Ilyinsky, A.	Lullaby	NK
Irons, E.	Echoes from the Painted Desert	CF
Isaac, M.-arr.	Sacred Music	CF
Jahrl	Frolic of the Keys	GFB
Jakma, F.	Cavatine	T-M
Jakma, F.	Sancta Lucia air varie	MM
Jakma, F.	2e Concertino	T-M
Jakma, H.	Starlight Dreams	T-M
Jarnefelt, A.-Pardee	Berceuse	Ken
Jessel, L.-Polla	Parade of the Wooden Soldiers	EBM
Johnson, C.	Waltz Moods	Rub
Karel, L.	Cypress Song	B&H
Karel, L.	Hexaphon	SM
Karel, L.	Metrax	SM
Karel, L.	Quintra	SM
Karlins, W.	Music for Tenor Sax	SM
Keithley	I'll Never Find a Pal Like You	McK
Keithley	When Shadows Fall	McK
Ketèlbey, A.-Sears	In a Monastery Garden	War
Ketèlbey, A.	In a Persian Market	Bos

Tenor Saxophone and Piano

Ketèlbey, A.	Remembrance	Bos
Ketèlbey, A.	Sanctuary of the Heart	Bos
Khachaturian, A.-Schoebel	Sabre Dance	MCA
Kiefer, W.-Holmes	Elena Polka	Bar
King-Garrison	Song of the Islands	EBM
Kinyon, J.	Recital Pieces	War
Klauss, N.	Aria	Ken
Klickmann, F.	Sweet Hawaiian Moonlight	McK
Klickmann, F.	Trail to Long Ago	McK
Klickmann, F.	Weeping Willow Lane	McK
Knight-Clement	Rocked in the Cradle of the	
	Deep	Vol
Koepke, P.	Intermezzo	Rub
Koepke, P.	Reminiscence	Rub
Kosteck, G.	Mini-Variations	MeP
Kuhlau, F.	Menuett	NK
Labate, B.	Villanella	CF
Lack, T.	Idilio	Cen
Lacome, P.	Rigaudon	SM
Lake, M.	Annie Laurie	CF
Lalo, E.	Le Roi d'Ys	MM
Lamote de Grignon, J.-Amaz	Canço de Maria	UME
Lamote de Grignon, J.-Amaz	Rêverie (Schumanniana)	UME
Lancen, S.	Espièglerie	HeE
Lancen, S.	Intimité	MM
Lancen, S.	Introduction et Allegro Giocoso	MM
Lancen, S.	Pastorale	HeE
Lancen, S.	Romance	HeE
Lange, G.	Blumenlied (Flower Song)	Cen
Lange, G.	Blumenlied (Flower Song)	CF
Lansing, A.	Darkey's Dream	McK
Lara, A.	Granada	SMP
Lassen, E.	At Devotions	EdM
Lebierre	Airs Bohemiens	T-M
Leclair, J.	Danse Provençale	EdM
Leclair, J.-Mule	Musette	ALe
Leclercq, E.	Intimité	EMb
Leclercq, E.	Moment heureux	EMb
Lemare, E.-Trinkaus	Andantino	CF
Lemare, E.-Long	Andantino	Vol
Lenom, C.-Findlay	Lullaby	CF
Leonard, B.	The Dreamer	B-M
Leonard, B.	Fun Tune	B-M
Leoncavallo, R.	Arioso (Pagliacci)	Cen
Levy-DeVille	Rode's Air Variations	CF
Liliuokalani, Queen	Aloha Oe	CF
Liliuokalani, Queen	Aloha Oe	McK
Lincke, P.-Polla	Fireflies	EBM
Lincke, P.-Polla	Glow-Worm	EBM
Lincke, P.-Polla	March of the Siamese	EBM

Lincke, P.-Polla	Spring Beautiful Spring	EBM
Liszt, F.-Smith	Liebestraum	Bar
Llewellyn, E.	My Regards	CF
Llewellyn, E.	My Regards	War
Londeix, J.-arr.	A la découverte de la musique des XVIIe et XVIIIe siècles	HLe
Lorey, W.	Valse Roulette	RuE
Lotter, A.	Rouge et Noir	B&H
Lotti, A.	Arietta	EdM
Lully, J.-Londeix	Ballets du Roi	ALe
Lully, J.	Dances for the King	EdM
Lully, J.-Mule	Passacaglia and Passepied	ALe
Macbeth, A.	Intermezzo "Forget Me Not"	CF
MacDowell, E.-Coggins	To a Wild Rose	B-M
MacDowell, E.-Isaac	To a Wild Rose	CF
MacDowell, E.	To a Wild Rose	MM
Maertens, J.	Moments tristes	Mau
Maganini, Q.	La Romanesca	EdM
Maganini, Q.	Song of a Chinese Fisherman	EdM
Mahy, A.	Bourrée, Cadenze e Finale	MM
Malotte, A.-Lake	The Lord's Prayer	Sch
Manuel, J.-Dedrick	Lynne	Ken
Marcello, A.-Joosen	Concerto, c	MM
Marchetti, F.-Hurrell	Fascination	Rub
Martin, F.	Ballade	UE
Martini, G.	Canzona	MM
Martini, P.-Leonard	Gavotte	B-M
Martini, P.	Plaisir d'Amour	EdM
Martini, P.-Overveld	Plaisir d'Amour	T-M
Mascagni, P.	Intermezzo (Cavalleria Rusticana)	CF
Mascagni, P.	Intermezzo	McK
Massenet, J.-Trinkaus	Elegy	CF
Massenet, J.	Virgin's Last Slumber	CF
Masten, I.	Bonnie Eloise	Lud
McCathren, D.	Saxophones on Parade	Hal
McHugh-Ventura	On the Sunny Side of the Street	ShB
McKay, G.	Arietta and Capriccio	BM
McKay, G.	Concert Solo Sonatine	BM
Meacham, F.-Kent	American Patrol	CF
Mellish-arr.	Drink To Me Only With Thine Eyes	GFB
Mendelssohn, F.-Trinkaus	Nocturno	CF
Mendelssohn, F.-Weber	On Wings of Song	B-M
Mendelssohn, F.-Trinkaus	On Wings of Song	CF
Mendelssohn, F.-Mule	Spring Song	ALe
Mendelssohn, F.	Spring Song	Cen
Mendelssohn, F.	Frühlingslied	MM
Meyerbeer, G.-Trinkaus	Coronation March	CF
Moffat, J.-Rascher	Gavotte	B-M

357

Molloy, J.	Love's Old Sweet Song	McK
Monroe, S.	Rhapsodie	B-M
Monti, V. -Andreoni	Aubade d'amour	Ric
Monti, V. -Roberts	Csardas	CF
Moortel, A. van de	Nocturne	Mau
Morel	Norwegian Cradle Song	Cen
Morra, G.	Nocturnal Serenade	CF
Morra, G.	Romantique	CF
Morris -arr.	Drink To Me Only With Thine Eyes	Vol
Moszkowski, M. -Buchtel	Spanish Dance	NK
Mozart, W. -Mule	Adagio (Clarinet Concerto)	ALe
Mozart, W. -Rochon	Adagio, K. 411	HeE
Mozart, W. -Voxman	Adagio and Menuetto	Rub
Mozart, W. -Hautvast	Adagio en Romance	T-M
Mozart, W. -Londeix	Divertissement, D	ALe
Mozart, W. -Mule	Gavotte sentimentale (Les Petits Riens)	ALe
Mozart, W. -Rascher	Papageno's Aria	B-M
Mozart, W. -Coggins	Rondo	B-M
Myddleton, W. -Polla	Down South	EBM
Nelhybel, V.	Golden Concerto	EdM
Neukomm, S. -Kaplan	Aria	Spr
Norden, H.	The Court Jester	Hal
Offenbach, J.	Barcarolle (Tales of Hoffman)	Cen
Offenbach, J.	Barcarolle	CF
Offenbach, J.	Barcarolle	McK
Offenbach, J.	La Musette	CF
Olcott, C.	My Wild Irish Rose	NK
Olesen, W.	6 Saxophone Pieces, Bk. 2	WH
Ortolani, O.	More (Mondo Cane)	EBM
Ostransky, L.	Ballet Impressions	Rub
Ostransky, L.	Contest Caprice	Rub
Ostransky, L.	Night Piece	Rub
Ostransky, L.	Prelude and Allegro	Rub
Ozi, E.	Adagio et Rondo	Spr
Paderewski, I. -Trinkaus	Minuet a l'Antique	CF
Painparé, H.	Morceau de Salon	MM
Pala, J.	Bonjour	MM
Paquot, P. -arr.	10 Melodic Pieces	ALe
Parès, G. -Judy	Crépuscule (Twilight)	Rub
Pasquale, J. di	Sonata	SM
Paul, G.	Estilian Caprice	Rub
Pelz, W.	Portrait	B-M
Pelz, W.	Sophomore Waltz	B-M
Pergolesi, G. -Elkan	Se Tu M'Ami	HeE
Pergolesi, G.	Sicilian Air	EdM
Pergolesi, G.	Sonata No. 12	EdM
Pestalozza, A.	Ciribiribin	CF
Philidor, F. -Mule	Ego dis amicum (Chant	

	d'Eglise)	ALe
Pierné, G. -Gee	Canzonetta	SM
Pierné, G. -Gee	Piece, g	SM
Pinail -Rascher	Yearning	CF
Pinard, A.	Darling	CF
Pinard, A.	Just a Little Song of Love	CF
Pinard, A.	Yearning	CF
Porpora, N. -Rascher	Sinfonia, d	M&M
Porret, J.	Concertino No. 25	EdR
Porret, J.	Concertino No. 26	EdR
Porret, J.	19e Solo de Concours	MM
Porret, J.	20e Solo de Concours	MM
Prokofiev, S.	Kije's Wedding	EdM
Prokofiev, S. -Hummel	Romance and Troika	Rub
Puccini, G. -Andreoni	Che gelida manina (La Bohème)	Ric
Puccini, G. -Andreoni	O mio babbino caro (Gianni Schicchi)	Ric
Puccini, G. -Andreoni	Un Bel dì (Madama Butterfly)	Ric
Puccini, G. -Andreoni	E lucevan le stelle (Tosca)	Ric
Puccini, G. -Andreoni	Non piangere, Lùi (Turandot)	Ric
Purcell, H.	Dance Suite	EdM
Purcell, H.	Nymphs and Shepherds	NK
Purcell, H. -Kaplan	Saraband	Spr
Purcell, H.	Sonata, g	EdM
Purcell, H.	Suite, F	EdM
Rachmaninoff, S.	Vocalise	EdM
Rameau, J. -Rascher	Minuet	B-M
Rameau, J.	Rigadon de Dardanus	EdM
Rameau, J. -Mule	Saraband and Rigaudon (Les Fêtes de l'Hymen)	ALe
Rameau, J. -Mule	Tambourin	ALe
Ranger, A. -arr.	The Old Refrain	CF
Ranger, A. -arr.	Wreath of Holly	CF
Raphling, S.	Square Dance	EdM
Rascher, S. -arr.	All through the night	B-M
Rascher, S. -arr.	Blue Bells of Scotland	B-M
Rascher, S.	A Joyous tune	B-M
Rascher, S. -arr.	Let's sing a song of praise	B-M
Rascher, S. -arr.	Little Dance	B-M
Rascher, S. -arr.	March of the Finnish Cavalry	B-M
Rascher, S.	Noah's Ark	B-M
Rascher, S. -arr.	Shepherds' dance	B-M
Rascher, S. -arr.	Sweet Betsy from Pike	B-M
Ravel, M. -Branga	Boléro	Dur
Ravel, M.	Pavane pour une Enfante Défunte	EdM
Ravel, M.	Pièce en forme de habanera	ALe
Rehl, R.	The Duchess	Rub
Reilly, A.	2 Pieces	SM

359

Tenor Saxophone and Piano

Richards, J.	Sunbeams	Bar
Rimmer, H.	Autumn Even Song	HeE
Rimsky-Korsakov, N.	Flight of the Bumble Bee	CF
Rimsky-Korsakov, N.	Song of India	Cen
Rimsky-Korsakov, N.	A Song of India	CF
Rimsky-Korsakov, N.	Song of India	NK
Rimsky-Korsakov, N.-Davis	Song of India	Rub
Ritter, R.	Long Ago air varie	MM
Robel	Kitty's Waltz	Vol
Robert, C.	Concerto	T-M
Rocereto-Morgan	Meditation	Vol
Rooij, P. De	Greensleeves	HeE
Ropartz, G.	Andante and Allegro	NK
Rossini, G.-Lemarc	Cavatine	T-M
Rossini, G.-Paque	Cavatine de Tancrede	T-M
Rossini, G.	Inflammatus	CF
Rougnon, P.	Valse lente	GrF
Round, H.	Zenobia	MM
Rubinstein, A.	Melodie in F	CF
Rubinstein, A.	Mélodie	MM
Rubinstein, A.	Romance	SF
Rubinstein, A.-Long	Romance	Vol
Ruby-Ventura	I'll Always Be In Love With You	ShB
Saint-Saens, C.-Whear	Amour Viens Aider	Lud
Saint-Saens, C.-Goldman	My Heart At Thy Sweet Voice	CF
Saint-Saens, C.	Romance	EdM
Saint-Saens, C.	Le Cygne (The Swan)	Cen
Saint-Saens, C.-Trinkaus	The Swan	CF
Saint-Saens, C.	2 Pavanes	EdM
Sammartini, G.	Canto Amoroso	MM
Schaefer, A.	The Soloist	CF
Schaeffer, D.	Licorice and Lollipops	PrA
Schmidt, W.	Sonatina	Wes
Scholtens	Claus Fantaisie	T-M
Schubert, F.-Rascher	Andante	B-M
Schubert, F.-De Rooij	Ave Maria	HeE
Schubert, F.-Overveld	Du bist die Ruh'	T-M
Schubert, F.-Tobani	The Erl King	CF
Schubert, F.-Londeix	Impromptu	ALe
Schubert, F.-Andreoni	Moment musical, op. 94/3	Ric
Schubert, F.	Rosamunde	MM
Schubert, F.	Sei Mir Gegrüsst	MM
Schubert, F.	Serenade	Cen
Schubert, F.-Damm	Serenade	CF
Schubert, F.-Andreoni	Serenade	Ric
Schubert, F.-Overveld	Ständchen	T-M
Schubert, F.-Londeix	Suite de Valses	ALe
Schumann, R.-Merriman	Andantino, op. 94	SM
Schumann, R.	Einsame Blumen	Spr

Tenor Saxophone and Piano

Schumann, R.-Merriman	Folk Song	SM
Schumann, R.	Reverie	MM
Schumann, R.	Romance	CF
Schumann, R.	Traumerei	CF
Schumann, R.-Andreoni	Traumerei, op. 15/7	Ric
Schwartz, G.	International Folk Suite	SM
Seleski, G.	Interlude Romantique	Ken
Semler-Collery, J.	Mélodie Expressive	EME
Sherman, R.	Sonata	CoF
Shostakovich, D.	Danses Fantastiques	EdM
Shostakovich, D.	Satirical Dance (The Bolt)	EdM
Sibelius, J.	Valse Triste	Cen
Sibelius, J.-Trinkaus	Valse Triste	CF
Simonetti-Leonard	Madrigal	B-M
Simpson	Canzona	Wat
Singelée, J.	Fantaisie Pastorale	MM
Singelée, J.	4e Solo de Concert	MM
Singelée, J.-Voxman	Solo de Concert	Rub
Singer	Marionettes Modernes	CF
Skolnik, W.	Meditation	Ten
Smetana, B.-Harris	Polka (Bartered Bride)	Lud
Smith, C.	Among the Sycamores	Bar
Smith, C.	Eb'ry Rose Is Sweeter For de Rain	Bar
Smith, C.	Fancy Free	Bar
Smith, C.	From Day to Day	CF
Smith, C.	Harbor Lights	Bar
Smith, C.	Italiana	Bar
Smith, C.	Life's Lighter Hours	Bar
Smith, C.	Memories of the Past	Bar
Smith, C.	Milady's Pleasure	Bar
Smith, C.	Miraflores	Bar
Smith, C.	My Song of Songs	CF
Smith, C.	On Pleasure Bent	CF
Smith, C.	Philistine	Bar
Smith, C.	Pipes o' Pan	Bar
Smith, C.	Rainbow Hues	Bar
Smith, C.	Smithsonian	Bar
Smith, C.	The Spirit of Joy	CF
Smith & Holmes -arr.	Believe Me If All Those Endearing Young Charms	CF
Smith & Holmes	Call of the Sea	Bar
Smith & Holmes	The Caribbean	CF
Smith & Holmes -arr.	Drink To Me Only With Thine Eyes	CF
Smith & Holmes -arr.	Massa's in the Cold, Cold Ground	Bar
Smith & Holmes -arr.	Old Black Joe	CF
Smith & Holmes -arr.	Silver Threads Among the Gold	Bar

Smith & Holmes	Through Shadowed Vales	Bar
Smith & Holmes	Wayfarer	Bar
Sontag, C.	An Evening Serenade	CF
Speaks, O.-Leidzen	Sylvia	BM
Sporck, G.	Virelai	Bil
St. Clair, F.	Admiration	Vol
St. Clair, F.	Dream Time	Vol
St. Clair, F.	Golden Days	Vol
Stein, L.	Sonata	SM
Stoutamire, A.	Prelude and Fugue	Lud
Strauss, J.	Waltz from the Gypsy Baron	NK
Strauss, O.-Harris	A Waltz Dream	Lud
Strauss, R.-Walters	Allerseelen	Rub
Strauwen, J.	Andante Varié	EMb
Stravinsky, I.	Dance of the Princesses	
	(The Firebird)	EdM
Sullivan, A.	The Lost Chord	Cen
Sullivan, A.	The Lost Chord	CF
Suppé, F. von -Long	Andante Maestoso (Poet and	
	Peasant)	Vol
Tartini, G.-Mule	Grave	ALe
Tartini, G.-Reff	Larghetto	HeE
Tchaikovsky, P.-Gurewich	Andante Cantabile (Quartet, F)	CF
Tchaikovsky, P.	Chanson Triste	CF
Tchaikovsky, P.	Chanson Triste	MM
Tchaikovsky, P.	Chant sans Paroles	MM
Tchaikovsky, P.-Lemarc	Chant sans Paroles	T-M
Tchaikovsky, P.	Nocturne	MM
Tchaikovsky, P.-Coggins	Reverie	B-M
Tchaikovsky, P.-Trinkaus	Song Without Words	CF
Tchaikovsky, P.	3 Pieces (Album for Children)	EdM
Tchaikovsky, P.-Harris	Waltz	Lud
Teal, L.-arr.	Solos for the Tenor Saxophone	
	Player	Sch
Telemann, G.-Barnes	Arie (Pimpinone)	Spr
Telemann, G.	Concerto, F	MM
Telemann, G.-Voxman	Sonata, c	Rub
Templeton, A.	Elegie	MCA
Tenaglia, A.	Aria Antica	EdM
Thiry	Dialogue	MM
Thiry	Dimanche Matin	MM
Thiry	Promenade	MM
Thomas, A.-Lureman	Aria, Drinklied en Allegretto	T-M
Thomas, A.-Gatley	Mignon Selection	CF
Thomas, A.-Lureman	Recitatief, Aria, Cavatine	
	en Rondo	T-M
Thomas, A.	Romance (Raymond)	Cen
Thomé, F.	Simple Aveu (Confession)	Cen
Thompson	Remembrance	Vol
Thompson	Song of Spring	Vol

Thompson	Suite d'amour	Vol
Thompson	Valse Minah	Vol
Thornton, E.	Columbus	CF
Titl, A.	Serenade	CF
Toldra, E.-Amaz	Ave Maria	UME
Toldra, E.-Amaz	Dels Quatre Vents	UME
Toldra, E.-Amaz	La Font	UME
Toldra, E.-Amaz	Oracio al Maig	UME
Toldra, E.-Amaz	Soneti de la Rosada	UME
Tomasi, H.	Chant Corse	ALe
Toselli, E.-Leonard	Serenade	B-M
Tosti, F.	Good-Bye	Cen
Tosti, F.-Andreoni	Ideale	Ric
Trinkaus, G.	Lament	CF
Trinkaus, G.-arr.	World's Best-Known Pieces	CF
Tufilli, W.	Random Reverie	B-M
Tuthill, B.	Concerto	SM
Tuthill, B.	Sonata	SM
VanderCook, H.	Daisies	NK
Vasilenko, S.	Rhapsodie Orientale	EdM
Veracini, F.	2 Classic Dances	EdM
Verdi, G.-Andreoni	Addio, del passato (La Traviata)	Ric
Verdi, G.	Celeste Aida (Aida)	Cen
Verdi, G.-Andreoni	Deserto sulla terra (Il Trovatore)	Ric
Verdi, G.-Andreoni	Di quella pira (Il Trovatore)	Ric
Verdi, G.	La Donna è Mobile	Cen
Verdi, G.-Andreoni	La Donna è mobile (Rigoletto)	Ric
Verdi, G.-Andreoni	Libiam ne' lieti calici (La Traviata)	Ric
Verdi, G.	Misere, Il Trovatore	Cen
Verdi, G.-Andreoni	Questa o quella (Rigoletto)	Ric
Verdi, G.-Andreoni	Tutte le feste al tempio (Rigoletto)	Ric
Verdi, G.-Andreoni	Va, pensiero (Nabucco)	Ric
Verroust, S.	12e Solo	MM
Vivaldi, A.-Rascher	Sonata, g	M&M
Vivaldi, A.	Suite, c	EdM
Vogt	Boat Song	Cen
Vogt	Dream Waltz	Cen
Vogt	Remembrance	Cen
Vogt	Sax-o-moan	Cen
Vogt	Saxonade	Cen
Vogt	Saxonola	Cen
Voxman, H.-arr.	Concert and Contest Collection	Rub
Vries, K. de	March. 1972	SD
Wagner, R.	Bridal Chorus	McK
Wagner, R.	Romance (Tannhauser)	Cen
Wagner, R.-Roberts	Song to the Evening Star	CF

363

Wagner, R.-Trinkaus	Song to the Evening Star	CF
Wagner, R.	Evening Star	McK
Wagner, R.-Trinkaus	Walther's Prize Song	CF
Wagner, R.-Buchtel	Walther's Prize Song	NK
Walker, R.	Valse Casuel	BM
Wallace-Round-Henton	Scenes that Are Brightest (Maritana)	CF
Walters, H.	Sakura, Sakura (Cherry Blossoms)	Rub
Walters, H.	Tarantelle	Lud
Ward, N.	Impressions	Ken
Warren, D.	Chorale Fantasy	Lud
Warren, D.	Danish Dance	Lud
Warren, D.	Sonatina	Lud
Webber, C.-arr.	First Solo Album	TP
Weber, C.M. von-Bayer	Concerto op. 73, No. 1	UME
Weber, C.M. von-Mule	Waltz (Der Freischütz)	ALe
Weber, F.	Evening Shadows	B-M
Weber, F.	Sentimental Lady	B-M
Westendorf, T.	I'll Take You Home Again Kathleen	GFB
Wettge, G.	Fantaisie Varié	MM
Whitney, M.	Melancholy	Spr
Williamson, M.	Evening Lament	Ken
Wilson, G.	Moonlight on the Hudson, op. 60	Cen
Wilson, G.	The Wayside Chapel	Cen
Wolpe, D.	Turn Yourself Around	Ken
Young-Ventura	Sweet Sue--Just You	ShB
Yradier, S.	The Dove	Cen
Yuste, M.	Solo de concurso	UME
Zamacois, J.-Amaz	Serenada d'Hivern	UME
Zimmerman, R.	Play A Song of America	TP
Zimmerman, R.-arr.	Play A Song of Christmas	TP
Zobel, E.	Spruce Shadows	NK

Tenor Saxophone and Orchestra

Hespos, H.	dschen--das Erregende ist wie eine offene Schale	EMo
Ravel, M.	Pièce en forme de habanera	ALe

Tenor Saxophone and Band

Blémant, L.	Sous les sapins	ALe
Buschmann, R.	Tenor Tales. 1965	HG
Chopin, F.-Beeler	Minute Waltz	CF
DeLuca, J.-Roberts	Beautiful Colorado	CF
Godard, B.-Fernand	Berceuse de Jocelyn	EdR
Groot, de	Tyrolienne	MM
Hubert, R.	Elégie	EdR
Masten, I.	Bonnie Eloise	Lud

Tuthill, B.	Concerto	SM
Wallace-Round-Henton	Maritana	CF
Walters, H.	Tarantelle	Lud
Ward, N.	Impressions	Ken

Baritone Saxophone

Baritone Saxophone and Piano

Alschausky, J.	Walzer-Arie No. 2	CF
Bach, J.C.F.-Johnson	Andante	B-M
Bach, J.S.-Davis	Fugue 21 (Well-tempered Klavier)	Wes
Bach, J.S.-Rascher	If Thou Be Near	B-M
Barnhouse, C.	Barbarossa	Bar
Barnhouse, C.	God Be With You	Bar
Barnhouse, C.	Let the Lower Lights be Burning	Bar
Barnhouse, C.	Meditation Religioso	Bar
Barnhouse, C.	Refuge	Bar
Barnhouse, C.	Sweet By and By	Bar
Beethoven, L. van-Bettoney	Adagio (Sonata Pathetique)	CF
Beethoven, L. van	Allegro (Sonata Pathetique)	CF
Bisselink, P.	Izegrim	MM
Brahms, J.-Rascher	Theme (1st symphony)	B-M
Brown, R.	Sonata breve	Wes
Buchtel, F.	First Book of Solos for Baritone Saxophone	Col
Buchtel, F.	Golden glow waltz	B-M
Buchtel, F.	High stepper's march	B-M
Carissimi, G.-Barnes	Heart Victorious	Spr
Coggins, W.	Andantino	B-M
Coggins, W.	Little waltz	B-M
Corelli, A.-Coggins	Gavotte	B-M
Corelli, A.-Voxman	Sarabande and Gigue	Rub
Crawford-Kent	The Army Air Corps	CF
Cui, C.-Leonard	Orientale	B-M
Donjon, J.	Invocation	CF
Fesch, W. de-Kaplan	Canzonetta	Spr
Fontaine, E.	Interlude Melodie	PrA
Franck, C.-Leonard	Panis Angelicus	B-M
Frangkiser, C.	Canzona	B-M
Girlamo-Coggins	Canzonetta	B-M
Glière, R.-Hurrell	Russian Sailor's Dance	Rub
Godfrey, F.-Harris	Lucy Long	CF
Grieg, E.-Rascher	Walzer	B-M
Gruber-Kent	The Caissons Go Rolling Along	CF

Handel, G. -Barr	Allegro (Concerto, f)	Lud
Handel, G. -Coggins	Bourrée	B-M
Handel, G.	Honor and Arms	EdM
Handel, G. -Rascher	Hornpipe	B-M
Handel, G. -Barr	Sarabande (Concerto, f)	Lud
Handel, G. -Barnes	Sound an Alarm	Spr
Heller, S.	L'Avalanche	NK
Hoffmann, A.	Serenade Basque	B-M
Hurrell, C.	Echo of Romany	Rub
Jakma, F.	Parade der Olifanten	MM
Jarnefelt, A. -Leonard	Berceuse	B-M
Johnson, C.	Scene Forestal	Rub
Klughardt, A.	Romanze	Spr
Koepke, P.	Recitative and Rondino	Rub
Lamb, J. -Rascher	Romp	B-M
Leonard, B.	Happy Valley	B-M
Leonard, B.	Uno poco rondo	B-M
Long, N.	Undercurrent	Rub
Marcello, B. -Voxman	Andante and Allegro (Sonata, G)	Rub
Marcello, B. -Coggins	Grave and Allegro	B-M
Mattei, T. -Walters	The Mariner	Rub
McCathren, D.	Latin Holiday	Hal
Meacham, F. -Kent	American Patrol	CF
Mendelssohn, F.	It Is Enough	EdM
Mozart, W. -Rascher	Aria (Magic Flute)	B-M
Mozart, W. -Voxman	Menuetto (Divertimento No. 1)	Rub
Mozart, W. -Barnes	Per Questa Bella Mano	Spr
Norden, H.	Carousel	Hal
Offenbach, J.	La Musette	CF
Ostransky, L.	Contest Etude No. 1	Rub
Ostransky, L.	Variations on a Theme by Schumann	Rub
Paganini, N. -Leonard	Introduction and Theme	B-M
Parès, G. -Judy	Crépuscule (Twilight)	Rub
Pergolesi, G. -Barnes	Canzona	Spr
Pestalozza, A.	Ciribiribin	CF
Petrie, H.	Asleep in the Deep	NK
Petrie, H. -Walters	Asleep in the Deep	Rub
Porret, J.	1st Pièce de concours	Bil
Presser, W.	Prelude. 1966	TP
Purcell, H. -Rascher	Rondeau	B-M
Rascher, S. -arr.	Deep in the cellar I sit	B-M
Rascher, S. -arr.	Flow Gently Sweet Afton	B-M
Rascher, S. -arr.	Gently the moon has risen	B-M
Rascher, S. -arr.	Heavens Resound	B-M
Rascher, S. -arr.	In dulci jubilo	B-M
Rascher, S. -arr.	Loch Lomond	B-M
Rascher, S. -arr.	Song of the Tower Watchman	B-M
Regi, A. -Voxman	Ancient Melody	Rub
Rollinson, T.	Rocked In The Cradle of the	

	Deep	CF
Saint-Saens, C.-Coggins	The Elephant	B-M
Scarlatti, A.-Barnes	Aria (Tigraine)	Spr
Schaefer	Spring in the Forest	CF
Schulz, J.-Rascher	Little March	B-M
Schumann, R.	Einsame Blumen	Spr
Schumann, R.-Rascher	Happy Farmer	B-M
Senaillé, J.-Gee	Allegro Spiritoso	SM
Tchaikovsky, P.-Seay	Impromptu	Spr
Telemann, G.-Coggins	Vivace	B-M
VanderCook, H.	Columbine	NK
VanderCook, H.	The Message	NK
VanderCook, H.	Peony	NK
Van Der Pals, L.-Rascher	Song of Joy	B-M
Veach, D.	Wind Currents	CF
Walters, H.	Forty Fathoms	Rub
Weber, F.-arr.	Deep River	B-M
Weber, F.	Elephant Dance	B-M
Weber, F.	Evening Shadows	B-M
Whitney, M.	Melancholy	Spr
Wieniawski, H.	Romance	CF

Baritone Saxophone and Band

Hartzell, D.	Egotistical Elephant	Sha
Petrie, H.-Walters	Asleep in the Deep	Rub

Bass Saxophone

Bass Saxophone and Piano

Frangkiser, C.	Melody Variante	B-M

Saxophone Methods and Studies

	Fun with Sax	War
	Phrasing Modern Melodies	McK
	Pro Art Saxophone Method	PrA
	Saxophone Method	MS
	Scale for Saxophones	CF
	Rubank Instrumental Chart	Rub
Ajosa, A.	8 Grand Etudes	Ric
Allard, J.	Three-Octave Scales & Chords	CCo
Allard, J.	60 Varied studies (based on A. Gabucci's 60 Divertimenti for clarinet)	Ric
Ameller, A.	Etudes expressives	HE
Anzalone, V.	Breeze-Easy Method, 2 vols.	War
Arfine, L.	Comprehensive Choral Etudes	McK

367

Arnold, J.	Fingered Scales	ShB
Arnold, J.	Modern Fingering System	ShB
Arnold, J.	25 Klosé Daily Exercises	ShB
Bach, J.S.-Faulx	20 Etudes de virtuosité	EMb
Bassi, L.-Iasilli	27 Virtuoso Studies	CF
Beltrán	Método completo y progresivo	UME
Bernards, B.	24 Virtuoso Studies	WZ
Bernards, B.	125 Etudes as Daily Studies	WZ
Bichon, S.	Play the Saxophone, Vol. 1	ECh
Blatt, F.	15 Entertaining Etudes	EdM
Blatt, F.	20 Exercices	Bil
Blémant, L.	New Practical Method, 2 vols.	ALe
Blémant, L.	20 Melodic Studies, 2 vols.	ALe
Blücker, N. & O. Rönn	Saxofonskola	Nor
Bosch, A. Jr.	Concert Studies	HeE
Boucek, J.	Zaciname	Art
Bozza, E.	12 Study-Caprices	ALe
Bräu, A.	Übungen	HG
Briard, R.	Nouvelle Méthode	Bil
Busser, H.-Paquot	12 Melodic Studies	ALe
Bumcke, G.	Scale Exercises, op. 70	Sim
Bumcke, G.	36 Studies, op. 43/1, 2	Sim
Bumcke, G.	24 Jazz Studies, op. 43/3	Sim
Bumcke, G.	Daily Technical Exercises, op. 43/5	Sim
Bumcke, G.	Saxophone School	Sim
Busser, H.-Paquot	12 Melodic Studies	ALe
Cailliet, L.	Method for Alto and Tenor Saxophone, 2 vols.	B-M
Capelle, F.	20 Grand Studies, 2 vols.	ALe
Cardoni, A.	Introductory Studies	Ric
Carney, H.	Warm-Up Book for Baritone Sax	MCA
Cavallini, E.-Iasilli	30 Caprices, 2 vols.	CF
Chauvet, G.	Etudes de perfectionnement	Com
Chauvet, G.	15 Grandes études	Com
Coggins, W. & J. Ployhar	Alto Saxophone Student, 3 vols.	B-M
Coggins, W. & F. Weber	Studies and Melodious Etudes (Level 1)	B-M
Coggins, W. & J. Ployhar	Studies and Melodious Etudes (Level 2)	B-M
Coggins, W. & J. Ployhar	Studies and Melodious Etudes (Level 3)	B-M
Coggins, W. & J. Ployhar	Tunes for Alto Saxophone Technic (Level 3)	B-M
Coggins, W. & F. Weber	Studies and Melodious Etudes (Level 1) (ten sax)	B-M
Coggins, W. & J. Ployhar	Studies and Melodious Etudes	

	(Level 2) (ten sax)	B-M
Coggins, W. & J. Ployhar	Studies and Melodious Etudes	
	(Level 3) (ten sax)	B-M
Coggins, W. & F. Weber	Tenor Saxophone Soloist	
	(Level 1)	B-M
Coggins, W, J. Ployhar,		
& Weber	Tenor Saxophone Student,	
	3 vols.	B-M
Coggins, W. & J. Ployhar	Tunes for Tenor Saxophone	
	Technic (Level 3)	B-M
Coggins, W. & F. Weber	Baritone Saxophone Soloist	
	(Level 1)	B-M
Coggins, W. & F. Weber	Studies and Melodious Etudes	
	(Level 1) (bar sax)	B-M
Coggins, W. & J. Ployhar	Studies and Melodious Etudes	
	(Level 2) (bar sax)	B-M
Coggins, W. & J. Ployhar	Studies and Melodious Etudes	
	(Level 3) (bar sax)	B-M
Coggins, W. & J. Ployhar	Tunes for Baritone Saxophone	
	Technic (Level 3)	B-M
Corre, J.	Warm-Ups for Woodwinds	PDS
Couf, H.	Let's Play Saxophone	Cha
Cragun, J.	Business Saxophonist	Rub
Cragun, J.	Conservatory Method, 3 vols.	Rub
Cragun, J.	20 Etudes	Rub
Cragun, J.	30 Melodic Caprices	Rub
Cuneo, A.	Metodo completo	Ric
Cuneo, A.	Scale e 24 Studi in tutti i toni,	
	op. 197	Ric
Dalby, C.	All Melody Method, 2 vols.	PrA
Daneels, F.	The Budding Saxophonist	ScF
Debondue, A.	25 Etudes-déchiffrages	ALe
Debondue, A.	48 Etudes-déchiffrages	ALe
Debondue, A.	50 Etudes-déchiffrages	ALe
Decouais, R.	35 Etudes techniques	Bil
Decruck, M. & F. Breilh	Modern Saxophone School	ALe
DeVille, P.	Universal Method	CF
Dorsey, J.	Method	Big
Druet, R.	L'Ecole française	Bil
	du saxophone, 3 vols.	
Eby, W.	Scientific Method	Big
Eisenhauer, W.	Elementary Supplement Series	Alf
Eisenhauer & Gouse	Saxophone Method, Bk. 2	Alf
Endresen, R.	Saxophone Etudes and Solos	Col
Endresen, R.	Supplementary Studies	Rub
Faulx, J.	20 Virtuoso Studies after Bach	HeE
Fedoroff & Baresel	Method for Saxophone	WZ
Ferling, W.-Pierlot	18 Etudes, op. 12	Bil
Ferling, W.-Bleuzet	48 Etudes	EdR
Ferling, W.-Pierlot	48 Etudes	Bil
Ferling, W.-Pierlot	144 Préludes et études, 2 bks.	Bil

Froseth, J.	The Individualized Instructor, 2 vols.	GIA
Gatti, D. -Iasilli	Studies on Major and Minor Scales	CF
Gatti, D. -Iasilli	35 Melodious Technical Exercises	CF
Gaudriot -Schneider	20 Etüden, 2 vols.	LDo
Gee, H. -ed.	20 Progressive Etudes	SM
Gekeler, K. -Hovey	Belwin Saxophone Method, 3 vols.	B-M
Giampieri, A.	Progressive Method	Ric
Giampieri, A.	16 Daily Studies for Perfection	Ric
Gillette, M.	Saxophone Method	Big
Glassman, B.	Saxophone Studies, 4 vols.	KPM
Gornston, D.	Saxophone Mechanisms	MCA
Gornston, D.	Velocity Series	SF
Gornston, D. & B. Paisner	Beethoven Sonatas	SF
Gornston, D. & B. Paisner	Chopin Studies	SF
Gornston, D. & B. Paisner	Fun with Scales	MCA
Grooms, C.	Scales and Chords for the Saxophone	Cen
Hartmann, W.	Rhythmisch-stilistische Studien, Vol. 1 (Jazz Studies)	Deu
Hauck, F.	Neue Saxophonschule	SS
Hawkins, C.	Warm-Up Book for Tenor Sax	MCA
Hegvik, A.	Modern Course for the Saxophone, 2 vols.	HeE
Hegvik, A.	Scales and Arpeggios	HeE
Hendrickson, C.	Handy Manual of Fingering Charts	CF
Herfurth, P.	A Tune a Day, 2 vols.	BM
Herfurth & Stuart	Sounds of the Winds, 2 vols.	CF
Herman, W.	Sax Scales--Chords & Solos	Han
Herrer, P.	Saxophonschule	EMB
Hovey, N.	Daily Exercises for Saxophone	B-M
Hovey, N.	Elementary Method	Rub
Hovey, N.	Practical Studies for Saxophone, 2 vols.	B-M
Huff, G.	Saxophone Method, 2 vols.	Col
Iasilli, G.	Modern Conservatory Method, 2 vols.	CF
Jacobs, M.	Saxophone Method	Alf
Jettel, R.	Method, 3 vols.	Wel
Jettel, R.	Neue Saxophonstudien, 2 vols.	FrH
Jettel, R.	24 Etüden	Wel
Karg-Elert, S.	25 Caprices and Sonata, op. 153, 2 vols.	WZ
Klosé, H. -Gay	Complete Method	ALe
Klosé, H. -Jeanjean	Études de genre et de mécanisme	ALe

Klosé, H.-Buyzer	Saxofoon Methode	MM
Klosé, H.-Mule	15 Melodious Studies	ALe
Klosé, H.	20 Studies	SF
Klosé, H.-Mule	25 Exercises journaliers	ALe
Klosé, H.-Mule	25 Technical Studies	ALe
Klosé, H.	25 Daily Exercises	CF
Kregcyk, R.	100 Stilistische Übungen	Wel
Krtička, S.	Schule für Saxophon	Art
Kucinski	Brahms Studies	SF
Labanchi, G.-Iasilli	33 Concert Etudes, 3 vols.	CF
Lacour, G.	8 Etudes brillantes	ALe
Lacour, G.	28 Etudes (sur les modes d'Olivier Messiaen)	Bil
Lacour, G.	50 Etudes faciles et progressives, 2 vols.	Bil
Lacour, G.	100 Déchiffrages manuscrits en forme de petites études mélodiques et rhythmiques, 2 vols.	Bil
Lamotte, A.	18 Etudes	Bil
Lamotte, A.-Marx	First Book of Scale and Arpeggio Studies	M&M
Lang, R.	Beginning Studies in the Altissimo Register (Harmonics)	Lan
Lang, R.	Principles of the Saxophone	Lan
Langenus, G.	Practical Transposition	CF
Langey, O.-Fitzgerald	Practical Tutor	B&H
Langey, O.	Tutor	CF
Laurent, L.	Nouvelle Méthode Pratique de Saxophone	EdS
Lee, S.	20 Studies	CF
Lefèbvre, P.	De la technique du son	ALe
Lefèvre, X.-Savina	20 Melodious Studies	Ric
Lester, L.	50 Rambles	CF
Letellier, R.	40 Etudes de style	EdR
Letellier, R.	Gammes	EdR
Letellier, R.	Méthode nouvelle	EdR
Letellier, R.	Tablature	EdR
Levy, H.	The Time Revolution	CrW
Lindeman, B.	Melodious Fundamentals, 2 vols.	CCo
Lindeman, B.	Saxophone Made Easy, 2 vols.	CCo
Londeix, J.	Le Détaché (Staccato)	HLe
Londeix, J.	Gammes et Modes, 2 vols.	ALe
Londeix, J.	Scales, Conjunct and Arpeggiated	HLe
Londeix, J.	Tablature des doigtés comparés des notes suraigues	ALe
Lowry, R.	Von Weber Studies	SF

Loyon, E.	32 Etudes	Bil
Lubin	Tchaikovsky Studies	SF
Luft, J.	24 Etudes	Bil
Mangelsdorff, E.	Anleitung zur Improvisation	SS
Mantovani, M.	Invito al saxofono, 2 vols.	EBe
Massis, A.	6 Study-caprices	ALe
Masuy, F.	10 Etudes de Force moyenne	EMb
Masuy, F.	10 Etudes difficiles et très difficiles	EMb
Mayeur, L.	50 Exercises	CF
Mayeur, L.-Perrin	Grande Méthode	ALe
Mayeur, L.	New and Grand Method	CF
Mayeur, L.-Chauvet	Grande méthode, 2 vols.	Com
Mayeur, L.	Scales, Arpeggio Exercises and Studies in Interpretation	CF
McKusick	Supplementary Studies for the Modern Saxophonist	B-M
Meriot, M.	Le Saxophoniste--Méthode pratique	Com
Miller, R.-Skornicka	The Master Method	B&H
Moore, E.	Daily Routine	Leb
Mule, M.-ed.	Difficult Passages, 3 vols.	ALe
Mule, M.	18 Exercises after Berbiguier	ALe
Mule, M.	Etudes variées	ALe
Mule, M.	Exercises journaliers d'après Terschak	ALe
Mule, M.	24 Easy Studies after Samie	ALe
Mule, M.	30 Grand Exercises after Soussmann, 2 vols.	ALe
Mule, M.	48 Studies after Ferling	ALe
Mule, M.	53 Studies, 3 vols.	ALe
Mule, M.	Gammes et arpèges, 3 vols.	ALe
Murphy, S.	Daily Exercises	Big
Murphy, S.	36 Modern Harmonic Patterns	Wes
Nash, T.	Studies in High Harmonics	MCA
Niehaus, L.	Advanced Jazz Conception	PDS
Niehaus, L.	Basic Jazz Conception	PDS
Niehaus, L.	Intermediate Jazz Conception	PDS
Olesen, W.	Saxofonskole	WH
Oltersdorf, H.	Tutor	FrH
Orsi, R.-Giampieri	Popular Method	Ric
Ostling, A. & F. Weber	Tunes for Alto Saxophone Technic (Level 2)	B-M
Ostling, A. & F. Weber	Tunes for Tenor Saxophone Technic (Level 2)	B-M
Ostling, A. & F. Weber	Tunes for Baritone Saxophone Technic (Level 2)	B-M
Pala, J.	Hulpgrepen	T-M
Pantaleo-Iasilli	6 Virtuoso Caprices	CF
Parès, G.	Daily Exercises and Scales	CF

Parès, G.-Whistler	Parès Scales	Rub
Parisi -Iasilli	40 Technical & Melodious Studies, 2 vols.	SM
Pease, D.	Fundamental Method	UMI
Pease, D.	Follow-Up Method	UMI
Pellegrini, G.	Method	Car
Perrin, M.	Technique du Saxophone	GD
Perrin, M.	Travail journalier des gammes et arpèges	ALe
Perrin, M.	22 Transcendental Studies	ALe
Phillips, S.	Saxophone Method	Pax
Porret, J.	Mémento du saxophoniste	EdR
Porret, J.	24 Déchiffrages manuscrits	EdR
Porret, J.	25 Déchiffrages manuscrits	EdR
Prescott, G.	Outlines of Technic	CF
Rascher, S.	Complete Chart for All Saxophones	CF
Rascher, S.	158 Saxophone Exercises	Sch
Rascher, S.	Scales for the Saxophone	M&M
Rascher, S.	Top-Tones for the Saxophone, Revised Ed.	CF
Rascher, S.	24 Intermezzi	Bou
Rivchun, A.	40 Etudes	MCA
Rivchun, A.	150 Exercises	MCA
Rose, C.-Gornston	22 Selected Studies	PrA
Rossari -Iasilli	53 Melodious Etudes, 2 vols.	SM
Rousseau, E.	Eugene Rousseau Saxophone Method, 2 vols.	NK
Rousseau, E.	Saxophone Method for Beginning Students	Leb
Ruggiero, G.	15 Studies for Perfection	ALe
Ruggiero, G.	20 Technische u. melodische Studien	GZ
Rusch, H. & A. Barto	Breath Control and Tuning and Intonation Studies	
Sabon, E.	12 Etudes d'après Bochsa	Bil
Salviani, C.-Iasilli	Exercises in All the Practical Keys	CF
Salviani, C.-Giampieri	Studies from the Oboe Method, 4 vols.	Ric
Schiemann, C.	7 Characteristic Studies	EdM
Schmidt, W.	10 Contemporary Etudes	Wes
Segouin, P.	25 Etudes artistiques, 2 vols.	Bil
Sellner, J.-Bleuzet	Etudes élémentaires	EdR
Sellner, J.-Bleuzet	Etudes progressives	EdR
Sellner, J.-Bleuzet	Méthode pour hautbois ou saxophone, 2 vols.	Bil
Skornicka, J.	Intermediate Method	Rub

Small, J.	27 Melodious and Rhythmical Exercises	CF
Snavely, J.	Basic Technique for All Saxophones	Ken
Spear	Basic Syncopation	PrA
Stabile, D.	Saxophone Studies	Han
Starita, A.	First Step Series--Saxophone	KPM
Teal, L.	Daily Studies for the Improvement of Saxophone Technique	EQM
Teal, L.	Saxophonist's Workbook	Uni
Thiriet, A.	24 Etudes d'expression	EMT
Universal-Prescott	First and Second Year	CF
Van Bodegraven, P.	Adventures in Saxophone Playing	Sta
Vereecken, B.	Complete Chart for All Saxophones	CF
Vereecken, B.	Foundation to Saxophone Playing	CF
Vereecken, B.	Junior Saxophone Method	Rub
Vereecken, B.	Saxophone Virtuoso	CF
Verroust, S.-Marx	24 Melodic Studies, Bk. 1	M&M
Vincent, H. & F. Weber	Tunes for Alto Saxophone Technic (Level 1)	B-M
Vincent, H. & F. Weber	Tunes for Tenor Saxophone Technic (Level 1)	B-M
Vincent, H. & F. Weber	Tunes for Baritone Saxophone Technic (Level 1)	B-M
Viola, J.	The Technique of the Saxophone, 3 vols.	BPP
Votquenne, V.	Technique Moderne, 2 vols.	EMb
Voxman, H. & W. Gower	Advanced Method, 2 vols.	Rub
Voxman, H.	Selected Studies	Rub
Wahls, H.	Anfangsstudien, 2 vols.	FrH
Weber, F. & W. Coggins	Alto saxophone student	B-M
Weber, F. & W. Coggins	Tenor saxophone student	B-M
Weber, F. & W. Coggins	Baritone sax student	B-M
Webster, M.	Saxophone Instructor	Lud
Werner, M.	Vibrato Tone Studies	McK
Wunderlich, F.	Arpeggios (Chords)	CF

Treble Instrument

Treble Instrument

Gates, E.	Odd Meter Etudes	SF
Gornston, D.	Weird Etudes	SF

Treble Instrument

Hunt	Modern Syncopation	Rub
Kagel, M.	Atem	UE
LaPorta, J.	Developing Sight-reading Skills in the Jazz Idiom	BPP
Lehmann, H.	Monodie für ein Blasinstrument	SS
Racusen, D.	Canonic Etudes	Sha
Stockhausen, K.	Plus Minus, 2 x 7	UE
Tustin, W.	Technical Studies	PIC

Treble Instrument and Piano

Breck, E.-arr.	Christmas Joys	CF
Buchtel, F.	Chant d'Amour	Vol
Buchtel, F.	Valse Romantique	Vol
Clement, F.	Silvertone Polka	Vol
Hedges, A.	Count Down	BrH
Isaac, M.-arr.	Sacred Music	CF
Knight, J.-Clement	Rocked in the Cradle of the Deep	Vol
Kraus, E.	7 Choralbearbeitungen (C instr, org)	Hei
Long	Home Sweet Home	Vol
McCall, H.-arr.	Instrumental Hymn Favorites	CF
Phillips, H.	8 Bel Canto Songs	Sha
Rubinstein, A.-Long	Romance	Vol
St. Clair, F.	Admiration	Vol
St. Clair, F.	Dream Time	Vol
St. Clair, F.	Golden Days	Vol
Suppé, F. von-Long	Andante Maestoso (Poet and Peasant)	Vol
Webb-Clement	Stand Up for Jesus	Vol

B♭ Instrument

B♭ Instrument and Piano

Code, P.	At Dawn	All
Code, P.	At Sunset	All
Code, P.	Miranda	All
Code, P.	Wendouree	All
Code, P.	'Neath Austral Skies	All
Code, P.	Prelude de Concert	All
Code, P.	Valse Caprice	All
Code, P.	Zanette	All
Code, P.	Zelda	All
Cutter, B.-arr.	Debut Solo Time	ShB
Cutter, B.-arr.	Solo Time Encores	ShB
Johnston, H.	Anna Karenina	All

Johnston, H.   Leonie   All

Eb Instrument

Eb Instrument and Piano
Cutter, E.-arr.   Debut Solo Time   ShB
Cutter, B.-arr.   Solo Time Encores   ShB

Miscellaneous Instrument

Miscellaneous Instrument
                                  Carnival of Venice
                                     (Bb or bass instr, pf)   CCo
Giuffre, J.   Jazz Phrasing & Interpretation
                                     (C, Bb, Eb, or bass instr)   AMP
Glantz, H.   6 Great Modern Solos
                                     (Bb or Eb instr, pf)   CCo
Williams, E.   Little Classics (Bb, Eb, or
                                     bass instr, pf)   CCo

Miscellaneous Instrument and Orchestra
Bucci, M.   Concerto for a Singing Instru-
                                     ment (Bb or C treble instr
                                     or C bass instr)   FrM

Multiple Instruments with Orchestra or Band

2 Instruments with Orchestra

> *In numerous instances listings of early music in publishers' catalogs do
> not distinguish between concertant or continuo usage of the bass instruments.
> Many bassoon or cello parts are probably accompanimental rather than solo-
> istic. Therefore some of the items listed for three or more solo instruments
> are actually for two or more solo instruments and orchestra.*

Albinoni, T.   Concerto a cinque, op. 7/5,
                                     C (2 ob, str)   EK
Albinoni, T.   Concerto, op. 9/3 (2 ob, str)   MR
Albinoni, T.   Concerto, op. 9/6 (2 ob, str)   MR
Albinoni, T.   Concerto, op. 9/9 (2 ob, str)   MR
Albinoni, T.-Giazotto   Concerto, C, op. 9/9 (2 ob, str) Ric
Albinoni, T.   Concerto, op. 9/12 (2 ob, str)   MR
Altens, L. van   Divertimento (fl, ob, O)   SD
Ancelin, P.   Concerto op. 14 (ob, pf, str)   ECh
Bach, J.C.   Concerto (ob, bsn, str)   Eul

Bach, J.C.-Moyse	Divertissement (2 fl, O)	SM
Bach, J.C.-Dawes	Sinfonia concertante, F	
	(ob, vc, O)	Eul
Bach, J.S.-Fischer	Concerto, c, BWV 1060	
	(ob, vn, O)	B&N
Bach, J.S.-Schneider	Concerto, d, BWV 1060	
	(ob, vn, O)	BrH
Bach, J.S.-Winschermann	Doppelkonzert, d, BWV 1059	
	(ob, hpcd, str)	HSM
Bach, W.F.-Lebermann	Adagio and Fugue, d (2 fl, str)	SS
Bach, W.F.	Sinfonia, d (2 fl, str)	Eul
Bach, W.F.	Sinfonia (2 fl, str)	M&M
Beck, C.	Concertino (cl, bsn, O)	SS
Beck, C.	Serenade (fl, cl, O)	SS
Beckerath, A. von	Concerto fugato (2 fl, str)	HSM
Beckwith, J.	Fall Scene & Fair Dance	
	(cl, vn, str)	Ber
Behrend, S.	Legnaniana, based on themes	
	by Legnani (fl, guit, str)	Pet
Benguerel, X.	Concerto. 1961 (2 fl, O)	B&N
Berger, J.	Concert Piece (2 fl, str)	Sch
Berkovec, J.	Concerto (fl, hp, O)	Art
Bloch, E.	Concertino (fl, cl, str)	Sch
Borris, S.	Shakespeare-Suite, op. 39/1	
	(fl, ob, str)	S-V
Bottje, W.	Concerto (fl, tpt, O)	ACA
Bräutigam, H.	Fröhliche Musik. 1938-39	
	(fl, ob, str)	BrH
Breval, J.	Symphonie Concertante, F,	
	op. 31 (fl, bsn, O)	MR
Briegel, G.	Soloette (asax, tsax, O)	GFB
Briegel & Tucker	Triplets (asax, tsax, O)	GFB
Burkhard, W.	Canzona, op. 76 (2 fl, O)	B&N
Burkhard, W.	Concertino op. 94. 1954	
	(2 fl, O)	B&N
Canino, B.	Concerto da Camera No. 3	
	(ob, vn, O)	ESZ
Capoianu, D.	Divertisment (2 cl, str)	EdR
Chevreuille, R.	Double Concerto op. 34. 1946	
	(asax, pf, O)	CBD
Chopin, F.	Minute Waltz (asax, tsax, O)	GFB
Chopin, F.	Minute Waltz (2 cl, O)	GFB
Cimarosa, D.-Oubradous	Concertante (2 fl, O)	EMT
Cimarosa, D.-Piccioli	Concerto, G (2 fl, O)	Int
Cimarosa, D.-Moyse	Concerto, G (2 fl, O)	SM
Cimarosa, D.	Sinfonie concertante (2 fl, O)	SS
Csonka, P.	Concertino (ob, bsn, O)	PIC
Danzi, F.	Sinfonia Concertante (cl, bsn, O)	EBM
David, J.	Variations on a Theme of	
	Josquin des Prés, op. 62	

	(fl, hn, str)	BrH
Delden, L. van	Concerto op. 64. 1959 (2 ob, O)	SD
Delden, L. van	Concerto op. 91. 1967	
	(2 sop sax, O)	SD
Depelsenaire, J.	Concertino (ob, asax, O)	ECh
Depelsenaire, J.	Dialogue (asax, tpt, O)	EMT
Devienne, F.	Symphonie Concertante (2 fl, O)	MR
Devienne, F.-Voxman	Symphonie Concertante, op. 25	
	(2 cl, O)	MR
Diamond, D.	Elegies (fl, ehn, str)	SMP
Dijk, J. van	Suite Pastorale. 1953	
	(ob, ehn, O)	SD
Doppler, F.-Adorjan	Concerto, d (2 fl, O)	Bil
Doppler, F.	Hungarian Phantasy, op. 35	
	(2 fl, O)	MR
Dubois, P.	Double Concertino (ob, bsn, O)	ALe
Duclos, P.	Concert Champêtre (ob, vn, str)	EMT
Durkó, Z.	Una Rapsodia ungherese.	
	1964-65 (2 cl, O)	EMB
Fasch, J.-Winschermann	Concerto, D (fl, ob, str)	HSM
Fasch, J.-Winschermann, Buck	Doppelkonzert, d (ob, vn, str)	HSM
Fasch, J.	Concerto, G (fl, ob, O)	HG
Feld, J.	Concert music. 1964 (ob, bsn, O)	CHF
Feld, J.	2 Lausbuben (2 fl, O)	CHF
Ferlendis, G.	Concerto, F, No. 1 (ob, hn, str)	Ric
Fesch, W. de -Ruf	Concerto, G, op. 10/8 (2 fl, O)	SS
Festing, M.-Ruf	Concerto a 7, op. 3/10 (2 fl, O)	B&N
Fiorillo, F.	Sinfonia Concertante (2 fl, O)	MR
Flothuis, M.	Sinfonietta concertante, op. 55.	
	op. 55. 1955 (cl, asax, O)	SD
Françaix, J.	Duo concertante (fl, vn, O)	SS
Frid, G.	Nocturnes, op. 24 (fl, hp, str)	SD
Frommel, G.	Concerto, b (cl, pf, O)	R&E
Fuchs, C.	Improvisation (fl, cl, str)	R&E
Fürst, P.	Bavy-Concerto, op. 32	
	(bcl, vib, O)	LDo
Furstenau, A.	Concertino op. 87, No. 2	
	(2 fl, O)	EdH
Galuppi, B.-Jenkins	Concerto, d (2 fl, O)	Sch
Galuppi, B.-Schroeder	Concerto, e (2 fl, str)	Hei
Genzmer, H.	Concertino (fl, pf, O)	SS
Ghedini, G.	Concerto (L'Alderina) (fl, vn, O)	Ric
Glanville-Hicks, P.	Gymnopédie No. 1 (ob, hp, O)	AMP
Gluck, C.	Iphigenie en Aulide, Gavotté	
	(2 ob, str)	Dur
Gluck, C.	Orphée, Menuet (2 fl, O)	Dur
Godron, H.	Hommages classiques. 1950	
	(fl, pf, O)	SD
Haller, H.	Doppelkonzert (fl, cl, str)	S-V
Handel, G.-Gevaert	Andante et Menuet (Concerto	

	No. 4) (ob, bsn, str)	Dur
Handel, G.	Concerto, Bb, op. 4, No. 6	
	(2 fl, str)	B&N
Handel, G. -Gevaert	Fragment du 5e Concerto	
	(2 ob, str)	Dur
Hanus, J.	Concerto doppio, op. 59. 1965	
	(ob, hp, O)	Art
Haydn, F. -Landon	Concerto, C, No. 1 (Lira	
	Concerti) (2 fl, O)	LDo
Haydn, F. -Landon	Concerto, G, No. 2 (Lira	
	Concerti) (fl, ob, O)	LDo
Haydn, F. -Landon	Concerto, G, No. 3 (Lira	
	Concerti) (fl, ob, O)	LDo
Haydn, F. -Landon	Concerto, F, No. 4 (Lira	
	Concerti (fl, ob, O)	LDo
Haydn, F. -Landon	Concerto, F, No. 5 (Lira	
	Concerti (fl, ob, O)	LDo
Heinichen, J. -Bachmair	Weihnachts-Pastorale (2 ob, O)	BrH
Hertel, J.	Concerto, Eb (ob, tpt, str)	MR
Hertel, J. -Tarr	Doppelkonzert, Eb (ob, tpt, str)	SS
Hertel, J.	Sinfonia à 6 (2 fl, str, bc)	MV
Hindemith, P.	Concerto. 1949 (bsn, tpt, O)	SS
Hirsch, H.	Concerto (ob, bsn, str)	Pet
Hobson, M.	Serenata (fl, ob, str)	Che
Hoffmeister, F.	Concerto, Eb (2 cl, O)	MR
Holmboe, V.	Chamber Concerto op. 20,	
	No. 2. 1940 (fl, vn, O)	SPD
Honegger, A.	Concerto da camera. 1948	
	(fl, ehn, O)	EdS
Hurnik, I.	Concerto (ob, pf, str)	Art
Jahrl	Frolic of the Keys	
	(asax, tsax, O)	GFB
Jelinek, H.	Fantasie, op. 18 (cl, pf, O)	UE
Jež, J.	Strophes (ob, cl, O)	EdD
Johns, D.	Concerto piccolo (fl, cl, O)	LDo
Koch, E. von	Concerto piccolo. 1962	
	(sop sax, asax, O)	BrH
Koch, E. von	Double Concerto. 1971	
	(fl, cl, str)	STI
Koetsier, J.	Duo concertante, op. 14/3.	
	1937 (fl, vn, O)	SD
Koetsier, J.	Siciliano e Rondino. 1942	
	(2 ob, O)	SD
Korte, O.	Geschichte zweier Flöten	
	(2 fl, O)	Art
Koutzen, B.	Concertante (2 fl, O)	Gen
Krommer, F.	Concerto, op. 35 (2 cl, O)	MR
Krommer, F.	Konzert, Eb, op. 91 (2 cl, O)	Art
Krommer, F.	Concerto op. 91 (2 cl, O)	M&M
Kubinsky, R.	Legende (cl, hp, str)	LK

Laderman, E.	Double Helix (fl, ob, O)	OxU
Langer, A.	A Promenade through the keys (March variations in Folk Tone) (2 cl, O)	CHF
Leighton, K.	Veris gratia, op. 9 (ob, vc, str)	Nov
Lier, B. van	Concertante muziek. 1959 (ob, vn, O)	SD
Ligeti, G.	Doppelkonzert (fl, ob, O)	SS
Lilien, I.	Concert arcadique. 1953 (2 fl, O)	SD
Luke, R.	Symphonic Dialogues (ob, vn, O)	OxU
Maconchy, E.	Concerto (ob, bsn, str)	AlL
Maderna, B.	Grande Aulodia (fl, ob, O)	Ric
Magdič, J.	Apeiron (fl, cl, O)	EdD
Mannino, F.	Suite Galante (fl, trb, O)	Ric
Marinuzzi, G.	Concerto (ob, asax, str)	Car
Martelli, H.	Concerto (cl, bsn, O)	HMo
Martinu, B.	Concerto. 1936 (fl, vn, O)	B&N
Masseus, J.	Concerto op. 29. 1956 (2 fl, O)	SD
Mersson, B.	Notturno (fl, hp, str)	Kaw
Meyer, K.	Concerto da Camera (fl, perc, str)	HMo
Meyer, T.	Concerto (ob, ehn, O)	For
Milhaud, D.	Concerto (fl, vn, O)	EdS
Möckl, F.	Bicinien (fl, ob, str)	S-V
Mozart, W.	Concerto, C, K. 299 (fl, hp, O)	BrH
Mozart, W.	Concerto, C, K. 299 (fl, hp, O)	CF
Mozart, W.	Concerto K. 299 (fl, hp, O)	EdK
Mozart, W.-Jongen	Cadenzas for Concerto, K. 299 (fl, hp, O)	EMb
Mozart, W.-Müller	Cadenzas to the Concerto for Flute and Harp	Hug
Mozart, W.-Pillney	Cadenzas for Concerto, K. 299 (fl, hp, O)	WZ
Mozart, W.	Idoménée, marche (2 ob, str)	Dur
Muscaro, M.	Ode (bsn, hn, str)	Cor
Natanson, T.	Double Concerto. 1959 (2 sax, O)	AP
Nemiroff, I.	Concertino (fl, vn, str)	M&M
Nessler, R.	Kammerkonzert (cl, pf, str)	EMo
Newlin, D.	Chamber Concerto, F (ob, vn, O)	ACA
Niederste-Schee, W.	Konzertantes Spiel. 1966 (fl, cl, str)	WH
Noetel, K.	Concertino (fl, vn, str)	B&N
Osieck, H.	Romance. 1952 (fl, hp, O)	SD
Palmer, R.	Chamber Concerto No. 1 (ob, vn, str)	PIC
Petermann, R.	Concerto op. 25 (fl, ob, O)	BrH
Piston, W.	Fantasy (ehn, hp, O)	AMP

Poradowski, S.	Nocturne, op. 59b (fl, hp, O)	A&S
Porcelijn, D.	Concerto. 1973 (fl, hp, O)	SD
Praag, H. van	Fantasia concertante. 1957 (fl, bsn, O)	SD
Quantz, J.	Concertos 1, 2; published separately (2 fl, O)	MR
Regteren Altena, L. van	Divertimento (fl, ob, O)	SD
Reinhold, O.	Konzert op. 111 (fl, pf, str)	B&N
Reuland, J.	Concertino. 1966 (2 cl, O)	SD
Rietz, J.	Concertino. 1963 (ob, va, str)	BrH
Rohwer, J.	Kammerkonzert. 1960 (2 fl, O)	BrH
Saint-Saens, C.	Tarantelle, op. 6 (fl, cl, O)	CF
Salieri, A.-Sabatini	Concerto, C (fl, ob, O)	LDo
Salieri, A.-Wojciechowski	Concerto, C (fl, ob, O)	Pet
Sammartini, G.-Lauschmann	Concerto (2 ob, str)	For
Schibler, A.	Elegische Musik, op. 52. 1957 (fl, vc, O)	BrH
Schibler, A.	Lyrische Musik, op. 12c (ob, hp, O)	A&S
Schneider, G.-Wollheim	Sinfonie concertante, F (cl, bsn, O)	B&B
Schoeck, O.	Serenade, op. 27 (ob, ehn, O)	BrH
Schönherr, M.	Im Duett (2 cl, O)	LK
Schulhoff, E.	Double Concerto. 1927 (fl, pf, O)	Art
Sehlbach, E.	Kammerkonzert, op. 97/1 (ob, hp, str)	MV
Sehlbach, E.	Kammerkonzert, op. 97/3 (fl, cl, str)	MV
Simeone, H.	Flute Cocktail (2 fl, O)	Sha
Soukup, V.	Sonate. 1966 (ehn, pf, str)	Art
Stamitz, A.-Lebermann	Concerto, G (2 fl, str)	SS
Stamitz, K.-Lebermann	Concerto, Bb (2 cl, O)	Pet
Stamitz, K.-Wojciechowski	Doppelkonzert, Bb (cl, bsn, O)	HSM
Stibilj, M.	Impressionen. 1963 (fl, hp, str)	B&N
Stölzel, G.-Tessmer	Concerto, e (fl, ob, str)	HSM
Stölzel, G.-Winschermann, Buck	Doppelkonzert, F (ob, vn, str)	HSM
Stölzel, G.	Concerto, F (ob, vn, str)	MV
Strategier, H.	Concertante Speelmuziek (fl, bsn, O)	SD
Strohbach, S.	Concerto, G. 1959 (2 fl, O)	BrH
Stutschewsky, J.	Phantasy (ob, hp, str)	See
Suchý, F.	Scherzo bifiatato. 1965 (fl, hn, O)	CHF
Šust, J.	Trauermusik (ob, vc, O)	CHF
Sydeman, W.	Concertino. 1956 (ob, pf, O)	See
Tausch, F.	Concerto (2 cl, O)	MR
Tcherepnin, A.	Concerto op. 33 (fl, vn, O)	SS
Telemann, G.-Oubradous	Concerto (2 fl, O)	EMT
Telemann, G.-Hinnenthal	Concerto, A (fl, vn, O)	B&N

Telemann, G. -Koelbel	Concerto, A (2 fl, O)	Pet
Telemann, G.	Concerto, a (2 fl, O)	AMP
Telemann, G. -Stein	Concerto, a (2 fl, O)	B&N
Telemann, G.	Concerto, d (ob, tpt, str)	Bil
Telemann, G.	Concerto, d (2 cl, O)	MR
Telemann, G. -Kölbel	Concerto, e (fl, rec, O)	B&N
Telemann, G. -Angerhofer	Concerto, F (rec, bsn, O)	BrH
Telemann, G. -Hofmann	Concerto, G (fl, ob d'amore, O)	Pet
Telemann, G. -Hinnenthal	Ouverture und Conclusion (Tafelmusik) (2 fl, O)	B&N
Telemann, G. -Hinnenthal	Ouverture and Conclusion, D (Tafelmusik II) (ob, tpt, str)	B&N
Valentini, R. -Fassano	Concerto, C, No. 3 (ob, vn, str)	Ric
Veale, J.	Elegy (fl, hp, str)	AlL
Vivaldi, A.	Concerto (fl, hpcd, O)	EdK
Vivaldi, A. -Müller	Concerto (2 fl, O)	NK
Vivaldi, A.	Concerto, a, P. 53 (2 ob, str)	MR
Vivaldi, A. -Oubradous	Concerto, C, No. 2 (2 fl, str)	EMT
Vivaldi, A. -Schroeder	Concerto, C, op. 47/2 (2 fl, O)	Eul
Vivaldi, A. -Ghedini	Concerto, C (2 fl, O)	Int
Vivaldi, A.	Concerto, C, F. VI, No. 2 (2 fl, O)	Ric
Vivaldi, A.	Concerto, C, F. VII, No. 3 (2 ob, O)	Ric
Vivaldi, A.	Concerto, C, P. 85 (2 ob, str)	MR
Vivaldi, A. -Lund	Concerto, c (ob, vn, str)	MR
Vivaldi, A.	Concerto, d, P. 302 (2 ob, str)	MR
Vivaldi, A.	Concerto, d, F. VII, No. 9 (2 ob, O)	Ric
Vivaldi, A. -Lasocki	Concerto, G, F. XII/36, P. 129 (ob, bsn, str)	MR
Vivaldi, A. -Oubradous	Concerto, G, No. 22 (ob, bsn, str)	EMT
Vivaldi, A. -Schroeder	Concerto, G, op. 42/3 (ob, bsn, O)	Pet
Vivaldi, A.	Concerto, G, F. XII, No. 36 (ob, bsn, str)	Ric
Vivaldi, A. -Torrefranca	Concerto, g, No. 1 (ob, vn, O)	Car
Voormolen, A.	Concerto. 1933 (2 ob, O)	SD
Voormolen, A.	Sinfonie concertante. 1951 (cl, hn, O)	SD.
Vorlova, S.	Double concerto, op. 59. 1962 (ob, hp, O)	CHF
Vranický, P. -Muclinger	Concerto, C, op. 39 (fl, ob, O)	CHF
Werdin, E.	Concertino (fl, guit, str)	HG
Werdin, E.	Concertino (2 fl, str)	SS
Wiechowicz, S.	Kate, Folk Suite in 5 Movements. 1946 (2 cl, O)	AP
Winter, P. von -Michaels	Concertino, Eb (cl, vc, O)	HSM

2 Instruments with Orchestra

Wiszniewski, Z.	Concerto (2 cl, str)	PWM
Wiszniewski, Z.	Concerto (2 cl, str)	EMo
Zipoli, D.	Adagio (ob, vc, str)	EdC

2 Instruments with Band

Bennett, D.	Clarinet Carousel (2 cl, B)	SM
Bennett, D.	Treatise for Two (fl, cl, B)	SM
Bishop, H.-Lax	Lo, Hear the Gentle Lark (fl, cl, B)	CF
Briegel & Tucker	Triplets (asax, tsax, B)	GFB
Briegel, G.	Soloette (asax, tsax, B)	GFB
Bruniau, A.	Toi et moi (cl, asax, B)	EdR
Bruniau, A.	Toi et moi (ob, asax, B)	EdR
Bruniau, A.	Toi et moi (sop sax, asax, B)	EdR
Chopin, F.	Minute Waltz (2 cl, B)	GFB
Chopin, F.	Minute Waltz (asax, tsax, B)	GFB
Coiteux	Les Gais troubadours (2 asax, B)	EdR
Crusell, B.	Concertante, Eb (2 cl, B)	Fin
Delbecq, L.	Dans les Montagnes (2 cl, B)	MM
Delbecq, L.	Doublette (2 asax, B)	EdR
Delbecq, L.	Fantasie Duo No. 1 (asax, asax, B)	MM
Delbecq, L.	Fantasie Duo No. 1 (asax, asax(tsax), B)	MM
DeVille, P.	Swiss Boy (2 cl, B)	CF
Endresen, R.	Pepperino (2 cl, B)	Rub
Fote, R.	Tutti Flutti (2 fl, B)	Ken
Jahrl	Frolic of the Keys (asax, tsax, B)	GFB
Kinyon, J.-arr.	Brothers Two (2 asax, B)	CFC
Labole, P.	Les Tourbillons (2 cl, B)	EdR
Labole, P.	Les Tourbillons (sop sax, asax, B)	EdR
Livingston, S.	Symphonic Poem (cl, asax, B)	Vol
Magnan	Les Deux amis (2 cl, B)	EdR
Marsal, E.	Grande fantaisie polka (sop sax, asax, B)	EdR
Mendelssohn, F.-Gee	Concert Piece No. 2 (2 cl)	SM
Nattes, de	Les Deux virtuoses (2 cl, B)	EdR
Paganini, N.-Falcone	Perpetual Motion (2 cl, B)	SM
Reynolds	Air and Dance (2 cl, B)	CFC
Reynolds	Flattery for Flutes (2 fl, B)	CFC
Reynolds	Song and Polka (2 asax, B)	CFC
Rosen, J.	Concerto (cl, trb, B)	ACA
Schubert, F.-Martin	Ave Maria (asax, tsax, B)	EdR
Simeone, H.	Flute Cocktail (2 fl, B)	Sha
Smith & Holmes	Friends (2 cl, B)	Rub
Taylor, C.	Sinfonia Seria (fl, bar, B)	ACA

3 Instruments with Orchestra*

Amram, D.	Shakespearean Concerto	
	(fl, 2 hn, str)	Pet
Andriessen, J.	Movimenti II (ob, cl, bsn, O)	SD
Bach, J.S.-Soldan, Landshoff	Brandenburg Concerto No. 4	
	(2 fl, vn, str)	Pet
Bach, J.S.	Brandenburg Concerto, D,	
	No. 5, BWV 1050	
	(fl, vn, hpcd, str)	BrH
Bach, J.S.	Concerto, a, BWV 1044	
	(fl, vn, hpcd, str)	BrH
Bach, J.S.	Concerto, a, No. 8, BWV 1044	
	(fl, vn, hpcd, str)	CF
Bach, J.S.	Concerto, F, BWV 1057	
	(2 fl, pf, str)	BrH
Bach, J.S.	Concerto, F, BWV 1957	
	(2 fl, hpcd, str)	CF
Bach, J.S.	Triple Concerto (fl, vn, pf, str)	EdK
Barber, S.	Capricorn Concerto, op. 21	
	(fl, ob, tpt, str)	Sch
Baumann, M.	Petite Suite (fl, ob, cl, str)	S-V
Beethoven, L. van-Hess	Romance cantabile, e	
	(fl, bsn, pf, O)	BrH
Bentzon, N.	Triple Concerto, op. 94	
	(ob, cl, bsn, O)	WH
Bialas, G.	Sinfonia piccola (fl, ob. cl, str)	B&N
Biscogli	Triple Concerto (ob, bsn, tpt, O)	MR
Blacher, B.	Dialog (fl, vn, pf, str)	UE
Bräutigam, H.	Konzert (fl, ob, bsn, O)	BrH
Breval, J.-Brook	Symphonie Concertante	
	(cl, bsn, hn, str)	FrM
Breval, J.-Petit	Concertante, F, op. 38	
	(cl, bsn, hn, O)	Kaw
Briegel, G.	Soloette (2 asax, tsax, O)	GFB
Briegel & Tucker	Triplets (2 asax, tsax, O)	GFB
Cannabich, C.-Päuler	Concerto (fl, ob, bsn, O)	Eul
Crusell, B.-Weelink	Concertante, Bb, op. 3	
	(cl, bsn, hn, O)	Kaw
Cunningham, M.	Dialogue (fl, cl, bsn, O)	CoA
Dressel, E.	Konzert (ob, cl, bsn, O)	R&E
Driessler, J.	Concerto da camera I, op. 51	
	(fl, ehn, vn, O)	BrH
Eckhardt-Gramatté, S.	Tripel-Konzert (cl, bsn, tpt, O)	UE
Emborg, J.	Concerto Grosso, op. 51	
	(ob, vn, vc, O)	Kis
Fasch, J.	Triple Concerto, E	
	(ob d'amore, tpt, vn, O)	MR
Felix, V.	Concertino (concerto	
	romantico). 1953	
	(cl, vn, hp, O)	CHF

* See footnote page 376.

Gallon, N.	Concerto (ob, cl, bsn, O)	ALe
Handel, G. -Hoffmann, Redlich	Concerto, G, op. 6, No. 1	
	(2 ob, bsn, str)	B&N
Handel, G. -Hoffmann, Redlich	Concerto, F, op. 6, No. 2	
	(2 ob, bsn, str)	B&N
Handel, G. -Hoffmann, Redlich	Concerto, D, op. 6, No. 5	
	(2 ob, bsn, str)	B&N
Handel, G. -Hoffmann, Redlich	Concerto, g, op. 6, No. 6	
	(2 ob, bsn, str)	B&N
Handel, G. -Schering	Mirtillo Suite (Il Pastor Fido)	
	(fl, 2 ob, str)	Pet
Hervig, R.	Trio-Concertino (cl, vn, pf, O)	AMC
Holst, G.	Brook Green Suite	
	(fl, ob, cl, str)	Sch
Hovhaness, A.	Tzaikerk (Evening Song)	
	(fl, vn, timp, str)	SMP
Hummel, J. N.	Fantasia (2 cl, va, str)	MR
Indy, V. d'	Concert (fl, vc, pf, str)	EdS
Jahrl	Frolic of the Keys	
	(2 asax, tsax, O)	GFB
Kattnigg, R.	Serenata Chioggiota (3 bsn, str)	UE
Kramar-Krommer, F.	Sinfonia Concertante, op. 70	
	(fl, cl, vn, O)	MR
Kramar-Krommer, F.	Sinfonia Concertante, op. 80	
	(fl, cl, vn, O)	MR
Krenek, E.	Concertino, op. 27	
	(fl, vn, hpcd, str)	UE
Krol, B.	Concerto Grosso, op. 15	
	(ob, ehn, bsn, O)	B&B
Michaelides, S.	Suite Archaiique. 1955	
	(fl, ob, hp, str)	See
Orlinski, H.	Evoë (fl, vc, hpcd, str)	Hug
Piños, A.	Triple Concerto. 1967	
	(bcl, vc, pf, O)	Art
Quinet, M.	Concertino. 1960 (ob, cl, bsn, O)	CBD
Ranta, S.	Concertino No. 2. 1934	
	(fl, hp, va, str)	Fin
Reiner, K.	Divertimento (cl, ph, perc, str)	Art
Salieri, A. -Wojciechowski	Tripelkonzert, D (ob, vn, vc, O)	HSM
Schenker, F.	Triple Concerto (ob, bsn, pf, O)	Deu
Schollum, R.	3 Stücke, op. 51a (fl, vn, va, O)	LDo
Simeone, H.	Flute Cocktail (3 fl, O)	Sha
Starer, R.	Concerto a Tre (cl, tpt, trb, O)	MCA
Telemann, G. -Stein	Concerto, E (fl, ob d'amore,	
	va d'amore, O)	Pet
Telemann, G.	Concerto, e (2 fl, vn, str)	EdK
Telemann, G. -Schroeder	Concerto, e (2 fl, vn, O)	Eul
Tomasi, H.	Divertimento Corsica	
	(ob, cl, bsn, O)	ALe
Tomasi, H.	Pastorales Provençales	

	(fl, 2 guit, str)	ALe
Viozzi, G.	Triple Concerto (cl, vc, pf, O)	B-M
Vivaldi, A.-Schroeder	Concerto, F, op. 44/16, "La Tempesta di mare" (fl, ob, bsn, O)	Eul
Vivaldi, A.-Oubradous	Concerto, g, No. 25 (fl, ob, bsn, O)	EMT
Vivaldi, A.-Rampal	Concerto, P. 402 (fl, ob, bsn, O)	Int
Wennig, H.	3 Orchesterstücke, op. 36 (ob, 2 cl, O)	JS
Zender, H.	Divertimento, op. 7b (fl, vn, vc, O)	BrH

3 Instruments with Band

Barsotti, R.	Clarinet Cameo (3 cl, B)	Vol
Briegel, G.	Soloette (2 asax, tsax, B)	GFB
Briegel & Tucker	Triplets (2 asax, tsax, B)	GFB
Bright, H.	Concerto Grosso No. 1-- Allegro Moderato (fl, ob, cl, B)	Sha
Bright, H.	Concerto Grosso No. 1-- Lento Cantabile (fl, ob, cl, B)	Sha
Bunton, E.	Tropical Flutes (3 fl, B)	Vol
Cacavas, J.-Wilkes	Shimmering Flutes (3 fl, B)	SM
Cacavas, J.	Midnight Soliloquy (3 sax, B)	Vol
Eisch	Dancing Reeds (3 cl, B)	Hal
Estes, A.	Claristhenics (3 cl, B)	Ken
Fote, R.	Tutti Flutti (3 fl, B)	Ken
Frackenpohl, A.	Flute Rag (3 fl, B)	EBM
Frank, M.	Minka, Minka (3 sax, B)	Rub
Grundman, C.	Flutation (3 fl, B)	B&H
Handel, G.-Malin	Concerto Grosso (2 fl, cl, B)	War
Hayes	Visions (2 asax, bar sax, B)	CF
Jahrl	Frolic of the Keys (2 asax, tsax, B)	GFB
Langlois	Les Trois inséparables (Eb cl, 2 cl, B)	EdR
Madden	Flutes, Flutes, Flutes (3 fl, B)	CFC
Morrissey, J.	Waltzing Clarinets (3 cl, B)	B-M
Osterling, E.	Beguine for Flutes (3 fl, B)	Lud
Osterling, E.	Samba for Flutes (3 fl, B)	Lud
Ostling, A.	Swing low, sweet saxes, based on "Swing low, sweet chariot" (2 asax, tsax, B)	B-M
Ployhar, J.	Beguine for Shimmering Flutes (3 fl, B)	CFC
Reynolds	Flattery for Flutes (3 fl, B)	CFC
Scarmolin, L.-Kepner	3 Swingsters (3 sax, B)	Lud
Simeone, H.	Flute Cocktail (3 fl, B)	Sha
Vitello	A Trio Grows in Brooklyn	

	(cl, tpt, trb, B)	CF

4 Instruments with Orchestra *

Amram, D.	Triple Concerto	
	(fl, ob, cl, bsn, O)	Pet
Andriessen, H.	Chromatische Variaties	
	(fl, ob, vn, vc, str)	SD
Bach, J.S.-Soldan, Landshoff	Brandenburg Concerto No. 2	
	(fl, ob, tpt, vn, str)	Pet
Baksa, R.	Chamber Concerto	
	(fl, ob, cl, bsn, str)	AlB
Barati, G.	Baroque Quartet Concerto	
	(fl, ob, db, hpcd, O)	ACA
Baur, J.	Concertino. 1959	
	(fl, ob, cl, timp, O)	BrH
Bentzon, N.	Concerto No. 1, op. 167	
	(fl, hn, tpt, hpcd, str)	WH
Bentzon, N.	Concerto No. 2, op. 168	
	(ob, vn, vc, hpcd, str)	WH
Bentzon, N.	Concerto No. 3, op. 169	
	(bsn, va, pf, hpcd, str)	WH
Bentzon, N.	Concerto No. 4, op. 170	
	(cl, trb, db, hpcd, str)	WH
Berio, L.	Concertino. 1050–51	
	(cl, vn, cel, hp, str)	AlB
Berio, L.	Tempi Concertati. 1958	
	(fl, vn, 2 pf, O)	AlB
Birtwistle, H.	Nomos (fl, cl, bsn, hn, O)	UE
Boguslawski, E.	Concerto (ob, ob d'amore, ehn,	
	musette, O)	PWM
Bonneau, P.	Divertissement (4 fl, O)	ALe
Buschmann, R.	Concerto Piccolo	
	(cl, db, guit, perc, str)	GBV
Calmel, R.	Concerto (sop sax, asax, tsax,	
	bar sax, str)	ECh
Danzi, F.	Sinfonia Concertante	
	(fl, ob, bsn, hn, O)	MR
Danzi, F.-Zirnbauer	Sinfonia concertante	
	(fl, ob, bsn, hn, O)	SS
Dubois, P.	Concertino (4 sax, O)	ALe
Dubois, P.	Concerto Printanier (4 fl, O)	ALe
Françaix, J.	Quadruple Concerto	
	(fl, ob, cl, bsn, O)	SS
Gabaye, P.	Symphonie Concertante	
	(fl, ob, hn, bsn, str)	ALe
Grabner, H.	Konzert, op. 48	
	(fl, cl, hn, bsn, str)	Kis
Hasquenoph, P.	Troisième symphonie (4 sax, O)	ECh
Haydn, F.	Sinfonie Concertante, op. 84	
	(ob, bsn, vn, vc, O)	BrH

* *See footnote page 376.*

Haydn, F.	Sinfonia Concertante, op. 84	
	(ob, bsn, vn, vc, O)	EdK
Heinichen, J.	Concerto (4 fl, O)	BrH
Henkemans, H.	Elégies. 1967 (4 fl, O)	SD
Levy, F.	Concerto (ob, bsn, hn, timp, str)	Cor
Lothar, M.	Concertino, op. 63 (4 cl, O)	R&E
Maasz, G.	Tripartita (3 fl, hpcd, str)	HSM
Martelli, H.	Concertino (ob, cl, hn, bsn, str)	Ric
Milhaud, D.	Symphonie Concertante	
	(tpt, hn, bsn, db, O)	Heu
Mozart, W.	Sinfonia Concertante, Eb,	
	KV 9 (ob, cl, hn, bsn, O)	BrH
Mozart, W.	Sinfonia Concertante, Eb, KV 9	
	(ob, cl, hn, bsn, O)	EdK
Pleyel, I.	5th Symphonie Concertante	
	(fl, ob, hn, bsn, O)	EMT
Pleyel, I.	Sinfonia Concertante	
	(fl, ob, bsn, hn, O)	MR
Quinet, M.	Concerto grosso. 1964 (4 cl, O)	CBD
Ronnefeld, P.	Concertino (fl, cl, bsn, hn, str)	EMo
Rudajev, A.	Concerto grosso (fl, 2 ob, hp, O)	CHF
Rytel, P.	Sinfonia Concertante. 1060	
	(fl, cl, hn, hp, O)	AP
Schulhoff, E.	Doppelkonzert (fl, 2 ob, pf, str)	Art
Trimble, L.	Concerto (fl, ob, cl, bsn, str)	Pet
Vivaldi, A. -Meylan	Concerto in due Cori (4 fl, O)	UE
Winter, P. von -Stefan	Concertino (cl, bsn, hn, vn, O)	Kaw

4 Instruments with Band

Bennett, D.	Sax-Soliloquy (4 sax, B)	SM
Budka, H.	Four Winds--Suite	
	(fl, ob, cl, asax, B)	S-B
Cacavas, J.	Midnight Soliloquy (4 sax, B)	Vol
Palange, L.	The Southern Four	
	(cl, tsax, tpt, trb, B)	TP
Schwarz, I.	Sax Serenade (2 asax, tsax,	
	bar sax, B)	Bar
Stevens, N.	Cameos (asax, ehn, trb, tpt, B)	CF

5 Instruments with Orchestra*

Baur, J.	Pentagramm. 1966	
	(fl, ob, cl, bsn, hn, O)	BrH
Bentzon, N.	Concerto No. 5, op. 171	
	(fl, ob, cl, bsn, hn, O)	WH
Berger, A.	Serenade Concertante	
	(fl, ob, cl, bsn, vn, O)	Pet
Blacher, B.	Konzertstück. 1963	
	(fl, ob, cl, bsn, hn, str)	B&B
Burghauser, J.	Concerto for wind quintet. 1942	
	(fl, ob, cl, bsn, hn, O)	CHF

* *See footnote page 376.*

5 Instruments with Orchestra

David, T.	Concerto (fl, ob, cl, bsn, hn, O)	LDo
Di Domenica, R.	Concerto (fl, ob, cl, bsn, hn, O)	EBM
Flosman, O.	Concertante music. 1965	
	(fl, ob, cl, bsn, hn, O)	CHF
Heinichen, J.-Hausswald	Concerto (fl, ob, vn, vc,	
	theorbo, str)	Eul
Helm, E.	Concerto (fl, ob, bsn, vn, tpt, O)	SS
Hindemith, P.	Concerto. 1949 (fl, ob, cl,	
	bsn, hp, O)	SS
Husa, K.	Concerto (fl, ob, cl, bsn, hn, str)	ALe
Husa, K.	Sérénade (fl, ob, cl, bsn, hn, O)	ALe
Klusák, J.	Concerto grosso	
	(fl, ob, cl, bsn, hn, str)	B&N
Kunert, K.	Concerto (fl, ob, cl, hn, bsn, O)	BrH
Kurz, S.	Kammerkonzert, op. 31	
	(fl, ob, cl, bsn, hn, O)	BrH
Lachman, H.	Symphonie Concertante	
	(fl, ob, cl, bsn, hn, O)	SD
Linde, B.	Liten konsert op. 35. 1965	
	(fl, ob, cl, bsn, hn, str)	STI
Rieti, V.	Concerto (fl, ob, cl, hn, bsn, O)	UE
Roger, K.	Concerto Grosso, op. 71	
	(fl, ob, cl, trb, perc, str)	HMo
Schäfer, K.	Concerto (fl, vn, tpt, pf, perc, str)	GBV
Sköld, Y.	Concertino op. 63. 1963	
	(fl, ob, cl, bsn, hn, O)	STI
Swann, J.	Sinfonie Concertante	
	(fl, ob, cl, bsn, hn, O)	CoA
Vivaldi, A.-Raphael	Concerto, F (2 ob, 2 hn, vn, O)	BrH

5 Instruments with Band

Davis, A.	Sweet Winds	
	(cl, 2 asax, 2 tsax, B)	Vol
Haddad, D.	Air and Adagio	
	(fl, ob, cl, bsn, hn, B)	Sha
Long, N.	Concertino (fl, ob, cl, bsn, hn, B)	Vol
Nowak	Suite (fl, ob, cl, bsn, hn, B)	CFC
Schanke, D.	Bubbling Woodwinds	
	(2 fl, 3 cl, B)	Bar
Schanke, D.	5 Mellow Winds (5 sax, B)	Cha
Schanke, D.	Latin Reeds	
	(cl, 2 asax, 2 tsax, B)	Bar

KEY TO PUBLISHERS

ABe	Anton J. Benjamin, Werderstrasse 44, Hamburg 13, Germany (AMP)
ABS	Anton Bohm & Sohn, Lange Gasse 26, 89 Augsburg 2, Germany
ACA	American Composers Alliance, 170 West 74th Street, New York, New York 10023
Acc	Accura Music, Box 887, Athens, Ohio 45701
AE	Autograph Editions, New York (AM)
AHC	Ascherberg, Hopwood & Crew, Ltd., 16 Mortimer Street, London, W. 1, England
AlB	Alexander Broude, Inc., 225 West 57th Street, New York, New York 10019
Alb	Albersen & Company, The Hague, Holland
ALe	Alphonse Leduc, 175 Rue Saint-Honoré, Paris, France
Alf	Alfred Music Co., Inc., 75 Channel Drive, Port Washington, New York 11050
AlL	Alfred Lengnick & Co., Purley Oaks Studios, 421a Brighton Road, South Croydon, Surrey, England (FH)
Als	G. Alsbach & Co., Leidsegracht 11, Amsterdam, Holland (Pet)
AM	Atlantic Music Supply, Box 180, West Nyack, New York 10994 (Philharmusica Corporation)
AMC	American Music Center, Inc., 2109 Broadway, Suite 15-79, New York, New York 10023
AME	American Music Edition, 263 East 7th Street, New York, New York 10009 (CF)
AMP	Associated Music Publishers, Inc., 866 Third Avenue, New York, New York 10022
Amp	Amphion Editions Musicales, 9 Rue d'Artois, Paris 8e, France (B-M)
AP	Ars Polona, Krakowskie Przedmiescie 7, Warsaw, Poland
ArM	Artisan Music Press (AM)
Art	Artia, Ve Smečkách 30, Praha 1, Czechoslovakia (B&H)
A&S	Ahn & Simrock, Mommsenstrasse 71, 1000 Berlin 12, Germany or Taunusstrasse 66, 6200 Wiesbaden, Germany
Ash	Ashley Dealers Service, Inc., 263 Veterans Blvd., Carlstadt, New Jersey 07072
ATL	A.T.L. Publishing Co., 3105 S. Hughes Avenue, Fresno, California 93706
Aug	Augsburg Publishing House, 426 S. Fifth Street, Minneapolis, Minnesota 55415
Ba	Barry E.C.I., Buenos Aires, Argentina (B&H)
Bar	C.L. Barnhouse Co., Oskaloosa, Iowa 52577
BB	Broude Brothers, 56 West 45th Street, New York, New York 10036
B&B	Bote & Bock, Hardenbergstrasse 9a, 1 Berlin 12, Germany (AMP)
Be	M.P. Belaieff, Kronprinzenstrasse 26, Bonn, Germany (Pet) Belwin (See B-M)
Ber	Berandol Music Limited, 11 St. Joseph Street, Toronto, Canada
B&H	Boosey & Hawkes, Lawson Blvd., P.O. Box 130, Oceanside, New York 11572
Big	The Big 3 Music Corporation, 729 7th Avenue, New York 10019
Bil	Billaudot Editions Musicales, 14, Rue de l'Echiquier, Paris 10e, France (TP)
BM	Boston Music Company, 116 Boylston St., Boston, Massachusetts 02116 (FrM)
B-M	Belwin-Mills Publishing Corp., 25 Deshon Drive, Melville, New York 11746
B&N	Bärenreiter & Neuwerk, Heinrich-Schütz-Allee 35, 35 Kassel-Wilhelmshöhe, Germany
Bos	Bosworth & Co., Ltd., 14/18, Heddon Street, London, W. 1, England (B-M)
Bou	Bourne Co., 1212 6th Ave., New York, New York 10036 (Cha)
Bow	Bowdoin College Music Press, Brunswick, Maine 04011
BPP	Berklee Press Publications, 1140 Boylston Street, Boston, Massachusetts 02215
Bra	Branden Press, Inc., 221 Columbus Ave., Boston, Massachusetts 02116
BrH	Breitkopf & Härtel, Walkmühlstrasse 52, D 6200 Wiesbaden 1, Germany (AMP)
Bro	Brodt Music Co., P.O. Box 1207, Charlotte, North Carolina 28201
B&V	Broekmans & Van Poppel, Van Baerlestraat 92-94, Amsterdam, Holland (Pet) B. Schott's Söhne (See SS)
BVC	Bregman, Vocco and Conn, Inc., c/o Big Bells Inc., 33 Hovey Ave., Trenton, New Jersey 08610
Byr	Byron-Douglas Publications, 25 Deshon Drive, Melville, New York 11746
Cam	Camara Music Publishers, 25 Elk Street, San Francisco, California 94131
Can	Canadian Music Centre, 33 Edward Street, Toronto 2, Ontario, Canada
Car	Carisch S.P.A. 20124 - Via General Fara, 39, Milan, Italy
CBD	Centre Belge de Documentation Musicale, Rue de l'Hôpital, 31, B-1000 Bruxelles, Belgium (HeE)
CBP	Claude Benny Press, 1401 State St., Emporia, Kansas 66801
CCo	Chas. Colin, 315 West 53rd Street, New York, New York 10019
Cen	Century Music Publishing Co. Inc., 263 Veterans Blvd., Carlstadt, New Jersey 07072
CF	Carl Fischer, Inc., 62 Cooper Square, New York, New York 10003
CFC	Carl Fischer of Chicago, 312 South Wabash, Chicago, Illinois 60604
CFo	Charles Foley, Inc. (CF)
CFV	Chr. Friedrich Vieweg, Limonenstr. 10, 1 Berlin 45, Germany (Pet)
CGM	Carl Gehrmans Musikförlag, Vasagatan 46, Box 505, 101 26 Stockholm 1, Sweden (B&H)
Cha	Chappell & Co., Inc., 810 7th Ave., New York, New York 10019
Che	J.&W. Chester Ltd., Eagle Court, London, EC1, England (M-B)
CHF	Český Hudebni Fond, Ústredni archiv, Pařízská 13, Praha 1, Czechoslovakia
ChM	Le Chant du Monde, 32 Rue Beaujon, Paris 8e, France C.L. Barnhouse (See Bar)
CMP	Congress Music Publications, 4301 Adams Ave., Miami Beach, Florida 33140
CoA	Composers' Autograph Publications, P.O. Box 7103, Cleveland, Ohio 44128

CoF	Composers' Facsimile Edition, 170 West 74th Street, New York, New York 10023
Col	M.M. Cole Publishing Co., 251 East Grand Ave., Chicago, Illinois 60611
Con	Concordia Publishing House, 3558 South Jefferson Ave., St. Louis, Missouri 63118
CoP	The Composers Press, Inc., 177 East 87th Street, New York, New York 10028 (See)
Cor	Cor Publishing Co., 67 Bell Place, Massapequa, New York 11758
CP	Christlieb Products, 3311 Scadlock Lane, Sherman Oaks, California 91403
CPE	Composer Performer Edition, 330 University Ave., Davis, California 95616
Cra	J.B. Cramer, 139 New Bond Street, London, W.1, England
Cre	Crescendo Music Sales, Box 395, Naperville, Illinois 60540
CrW	Creative World, Inc., Box 35216, Los Angeles, California 90035
Cur	J. Curwen & Sons Ltd., 29 Maiden Lane, London, W.C.2, England
	J.&W. Chester (See Che)
Deu	VEB Deutscher Verlag, Postfach 147, 701 Leipzig, East Germany (AlB)
DGo	David Gornston (SF)
Dor	Dorn Productions, 391 Concord Street, Framingham, Massachusetts 01701
DSS	DSS Editions, Misarska 12-14, Belgrade, Yugoslavia
Dur	Editions Durand & Cie, 4, Place de la Madeleine, 4 Paris 8e, France (E-V)
EB	Edition Boileau, Post Box 6026, Barcelona, Spain
EBe	Edizioni Musicali Bèrben (TP)
EBM	Edward B. Marks Music Corporation, 1790 Broadway, New York, New York 10019 (B-M)
EbM	Eble Music, 11-1/2 South Dubuque, Iowa City, Iowa 52240
E&C	Enoch & Cie., 27 Boulevard des Italiens, Paris 2e, France (AMP)
ECh	Editions Choudens, 38 Rue Jean Mermoz, Paris 8e, France (Pet)
ECK	E.C. Kerby, Ltd., 198 Davenport Road, Toronto 5, Ontario, Canada (JB)
ECM	Editions A. Cranz Musikverlag, Adelheidstrasse 68, 62 Wiesbaden, Germany (HeE)
ECS	E.C. Schirmer Music Co., 112 South Street, Boston, Massachusetts 02111
EdA	Editorial Alpuerto, S.A., Agustin de Bethencourt, 19, Madrid, Spain
EdB	Edizioni Bongiovanni, Via Rizzoli, 28/E, Bologna, Italy (B-M)
EdC	Editions Costallat, 60 Rue de la Chaussée-d'Antin, Paris 9e, France (Bil)
EdD	Edicije Društva slovenskih skladateljev, Trg francoske revolucije 6, 61000 Ljubljana, Yugoslavia
EdF	Edition Fazer, Postbox 260, 00101 Helsinki 10, Finland
EdH	Edition Heuwekemeyer, Weteringstraat 19, Amsterdam 1002, Holland (HeE)
Edi	Edizioni Curci, Galleria del Corso, 4, Milan, Italy
EdK	Edwin F. Kalmus, Opa Locka, Florida 33054
EdL	Editions de L'Oiseau-Lyre, Les Remparts, Monaco
EdM	Edition Musicus-New York, Inc., Box 1341, Stamford, Connecticut 06904
EdO	Les Editions Ouvrières, 12, Avenue Soeur-Rosalie, Paris 13e, France
EdR	Editions Robert Martin, 106, Grande-rue de la Coupée, 71, Charnay-Les-Macon, France
EDS	Edizioni De Santis, Via Cassia, 13, Rome, Italy
EdS	Editions Salabert, 22 Rue Chauchat, Paris 9e, France or 575 Madison Ave., New York, N.Y. 10022
EdT	Edition Tonos, Ahastrasse 7-9, 6100 Darmstadt, Germany
EFM	E.F. Technisonor, 14 Rue Magellan, Paris 8me, France
EHe	Edition Helbling, 8604 Volketswil, Zürich, Switzerland
Ehr	Ehrling Musik AB, Stockholm, Sweden
EK	Edition Kneusslin, Amselstrasse 43, Basel 24, Switzerland (Pet)
Elk	Elkin and Co., Ltd., Borough Green-Sevenoaks, Kent, England (GaM)
EM	Edwin H. Morris & Co., Inc., 810 7th Ave., New York, New York 10019 (Han)
EMB	Editio Musica Budapest, Pf. 322, Budapest 5, Hungary (B&H)
EMb	Editions Musicales Brogneaux, 73 Avenue Paul Janson, Bruxelles, Belgium (HeE)
EMC	Eastlane Music Corp., 623 Latona Ave., Trenton, New Jersey 08618
EME	Editions Max Eschig, 48 Rue de Rome, Paris 8e, France (AMP)
EMe	Editions Metropolis, Frankrijklei 24, Antwerpen, Belgium (HeE)
EMF	Eriks Musikhandel & Forlag AB, Karlavagen 40, Stockholm, Sweden
EMG	Edition Marbot GmbH., Bornstrasse 12, Hamburg 13, Germany
EMM	Editorial Musical Moderna, Marqués de Cubas 6, Madrid 14, Spain
EMo	Edition Modern, Franz Joseph Strasse 2, 8 Munich, Germany
EMP	Edition Maurice et Pierre Foetisch, 6 Rue de Bourg, Lausanne, Switzerland
EMT	Editions Musicales Transatlantiques, 14 Avenue Hoche, Paris 8e, France (TP)
EMU	Editura Muzicala, Compozitorilor Din R.S.R., Bucharest, Rumania
Ens	Ensemble Publications, Inc., Box 98, Bidwell Station, Buffalo, New York 14222
EPC	Editions Philippo-Combre, 24 Boulevard Poissonnière, Paris 9e, France (TP)
EQM	Etoile Quality Music, Box 651, Bloomington, Indiana 47401
Eri	E.J. Erickson Co., 606 N. 4th St., St. Peter, Minnesota 56082
ERM	Emil Ruh Musikverlag, Zürichstrasse 33, Ch-8134 Adliswil, Zurich, Switzerland
ERR	Editions Rideau Rouge, 24 Rue de Longchamp, Paris 16, France (E-V)
ERS	Edouard Richli Siècle Musical, 16 Boulevard Helvétique, Geneva, Switzerland
ES	Editio Supraphon, Palackého 1, Praha 1, Czechoslovakia
ESu	Edition Suecia, Stockholm, Sweden
ESZ	Edizioni Suvini Zerboni, Corso Europa 5/7, Milan, Italy
Eul	Eulenburg GmbH., Grütstrasse 28, 8134 Adliswil-Zurich, Switzerland (Pet)
	Henri Elkan (See HeE)

E-V Elkan-Vogel Co., Inc., c/o Theodore Presser, Presser Place, Bryn Mawr, Pennsylvania 19010
ExM Experimental Music, 208 Ladbroke Grove, London W 10, England
Fab Faber Music Ltd., 38 Russell Square, London WC1B 5 DA, England (Sch)
FaM Fana Music, Box 393, Amherst, Maine 01002
Fer Fereol Publications, Box 6007, Alexandria, Virginia 22306
F.E.C. Leuckart (see Leu)
FH Frederick Harris Music, Box 670, Oakville, Ontario, Canada
Fin Finnish Music Information Centre, Runeberginkatu 15 A, 00100, Helsinki 10, Finland
Fit H.T. FitzSimons Co., 615 N. LaSalle Street, Chicago, Illinois 60610
Carl Fischer (See CF)
Charles Foley (See CFo)
Sam Fox (See SF)
For Robert Forberg Verlagsverzeichnis, Mirbachstrasse 9, 53 Bonn-Bad Godesberg, Germany
FrC Franco Colombo Publications, 25 Deshon Drive, Melville, New York 11746 (B-M)
FrH Friedrich Hofmeister-Verlag, Ubierstrasse 20, 6238 Hofheim am Taunus, Germany (AMP)
FrM Frank Music Corp., 116 Boylston Street, Boston, Massachusetts 02116
Gal Galliard Ltd., Queen Anne's Road, Great Yarmouth, Norfolk, England (GaM)
GaM Galaxy Music Corporation, 2121 Broadway, New York, New York 10023
GBV Gustav Bosse Verlag, Postfach 417, 84 Regensburg 2, Germany
GD Georges Delrieu & Cie, 45, Avenue de la Victoire, Nice, France (GaM)
Gen General Music Publishing Co., Inc., P.O. Box 267, Hastings-on-Hudson, New York 10706
GFB George F. Briegel, Inc., 4 Summit Court, Flushing, New York 11355
GIA G.I.A. Publications, 7404 S. Mason Avenue, Chicago, Illinois 60638
Gor Gordon Music Co., 2680 Cherokee Way, Palm Springs, California 92262
G. Ricordi (See Ric)
Gra H.W. Gray Co., Inc., c/o Belwin-Mills, Melville, New York 11746
GrF S.A.R.L. Gras Frères, 36 Rue Pape-Carpentier, 72-La Flèche, France (MB)
Ph. Grosch (See PG)
G. Schirmer (See Sch)
GZ G. Zanibon, Piazza Dei Signori 24/26, 35100 Padova, Italy (Pet)
Hal Hal Leonard Publishing, Inc., 8112 W. Bluemound Rd., Milwaukee, Wisconsin 53213
Ham Hamelle & Cie, 24, Boulevard Malesherbes, Paris 8e, France
Han Charles Hansen Publishing, 1842 West Avenue, Miami Beach, Florida 33139
Har T.B. Harms Co., c/o Cimino Publications, 1646 New Highway, Farmingdale, New York 11735
HE Hinrichsen Edition, Ltd., 10 Baches Street, London, England (Pet)
HeE Henri Elkan Music Publisher, 1316 Walnut Street, Philadelphia, Pennsylvania 19107
Hei Heinrichshofen Verlag, Liebigstrasse 4, Wilhelmshaven, Germany (Pet)
Heu Heugel & Cie, 2 bis, Rue Vivienne, Paris 2e, France (TP)
HG Hans Gerig Musikverlag, Drususgasse 7-11, D-5, Cologne, Germany (MCA)
HL Harold Lyche & Co., Kongenst, 2, Oslo, Norway
HLe Henry Lemoine & Cie, 17 Rue Pigalle, Paris 9e, France (E-V)
HMo Hermann Moeck Verlag, Postfach 143, D 31 Celle, Germany
HMP Hargail Music Press, 28 West 38th Street, New York, New York 10018
H. Litolff's (See Lit)
H-O Hall-Orion Music Press, P.O. Box 145, University Station, Berrien Springs, Michigan 49104
Hoh Hohner Verlag, 7218 Trossingen, Würtemberg, Germany
HSM Hans Sikorski Musikverlag, Johnsalle 23, 2 Hamburg 13, Germany (B-M)
HU Harmonia-Uitgave, Roeltjesweg 23-Postbus 126, Hilversum, Holland (Pet)
H.T. FitzSimons (See Fit)
Hug Hug & Co., Musikverlag, CH-8022 Zürich, Switzerland (Pet)
H-V Hänssler-Verlag, Neuhausen-Stuttgart, Germany (Pet)
H.W. Gray (See Gra)
IA Inter Art Co. Ltd., 10-16 Rathbone Street, London W1P 2BJ, England
IMP Israeli Music Publications Ltd., (AlB)
ImV Impero Verlag (TP)
InM International Music Company Ltd., 16 Mortimer Street, London W. 1, England (Sch)
Int International Music Company, 511 Fifth Avenue, New York, New York 10017
Isr Israel Music Institute, P.O. Box 11253, Tel Aviv, Israel (B&H)
I-V Ichthys Verlag GmbH., Postfach 834, 7000 Stuttgart 1, Germany
J. Maurer (See Mau)
JB Joseph Boonin, Inc., P.O. Box 2124, South Hackensack, New Jersey 07606
Edwin F. Kalmus (See EdK)
JE June Emerson-Wind Music, Ampleforth York, England
JKM Johann Kliment Musikverlag, Kolingasse 15, 1090 Vienna, Austria
JoA Johann André Musikverlag, Postfach 141, 605 Offenbach am Main, Germany
Job Jobert & Cie, 44, Rue du Colisée, Paris 8e, France (E-V)
J. Curwen (See Cur)
JoW Josef Weinberger Musikverlag, Oederweg 26, Frankfurt, Germany (TP)
JS J. Schuberth & Co., Zietenring 3, Wiesbaden, Germany
J.&W. Chester (See Che)
Kaw KaWe, Brederodestraat 90, Amsterdam 13, Holland
Ken Kendor Music, Inc., Delevan, New York 14042

393

	E.C. Kerby (See ECK)
Kis	Kistner & Siegel & Co., Postfach 101, Cologne, Germany
KMC	Karnes Music Co., 9800 Milwaukee Avenue, Des Plaines, Illinois 60016
KMV	Karl Merseburger Verlag, Alemannenstrasse 20, 1000 Berlin 38, Germany (Pet)
	Neil A. Kjos (See NK)
Kof	Koff Music Co., Box 1442, Studio City, California 91604
Kov	S. Kovar, 4974 Noeline, Encino, California
KPM	Keith Prowse Music Publishing Co., Ltd., 21 Denmark Street, London WC2H 8NE, England
	E.C. Kerby (See ECK)
Lan	Lang Music Publications, P.O. Box 11021, Indianapolis, Indiana 46201
LDo	Ludwig Doblinger Verlag, Dorotheergasse 10, Vienna, Austria (AMP)
Leb	Leblanc Publications, Inc., 7019 30th Avenue, Kenosha, Wisconsin 53141 (SM)
Leu	F.E.C. Leuckart Verlag, Nibelungenstr. 48, Munich 19, Germany (AMP)
Lit	H. Litolff's Verlag, Forsthausstrasse 101, Frankfurt, Germany (Pet)
LK	Ludwig Krenn, Reindorfgasse 42, Vienna 15, Austria
LMP	Littlehall Music Publishers, 3315 Dellwood Drive, Parma, Ohio 44134
LP	Lariken Press, 2808 25th Street, Lubbock, Texas 79410
Lud	Ludwig Music Publishing Co., 557-67 East 140th Street, Cleveland, Ohio 44110
MaM	Mannheimer Musikverlag Gmbh., Mollstrasse 35, Mannheim 2, Germany
Man	Manuscript Publications, 2550 Faulkner Drive, Colorado Springs, Colorado 80916
Mau	J. Maurer, Avenue de Verseau 7 Watermanlaan, Bruxelles 15, Belgium
MB	Maurice Baron Co., P.O. Box 149, Oyster Bay, Long Island, New York 11771
M-B	Magnamusic-Baton, Inc., 10370 Page Industrial Parkway, St. Louis, Missouri 63132
MCA	MCA Music, 445 Park Avenue, New York, New York 10022 (B-M)
McK	McKinley Publishers, Inc., 797 8th Avenue, New York, New York
Men	Mentor Music, Inc., Broadview Drive, Brookfield, Connecticut 06804 (SF)
MeP	Media Press, Box 895, Champaign, Illinois 61820
	Mills (See B-M)
MiR	Minkoff Reprints, 46 Chemin de la mousse, 1225 Chene-Bourg, Geneva, Switzerland
Mit	Mitteldeutscher Verlag, Robert-Blum-Strasse 37, Halle/Saale, East Germany
	M.M. Cole (See Col)
MJQ	MJQ Music, Inc., 200 West 57th Street, New York, New York 10019
MKE	Mezhdunarodnaya Kniga Editions (USSR), (Sch)
MM	Molenaar's muziekcentrale nv, Zuideinde 18, Wormerveer, Holland (HeE)
M&M	McGinnis & Marx, 201 West 86th Street, New York, New York 10024 (PD)
	M.P. Belaieff (See Be)
MR	Musica Rara, 2 Great Marlborough Street, London W. 1, England
MRL	Musikverlag Robert Lienau, Lankwitzer Strasse 9, 1 Berlin 45, Germany (Pet)
MS	Music Sales Corporation, 33 W. 60th Street, New York, New York 10023
MT	Musiikin Tiedotuskeskus, Runeberginkatu 15 A 11, 00100 Helsinki 10, Finland
MV	Möseler Verlag, 3340 Wolfenbüttel, Germany
NK	Neil A. Kjos Music Co., 525 Busse Highway, Park Ridge, Illinois 60068
Nor	Nordiska Musikforlaget, Drottninggatan 37, 101 30 Stockholm 1, Sweden (AMP)
Nov	Novello & Co., Ltd., Borough Green, Sevenoaks, Kent, England or
	Box 1811, Trenton, New Jersey 08607
NV	Nagels Verlag, Heinrich Schütz Allee 31, Kassel, Germany (AMP)
NVM	New Valley Music Press, Sage Hall, Smith College, Northampton, Massachusetts 01060
	N. Simrock (See Sim)
OHN	Otto Heinrich Noetzel, Liebigstrasse 4, Wilhelmshaven, Germany (Prt)
OJ	Otto Junne GmbH., Sendlinger-Tor-Platz 10, 8 Munich 2, Germany
OM	Omega Music Co., 353 E. 52nd, New York, New York 10022
OxU	Oxford University Press, Inc., 200 Madison Avenue, New York, New York 10016
Pan	Panton, Říční 12, Prague, Czechoslovakia
Pat	Paterson's Publications Ltd., 38-40 Wigmore Street, London W1HOEX, England (CF)
Pax	W. Paxton & Co., Ltd., 36-38 Dean Street, Soho, W1V 6EP, London, England (Nov)
PD	Pietro Deiro, 133 7th Avenue South, New York, New York 10014
PDS	Professional Drum Shop, Inc., 854 Vine Street, Hollywood, California 90038
Pel	Pelikan Musikverlag, CH-8034 Zurich, Switzerland
Pet	C.F. Peters Corporation, 373 Park Avenue South, New York, New York 10016
PG	Ph. Grosch Musikverlag, 8000 Munich 8, Germany
PIC	Peer International Corporation, 1740 Broadway, New York, New York 10019
	P.J. Tonger (See Ton)
PMP	Providence Music Press, P.O. Box 2362, East Side Station, Providence, Rhode Island 02906
Pod	Podium Music Inc., 4 Broadway, Valhalla, New York 10595
	Theodore Presser (See TP)
PP	Progress Press, Box 12, Winnetka, Illinois 60093
PrA	Pro Art Publications, Inc., 469 Union Avenue, Westbury, New York 11590
PrM	Pro Musica Verlag, Karl-Liebknecht-Strasse 12, 701 Leipzig 1, East Germany
PWM	Polskie Wydawnictwo Muzyczne, Krakowskie Przedmieście 7, 00-068 Warszawa, Poland
Pyr	Pyraminx Publications, 358 Aldrich Road, Fairport, New York 14450
RBM	Richard Birnbach Musikverlag, Dürerstrasse 28, 1000 Berlin 45, Germany
R&E	Ries & Erler, Charlottenbrunner Strasse 42, Berlin 33 (Grunewald) Germany (Pet)

Reb   Rebo Music Publications, P.O. Box 9481, 425 East Alameda Avenue, Denver, Colorado 80209
Reu   Reuter & Reuter, Stockholm, Sweden
Ric   G. Ricordi & Co., Via Salomone 77, Rome, Italy (B-M)
Roc   Rochester Music Publishers, Inc., 358 Aldrich Road, Fairport, New York 14450
Ron   Rongwen Music, Inc., 56 West 45th Street, New York, New York 10036 (BB)
RS   Richard Schauer, 67 Belsize Lane, Hampstead, London NW3 5AX, England
Rub   Rubank, Inc., 16215 N.W. 15th Avenue, Miami, Florida 33169
RuE   Rud. Erdmann, Postfach 471, Wiesbaden, Germany
S-B   Summy-Birchard Co., 1834 Ridge Avenue, Evanston, Illinois 60204
S&C   Schott & Co., Ltd., 48 Great Marlborough Street, London W.1, England (B-M)
ScF   Schott, Freres, 30 Rue Saint-Jean, Bruxelles 1, Belgium (Pet)
Sch   G. Schirmer, Inc., 866 Third Avenue, New York, New York 10022
       E.C. Schirmer (See ECS)
       J. Schuberth (See JS)
SD   Stichting Donemus, Jacob Obrechtstraat 51, Amsterdam, Holland (Pet)
See   Seesaw Music Corporation, 177 East 87th Street, New York, New York 10028
SEM   S.E.M.I., 5 Rue Lincoln, Paris 8e, France
SF   Sam Fox Music Sales Corporation, 62 Cooper Square, New York, New York 10003
       S.A.R.L. Gras Frères (See GrF)
Sha   Shawnee Press, Inc., Delaware Water Gap, Pennsylvania 18327
ShB   Shapiro, Bernstein & Co., Inc., 10 East 53rd Street, New York, New York 10022
SHF   Slovenský Hudobný Fond, Gorkeho 19, Bratislava, Czechoslovakia
SHM   Schmitt Music Centers, 110 N. 5th Street, Minneapolis, Minnesota 55403
Sid   Sidem Editions, 8 Rue de Hesse, Geneva, Switzerland
Sim   N. Simrock, Werderstrasse 44, Hamburg 13, Germany (AMP)
SkB   Skandinavisk og Borups Musikforlag, Bredgade 31, Copenhagen, Denmark
SLP   Swing Lane Publications, Box 128, Beverly, New Jersey 08010
SM   Southern Music Co., 1100 Broadway, Box 329, San Antonio, Texas 78292
Smo   SHALL-u-mo Publications, P.O. Box 2824, Rochester, New York 14626
SMP   Southern Music Publishing Co., Inc., 1740 Broadway, New York, New York 10019
SP   Studio Publications, 224 South Lebanon, Lebanon, Indiana 46052
SPD   The Society for Publishing Danish Music, Graabrodretorv 7, 1154 Copenhagen, Denmark (Pet)
Spr   Spratt Music Publishers, 17 West 60th Street, New York, New York 10023
SS   B. Schott's Söhne, Weihergarten 1-9, 65 Mainz, Germany (B-M)
Sta   Staff Music Publishing Co., Inc., 17 West 60th Street, New York, New York 10023
STI   STIMS Informationscentral för Svensk Musik, Tegnerlunden 3, 111 85 Stockholm, Sweden
StM   Standard Music Publishing, Inc., P.O. Box 1043-Whitman Square, Turnersville, New Jersey 08012
S-V   Sirius-Verlag, Wiclefstrasse 67, Berlin 21, Germany
       T.B. Harms (See Har)
Tem   Tempo Music Publications, Inc., P.O. Box 392, Chicago, Illinois 60690
Ten   Tenuto Publications, c/o Theodore Presser Co., Bryn Mawr, Pennsylvania 19010
T-M   Tierolff-Muziekcentrale, Markt 90/92, Roosendaal, Netherlands (HeE)
Ton   P.J. Tonger Musikverlag, Bergstrasse 10, 5038 Rodenkirchen/Rhein, Germany (Pet)
TP   Theodore Presser Co., Bryn Mawr, Pennsylvania 19010
TrA   Trio Associates, Box 2572, Culver City, California 90230
Tri   Tritone Press c/o Theodore Presser Co., Bryn Mawr, Pennsylvania 19010
TRY   TRY Publications, 854 Vine Street, Hollywood, California 90038
UE   Universal Editions, Karlsplatz 6, Wien 1, Austria (JB)
UME   Union Musical Espanola, Carrera de San Jeronimo 26, y Arenal, 18 Madrid 14, Spain (AMP)
UMI   Universal Musical Instrument Co., 732 Broadway, New York, New York 10003
UMP   United Music Publishers Ltd., 1, Montague Street, Russell Square, London, W.C.1, England
Uni   University Music Press, P.O. Box 1267, Ann Arbor, Michigan 48103 (SF)
Vol   Volkwein Bros., Inc., 117 Sandusky Street, Pittsburgh, Pennsylvania 15212
       W. Paxton (See Pax)
Wah   George Wahr Publishing Co., 304-1/2 South State Street, Ann Arbor, Michigan 48108
War   Warner Bros. Publications, 75 Rockefeller Plaza, New York, New York 10019
Wat   Waterloo Music Co., Ltd., 3 Regina Street N., Waterloo, Ontario, Canada (AMP)
Wel   Weltmusik Edition International, Seilergasse 12, Wien 1/15, Austria
Wes   Western International Music, Inc., 2859 Holt Avenue, Los Angeles, California 90034
WH   Wilhelm Hansen Musik-Forlag, Gothersgade 9-11, 1123 Copenhagen, Denmark (M-B)
Wil   Willis Music, 7380 Industrial Road, Florence, Kentucky 41402
WIN   W.I.N.D.S., Box 513, Northridge, California 91324
Wit   Witmark & Sons, c/o Warner Bros. Publications, 75 Rockefeller Plaza, New York, New York 10019
W-J   Wingert-Jones Music, Inc., P.O. Box 1878, Kansas City, Missouri 64141
WLP   World Library Publications, 2145 Central Parkway, Cincinnati, Ohio 45214
WMI   Wind Music Inc., 1014 South Goodman Street, Rochester, New York 14620
WMS   Willy Müller-Süddeutscher Musikverlag, Marzgasse 5, Heidelberg, Germany (Pet)
WZ   Wilhelm Zimmermann Musikverlag, Zeppelinallee 21, 6000 Frankfurt, Germany (Pet)
YM   Ybarra Music, Box 665, Lemon Grove, California 92045
Za   Zalo Publications, P.O. Box 913, Bloomington, Indiana 47401
       G. Zanibon (See GZ)
Z-O   Zen-On Publishers Co., Ltd., Japan (S-B)